Proceedings of the 11th ICOM-CC Group on Wet Organic Archaeological Materials Conference

Greenville 2010

Editors:

Kristiane Strætkvern and Emily Williams

Published by the International Council of Museums (ICOM), Committee for Conservation Working Group on Wet Organic Archaeological Materials

ISBN: 978-1-257-86709-7

Printed in the USA by Lulu.com

Table of contents

Jill Barnard, Liz Goodman and Nancy Shippen

Introduction

The 11th ICOM-CC Working Group meeting for Wet Organic Archaeological Materials (WOAM) took place at East Carolina University, in Greenville, North Carolina, USA, in May 2010. The conference and excursions were wonderfully organized by Sarah Watkins-Kenney and Emily Williams and their colleagues from East Carolina University, North Carolina Department of Cultural Resources (NCDCR), the NCDCR *Queen Anne's Revenge* Archaeological Conservation Laboratory, North Carolina Division of Parks and Recreation Pettigrew State Park, and the Colonial Williamsburg Foundation. Again, the WOAM week was inspiring and interesting for the approximately 80 engaged participants. In addition to the 54 presentations of papers and posters there was time and intellectual capacity for several discussions during the week.

New generations are entering the WOAM forum – fortunately, it seems that we still have a good overlap and communication between the seniors and the younger generations. Even more promising is that the new generations come in with good skills, open minds and a lot of enthusiasm and energy. As long as the group remain communicative, skeptical but still open minded, we will learn from each other and hopefully achieve a general better understanding of the skills that are required in the preservation of archaeological cultural heritage. I strongly recommend readers to take their time and read the questions and answers after the presentations – as well as the general discussions related to themes 3 and 4.

After the Amsterdam conference, colleagues were recommended to try out some of the methods presented during the conference – and to report back to the group. It is nice to observe that this is actually happening. Thus, many colleagues working in this specialized niche get a chance to have a second or third opinion on a method or material before trying it out in their laboratories. Moreover, receiving professional responses to ones' methods, techniques or suggested new materials are invaluable. So, please continue to try out and test the theories, the materials and the techniques presented during the conference and in this book. The authors' contact information is meant to promote this idea, also for the next triennial.

Again, the WOAM Proceedings contains many well written articles based upon a wide spectrum of highly qualified work. This volume holds the manuscripts of 54 presentations, 42 of them presented as talks, the remaining 12 as posters during the conference. As in 2007, the authors were offered the possibility of having the manuscripts scientifically peer reviewed. 11 manuscripts passed the scientific review. In this volume, these manuscripts will be recognized by a special font (Times New Roman) and by the 'SC Pr' abbreviation after the manuscript number.

The scientific committee consisted of the following people: Yvonne Fors, Tara Grant, David Gregory, Per Hoffmann, Ida Hovmand, Hans Huismann, Jan Bruun Jensen, Poul Jensen, Henning Matthiesen, Vicky Richards, Theo Skinner, Jeremy Spriggs and Khoi Tran.

An academic review has been undertaken for the remaining manuscripts. This work was carried out by: Ian Godfrey, Tara Grant, David Gregory, Vicky Richards, Kristiane Strætkvern, Khoi Tran, Gordon Turner Walker and Emily Williams (who also transcribed the 50 pages of discussions from the meeting!).

The reviews have been time consuming and a lot of energy and expertise were invested. It is very important to the working group to have this strong network of colleagues and institutions with the will, skill and ability to invest resources in such projects. On behalf of the WOAM working group, I wish to express my deepest gratitude to all these institutions and people who made this conference and proceedings possible. In particular, we are grateful to the Colonial Williamsburg Foundation, East Carolina University, the North Carolina Department of Cultural Resources (NCDCR), the NCDCR *Queen Anne's Revenge* Archaeological Conservation Laboratory and the Danish National Museum for their support. I hope, for our future meetings, that the institutions, managers and directors continue to acknowledge the significance of the WOAM conferences and allow our colleagues to participate on all levels of engagement. The WOAM meetings offer the participants an outstanding opportunity to gain knowledge, to discuss recent research, methods and results in the field and in general improve the conservation of wet organic archaeological materials.

During the opening session of the 11th WOAM meeting, we agreed to dedicate this volume of proceedings to our colleague Kate Hunter, who passed away in January 2010. All the way through her professional life, she worked wholeheartedly for the future of our cultural heritage. We missed her during the conference and she would have loved to read this book. As Jim Spriggs says: *'Kate was(...) inspiring to others with her knowledge, passion and tireless energy..'* It is my hope, that you all will enjoy this volume of WOAM Proceedings and find inspiration and to continue your passionate work in the laboratories, in the fields, in the museums and in the worn down factory halls.

Kristiane

Kristiane Strætkvern
Coordinator
ICOM-CC working group for Wet Organic Archaeological Materials

Kate Hunter as we remember her - in the field with a shipwreck.

1.1

Deepwater Preservation and Management of Archaeological Sites. Outlining the DePMAS Project

Elizabeth E. Peacock*, Norwegian University of Science and Technology (NTNU), NO-7491 Trondheim, Norway and University of Gothenburg, Sweden
*E-mail: elizabeth.peacock@vm.ntnu.no

Fredrik Skoglund, Norwegian University of Science and Technology (NTNU), NO-7491 Trondheim, Norway

Jørgen Fastner, Norwegian University of Science and Technology (NTNU), NO-7491 Trondheim, Norway

Abstract
The deepwater coastal areas of Scandinavia are increasingly being exploited and developed for the harvesting of energy resources such as oil, natural gas and wind power, and for aquaculture. These activities come in conflict with the underwater cultural heritage, especially shipwrecks. The Deepwater Preservation and Management of Archaeological Sites (DePMAS) Project seeks to develop informed protocols for in-situ preservation, management and monitoring of shipwrecks in deepwater environments. DePMAS's 2008 pilot project successfully tested the design and feasibility, and remote deepwater installation and retrieval of sample modules, groundwork for the long-term project program of in-situ environmental monitoring and deterioration of artifact analogues at two deepwater localities in Central Norway.

Keywords: cultural heritage management, deepwater, shipwrecks, DePMAS, in-situ, artifact analogues, environmental monitoring

Background
The deepwater coastal areas of Scandinavia are increasingly being exploited and developed, not only for the harvesting of energy resources such as oil, natural gas and wind power but also numerous aquaculture facilities. The inevitable disturbance of the seabed as a direct consequence of the installation of massive pipelines, platforms, wind turbines and other structures, can lead to the disruption of the continued long-term preservation of underwater cultural heritage (UCH), such as shipwrecks.

Norway ratified the United Nations Convention on the Law of the Sea (UNCLOS)[1]in 1996. In 2004, in accordance with the Convention, Norway extended its territorial limit from 4 to 12 nautical miles from the baseline, and declared a contiguous zone of 12 nautical miles[2]. This zone is protected by Norway's Cultural Heritage Act[3], the ramifications of which mean that Norway's underwater cultural heritage management encompasses not only a much larger area, but also much deeper waters (Dromgoole 2006).

Norway's coastal waters present some of the most extreme and difficult conditions for in-situ preservation in and on the seabed. This is due to such diverse factors as wave energy, high salinity content, the steep near-coastal shelf drop-off, and the presence of *teredo navalis*. The conditions for preservation of archaeological remains are better in deepwater environments, but little is known about site formation processes and the actual agents of preservation at these depths. There is a great potential for finds of shipwrecks in deep waters. Studies show that in the 19th century as many as 17% of Norwegian sailing ships were lost in open waters (Nymoen and Nævestad 2006); and at that time the Norwegian merchant fleet was among the largest in the world.

Extensive experience is being gained in deepwater marine archaeological exploration and ROV technology by the maritime archaeology group at the Norwegian University of Science and Technology (NTNU) in Trondheim, Norway. Because underwater surveys are now technologically feasible at greater depths, shipwrecks and other archaeological remains are increasingly being located, investigated and documented. But much of the work being carried out relies on educated guesswork. Presently, we more anticipate rather than know what we might find: what types of remains can be preserved in/on the seabed at different sites, at different depths and in what conditions. Furthermore, we do not know how to protect them in-situ once we discover them.

The deepwater survey work driven by energy exploitation is raising vital and pressing issues. It highlights that, at present, cultural heritage management has too few facts at its disposal to understand our multitudinous deepwater cultural heritage. Threats to its continued survival are difficult to assess using the existing knowledge base. Too little is known about the environmental conditions and formation processes at deepwater sites, and how they affect cultural remains and their long-term preservation. In addition, it is now recognized that wrecks play an important role in marine environments in terms of fish spawning sites and safe havens.

This lack of baseline information about the actual preservation and deterioration processes, as well as practical, appropriate, in-situ preservation and monitoring guidelines has led to the development of the DePMAS Project coordinated by the NTNU.

The DePMAS Project

The DePMAS project seeks to fill the knowledge gap about the protective and destructive mechanisms that influence the preservation of underwater cultural heritage in deepwater environments. Currently, these are poorly understood and inadequately documented. As a consequence, threats to underwater cultural heritage's continual survival are difficult to assess using our existing knowledge base. The project seeks to provide methodologies to characterize, understand and assess the significance of these threats in a local, national and international context. The research aims to establish a sound research foundation for the development of deepwater cultural heritage management protocols to address the shortfall in current knowledge. A core goal of the project is to provide heritage management authorities with informed guidelines for specific measures that can, and should be, taken for the in-situ management, protection and environmental monitoring of these deepwater sites.

DePMAS aims to initiate a long-term study of the processes of deterioration in deepwater coastal environments, for the most common organic and inorganic materials that make up shipwreck assemblages. Baseline geological, geochemical and biological mapping of the field sites prior to installation, and environmental monitoring over the course of the program period, will establish a sound research foundation for the development of deepwater cultural heritage management protocols.

DePMAS will span a projected 32 years. Thus far, it consists of a pilot project undertaken in 2008, to be followed by several multi-year phases. It is coordinated by a research group based at the university museum (Vitenskapsmuseet) of NTNU. The Museum has the responsibility for managing both the land-based and underwater cultural heritage in Central Norway. Its staff has extensive experience in management, fieldwork, survey methodology and conservation in the marine environment. The full DePMAS team will be an international consortium of specialists from institutions representing universities, museums and conservation laboratories in Scandinavia and beyond.

In developing DePMAS, the work of two recent research projects has provided valuable insight: Reburial and Analyses of Archaeological Remains (RAAR) (Bergstrand and Godfrey 2007, Peacock et al. 2008), and Monitoring of Shipwreck Sites (MoSS) (Palma 2005). Both focus on the degradation/preservation processes associated with underwater cultural heritage. While RAAR addresses deterioration and environmental monitoring in shallow ocean waters, MoSS focuses on the preservation status of known shipwrecks. DePMAS will focus not on specific wreck sites, but on the key factors associated with deterioration in deepwater seabed environments to identify the more general characteristics that can be applicable to a more global arena.

The primary objective of DePMAS is the development of protocols for the in-situ preservation, management and monitoring of underwater cultural heritage landscapes in deepwater environments. This will be achieved through several lines of research. One is the development of methods to monitor deepwater underwater cultural heritage. Another is the long-term environmental monitoring of two deepwater localities along Norway's coast. The deepwater deposition of sample materials to (1) act as analogues for the materials that make-up pre-modern wooden shipwrecks and (2) modern polymeric materials for use in in-situ preservation of shipwrecks constitute an additional avenue of critical research. Finally, experimental methodologies to

facilitate the practical execution of actualistic degradation studies in deepwater will be developed.

Deepwater operations and DePMAS
DePMAS is completely dependent upon technology that facilitates access to the seabed in deep water. For all oceanographic operations, it will utilize vessels and equipment available at NTNU. These include the recently acquired, specially designed research vessel and floating laboratory R/V "Gunnerus". This state-of-the-art ship is equipped with the latest technology for a variety of research activities within biology, geology, technology, archaeology and oceanographic research. Dynamic positioning (DP) system and a HiPAP 500 unit makes it optimal for positioning ROV and submergible equipment. For all underwater activities, including surveys, documentation and monitoring, DePMAS will utilize the University Museum's work-class SUB-fighter 30k ROV custom-built for marine archaeological purposes by Sperre AS. The 2008 pilot project investigated adaptation of the ROV and research ship to the challenges of the DePMAS project.

Investigation, surveying and selection of two deepwater test sites for environmental and shipwreck degradation studies
In order to produce a solid transferable database it is important that DePMAS carries out fieldwork at more than one site to provide a comparative basis. Because it seeks to study deterioration of ship-related materials from the moment of wrecking, i.e., impact on the seabed, it will select culturally neutral sites. It will not employ existing shipwreck sites as their degradation history from day one is unknown. Selection of the test sites is based not on site-specific criteria, but rather on their potential for application to a broader range of wreck site scenarios. In this way, research results will be transferable to prospection and

management – such as surveys, security and monitoring of wreck circumstances and environments both nationally and internationally.

Fieldwork will be carried out at two sites localized in Trondheimsfjord, which is NTNU's maritime research platform. Proximity to Trondheim facilitates monitoring and retrieval. Two test sites have been selected where test materials will be exposed to different environmental influences. One is an exposed environment along the Norwegian coast; the other site is a more-protected inner-fjord environment. Similar seabed conditions are sought, and both sites will be at the same 200-250 m depth to minimize depth-related variations. DePMAS is drawing upon existing NTNU research and monitoring of Trondheimsfjord to provide long-term perspectives on the area's general nature and conditions.

Characterization and environmental monitoring of deepwater cultural heritage environments

Site monitoring is crucial to DePMAS, and changes in the environment of the study sites will be closely supervised. Existing environmental data from research and governmental institutions will be supplemented by the collection of data using remote geophysical techniques, water sampling, in situ measurements and taking of sediment samples for subsequent laboratory analysis. Data logging devices will be deployed throughout the project in order to assess seasonal variation and the results combined with historical data collected by other institutions to examine what effect climate change in the recent past has had.

Extensive monitoring of the sites, and detailed analysis of the test materials, will provide insights into the processes that affect shipwrecks from the moment of wrecking. Research on deterioration "from day one" addresses a fundamental need to

understand the whole and complete interrelationship of the condition of a shipwreck and its environs as found (Ward et al. 1999, Gibbs 2006). A detailed understanding of wreck- and site-formation processes in different deepwater environments, including how long it takes for a wreck and associated materials to reach equilibrium at a site, is crucial to evaluate the potential for in-situ protection and stabilization.

The actualistic study of degradation/preservation agents and site-impact parameters will provide options for monitoring sites. Informed understanding of degradation/preservation of deepwater shipwrecks will provide a more nuanced insight into robust relevant methods for future survey, excavation and monitoring. This will lead to development of appropriately tailored equipment for these tasks. Since DePMAS's results will point to what materials are preserved and/or lost, archaeologists can be better prepared when documenting a shipwreck in terms of what is absent and why.

Taphonomy of tangible cultural heritage materials in deepwater environments

DePMAS seeks to gain insight into how, and under what circumstances archaeological materials are preserved at various depths at different sites, and how quickly equilibrium is established. Here DePMAS draws heavily on the Reburial and Analyses of Archaeological Remains (RAAR), also known as the Marstrand Project. A range of proxy artifact materials will be mounted in sample modules and deployed at two sites to gain insight into site- and wreck-formation processes in deep water. The degradation of ships, as well as their contents and surrounding environments will be studied as an integrated unit.

Modules will be inserted in the seabed for retrieval after exposure to the deepwater environments for 1, 2, 4, 8, 16 and 32 years. An additional reserve set of modules will be installed on each site. All materials will be subjected to post-retrieval analyses to identify biological and chemical degradation pathways, and to distinguish environments with long-term survival potential. The effects of burial above and at different depths within the seabed, and of burial in two environmentally different deepwater sites, at 200-250m, will be studied.

Every shipwreck is unique in terms of the artifacts and materials present. Materials selected for inclusion in the DePMAS program are the most common organic and inorganic artifactual materials found in ships: materials that might be found on pre-20th century wooden shipwreck sites. These will be supplemented by modern polymeric materials that might be used for in-situ preservation.

Standard copper and iron alloy metal coupons will be included, as well as a special set of composite modules that will include metal and wood in close association to simulate concreted organics common to shipwreck sites. The silicates group will be represented by Roman and medieval potash glass replicates, and modern traditional faience and Trønder ceramics replicates. Fresh oak and pine will be investigated, as will samples of modern, uncooked cow bone and cow horn. Vegetable-tanned leather, rope and textiles will be included in the DePMAS program.

Finally, the inclusion of modern polymeric materials, such as netting and geotextiles, used in site protection of shipwreck sites will provide an additional window on the impact of modern plastics (e.g. fishing nets, polyethylene bags, etc.) on the wider marine environment.

Development of in-situ methodology for investigating material taphonomy during long-term deepwater exposure

To safely install and successfully retrieve the artifact analogues in the seabed, and to ensure comparable conditions and exposure for the duration of the project, has demanded the development of both a prototype deepwater sample module adaptable for the various test materials and shapes, as well as a module containment system. The sample modules must withstand the deepwater environmental conditions for long-term deployment; they must facilitate exposure at different depths within the sediment; and, they must be robust enough to tolerate installation and retrieval by an ROV.

Pilot Project
The DePMAS pilot project was successfully carried to completion with full-scale deepwater tests of specially designed modules in October 2008. The pilot project focused on the development and evaluation of sample modules and module containment systems. A range of module solutions based on the standard sample modules (Turner-Walker and Peacock 2008) created for earlier, land-based, deterioration studies and that proved to be simple to install and retrieve were investigated. The challenging deployment practicalities associated with deepwater seabed installation and retrieval of the test material modules and containment systems were successfully met by both the ROV and the research ship. The pilot project fieldwork also included mapping of one of the test sites prior to the installment of the test modules.

Conclusion
DePMAS is developed to address the lack of baseline information about the actual preservation and deterioration processes of cultural heritage in deepwater environments, as well as the need for practical, appropriate, in-situ preservation and monitoring guidelines. It seeks to initiate a long-term study of the processes of deterioration in deepwater coastal

environments, of the most common organic and inorganic materials that make up shipwreck assemblages. Baseline geological, geochemical and biological mapping of the sites prior to installation, and environmental monitoring over the course of the program period, will establish a sound research foundation for the development of deepwater cultural heritage management protocols. The successful results of DePMAS's pilot study that focused on methodology, adaptation of equipment and practicalities confirmed that the project is technologically and practically feasible.

The project's study of wreck- and site-formation processes in deeper waters will lead to enhanced predictability for the energy sector, fisheries, coastal development and others. These sectors have a pressing need for information that highlights possible conflict their activities may have with underwater cultural heritage preservation. It is hoped that DePMAS's results can assist all sectors with better informed planning and decision making. In particular, for predicting what type of preservation conditions can be anticipated at different deepwater environments.

Notes
1) Also known as the Law of the Sea Convention or the Law of the Sea Treaty UNCLOS. Signed in Jamaica 1982 and taken into force 1994.
2) Act on Norwegian Territorial Waters of 2003 nr. 57.
3) Norwegian Act of 9 June 1978 No.50 Concerning the Cultural Heritage.

References
Bergstrand T. and Godfrey I.N., (eds.), (2007), *Reburial and Analyses of Archaeological Remains – Studies on the Effect of Reburial on Archaeological Materials Performed in Marstrand, Sweden 2002-2005, The RAAR Project*, Uddevalla, Bohuslåns Museum and Studio Våstsvensk Konservering.

Dromgoole S., (ed.), (2006), The protection of the underwater cultural heritage. National perspectives in light of the UNESCO convention 2001, *Publications on Ocean Development*, 55, Leiden, Martinus Nijhoff Publishers.

Gibbs M., (2006), Cultural site formation processes in maritime archaeology: Disaster response, salvage and Muckelroy 30 years on, *IJNA*, 35:1, 2006, pp 4–19.

Nymoen P. and Nævestad D., (2006), Hva blir borte av det vi ikke ser? Report comissioned by the Directorate for Cultural Heritage, *Norsk Sjøfartsmuseums Skrift*, nr. 50, Oslo, Norsk Sjøfartsmuseum.

Palma P., (2005), Monitoring of shipwreck sites, *IJNA*, 27:4, 2005, pp 343-358.

Peacock E.E., Bergstrand T., Nyström Godfrey I., Björdal C., Bohm C., Christensson E., Gregory D., MacLeod I., Nilsson T., Richards V., and Turner-Walker G., (2008), The Marstrand Reburial Project - overview, phase I and future work. *PARIS3 Preserving Archaeological Remains in Situ. Geoarchaeological and Bioarchaeological Studies* 10, Amsterdam, pp 253-263.

Turner-Walker G. and Peacock E.E., (2008), Preliminary results of bone diagenesis in Scandinavian bogs, *Palaeogeography, Palaeoclimatology, Palaeoecology*, 266:3-4, 2008, pp 151-159.

Ward I.A.K., Larcombe P., and Veth P., (1999), A new process-based model for wreck site formation, *JAS* 26, 1999, pp 561-570.

Questions and answers

Ellen Carrlee: Where do you define shallow water and deep water?

Elizabeth Peacock: I think there's a bit of a grey zone there but it is basically what is accessible and not accessible by divers.

1.2

WreckProtect – A European Project to Protect Wooden Historical Shipwrecks against Attack by Shipworm in the Baltic Sea

David Gregory*
National museum of Denmark, Conservation department, Research, Analysis and Consultancy, Brede, Kongens Lyngby, Denmark,
E-mail*: david.john.gregory@natmus.dk

Charlotte Gjelstrup Björdal
SP Technical Research Institute of Sweden, Drottning Kristinasväg 67, 114 86 Stockholm

Abstract
Wooden historical shipwrecks are subject to biological degradation in marine environments. Specialized fungi and bacteria are able to degrade the lignocelluolytic material present in the wood cell walls but this degradation is, however, very slow compared to the aggressive behavior of the marine borers like the shipworms. In the Baltic Sea, preservation conditions for shipwrecks have been uniquely favorable due to the absence of marine borers. The low salinity of this water has excluded marine borers and today the Baltic contains a unique collection of well preserved, historical shipwrecks and other ancient wooden constructions. Unfortunately, there have recently been indications of a spread of marine borers (*Teredo navalis*) into the Baltic, and climatic changes could be one of the reasons. A new project within the EC-7th framework program has started to provide stakeholders, archaeologists and conservators with guidelines in order to predict the spread of marine borers and to propose methods for preservation of wooden constructions and shipwrecks *in situ*.

Keywords: shipwreck, Baltic Sea, EC-project, WreckProtect, shipworm, protection

1. Marine Borers and Degradation of Archaeological Wood

Shipwrecks can be exposed to physical, chemical and biological deteriorative processes (Gregory 2009) and biological deterioration is one of the major threats to wooden shipwrecks in the marine environment (Jones et al. 2001). The most aggressive group of wood degraders is the marine borers, found in waters and oceans with high salinity (Eaton and Hale, 1993). Consequently, they are present in most of the oceans and seas worldwide, which include the Mediterranean, the North Sea and the Atlantic Ocean that surrounds Europe.

The marine borers, which include several different families and species, are able to totally decompose massive timbers within a relatively short period of time; within decades if not years. The larvae of the shipworm *Teredo navalis* settle on the wood surface, make a small hole and start degrading the interior of the wood, forming tunnels up to 1cm in diameter that with time expand to an open gallery (Turner 1966). The *Teredo navalis* lives inside the wood and develops from a small larva to a worm-like organism with a length of between 30 and 60 cm. The worm-like appearance and its effect on wooden ships has resulted in the popular name; shipworm, even though it is, in fact. a bivalve mollusk.

It is difficult for the untrained eye to see shipworm attack of wood. The wood may look seemingly intact on the outside and it is only when it breaks that the attack becomes visible (Figure 1). However, although marine borers are active in the saline and oxygenated water column, they are not active in sediment beneath the seabed (Gregory 1999, Björdal and Nilsson

2008). Consequently, where they are present, wrecks are often totally decomposed above the seabed, while the remaining parts protected by sediment are still available for archaeological studies.

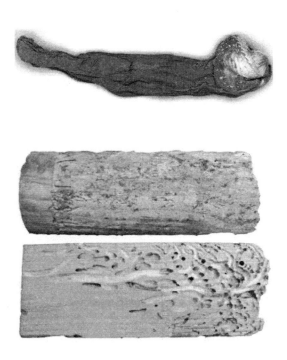

Figure 1. Upper: SEM of juvenile shipworm, actual size 3cm long. Lower: Attack of sound wood exposed 3 months in a marine saline environment. The upper photo showing the outside and the lower the inside of the same piece of wood after sectioning (Photo: David Gregory).

Another group of wood degraders in marine environments are micro-organisms. This group includes the soft rot fungi and two types of bacteria; tunneling bacteria and erosion bacteria (Björdal 2008, Blanchette et al. 1990). Compared to marine borers these micro-organisms decay wood very slowly and their main effects are softening of the wood surface. This group is found worldwide, both in brackish water systems as well as in saline marine waters.

2. Shipwrecks in the Baltic Sea and *In Situ* Preservation

Today the Baltic Sea is a unique resource for marine archaeology (Olsson 2006). The very low salinity of the water has limited the effects of aggressive marine borers and historical shipwrecks can be found intact both above and beneath the seabed. The Vasa ship, the number one tourist attraction of Stockholm, Sweden, is an example of the unique preservation conditions in the Baltic Sea (Figure. 2).

Figure 2. The Vasa ship exposed at the Vasa museum in Stockholm, Sweden. This ship was very well preserved, archaeologically speaking, both above and within the sediment due to the absence of marine borers. (Photo: Copyright Vasamuseum).

It is estimated that there around 100,000 shipwrecks in the Baltic and at least 6,000 are of significant archaeological and historical importance. The nine countries that surround the Baltic; Denmark, Sweden, Germany, Poland, Finland, Estonia, Latvia, Lithuania and Russia, frequently discover new wrecks and consequently the number of wrecks is still rising.

Salvaging each individual wreck is not a realistic option in the first instance due to the tremendous costs for excavation, conservation, storage, exhibition and curation (Manders et al., 2008). Furthermore, in-situ preservation is being increasingly seen as the preferred "first choice" for managing the underwater cultural heritage and has been politically galvanized by the 2001 UNESCO convention for the Protection of the Submerged Cultural Heritage (http://unesdoc.unesco.org/images/0012/001260/126065e.pdf).

3. The Spread of Shipworm: The Background to Wreck Protect

Within the past 20 years there have been increasingly frequent reports of the spread of shipworm into the Baltic. The reasons for this spread have been hotly debated and currently there are at least five different theories:

- Invasive species spread in ship's ballast water
- The marine / water environment in and around the Baltic has generally become cleaner
- Poorer quality wood used in marine constructions i.e. easier to attack
- Periodic increases of high salinity water into the Baltic. This is related to the meteorological phenomenon called the North Atlantic Oscillation.
- Higher than average summer temperatures in the waters of the Baltic leading to increased attacks.

Spread of shipworm into the Baltic was confirmed in a previous EU-Culture 2000 project, *MoSS* (Monitoring, Safeguarding and Visualizing North-European Shipwreck Sites), which describes attack by marine borers at shipwrecks sites along the German north coast at Rugen; areas that had not previously been affected by shipworm (Cederlund, 2004). This information together with other observations on attack in wooden harbor piling from the Danish east coast, as well as the southern parts of the Swedish west coast, indicated that shipworm were spreading into the southern and eastern parts of the Baltic Sea (Figure 3).

The WreckProtect project

May 2009 a project dedicated to assessing this problem started. The full title of the project is: *"Strategies for the protection of shipwrecks in the Baltic Sea against forthcoming attack by wood degrading marine borers. A synthesis and information*

project based on the effects of climatic changes". The short name is WreckProtect. It is financed mainly by the European Commission within the 7th framework program; Theme Environment, and is a coordination and support action with a duration of two years.

Figure 3. Map of the Baltic Sea. The marine borers extend from the saline "Kattegat" into the brackish "Baltic Sea". The circle illustrates an area where the new hot spots with decay by marine borers are found. This is also the area where brackish water meets the saline marine environment. Map: Modified after Wikipedia.

The pan-scientific project involves geophysicists, marine biologists, marine archaeologists, wood scientists, and conservators. The consortia consists of six partners from three countries; the Netherlands, Denmark, and Sweden. The project has an external advisory board with three marine archaeologists representing Germany, Finland and France.

The overall objective of the project is to protect archaeological shipwrecks and submerged settlements in the Baltic against forthcoming attack by shipworms. Two important questions are in focus:

> 1. How can the spread of shipworm be predicted, so that protection of a wreck can be given in time?

2. Which physical methods should be used for protection if the sites are   left in situ?

In this manner it will be possible to provide resource managers with a tool to assess and forecast where shipworm are, and where they are likely to be in the future. If used successfully it would enable a better assessment of which sites are threatened by attack and thus a means of prioritizing where resources should be targeted. Furthermore, if excavation is not a viable option, possible methods to protect the sites are given. To this end the project has been split up into various work packages described below.

4.   Scientific   Scope   and   Technical Objectives

The project is divided into the following five work packages:

4.1 Work package 1

The biological requirements for survival of the shipworm will be determined and related to their environmental parameters such as oxygen, temperature, currents, and salinity. Daily data relating to these parameters has been collected and collated from 1980 to 2006 and used in the DHI   Model   Mike   III (http://www.dhigroup.com/Software/Marine/MIKE3.aspx). The model has a horizontal resolution nine sea miles over the whole of the Baltic and two sea miles from the North Sea to Bornholm and a vertical resolution (depth) of two meters. The model takes into account meteorological changes, water currents, rain fall and changes in water level. The modeled data is then fed into a GIS (geographical information system) and is correlated with the biological information of the shipworm's ecology in order to identify where "Hot Spots" of shipworm activity are likely to be. Hindcast data (1980 – 2006) is being validated with evidence from documentary sources to see if "predicted" hot spots correlate with

what has been observed in the past. With the data available the model can also forecast spread until 2020.

4.2 Work package 2

A literature review of the wood industry, coastal engineering, off shore industry, archaeological and conservation literature is being carried out to identify suitable methods for stabilizing sites in situ and protecting them from attack by shipworm. These will be evaluated and efficient methods selected and a cost benefit analysis of conventional conservation included.

4.3 Work package 3

Two   guidelines   for   stakeholders, archaeologists, museums and conservators will be produced. The first will be on how to use the GIS model for predicting the spread of shipworm and the second discussing methods for physical protection of shipwrecks.

4.4 Work package 4

All accumulated knowledge from the project, such as guidelines, knowledge on shipworm in the light of climatic changes, etc. will be disseminated to stakeholders around the Baltic Sea as well as other parts of the world. Through international publications the guidelines will also be disseminated outside of Europe. A workshop   where   knowledge   is disseminated and demonstrated for interested stakeholders will be arranged at the end of the project.

4.5 Work package 5

This work package is focused on the actual management of the project.

5. Results

This paper is an introduction to the WreckProtect project. Results from the project will be published in scientific journals as well as presentations at conferences   related   to   marine archaeology, wood conservation, and marine biology. Moreover, the results from the project will be updated and can be followed on the website: www.wreckprotect.eu

Acknowledgments
The European Commission 7th framework program, Environment, is gratefully acknowledged for giving cultural heritage the opportunity to do research in this cross-disciplinary area. The organizers of Arc Nautica are gratefully acknowledged for the invitation to the symposia.

References
Björdal, C.G. and Nilsson, T., (2008) Reburial of shipwrecks in marine sediments: a long term study on wood degradation. *Journal of Archaeological Science* 35: 862-872.

Blanchette, R.A., Nilsson, T., Daniël, G. and Abad, A. (1990) Biological degradation of wood. In R.M Rowell & R.J. Barbour, (Eds.), *Archaeological Wood Properties, Chemistry and Preservation.* Advances in Chemistry Series 225. American Chemical Society, Washington, pp 158–161

Cederlund, C.O. (2004) MoSS: *Final Report*, Maritime Museum of Finland. PDF available at: http://www.mossproject.com/

Eaton, R.A. and Hale, M.D.C. (1993) *Wood. Decay, Pests and Protection.* Chapman and Hall London.

Gregory, D.J. (1999) Re-burial of timbers in the marine environment as a means of their long-term storage: experimental studies in Lynæs Sands, Denmark. In *The International Journal of Nautical Archaeology*, 27:4, 343 - 358. Academic Press.

Gregory, D. (2009) *In situ* Preservation of Marine Archaeological Sites: Out of Sight but Not Out of Mind. In V. Richards and J. Mckinnon (eds). *In situ Conservation of Cultural Heritage: Public, Professionals and Preservation*. Flinders University, Adelaide, p. 1-16.

Jones, E.B.G., Turner R.D., Furtado, S.E.J. and Kühne, H. (2001) Marine biodeteriogenic organisms I. Lignicolous fungi and bacteria and the wood boring mollusca and crustacea. *International Biodeterioration & Biodegradation* 48: 112-126.

Manders, M., Gregory, D. and Richards, V. (2008) The 'in situ' protection of archaeological sites under water. An evaluation of the techniques used. In E. May and M. Jones (Eds) *Proceedings of Heritage, Microbiology and Science, 2005.* Royal Society of Chemistry, London. 179 - 203

Olsson, A. (2006) The RUTILUS project. Strategies for a Sustainable Development of the Underwater Cultural Heritage in the Baltic Sea Region, *The Swedish Maritime Museums. Report 2006*, Stockholm.

Turner, R. D. (1966) *A survey and Illustrated Catalogue of the Teredinidae*, Harvard University, Cambridge, Mass.

Questions and answers

Lars I Elding: A question for David. You discussed various hypotheses for the invasion of ship worms in the Baltic, but I guess the salinity is one important parameter. Is there any long-term information about changes in the salinity of the Baltic Sea?

David Gregory: Nanna certainly found information when we were looking at the historical records, going back to 1870 and we can see quite nicely that there were several, they call them, I think, major periodic influxes of high saline water coming into the Baltic in 1920, in the 1930's, 1960. Very little happened in the

1970's and 1980's and then there was another very large one in 1993 and 2003. They believe it has something to do with what is called the North Atlantic Oscillation, which is a weather formation, a bit like El Niño, which is in the Pacific as far as I am aware. But the North Atlantic Oscillation is actually between Iceland and Europe. The pressure changes if you've got a lot of westerly wind coming over from Iceland. It's pushing the water into the Baltic, so you get an actual pressure change in the water levels and then when the easterly winds come in over the Baltic it actually changes the whole system, and we are finding that with the westerly winds, the high saline water is coming in from the Atlantic and North Sea into the Skagerrak/ Kattegat and then into the Baltic sea proper. So that's one side, also we've seen that there are these high saline incursions into the Baltic over the past 100 years or so. I shouldn't cherry pick but we've also seen when we've been looking at the evidence of outbreaks of shipworm certainly around Danish coastal waters and North Germany that we've actually seen that there are outbreaks of shipworm, it seems 2 or 3 years after these large incursions in the vicinity... I don't want to be too hasty here because Ziad is working on all that modeling at the moment so we are validating his model to see if it actually does tie in with both these high salt incursions and the shipworm outbreaks we have seen. So it could be a natural phenomenon in some respects, but it does seem the oscillation is actually increasing the frequency. So, even though it's not climate change necessarily in the Baltic, it's a bit like the Butterfly effect—in some way or another, things are changing and its having an effect all over the Baltic.

1.3
Monitoring In Situ Preservation of Shipwrecks

Michel Vorenhout*
Institute for Geo- and Bioarchaeology, Faculty of Earth and Life Sciences, VU University Amsterdam, De Boelelaan 1085, NI-1081 HV AMSTERDAM, The Netherlands
*E-mail: Michel.vorenhout@falw.vu.nl

Wouter Waldus
ADC ArcheoProjecten, ADC Maritiem, Nijverheidsweg Noord 114, 3812 PN Amersfoort
W.Waldus@archeologie.nl

Abstract
Previous research has shown that the groundwater table is the most dominating factor for the in situ preservation for wooden shipwrecks. However, also groundwater table quality and the fluctuation of the water table and moisture levels in the soil column will influence the condition of the wood. The preservation of six selected wrecks will be followed in a monitoring program in the city of Almere. This monitoring program is setup using the experiences and knowledge gained in two other projects: a study of the Roman vessel 'de Meern IV', and the study of two in situ preserved wrecks within the city of Almere. The monitoring program of groundwater table, redox potential and soil chemistry will be conducted at six wrecks. Three of the shipwrecks are covered by a simple layer of clay, three others have been protected by an artificial mound and plastic to actively raise the groundwater.

Keywords: Monitoring, in-situ preservation, ground water table, the Netherlands, burial

Introduction
A considerable part of the Dutch maritime archaeological heritage is found in the so called polders: former seabeds which were turned into dry land by large scale dike building and draining projects. The Province of Flevoland (central Netherlands) is the largest polder in the former Zuiderzee-area. Flevoland consists of several polder areas. The older one is the Noord-Oostpolder, which is connected to the mainland. The Noord-Oostpolder was converted to a polder in the 1940ies. The Flevopolder was brought into existence during the 1950s and 1960s, with the finalization of the pumping out of water in 1968. As these polders consist of a former seabed, it was to be expected that a number of shipwrecks would be uncovered. The number of shipwrecks and related finds in this polder currently exceeds over 400. New wrecks are still being discovered.

Soil characteristics in the polders create durable preservation circumstances for wooden shipwrecks in waterlogged conditions. The top soil is in general a thick clay, with good waterholding capacities. The city of Almere is a fast growing city in the Flevopolder, with large infrastructural building schemes. The average soil depth is -6 meter below mean sea level (2009). A large number of shipwrecks were uncovered in the years following the drainage of the polder, in the 1950ies and 1960ies. It would have been, and still is to date, impossible to preserve all these ex situ given the costs and time aspects of it.

Previous work
Previous research has shown that the groundwater table is the most dominating factor for the condition of the wrecks. The groundwater table is the depth at which the soil is saturated with water. This level can be measured using dipwells: plastic tubes with small holes that fill up with water. The dipwells can be equipped with dataloggers that record the level of water continuously. However, also groundwater

table quality and the fluctuation of the water table and moisture levels in the soil column will influence the condition of the wood. The preservation of six selected wrecks will be followed in a monitoring program in the city of Almere. This monitoring program is setup using the experiences and knowledge gained in two other projects: a study of the Roman vessel 'de Meern IV', and the study of two in situ preserved wrecks within the city of Almere.

De Meern IV

The Roman vessel Meern IV is located in a new living area in the city of Utrecht, the Leidsche Rijn area. It was discovered during groundworks during the construction of a underground dam. The wreck is located along the side of a former waterway, therefore it is "tilted". The excavations during 2003 and 2005 showed that the upper part was fully degraded. The lower parts were preserved very good, as wood analysis shows (de Groot & Morel 2007).

Two wrecks Almere

A short survey was carried out in the summer of 2007 to examine the current status of two different wrecks. These wrecks are located in the South Eastern part of the city of Almere, the developing area 'Poort'. Both wrecks were exposed after the drainage of the total area, letting it become the Flevopolder.

The first wreck, a 19th century small work boat, was protected by a layer of soil after discovery (Waldus 2008). The second wreck, a 17th century transport vessel was covered by a lining of soil and plastic (Waldus 2008a). The plastic is thought to diminish the evaporation, but let rainwater accumulate under the plastic (Figure 1). The plastic will thus raise the groundwater table around the wreck.

The two wrecks were both monitored during a period of three months. Existing dipwells were used for continuous groundwater table measurements. Just

before the pit excavation started, an additional dipwell was placed just above the expected location of the wreck. The soil brought up during the coring for the placement of the dipwell at the first wreck didn't show any finds. The placement of the dipwell at the second wreck showed the presence of chalk, indication that the inner parts of the wreck were hit during placement. The dipwells were equipped with dataloggers for waterlevel that took readings each 15 minutes.

Figure 1. *Covering a shipwreck with a raised layer of clay and plastic.*

Results of Pre-Studies
Experiences from 1 year monitoring of the Meern IV

The monitoring study of the Meern IV showed that the groundwater table is very important for the preservation of the wooden parts of the wreck. The level of loss of wood coincides with the position of the groundwatertable. A zone of several centimeters above mean groundwater table also contains wood in relatively good condition. This confirms that the presence of oxygen in the soil is the most important parameter, but also shows that a threshold might exist below which the fast degrading – oxygen dependant- fungi still might not grow. This will occur in the zone above the mean groundwater table. The moisture data shows that there might be a local influence of rainwater on the preservation of the wooden parts. Rain penetrates the soil, raising the moisture level in the soil and reducing the amount of oxygen available for oxic degraders. The soil just

16

above the groundwater table will have a higher sum of moisture than the layers higher up.

The wreck was uncovered for a small scale excavation. Results of the excavation have been published extensively before (de Groot & Morel 2007) and were also presented at WOAM 2008 (Amsterdam). After sampling and documentation, the excavation pit was closed with soil coming from that pit. The wreck was then under monitoring for one year. This monitoring included soil groundwater table, redox potential measurements and soil moisture content (Figure 2). The groundwater table was automatically recorded at three locations around the wreck. The redox potential and soil moisture were measured each month. In this way a soil profile of redox and moisture throughout the year was created.

Figure 2. *Monitoring at de Meern IV. Photo: A. Smit*

The recovering of the wreck had a strong influence on the redox potential in the soil above the wreck. A normal profile in depth of the redox potential will show lower redox potential with increasing depth. At the wreck however, such a profile did not

exist. Instead, a stable flat redox profile was found. The moisture content in the soil showed a good correlation with rain events, but also the dryness of the soil on top of the wreck.

It also showed however, that the reburial of a wreck will influence the burial environment strongly. As this might only be a temporal effect, more extensive research is needed.

Figure 3. *Covered shipwreck in Almere. Photo taken in 2007 during the pre-study (Waldus, 2008).*

Covered and Raised covered wreck
This study, in the area of Almere Poort, revealed a strong effect of coverage type of local hydrology. The first wreck (figure 3) which was covered by approximately one meter of clay in 1980 was near or below the groundwater table (figure 4).

The part of this wreck above the groundwater table was probably deteriorated and has since disappeared. Detailed study and comparison of wood samples below and the above groundwater table in the first wreck clearly demonstrated deterioration of the cell structures. The results show that the coverage with plastic and more soil is effective in actively raising the groundwater table around the wreck. In general, the second vessel was completely under the groundwater table, which is higher than in the surrounding areas (figure 5).

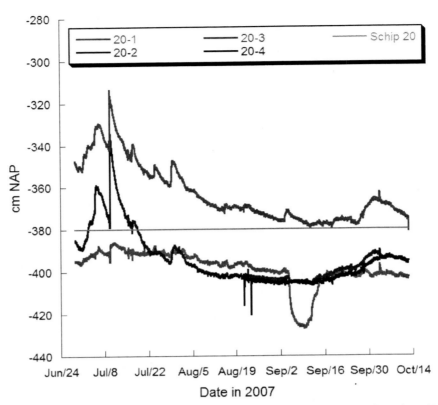

Figure 4. *Groundwater Tables around the covered wreck in Almere Poort. The short line (20-4) indicates groundwater table just above the wreck. Solid straight line is depth of highest part of the wreck.*

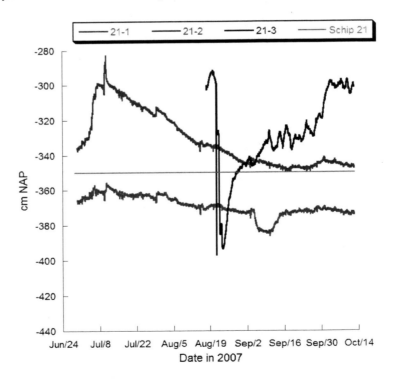

Figure 5. *Watertables at the raised coverage wreck in Almere Poort. The short line (21-3) indicates the groundwater table just above the wreck. Solid straight line is depth of highest part of the wreck.*

Vertical sampling of wood in the second wreck showed no differences in conservation between the two wrecks. A similar effect was found in de Meern IV where the ship is tilted. The highest part has greatly deteriorated and the lower parts show a more or less similar pattern of degradation.

The two types of coverage also have a different effect on the drainage at the site, for instance during a small excavation. The black lines in the graphs in figure 3 and 4 show the water table just above the wrecks. This line shows a sharp decline in the raised and covered (second) wreck. The effect is much less in the first wreck. The excavation pit at the first pit only needed short time drainage. The excavation pit at the second wreck was drained nearly all throughout the day. The groundwater at the first wreck was easily replenished from the surrounding area. At the second wreck however, it took nearly 2 months before the effect ceased and the original groundwater table was restored.

Outlook: Monitoring Program of a Selection of Wrecks
The building of complete new parts of the city of Almere can pose a serious threat to the burial environment of the shipwrecks. Besides the possible physical damage to the wrecks by building activities, one can summarize the threats to "changes in groundwater table". Related to this, the water quality can also change. The impact of these changes depends on the burial characteristics of the wreck, like its depth and type of coverage. As shown in the pre-studies, the artificial coverage of the wrecks with plastic and clay seems to force the groundwater to a higher level. If this coverage will stay intact, this type of protection may provide a long-lasting and durable solution. However, this has not been tested through time; the short study in 2007 only lasted a few weeks. The wrecks that are simply covered by a layer of clay or less will probably be influenced by the building activities as they are not protected in an additional way and the building activities will influence local groundwater tables and soil chemistry. The contact between these wrecks and the surrounding soil environment is much more direct.

To prevent damage to the wrecks in the building areas, and to gain a better understanding of the protective measures that work best, a large monitoring program will start in 2010. In this monitoring project we will follow the environmental conditions of six wrecks during at least 2.5 years. Three of the shipwrecks are covered by a simple layer of clay, three others have been protected by an artificial mound and plastic to actively raise the groundwater. The monitoring scheme involves groundwater table monitoring, continuous redox potential measurements and a combination of timed chemical analyses with possible characterization of the quality of the wood. The redox potential will show the intrusion of oxygen, or other electron acceptors, through time (Vorenhout et al 2004).

At the time of writing, the selection procedure was still under investigation. In the selection, two views have arisen. The first, as suggested by the authors, uses an a-select selection ("random") of shipwrecks. The selection is done by a random process, based on the input of some physical characteristics that group the wrecks in few groups. From these groups, one wreck is then selected at random. This will ensure that the results from the monitoring can be applied to all wrecks. However, this is also a bit counterintuitive for specialists that want to conserve the 'best' specimens. In that case, a selection should be made on the information content of the various wrecks, within the two main groups of coverage type. A combination of these two views will be needed in order to make a final decision on the method, and hence selection of monitoring locations.

The selection is expected to take place in July 2010, after which the monitoring can start. Main results are expected after one year, and at the end of this stage of the monitoring in the beginning of 2013.

References
De Groot T., Morel J.-M.A.W. eds. (2007). Het schip uit de Romeinse tijd De Meern 4 nabij boerderij de Balije, Leidsche Rijn, gemeente Utrecht. Rapportage Archeologische Monumentenzorg 147, RACM, Amersfoort.

Vorenhout, M., van der Geest, H.G., van Marum, D., Wattel, K., Eijsackers, H.J.P., 2004. Automated and Continuous Redox Potential Measurements in Soil. J. Environ. Qual. 33, 1562-1567.

Waldus W.B. (2008) Een negentiende-eeuws werkschip bij Almere-Poort. ADC Maratime report 1140, Amersfoort

Waldus W.B. (2008a) Een zeventiende-eeuws vrachtschip bij Almere-Poort. ADC Maratime report 1141, Amersfoort

Questions and answers
Sarah Watkins Kenney: I would like to thank the speakers for bringing us up to date on all the work that's been done over the last three years. Despite funding cuts etc., things are still moving forward. However, I have a couple of questions that I'd like to ask the speakers and then perhaps a more general one in relation to whether all these reburial issues are not putting archaeological material out of sight out of mind? If they are for the long-term—the very, very long-term—how do we decide what is long-term? First however, I'd like to ask Michel, how are you measuring the groundwater levels?

Michel Vorenhout: It's actually quite easy. You insert a plastic tube in the soil and the lower part has small slots in the plastic and it just fills up with the ground water. The water inside measures the pressure and you can actually calculate how long it takes. So, yes, you actually measure by the level the soil is saturated with.

Sarah Watkins Kenney: So your fluctuations were they seasonal or is there other development work going on around that is affecting them?

Michel Vorenhout: The fluctuations will be kind of seasonal. Regarding the watertable in these Polders, you will see that at some times, when they are pumping —when they expect a lot of rain they pre-pump, and you can see it in the lower tubes. We have tubes at different depths so you can have different layers of water. This is a relatively easy method.

Lars Anderson: I have a question for Michel. All these polders that have been pumped up—the water has been pumped out—have you seen any degradation of the soil? We have that in Denmark where the soil is oxidizing and getting lower and lower so your shipwrecks are getting higher and higher. So has that been considered?

Michel Vorenhout: Yes, we have a massive problem in, I think, one third of the Netherlands because there is a lot of pumping of the ground water and first the peat layers in your soil will degrade. And in the more recent polders the clay is still...the volume is too large so the volume is decreasing and lowering your ground level over time. This can start to about 2m in the next few years in some spots.

Lars Andersen: So it can get harder and harder to maintain these high (flood) water levels. Also we have some problems that these environments get very acidic. It seems like you have nice pH levels but...

Michel Vorenhout: Yes, that's why I mentioned it. I was at a meeting recently on Starr Carr where you have this massive pH flux, which doesn't happen yet in our area. But we do worry about sulfate and sulfite concentrations from the polders. In the deeper levels, there's already salt present.

Lars Andersen: So that could be a problem in the future?

Michel Vorenhout: Yes—it's a possible problem but in fact in the polders, the ground water table will just naturally rise because the soil depth is going down so we actually have most of the problems from the water and that will increase the problem. But the policy now is to decrease the pumping.

1.4

Reburial and Analyses of Archaeological Remains - The Raar Project.
Phase II - Project Status and New Findings

Inger Nyström Godfrey*, Thomas Bergstrand, Carola Bohm, Eva Christensson, Charlotte Gjelstrup Björdal, David Gregory, Ian MacLeod , Elizabeth E. Peacock and Vicky Richards
* E-mail and address corresponding author: inger.nystrom@vgregion.se
Studio Västsvensk Konservering (SVK), Västarvet, Gamlestadsvägen 2-4, 41502 Göteborg, Sweden.

Abstract

The general purpose of the RAAR project is to evaluate reburial as a method for long-term storage and preservation of waterlogged archaeological remains. The project and its findings after the first 3-year burial phase (2002-2005) have previously been presented at WOAM. It showed that reburial could become a valid tool for heritage management, although its usefulness might be less general than previously assumed. It was at that time too early to be conclusive and make any definitive statements regarding the long-term stability of some material such as leather, bone, antler and metals as well as some of the packing materials.

The project is designed to last for 50 years and is divided into 3 phases. With the retrieval of samples in September 2009 the second phase began. This paper will present a general overview of the project status and the recent results obtained after seven years of reburial.

Keywords: reburial, preservation, waterlogged archaeological material, cultural heritage management

1. Introduction

To protect the fragile and non-renewable archaeological heritage, non-destructive and non-intrusive conservation strategies, such as *in situ* preservation, are emphasized in the UNESCO convention of 2001. Reburial can be seen as the other side of the coin in that it seeks to emulate a pre-excavation (*in situ*) environment that has been benign for the preservation of archaeological remains for centuries. Therefore reburial and *in-situ* preservation of shipwrecks and other archaeological underwater sites represents a new field of interest that is being given increased attention. The approach offers the potential to understand and identify the processes of deterioration of archaeological materials in underwater environments. However, more importantly, it also offers the possibility to find methods of counteracting these processes and to create alternative storage for the preservation of underwater archaeological heritage.

The extensive archaeological investigations and reburial of recovered archaeological artifacts that took place in Marstrand harbor during 1998 to 1999, was the catalyst for the international reburial research project 'Reburial and Analyses of Archaeological Remains' (RAAR), which started in 2001. The project is coordinated by Bohus County Museum and Studio Västsvensk Konservering in Sweden and consists of six sub-projects coordinated in turn by museums and universities in Sweden, Denmark, Norway and Australia. (Table 1)

The general purpose of RAAR is to evaluate reburial as a method for long-term storage and preservation of waterlogged archaeological remains. Five sub-projects aim to investigate the effects of the burial environment in Marstrand harbor on a wide range of material types often encountered on archaeological

23

excavations. The stability of these materials, as well as packing and labeling products, is studied. The sixth sub-project monitors the reburial environment. (Table 1).

Figure 1. The reburial site at Marstrand.

In order to determine the long-term effects of reburial on the different material types, sufficient samples were buried to allow sampling to continue for up to 50 years. The wood, other organics, ceramics/silicates and polymeric samples were buried in Marstrand Harbor, Sweden in September 2002 (trench 1), whereas the metal sample units were buried in a separate trench (trench 2) the following year in September 2003 (Table 2 and Figure 1). The project, methodology and results from the first 3-year burial phase 2002-2005 have been reported extensively (e.g. Nyström and Bergstrand 2007; Nyström Godfrey et al. 2009). The final report for the first phase is available on the project website: http://www9.vgregion.se/vastarvet/svk/reburial/index.htm

Lack of funding meant that the 4th retrieval of samples was postponed from 2008 to 2009. With the retrieval of samples in September 2009, the second phase began. However, the funds received for the 4th retrieval were unfortunately, less than was required to follow through with the initial plan and we were forced to down size the project for this period. As it was most important to continue the analyses of materials less well studied or where results from phase

Table 1. The six subprojects and their coordinators

Sub-project	Coordinator	Institute/University
Silicates	Carola Bohm & Eva Christensson	The National Heritage Board, Sweden, (RAÄ)
Metals	Vicki Richards & Ian MacLeod	Western Australian Museum, Fremantle, Australia,(WAM)
Wood	Charlotte Björdal & Thomas Nilsson	Swedish University of Agricultural Science, Uppsala, Sweden, (SLU)
Organic non-wood material	Elizabeth Peacock	The Norwegian University of Science and Technology, Trondheim, Norway, (NTNU)
Packing and labeling materials	Inger Nyström Godfrey	Studio Västsvensk Konservering, Göteborg, Sweden, (SVK)
Environmental monitoring	David Gregory	The National Museum of Denmark, Brede, Denmark, (NM)

Table 2. *Retrieval program for the project.*

Phase	Proposed Retrieval Year	Proposed Reburial Interval (yr)	Retrieval Year	Reburial Interval (yr)	Comments
1	2003 2004 2005	1 2 3	2003 2004 2005	1 2 (1)[1] 3 (2)	Final report published in 2007
2	2008	6	2009	7 (6)	Final report due in 2010
2	2014	12			Subject to funding
3	2026	24			Subject to funding
3	2050	48			Subject to funding

[1] Number in brackets denotes the reburial interval for the metal samples, which were reburied in 2003 one year after the other sample units.

2. Summaries of the Sub Projects

2.1. Environmental monitoring

The environmental monitoring sub-project for Phase II of the RAAR project focused on three specific questions:

- What are the conditions within sediments deeper than 50cm below the sediment surface and is the 50cm reburial depth sufficient for protection?
- As the sediments in the metals reburial trench were not studied in Phase I, what are the conditions within these sediments?
- Is the environment in Marstrand harbor still conducive to the preservation of reburied archaeological material?

Following on from the completion of Phase I in 2006, sediments were examined in April 2007 and September 2009. A new system of coring was developed whereby it was possible to sample sediments to ca. 70cm below the sediment surface. Two systems were successfully used: the first, for analyzing pore water parameters and the second for analyzing sediment properties themselves. Cores were taken in an undisturbed area and from the organic and metals reburial trenches.

2.1.1 Pore water

Parameters were primarily measured using microelectrodes: dissolved oxygen, sulfide, redox potential, carbon dioxide and pH.

Aliquots of pore water were also taken for determination of sulfate content. Measurements were taken every 5cm through the cores. Results of the pore water analyses indicated that the conditions within the organic and metals reburial trenches were sub-oxic to anoxic and dominated by anaerobic processes. Dissolved oxygen levels were low: sub-oxic ($0.1 - 0.3$ mg dm^{-3}) to anoxic (<0.01 mg dm^{-3}). Redox potentials were strongly reducing with potentials between -150 and -200mV (vs SHE). pH of sediments were near neutral (pH $7 - 7.5$). The processes ongoing in the sediments were dominated by sulfate reduction, where generally a loss of sulfate was seen with increasing depth with the concomitant evolution of sulfide.

2.1.2 Sediment analyses

Were carried out on sections taken every 5cm through the cores. In each section the porosity, particle size, loss on ignition (organic content) and iron content were determined. The analyses of the sediments themselves showed there was a distinct difference between those used in the two reburial trenches. In both trenches the upper 30cm consisted of porous (porosity of 0.8), coarse silts with high organic content ($20 - 30\%$ weight/dry weight). In the metals trench (trench 2), sediments were graded to medium silts below 30cm and were still porous with a relatively high organic content. In the organic trench (trench 1) after 40 cm the sediment consisted of very fine, low porous (porosity of 0.4) sands with a low organic content (ca. 5% weight/dry weight).

In both trenches the profiles of sulfate and sulfide showed that the rates of sulfate reduction were highest in finer grained sediments with high organic contents (Figures 2 and 3). Seasonal changes in the rate of reduction were seen in the metals trench, surprisingly with rates higher in April than in September. Modeling mineralization of organic material due to sulfate reduction showed that ca. 80g and 44g of organic material per m^2 per year could be oxidized in the metals trench in April and September, respectively. Sulfate had been completely reduced at a depth of 50 – 60 cm in both April 2007 and September 2009. In the organic trench (trench 1) sulfate reduction was also the dominant process. The rate of mineralization of organic material was lower at ca. 20g per m^2 per year and there did not appear to be a significant seasonal variation. Not all sulfate had been utilized in the organic trench (trench 1), but sulfate reduction ceased at ca. 40 cm below the sediment surface where the concentration remained at about 7mM from 35 cm down to 65cm (Figure 3).

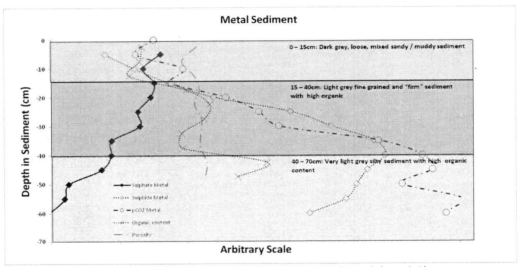

Figure 2. Results (September 2009) of sediment analyses in the Metal trench (trench 2).

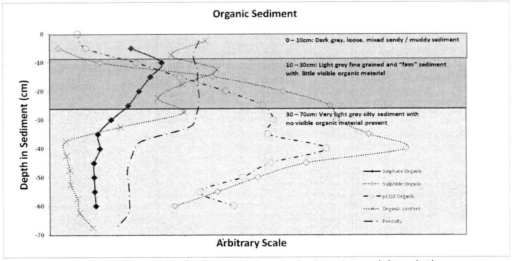

Figure 3. Results (September 2009) of sediment analyses in the Organic trench (trench 1)

26

2.1.3. General implications for reburial

Phase II has shown the importance of understanding the processes ongoing within a given sediment prior to carrying out any reburial. This was seen when comparing the results from the two trenches. The optimal depth of reburial has been a point of discussion throughout the project and the results of Phase II have assisted in answering some of the questions that have arisen over the years. These results show that it is not simply a matter of depth of burial per se, but the type of sediment used, its properties and the processes ongoing within it – all of which vary from sediment to sediment. Based on the results from Marstrand the implications for reburial are that sandy sediments, which are less porous and naturally contain less organic material due to their larger particle size, appear to have lower rates of mineralization when the dominant process is sulfate reduction. This contrasts with the higher rates of mineralization in more porous, finer grained sediment with higher organic contents.

These factors could be used to our advantage when reburying; for instance the use of coarse grained sediment with inclusion of a layer of "sacrificial organic matter" in order to "induce" mineralization in the upper sediment; in this way it may not be necessary to rebury archaeological materials so deeply.

In order to classify sediments for their potential use in future reburial projects it is recommended that the following parameters, at least, be measured and that the time (season) of sampling be considered:

- Pore water parameters: Dissolved oxygen, redox potential, pH, dissolved and total iron, sulfate and sulfide content, temperature.
- Sediment parameters: Particle size, porosity, organic content.

2.2. Metals

The aim of the metals sub-project is to investigate the corrosion behavior of metals buried in the marine environment. The corrosion of modern metal coupons reburied in the sediment and exposed to the open marine environment will be examined and compared over time. This study will ascertain the effect of reburial on the deterioration of archaeological metals commonly found on underwater cultural heritage sites and assist in evaluating the effectiveness of reburial as a long-term *in-situ* preservation strategy for metallic archaeological remains.

The sample units consisted of prefabricated proprietary metal coupons of known metal composition mounted utilizing high density polyethylene (HDPE) materials. The metal coupons deployed in the experiment were ferrous alloys: duplicate coupons of cast iron and mild steel and one standard Defense Science and Technology Organization (DSTO) copper steel coupon and copper alloys: duplicate coupons of brass, copper and bronze. The ferrous and copper alloys were mounted separately to minimize galvanic and proximity corrosion since the latter form of decay has been known to exert its effects over separation distances of many meters on historic shipwreck sites (North 1989). Each sample unit consisted of three sets of duplicate metal coupons mounted at three different depth intervals (totally exposed above the sediment, just below the sediment and buried 50cm in the sediment) on the HDPE rod (Figure 4).

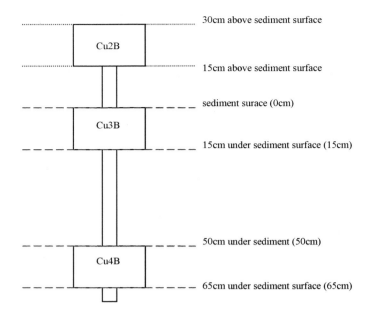

30cm above sediment surface

Cu2B

15cm above sediment surface

sediment surace (0cm)

Cu3B

15cm under sediment surface (15cm)

50cm under sediment (50cm)

Cu4B

65cm under sediment surface (65cm)

Figure 4. *Schematic diagram and image of the completed copper alloy coupon sample unit retrieved in 2004.*

In September 2009, six years after the initial reburial in 2003, the third set of metal sample units (copper and iron alloys) were retrieved. Each sample unit was removed by physically extracting the rods from the sediment and the corrosion parameters (E_{corr} and pH) of each coupon measured *in-situ* on the seabed prior to recovery. The metal coupons were documented and each coupon with the associated corrosion products was analyzed by scanning electron microscopy/electron dispersive x-ray analysis (SEM/EDAX). One of the duplicate coupons was then chemically stripped of all corrosion products, weighed and analyzed again by the same technique. Digital electron micrographs (SEM) and energy dispersive x-ray analyses (EDAX) were collected as the primary data.

At the end of six years it is clear that the precise burial microenvironment plays a major role in determining the fate of the metal coupons. From extended and detailed analyses of the surfaces and their corrosion products, weight loss data and the in-situ corrosion potential measurements it is possible to gain a good understanding of the parameters that dominate the deterioration of the metals. The effect of the reburial environment on the extent of corrosion of the metals after six years is summarized below.

- It is very important to fully understand the physico-chemical and biological nature of the local sedimentary environment prior to deployment of any reburial strategy.

- It was found that the behavior and characteristics of the metal surfaces that were fully exposed to the local microenvironment provided a better insight into long term corrosion of metals in a marine environment than the side that lay directly against the HDPE support plate despite the pre-drilled flow holes. However the complimentary data collected from this reverse side provided corroboration of the overall corrosion mechanism and provided an insight into how variations in the microenvironment affect the corrosion processes.

- The manner in which metals are packed for reburial is extremely important.

- Metals of significantly different composition must be physically separated by sufficient distance to avoid the complications of galvanic and proximity corrosion and even artifacts of similar composition should be separated in some way (e.g. geotextile barrier) to minimize abrasion and damage to the inherently protective corrosion product layer.

- Copper alloy artifacts recovered from a saline environment should always be stored wet. It was noted that desiccation can cause changes in the nature of the surface corrosion products that may not accurately reflect the microenvironment from which the object was recovered.

- If further analysis of the corrosion product layer and underlying residual metal will be undertaken in the context of the deposition and site formation processes then all metal artifacts should be stored in a similar environment to that from which they had been recovered (e.g. deoxygenated environments if the artifact is recovered from under the sediment). For example, both the copper and the ferrous alloy plates from above the sediment where stored in a low oxygen environment after recovery, which caused a significant change in the nature of the corrosion products. This could have lead to misinterpretation of the local microenvironment and the corrosion mechanisms and hence, the associated archaeological record.

- It is vitally important that metals are reburied to depths where there is no chance of partial exposure to the aerobic marine environment through sediment movement, since the non-ferrous metal coupons were found to be particularly sensitive to being in a mixed aerobic/anaerobic microenvironment.

- The resistance of a metal to corrosion is very dependent on the elemental composition and the associated microstructure, which records the impact of fabrication processes and depositional stress.

- The reburial environments surrounding the metal coupons have finally stabilized and as a result the long term corrosion processes and associated mechanisms are becoming better indicators of the final corrosion outcomes.

- The concretions and corrosion product layers on the metal coupons are more extensively developed than after the first two years of exposure/reburial and therefore, the coupons are beginning to more accurately reflect the corrosion behavior of marine archaeological metal artifacts.

- The extent of corrosion of all metal coupons decreased once the coupons were buried, even at shallow depths and this protective effect increased with increasing burial depth. This decrease was most marked for the brass and bronze coupons, but much less dramatic for the ferrous alloy coupons. Burial seemed to have the least effect on the pure copper coupons, however the extent of corrosion of the exposed copper coupons was also very low. The single phase and pure composition of the copper coupons combined with the benign marine environment to create a non-aggressive test.

- Despite a general decrease in the extent of corrosion with burial, all metal coupons exposed to the three different environments (exposed, buried just below the sediment and buried 50cm below the sediment), showed some increase in corrosion rate over the past four years. The greatest increases were found for the bronze and ferrous metal coupons buried at both depth intervals but the rate increases for the buried brass and copper coupons were considerably less. These results indicate that the greatest microenvironmental changes are occurring in the sediment and these changes are mainly affecting the corrosion behavior of the buried bronze and ferrous alloy coupons.

- It appears that reburial has the most positive effect on brasses and to a lesser extent, bronzes. This significant decrease in corrosion would be primarily due to the biological toxicity of copper, zinc and tin corrosion products, which inhibit concretion formation and corrosion by effectively limiting bacterial counts in the surrounding sediment. The bronze coupons show more corrosion than the brass coupons as the three different phases in the bronze microstructure have significantly different electrochemical voltages as compared to the brass microstructure, which causes increased intergranular (micro-galvanic) corrosion.
- Reburial has less affect on the preservation of pure copper as it is a single phase alloy, with uniform composition and therefore, exhibit less intergranular galvanic corrosion.
- This positive effect of burial is significantly reduced on ferrous alloys due to the fact that iron corrosion products can be utilized by microbes and therefore, microbially induce corrosion (MIC) can become more significant in controlling the corrosion rates than direct access to dissolved oxygen.
- Since the major process ongoing in the Marstrand sediments is sulfate reduction and the metals trench contains sulfate, albeit at low concentrations at deeper depths and significant quantities of organic

matter, , it is probable that sulfate reducing bacteria are causing microbially influenced corrosion of the buried ferrous alloy coupons.

Based on the 2009 results, copper alloys could be recommended for reburial in these types of sediments for a period of six years. It is probable that pure copper and brass alloy types may be buried for longer periods of time and at shallower depths, however more information from the next phase of the experiment is required to support this inference. On the other hand, due to the significant increase in corrosion rate of the bronze coupons over the past four years, it is not possible to recommend longer term reburial times for these alloy types at this point in time. Conversely, ferrous alloys could not be recommended for reburial even in the medium term, based on their extensive degradation after six years and the significant increases in their corrosion rates since 2005, which may indicate that corrosion will increase parabolically over time. Evidently, even after six years, it is still difficult to make any definitive statements regarding the longer term stability of these alloy types and therefore, it is of paramount importance that this project continues to the next phase, so as much information as possible regarding the corrosion processes of these metal coupons can be obtained, to establish whether or not the present conclusions are real indicators of the effects of the different microenvironments on long-term metal corrosion and whether reburial is indeed, an appropriate preservation strategy for maritime archaeological metals.

2.3. Silicates
In order to study the effects of reburial in a marine environment, twelve categories of silicate samples, typically found at shipwreck sites, were chosen for this sub-project. Each material category has been reburied in three different packing envelopes: zip-lock bags, plastic netting,

and geotextile to ascertain if preservation of the samples is affected by packing methods. Samples were deposited in perforated HDPE crates. In Tables 3 and 4 the material categories are listed along with the preliminary results from Phase I.

The analyses of the glass and ceramic samples retrieved in 2009, after seven years of burial, have, in many instances, been a confirmation of the results from the first phase of the project. However, it has also provided some new and intriguing features that have raised questions concerning local microenvironments in the burial trench, although this does not appear to be confirmed by the environmental data. It might simply be attributed to the longer period of burial.

An apparent difference in the deterioration process is manifested in the model potash glass samples. It is the texture, rather than the chemical composition of the weathering layers of these samples that differs strongly from that of the earlier samples, in that it is hard and sugary and adheres more strongly to the substrate. All the earlier samples have been conspicuously and increasingly flaking. The rate of deterioration – one of the questions raised by the results of Phase I – has not abated as is illustrated in Figure 5. The zip-lock bags still prove to be inhibiting, whereas the netting seems to allow for quicker leaching of the alkali components and thereby, loss of coherence in the surface layers.

Tables 3. Summary of the results for the glass samples

Archaeological samples		Model samples	
Clear table glass	Bottle glass, green	Soda glass	Potash glass
Thin iridescent surface layers with reduced alkali levels.	Thick silica-rich surface layers with areas of elevated NaCl, S, Fe	Accelerating depletion of Na	Depletion of alkali components in surface layers
Surface exfoliation	Heavy surface exfoliation		Severe disintegration and loss of surface
One sample in zip-lock bag broken	No clear difference between reburied sample and reference		Zip-lock bag represses leaching, but promotes biological growth
			Discoloration of weathered layers

Table 4. Summary of the results for the ceramic samples

Archaeological samples				Modern samples			
Porous			Non-porous	Porous		Non-porous	
Earthenware lead glazed	Flintware, lead glazed	Clay pipes	Stoneware, salt glazed	Earthenware low-fired	Flintware, lead glazed	Stoneware, feldspatic glaze	Porcelain, feldspatic glaze
No visible alteration	No visible alteration	Black stained in wet condition	No visible alteration	Severe disintegration	No visible alteration	No alteration	No alteration
Absorption of NaCl, S	Absorption of NaCl, S	Absorption of NaCl, S, Fe	Traces of NaCl, S	Absorbed NaCl, S	Some absorption of NaCl		

31

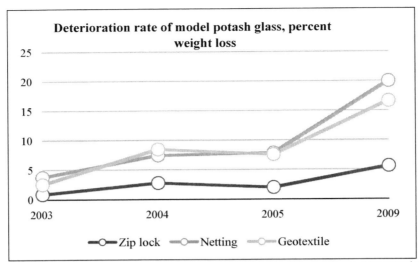

Figure 5. Model potash glass packed in zip-lock bags, netting and geotextile envelopes. Measured weight loss after reburial for1, 2, 3 and 7 years' burial

Another question that arose from the earlier retrievals was the nature of biological growth detected on all the samples of model potash glass deposited in zip-lock bags. The organisms are again present on the 2009 samples, but do not appear to have grown or expanded (Figure 6). At high magnification, groups of pits can be seen on the glass surface, which correspond in size and shape to the detected micro-organisms and could be a sign of etching caused by them (Figure 7). Investigations into these phenomena are on-going, but not conclusive and the organisms have not yet been identified.

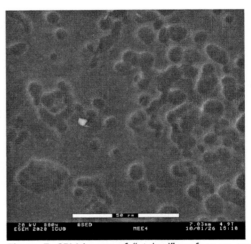

Figure 7. SEM-image of "etched" surface on model potash glass

Although the model soda glass samples still appear undeteriorated to the naked eye, the SEM-analyses reveal a continuing depletion of sodium from the superficial layers and the sample packed in the zip-lock bag is now starting to show tendencies of flaking. The leaching is most consistently observed in the samples deposited in netting where the sodium remaining at the surface after seven years of burial has decreased by a full third. Leaching is, however, observed in all three packing systems, but generally least in the zip-lock bags.

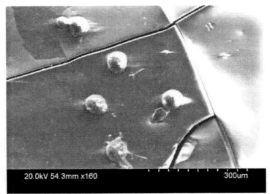

Figure 6. SEM-image of model potash glass with micro-organisms on the surface

On the archaeological glass, little change has been observed as compared to earlier retrievals.

Most samples of a porous nature, the earthenware, flintware and clay pipes, as well as the depleted, layered surfaces of the glass samples can be seen to include ever higher concentrations of both sulfides/sulfates and chlorides. Non-porous modern samples, porcelain and stoneware, are generally still quite unaltered, as seen both visually and in the elemental analyses.

Tentative recommendations for reburial provided after the conclusion of Phase I, still stand. The only material categories that might be considered "safe" for reburial are porcelain, stoneware and clay pipes.

2.4. Organic Non-Wood Materials

The non-wood organic materials sub-project of RAAR is evaluating the effect of burial in a marine environment on the more sensitive non-wood organic materials that make up the marine archaeological record. Samples have been drawn from modern materials of vegetable-tanned leather, undyed and dyed (madder, indigo and weld) woven wool fabric (vadmel), raw (grey) woven linen fabric, undyed woven silk fabric, hemp rope, tarred/treated cotton fishing net, antler, horn, and fresh bovine bone (metapodials). Dyestuffs, tanning agents and pre-treatments of the experimental materials were kept as close to those used in antiquity or historical times as practically possible. One sample of each material was sewn into a nylon open mesh envelope, and half of these envelopes were further enclosed in envelopes made of a non-woven geotextile fabric. One set each of the geotextile-covered and uncovered samples was laced side-by-side with nylon cord in the bottom of a perforated plastic tray (Figure 8).

The materials included in this study are modern in origin, and thus at the outset do not simulate burial-degraded archaeological artifacts of similar materials or artifacts recovered from a marine burial environment. For these materials the study is of burial rather than reburial. Moreover, the sample materials were not packed in polyethylene or similar slow-biodegradable packaging film to protect them from interaction with the surrounding sediment solution and sediment. Artifacts of these materials selected for deposition in a marine archive would undoubtedly be packaged prior to deposition. Therefore, these results reflect degradation of non-protected materials and of materials once the protective packaging fails either through leakage or failure of the packaging material itself.

Figure 8. The non-wood organic materials sample unit containing one uncovered and one covered set of samples before burial in September 2002 in the harbor at Marstrand

All the non-wood materials included in this study exhibited degradation as the result of one- to seven-years burial in 50cm of sediment in Marstrand harbor. In this seven-year timeframe there was no indication that the degradation was leveling off to establish an equilibrium state. Results indicate that the geotextile envelope offers protection from microorganisms within the sediment and isolates the material inside from some micro-structural alteration. The envelope does not appear to protect against chemical alteration.

One aim of RAAR has been to assist in evaluating the technique of reburial in the marine environment as an alternative to traditional museum storage for marine archaeological finds. The Phase I three-year burial period was sufficient to be able to draw conclusions for the fiber based materials included in the study, but was not long enough to be able to draw conclusions with regard to recommendations for or against long-term reburial for leather, bone and antler (Peacock 2007, Nyström Godfrey et al. 2009, Peacock and Turner-Walker 2009).

Results of the Phase II seven-year burial period support results of the Phase I burial period in that deterioration has progressed in the same manner as revealed at the end of Phase I. Based upon Phase II results, fiber artifacts and horn are not recommended for reburial; whereas, leather, bone and antler could be reburied for at least a period of seven years (Table 6). The twelve- and twenty-four year retrievals will be important determinants for making long-term recommendation for these latter materials.

Finds of the more perishable organic materials, especially fiber-based ones such as textile fabrics, basketry and rope make up a small percent of total recovered artifacts from the sea both in number of items and in physical bulk. Being a rarer category of find they are usually given a higher priority, and it is less likely that such finds would be selected for reburial. The exception could be in instances where large volumes of similar rope/cables, nets and sails are recovered, in which case representative samples might be conserved with the remaining finds reburied. Regardless, fiber materials are demanding in that their conservation is labor-intensive and therefore costly. In a water-degraded condition their polymer

substance is highly degraded and their physical structure disintegrated. Frequently in an attempt to preserve physical integrity such artifacts must be recovered together with their surrounding sediment matrix as blocklifts. Once documented, analyzed and accessioned into an archive, these artifacts are not likely to be robust enough to survive the reburial process. Finds of basketry, nets and rope/cables also fall into this category.

Based upon the Phase I results for the modern fiber-based materials investigated, buried at a depth of 50 cm in harbor sediment, it was already concluded after three years burial that reburial cannot be recommended for recovered fiber artifacts. The exception is tarred cables recovered in massive amounts, which due to their physical bulk and the biocidal effect of the tar coating will survive for a longer period.

Finds of leather can make up a sizeable portion of non-wood organic artifacts recovered from a marine site. It is possible that following full documentation leather artifacts may be selected for reburial in a marine environment. Based upon the Phase II results for the modern vegetable-tanned leather buried at a depth of 50 cm in porous and sandy sediment with a low organic content as in trench 1, short-term reburial can be recommended for recovered tanned leather artifacts.

The marine reburial of skeletal material poses several potential problems. Human skeletal remains require specialized handling and disposal protocols because of the obvious culturally sensitive nature of the material. It is highly unlikely that reburial at sea is suggested for human remains unless this involves returning bones to a recognized war grave. Horn and antler are such rare finds in marine archaeological sites that it is very unlikely that any finds made of these materials as well as worked bone would be selected for reburial. Only animal bones are likely to be selected for reburial/disposal at sea.

Based upon the Phase II results for the modern hard animal products investigated, buried at a depth of 50 cm in porous and sandy sediment with a low organic content as in trench 1, short-term reburial can be recommended for recovered bone ecofacts and antler; although, as mentioned above, antler may not be selected due to its less-frequent nature as a material.

It is advised that all material be packaged in materials recommended by the polymer sub-project, and buried in sediments with low microbiological activity. The burial depth should be determined based on the results of the environmental monitoring

2.5 Packing and labeling materials
As reburial of archaeological material is anticipated to last for an extended period, the packing and labeling materials need to be able to survive for the same period of time. Consequently the durability of these products is of great importance.

This sub-project focus on how a burial environment will affect the mechanical properties of some relevant packing products, mainly made from different polymers, and if different types of labels and written identifications can be read after being exposed to a marine sediment environment. Apart from in-situ exposure, Phase I also included accelerated ageing in the laboratory of some materials. Those results were reported at WOAM 2007 (Nyström Godfrey, 2009).

Table 5 shows all materials investigated in the sub-project. Due to lack of funding, tensile strength of some of these materials could not be tested in 2009. The materials excluded were chosen on the basis of bad preservation results in Phase 1 or their importance in the archaeological process.

The labeling materials were investigated using ocular inspection and colorimetric analyses and the mechanical strength of the packing materials was evaluated by tensile testing. Results were compared with references and previously retrieved samples.

When commercial products are studied a few problems arise. One is that the complete content of a specific product can be difficult to obtain because of trade secrets. Therefore only the main ingredient(s), the base material, of each product can be given in a study like this. Hence conclusions from the analyses in this study are valid primarily for the tested products and to a lesser extent for the base materials.

We know from previous results (Nyström Godfrey 2009) that the wooden crate (B) and the polyethylene net (D) had lost considerable strength already after 3 years. After seven years in the marine sediments the mechanical strength of the HDPE crate (A), the polyethylene bag (C), the polyethylene/polypropylene geotextile (F), the polyethylene rope and the PETR/PUR prefabricated tag (N) is unchanged. The polyester rope (J) is still strong, but the Max Load has decreased from 800 to 625 N and it could be considered a trend (Figure 9) that may make a polyester rope less suitable for long term reburials, however, this will have to be confirmed through future analyses.

The interpretation of the tensile tests on the polyamide products cord (L) and yarn (M) was inconclusive after phase I. Polyamide is a material sensitive to humidity. Moisture does not affect the ageing, but it strongly affects the strength of the material (Almström pers. comm.). The inconclusive and odd results for the mechanical strength in Phase I was thought to be a result of differences in moisture content and re-crystallization, despite all samples being conditioned in the same manner.

Table 5. *Packing and labeling materials tested*

Sample ID	Product	Material	Abbreviation	Tested in phase 1	Tested in phase 2 - 2009
A	Crate	Polyethylene	HDPE	x	x
B	Crate	Pine		x	.
C	Bag	Polyethylene	LDPE	x	x
D	Net	Polyethylene	PE	x	
E	Sack, woven	Polypropylene	PP	x	
F	Geotextile	Polyethylene/ Polypropylene	PP/PE	x	x
G	Geotextile	Polyester		x	
H	Tarpaulin	Synthetic rubber	EPDM	x	
J	Cord	Polyester		x	x
K	Cord	Polyethylene	PE	x	x
L	Cord, spun	Polyamide	PA	x	x
M	Yarn	Polyamide	PA	x	x
N	Tag, prefabricated	Polyether/ Polyurethane	PETR/PUR	x	x
O	Tag, Dymo ®	Polyvinyl chloride	PVC	x	x
P	Tag, Dymo ®	Steel		x	x
Q	Marker	Permanent ink on PE bag		x	x
R	Marker for OH	Permanent ink on PE bag		x	x
S	Pen, ball point	Archival proof ink on PE bag		x	x
T	Pencil	Graphite on PE - bag		x	x

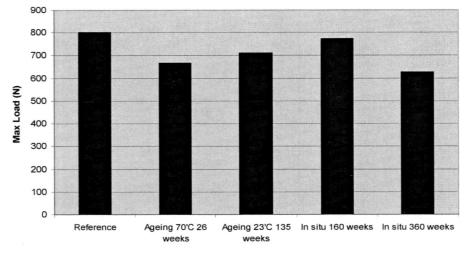

Figure 9. *Diagram showing the tensile strength of the polyester rope (J) after accelerated ageing in the laboratory and exposed in situ in the sediments in Marstrand.*

The tests performed on the 2009 in situ samples showed no degradation of the mechanical properties (Figure 10), smaller variations are within standard deviation. This suggests that it is be suitable for reburial. However, it would be wise to wait for future analyses before making statements of the long term preservation of polyamide in anaerobic reburial environments.

After seven years of burial all labels were easily readable with the naked eye. Ocular inspection and chromaticity readings show, however, that text written with the black marker, Stabilo OHpen Universal (R) and the blue archival proof pen, Svenskt arkiv (S) had continued to deteriorate and change quite considerable. The lead "graphite" pencil writing (T) had not changed at all, likewise with the permanent marker Edding 404 (Q).

It is therefore recommended to use pencils or markers of good permanent quality and not for example, over-head markers, as the one tested. As the archival ink pen (S) showed signs of degradation in this particular environment it is not suitable for anaerobic clay sediments. Another reason to avoid this pen is the fineness of the tip of the pen, which makes the lines very thin and difficult to read when the ink fades and changes in color.

Although the prefabricated and Dymo labels all looked good after seven years of burial, the steel label is difficult to read. It is also known that stainless steel corrodes in anaerobic environments due to the action of the sulfate reducing bacteria, which would make it a less attractive choice. A better choice for labeling artifacts reburied in sediments would be to use PVC Dymo labels or prefabricated embossed tags, so called "ear-tags". Table 7 summarizes the results and evaluations of the stability of the tested materials.

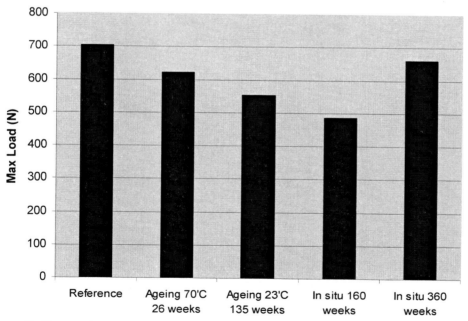

Figure 10. Diagram showing the tensile strength of the polyamide rope (L) after accelerated ageing in the laboratory and exposed in situ in the sediments in Marstrand.

3. Discussion and Conclusion

3.1. Findings of the RAAR project after seven years of burial

Phase II has so far confirmed most of the results from the previous phase, both with regards to the environmental and material studies. It has underlined the importance of understanding the processes ongoing within a given sediment prior to carrying out any reburial. If any form of reburial is to be successful, the primary aim should be to understand the agents of deterioration on a site or artifact and develop and implement mitigation strategies. Sites that are buried tend to be better preserved due to the limited oxygen levels, which minimizes chemical, physical and especially biological deterioration.

The optimal depth of reburial is not simply a matter of depth of burial per se, but the type of sediment used, its properties and the processes ongoing within it, which vary from sediment to sediment. Porosity and organic content in particular will have an effect on the rates of microbial activity. The lower the porosity and organic content the better the sediment is for preservation of archaeological materials.

The degradation processes have not yet stabilized for many of the tested materials and future analyses will be required in order to provide more conclusive evidence regarding reburial as a preservation strategy. Therefore, it is of paramount importance that this project continues so that as much information as possible can be obtained regarding the degradation processes of the test materials. This information, in conjunction with analyses of actual shipwreck artifacts, will allow evaluation of the long-term effectiveness of reburial as a preferred means of preservation for archaeological remains.

Although the RAAR Marstrand investigation aims to provide informed guidelines for the reburial of recovered marine artifacts in the seabed, the various sub-projects are yielding information of a much broader nature. At the outset, it might be questioned as to why more perishable organic materials are included in such a reburial study when it is not likely that artifacts of such materials would be selected for reburial. At the same time that the study provides information on the preservation of materials in and above the seabed, it sheds light on deterioration processes and contributes knowledge to artifact conservation. For example, the non-wood organic sub-project is providing insight into the properties of dyestuffs, which can slow the deterioration rate of dyed wool fabric. This confirms anecdotal evidence for the better preservation of madder-dyed wool in actual artifacts. Furthermore, it is noted that many of these same experimental materials have been or will be included in other actualistic burial studies; thus providing a comparative degradation/preservation dataset with broader implications than just the RAAR study (Peacock et al. this volume, Richards et al 2009, Turner-Walker and Peacock 2008, Peacock 2004).

Based on the results from the first and second phases (7 years of exposure) of the Marstrand reburial project, some conclusions can be drawn and recommendations made from a reburial viewpoint. These are summarized below and in Tables 6 and 7.

Table 6. *Recommendations on archaeological materials suited for reburial in anaerobic sediments with low microbiological activity (low porous, sandy sediments with low organic content). X marks the type of material suitable or not to reburials.*

Material	Long-term reburial possible*	Short-term reburial possible – at least 7 years	Reburial not recommended
Metals	copper & brass	bronze	ferrous alloys
Porcelain	x	x	
Stone ware	x	x	
Clay pipes	x	x	
Earthen ware, low-fired			x
Glass			x
Wood	x	x	
Fiber artifacts			x
Tanned leather		x	
Animal bones		x	
Antler		x	
Horn			x

*The suitability of these material types for long term reburial has been suggested but these predictions are to be confirmed through future retrievals.

Table 7. *Recommendations on packing and labeling materials suitable for reburial in anaerobic sediments with low microbiological activity.*

Sample ID	Product	Material	Long-term reburial possible*	Short-term reburial possible – at least 7 years	Reburial not recommended
A	Crate	Polyethylene, HDPE	x	x	
B	Crate	Pine			x
C	Bag	Polyethylene, LDPE	x	x	
D	Net	Polyethylene			x
E	Sack, woven	Polypropylene		x**	
F	Geotextile	Polyethylene/ Polypropylene	x	x	
G	Geotextile	Polyester		x**	
H	Tarpaulin	Synthetic rubber	x	x**	
J	Cord	Polyester		x	
K	Cord	Polyethylene	x	x	
L	Cord, spun	Polyamide		x	
M	Yarn	Polyamide		x	
N	Tag, prefabricated	Polyether/ Polyurethane	x	x	
O	Tag, dymo ®	Polyvinyl chloride	x	x	
P	Tag, dymo ®	Stainless steel		x	x
Q	Marker	Permanent ink	x	x	
R	Marker for OH	Permanent ink		x	x
S	Pen, ball point	Archival proof ink		x	x
T	Pencil	Graphite	x	x	

* The suitability of these material types for long term reburial has been suggested but these predictions are to be confirmed through future retrievals.
** These materials were only tested after 3 years of exposure, hence short term reburial of less than 3 years can only be safely recommended, however it is highly likely that at least the EPDM tarpaulin is suitable for long term reburial

The organic reburial trench (trench 1) in Marstrand appears to have generally good preservation conditions for the reburied artifacts and the experimental samples. The reburial sediments consisted of very fine, low porosity (0.4) sands with low organic content (ca. 5% weight/dry weight). At the depths where the artifacts and most of the material samples are buried (~ 50cm) the sediments are anoxic and strongly reducing with the predominant ongoing process being sulfate reduction.

1. It is recommended that the following pore water parameters are measured and that the season of sampling are considered: Dissolved oxygen, redox potential, pH, dissolved and total iron, sulfate and sulfide content, temperature.

2. It is recommended that the following sediment parameters are measured and that the season of sampling are considered: Particle size, porosity, organic content.

3. The reburial environments surrounding the metal coupons have finally stabilized and as a result the long term corrosion processes and associated mechanisms are becoming better indicators of the final corrosion outcomes.

4. The concretions and corrosion product layers on the metal coupons are more extensively developed than after the first two years of exposure/reburial and therefore, the coupons are beginning to more accurately reflect the corrosion behavior of marine archaeological metal artifacts.

5. The extent of corrosion of all metal coupons decreased significantly once the coupons were buried, even at shallow depths and this protective effect increased with increasing burial depth.

6. Despite a general decrease in the extent of corrosion with burial, all metal coupons showed some increase in corrosion rate over the past four years.

7. Copper alloys could be recommended for reburial in these types of sediments for a period of six years. It is probable that pure copper and brass alloy types may be buried for longer periods of time and at shallower depths, however more information from the next phase of the experiment is required to support this inference. On the other hand, due to the significant increase in corrosion rate of the bronze coupons over the past four years, it is not possible to recommend longer term reburial times for these alloy types at this point in time.

8. Ferrous alloys could not be recommended for reburial even in the medium term, based on their extensive degradation after six years and the significant increases in their corrosion rates since 2005, which may indicate that corrosion will increase significantly over time.

9. Reburial cannot be recommended for any type of glass.

10. Reburial cannot be recommended for low-fired earthenware. However, the resistance of earthenware in a marine environment varies, largely depending on the firing conditions during manufacture. The poor results for the very low-fired 'modern' earthenware samples after seven years of reburial cannot be extrapolated to issue a general recommendation against reburial of earthenware.

11. High-fired ceramic wares, such as porcelain, stoneware and also clay pipes are highly stable and should survive reburial processes but consideration should still be given to the problems of over-glaze decoration and gilding on porcelain and salt infiltration in clay pipes and less high-fired stoneware.

12. Reburial is a simple, useful and effective method for decreasing wood degradation. Wooden structures above

the sediment, in saline seawater degrade very fast.

13. A burial depth of at least 50 cm is recommended for wooden artifacts, and further studies on degradation on even greater depths in combination with knowledge on individual site parameters will be most important for decisions on the thickness of the applied protective layer.

14. Burial is not recommended for fiber artifacts, with the possible exception of large tarred cables/ropes, if similar representative samples are conserved.

15. Soft and hard animal products like leather, bone and antler can be considered for short-term reburial, at least 7 years, in porous and sandy sediment with low content of organic matter. The actual depth will have to be chosen according to the individual site. In Marstrand (trench 1) a depth greater than 40 cm was sufficient.

16. A general viewpoint is that reburial should be avoided if artifacts have decorative surfaces or show traces of production or wear.

17. With respect to packing materials, zip-lock bags generally seemed to offer the best protection against degradation and/or infiltration of salts. Geotextile readily allows for free flow of soluble salts, but protects against direct influence of the burial sediment. It possibly offers some protection from micro-organisms within the sediment and isolates the material inside from some micro-structural alteration, but it does not appear to protect against chemical alteration. Finally, polyethylene netting offers the least protection and should be avoided.

18. The zip-lock bags can cause a micro-climate. Micro-organisms were detected on the model potash glass deposited in zip-lock bags and corresponding pits were seen on the glass surface and could be a sign of etching.

19. Appropriate containers for groups of finds include high-density polyethylene crates, polyethylene bags and geotextile envelopes, with the former the most highly recommended.

20. Polyethylene, polyamide and polyester cords are suitable to tie and secure artifacts and labels for short term reburials (at least 7 years). For longer term reburials polyethylene ropes are recommended at this stage.

21. Preferred options for identifying finds include the use of prefabricated tags (live stock 'ear tags'), embossed PVC labels (eg. Dymo® labels), pencils or black permanent markers. Ballpoint pens, even those labeled, as 'archival' should not be used.

22. Recovered marine archaeological organic materials routinely undergo desalination at an early stage of post-excavation processing. It is important that the use of this method be re-evaluated in circumstances in which finds may be selected for later reburial in a saline marine environment. Problems may arise with rewetting dried-out organic materials for reburial.

3.2 Consequences for heritage management

The consequences for heritage management discussed previously in Nyström Godfrey et al. 2009 are still valid. The new findings from the last four years of exposure in the sediments have not changed the overall picture but have improved the overall understanding of reburial by providing information that was not conclusive after the completion of the first phase.

There remains three ways of dealing with physical finds from an excavation: conservation, reburial and disposal. Again, it is vital to stress that reburied artifacts are not meant to be forgotten in the sediments, nor should reburial be chosen instead of conscious disposal of artifacts that have been evaluated as of no use based on, for example, scientific, technological, educational, or aesthetic grounds. In the same way as traditional conservation and storage preserves an object for study or exhibition purposes, artifact reburial is also designed for preservation so that it can be accessed and researched in the future. If there are no thoughts or ideas about future needs or use of an artifact or a collection, there seems little point preserving it at all. This might lead to some problems, since it would perhaps be easy to use reburial as an "artifact dump" when the decision to discard is difficult or controversial. However, it is important to make a clear distinction between reburial and disposal.

It is possible and maybe even preferable, that stipulated time frames be part of a reburial strategy, i.e. depending on the materials to be reburied, a reburial program will be designed to last a certain number of years, decades or maybe even centuries. It should not however, become the end solution. Reburial could be used as a short-term storage solution while securing funding to cover conservation, traditional storage and/or extensive analyses. It could also be a preferred option for long-term storage if current analytical or investigative methods are not suitable, or if artifacts or collections are to be kept in a 'capsule' awaiting analysis to answer future research questions, improved analytical techniques and/or the development of more suitable conservation treatments. Concerning time frames, future intentions with regard to reburied artifacts or collections of artifacts should be stated before a reburial is commenced to force creative thinking and planning as well as to prevent creation of a 'reburial dump'. The idea that a reburial exists within a specified time frame is consistent with results of the physical preservation of material in anaerobic sediments. Neither analytical results nor any scientists would guarantee an unlimited preservation time for any type of material in anaerobic marine sediments or, for that matter, in most environments.

Following the above discussion a heritage institution could provide short- or long-term curation for some part of its archaeological archive by using reburial depots provided they are used within certain guidelines formulated based on the results of rigorous scientific research.

3.3 Future
The findings after seven years have revealed and confirmed many interesting results and have so far generally fulfilled the objectives of the project. However, seven years of exposure in the sediments of Marstrand is for some materials an insufficient time for degradation processes to take place and for other materials to stabilize. Some conclusions are therefore pending or awaiting confirmation from the results from next experimental phase. Further analyses and more comprehensive studies over a longer period of time is of great importance before more complete conclusions can be drawn on reburial as a tool for heritage management.

The participating institutions have all announced their willingness to continue with Phase II of the project, which also includes retrieval in 2014 and we hope that the project managers will find the funds to enable the second phase to continue.

Acknolwedgements
This phase of the RAAR project was undertaken thanks to funding provided by the National Heritage Board in Sweden, the Nordic Cultural Fund, Carl Jacob Lindebergs Fornminnesfond and Wilhelm och Martina Lundgrens Vetenskapsfond. Each co-coordinating institution has contributed funds to this project in varying degrees by providing work time for the co-coordinators, covering analytical costs, etc. This self-funding is quite substantial in

some cases and the project is in great debt to these institutions.

References

Almström S., (pers. comm. 2009), SP Technical Research Institute of Sweden.

Bergstrand T. and Nyström Godfrey I. (editors), (2007), Reburial and Analyses of Archaeological Remains. Studies on the Effect of Reburial on Archaeological Materials Performed in Marstrand, Sweden 2002-2005, Kulturhistoriska dokumentationer nr 20, Uddevalla, Bohusläns Museum and Studio Västsvensk Konservering.

Bohm C., Christensson E., Nord A. and Tronner K., (2007), Storing Large Quantities of Marine Archaeological Ceramics and Glass – Reburial as an Alternative Solution?, in L. Pilosi (editor), *Glass and Ceramics Conservation 2007, Preprints of the ICOM-CC Glass and Ceramics Working Group Interim Meeting*, Nova Gorica, 2007.

North, N.A., (1989) 'Proximity corrosion in seawater', *Corrosion Australasia* 14, 8–11.

Nyström Godfrey I., Bergstrand T., Bohm C., Christensson E., Gjelstrup Björdal C., Gregory D., MacLeod I., Nilsson T., Peacock E.E., Richards V., (2009), Reburial and Analyses of Archaeological Remains. The RAAR Project. Project Status and Cultural Heritage Management Implications Based on the First Preliminary Results, in K. Strætkvern and D.J. Huisman (editors), *Proceedings of the 10th ICOM Group on Wet Organic Archaeological Materials Conference, Amsterdam, 10-15 September 2007*, Rijksdienst voor Archeologie, Cultuurlandschap en Monumenten (RACM), Amersfoort, 2009, pp. 169-196.

Nyström Godfrey I., (2009), Reburial and Analyses of Archaeological Remains (RAAR). Investigation of the Effects of Burial on Materials Used at Archaeological Excavations to Separate and Mark Objects, in K. Strætkvern and D.J. Huisman (editors),

Proceedings of the 10th ICOM Group on Wet Organic Archaeological Materials Conference, Amsterdam, 10-15 September 2007, Rijksdienst voor Archeologie, Cultuurlandschap en Monumenten (RACM), Amersfoort, 2009, pp. 215-251.

Peacock E. E.,(2007), Reburial and Analyses of Archaeolgical Remains (RAAR): Investigation of the Effects of Burial on Organic Materials Other Than Wood (Textile, Leather, Antler, Horn and Bone), T. Bergstrand and I. Nyström Godfrey (editors), *Reburial and Analyses of Archaeological Remains – Studies on the Effect of Reburial on Archaeological Materials Performed in Marstrand, Sweden 2003-2005. The RAAR Project,* Uddevalla, Bohusläns Museum and Studio VästSvensk Konservering, pp. 35-38.

Peacock E. E., (2004), Moseforsøg – The Next Generation, J. Maik (editor), *Priceless Inventions of Humanity – Textiles*, Acta Archaeologica Lodziensia Nr. 50/1, Łódz, Polish Academy of Sciences, 2004, pp.185-193.

Peacock E. E., Skoglund F. and Fastner J. (submitted), Deepwater Preservation and Management of Archaeological Sites. Presentation of the DePMAS Project, in *Proceedings of the 11th ICOM Group on Wet Organic Archaeological Materials Conference, Greenville, North Carolina, USA,24-28 May 2010.*

Peacock, E. E. and Turner-Walker, G., (2009), Reburial and Analysis of Archaeological Remains (RAAR): Investigation of the Effects of Burial on Non-Wood Organic Materials. Preliminary Results, in K. Strætkvern and D.J. Huisman (editors), *Proceedings of the 10th ICOM Group on Wet Organic Archaeological Materials Conference, Amsterdam, 10-15 September 2007*, Rijksdienst voor Archeologie, Cultuurlandschap en Monumenten (RACM), Amersfoort, 2009, pp. 197-213.

Richards V., Godfrey I., Blanchette R., Held B., Gregory D. and Reed E., 2009, *In-Situ* monitoring and stabilization of the *James Matthews* site in *Proceedings of the 10th ICOM Group on Wet Organic Archaeological Materials Conference, Amsterdam, 10-15 September 2007*, eds K. Straetkvern & D.J. Huisman, Rijksdienst voor Archeologie, Cultuurlandschap en Monumenten (RACM), Amersfoort, pp. 113-160.

The RAAR web site: http://www9.vgregion.se/vastarvet/svk/reburial/index.htm

Turner-Walker G. and Peacock E. E. (2008), Preliminary Results of Bone Diagenesis in Scandinavian Bogs, *Palaeogeography, Palaeoclimatology, Palaeoecology, Vol.* 266, 2008, pp.151-159.

UNESCO, (2001), Convention on the Protection of the Underwater Cultural Heritage 2001. The General Conference of the United Nations Educational, Scientific and Cultural Organisation, 31st Session, Paris, 15 October to 3 November 2001http://portal.unesco.org/en/ev.php-URL_ID=13520&URL_DO=DO_TOPIC&URL_SECTION=201.html

Questions and answers

Kristiane Straetkvern: A question for Inger; you said that the wood and the packing material was taken out of the program. Is there the possibility for that material to be re-included in the program or what happened there?

Inger Nyström Godfrey: Well, we did actually retrieve the wooden material as well and we did retrieve the plastic samples—the packing and labeling samples—but we could not afford to analyze them. So they are there. I mean, Lotte has the wood material in the fridge, I think, somewhere. Yes, so it could be done

but we didn't have the money to pay for the analysis.

Shanna Daniel: I have a question for the people with the RAAR project. Your metal coupons that you were using, what was the back part of that...the white?

Vicki Richards: I'm sort of in charge of that bit. It is high density polyethylene. The rods are high density polyethylene, the screws and the nuts are high density polyethylene—everything is plastic. The cable ties are polyethylene—everything. The only metal bits on those units are the coupons themselves.

Sarah Watkins-Kenney: I have a question regarding the RAAR project. I was just wondering if your perception of reburial being a good or bad option has changed as you are getting some results through. Are you more or less confident that it might work and also whether you've looked at or might think about how? Because you are getting some deterioration of materials but how might that compare if you had kept that material recovered? Is there a different risk assessment between the deterioration of that material if it went into the usual storage environment on land versus whether it was reburied?

Inger Nyström Godfrey: Well, personally, I thought it would be an even better tool for heritage management than it actually is. That's my personal view. I thought there would not be so many restrictions so that's one thing. And then I have talked a bit with Carla Bohm, who is in charge of the silicates subproject, and eventually you start discussing is it worth reburying when it is so easy to desalinate, dry and store sherds? So, I think that is the next step you have to go to. First you have to find out— can we rebury or not and for how long? And then you have to decide whether it is it worth doing because it is easy to take care of materials in normal storage areas. So that is one aspect... and I didn't even say

44

anything about bone for instance; we're probably unlikely to rebury human bones for instance. And horn..we're probably not likely to find a lot of horn in marine environments. So there won't be that much horn to consider.

Vicki Richards: I'll hit the metals. What we are finding with copper alloys is that possibly they could be reburied, because the corrosion mechanisms haven't totally...they are starting to stabilize but they are not totally reflecting real historic artifacts at this moment based on comparisons of the corrosion potentials that we took and other measurements that we've taken over the last 20 years. I'm not happy. I'm sitting on the scientific fence. I'm not happy to say "Yeah, go bury them." What I can say though is that with ferrous alloys we are getting quite a lot of microbial bacteria corrosion—which is standard anyway. MIC is a big problem with iron alloy in the industry—oil, gas, mining industry anyway. So, I would probably say if I'm not on the fence, I'm saying no to ferrous and possibly to copper.

David Gregory: I think one of the problems we have is with the accessioning policies of the museums and heritage agencies. I'd just like to ask Inger what would happen if they'd said "No, we're not interested in accessioning those finds?" And I personally have it that we have a case in Denmark where they weren't interested in very important wrecks around 13 years ago and they were just tipped, I'm sorry to say.

Inger Nyström Godfrey: Yes, they would have gone to the tip.

David Gregory: So I expect nothing in some respects. I think it's nice...

Inger Nyström Godfrey: But there's a danger to that. You might fool yourself to think...

David Gregory: Yes, that's the thing.

Inger Nyström Godfrey: A reburial site, at least in Sweden goes under the Civil Act. So the museum is responsible for that storage area and they need to be able to survey it and control it so that means that you have to put money into that as well. You have to put in time. It's not as if it's not costly at all, because it is. I'm thinking that if you know these are materials we're not going to use ever again you should go the full way and do all the documentation and discard it. I don't want it to be "we don't know what to do so let's rebury it.

David Gregory: But in Europe certainly de-accessioning is very knee jerk—akin to psychological pornography. We've found the oldest ship; we've found the oldest this...so we're digging! And then two years later it's the conservators who are left with yesterday's/tomorrow's chip papers. But there is still a lot of money required and it's a long-term investment as one can see with the *Vasa* project. We've heard so many cases where the heritage agencies should actually come forward and have an accession or de-accession policy. But I think, as I often say, archaeologists are the men of the world and conservators are the women of the world...once they've had the baby, the men just bugger off and it's left for the conservators to actually keep things going. Sorry, I'm both archaeologist and, I won't say conservator, conservation scientist, and I feel very strongly about it. That's why I think having these options about reburial or stabilizing things *in situ*, it's fair to argue people are not sitting on the scientific fence or sitting on the fence not prepared to make decisions. At least we can say there is this site there, there is this material there for future research.

Susan Braovac: I'd like to ask this question to the RAAR project. It's very frustrating not to be involved in what archaeologists decide. So have you had any feedback from archaeologists about what they think of this? Often when you do this kind of research the archaeologists might simplify things and just sort of jump with the preliminary results and say this looks interesting but not think about the long-term consequences.

Inger Nyström Godfrey: We have a fairly good dialogue because we have done a few reburials not only at Marstrand but at some other sites as well. We have decided to conserve, to keep in the normal way, to rebury and also to discard. So we have discussions between the group of people and that works pretty well. You might not like to say you make a decision too quickly because you are under time pressure or because its contract archaeology—it's not everything that goes on properly there too. The excavators or whoever is going to build whatever are coming in one month and decisions have to be made. So you might say it's a decision you make under distress perhaps but nevertheless, I think it has worked pretty well. I think they, the archaeologists, probably tend to look at things with a summary of results and think "oh I can rebury this or I can rebury that" so it's important that that type of material is quite clear.

Susan Grieve: I have a question for all this morning's speakers. I'm wondering are the implications of the *in situ* preservation studies that we can perhaps quantitatively estimate what degree of preservation organics would be in on a shipwreck through soil samples or perhaps are there better techniques out there so we don't have to excavate the wreck site? We can take samples near certain areas and actually estimate what deterioration we are going to see?

David Gregory: If I may have my two pennies worth? There's quite a lot of work going on with marine geophysics certainly in the UK where they are using sub bottom profiles with an acoustic device where they can send the source down into the seabed

and they'll get a return and they will actually see things. At Southampton University a researcher called Justin Diggs has actually been taking out the signal they get from the sub-bottom profiler and relating it to the actual density of the wood for example. They've published a paper in the *Journal of Archaeological Science*, several papers actually, but they have one looking at the *Grace Dieu*, Henry IV's, ship, which sank in the River Hamble, just outside of Southampton and they've actually been able to map the whole site in three dimensions so they can use 3-d scanners with these sub-bottom profilers. So they've actually been able to identify the extent of the site by analyzing the return signal they get from it. It's related to the density of the material. That's how they can also see layers of stratigraphy, as the impedance of the material with the acoustic sources passing through has a different travel time, so they've actually extrapolated that to work with the densities. So that's a general method which can be used and also there's things like sidescan sonars where people are also trying to interpret the signal in other ways to see if they can relate it to the extent of preservation of the wood.

Vicki Richards: I think one of the issues with the problem is that the extent of degradation of the wood before it was actually buried is going to have a significant effect on the extent of degradation after it's buried. I know that we have ship's timbers that were very degraded obviously before the ship was actually encapsulated, the *Batavia* for instance, so I think that would maybe be one of the problems that you'd face by taking sediment samples and trying to extrapolate to the extent of degradation of the wood without actually sampling the wood itself. I think you would have a few problems with that because all ships are different. *Vasa* went down when she was brand new, the *Batavia* had been sailing around for how many years Ian?

Ian Godfrey: Not very long...from Holland to Western Australia anyway.

Vicki Richards: Longer than the *Vasa*, sorry. I think that might be an issue.

Suzanne Grieve: Sure, there is a lot of variability.

Ian Godfrey: Just one other comment as well. The other issue as well is that you do get additional burial exposure and reburial and that is something that does show up in the corrosion product layers in certain metals and if you get the same thing with an organic site, you can be sampling the sediments but you don't know whether it has actually suffered from a period of exposure to the open marine environment in which case it's going to be more degraded as well. So you really need to know a lot about the site other than just what the sediment composition is.

2.1

Bone, Antler and Ivory as Environmental Markers in Marine and Lacustrine Environments

Gordon Turner-Walker*
Graduate School of Cultural Heritage Conservation, National Yunlin University of Science & Technology, 123 University Road Sector 3, Douliou, 640 Yunlin, Taiwan
Current Address: De Naturhistorisk Samlinger, Bergen Museum, Universitetet i Bergen
Postboks 7800, 5020 Bergen, Norway
*E- mail: gordontw@yuntech.edu.tw

Kristina Gau
University of Applied Sciences Berlin, Campus Wilhelminenhof, Gebäude A, Wilhelminenhofstrasse 75A, D-12459 Berlin, Germany

Abstract
The long-term survival of many material types in the archaeological record is contingent on the objects' burial in favorable environments with which they can achieve some degree of equilibrium. This is especially true of organic artifacts. However, many burial environments evolve over time so that the sediments from which objects are eventually excavated may differ from those they experienced in the past. Many organic finds are so sensitive to changes in their chemical environment that their mere survival indicates that conditions have not changed dramatically since they entered the archaeological record. These materials are of limited use in understanding the history of an archaeological site's development. Skeletal materials, however, are composites comprising organic and inorganic phases in intimate association. Although subject to microbial and chemical degradation processes they differ from non-mineralized organics in that they persist in the archaeological record for thousands of years in a wide range of environmental conditions. These different degradation pathways leave very well-characterized changes in the mineralized tissues that can be used to identify different "diagenetic trajectories" and thus different environmental conditions. This work presents an SEM and chemical examination of bone, dentine and antler from three very different wet sites and compares these to both experimentally buried bones and skeletons with known burial histories. It is thus possible to reconstruct the burial histories of the finds from unknown environments.

Keywords: waterlogged environments, diagenesis, framboidal pyrite, bone, antler, dentine, collagen

1. Introduction

The long-term survival of human artifacts in the archaeological record is contingent on their rapid burial in favorable environments with which they can achieve some degree of equilibrium. This is especially true of organic artifacts which throughout history (and prehistory) have comprised a large proportion of material culture. Many organic finds are so sensitive to the nature of their chemical environment that their mere survival indicates that burial conditions were close to ideal in terms of thermodynamic equilibrium and microbial activity. As such most organic archaeological finds cannot tell us a great deal about the past evolution of the burial environment. In contrast to most organics, the mineralized vertebrate tissues, bone, antler, dentine and enamel are among the most durable materials in the archaeological and palaeontological records. They can persist in the burial environment for thousands of years in a wide range of environmental conditions.

Unlike other animal and vegetable tissues, such as leather, horn and hair, or the woody tissues, the proteins in skeletal materials are stabilized and protected by an extremely insoluble inorganic salt – hydroxyapatite or HAP. (At pH 5.5 the solubility of HAP is approximately 10^{-6} mol L^{-1}. For comparison the solubility of calcium carbonate at a similar pH is approximately 0.1 mol L^{-1}, assuming the solution is in equilibrium with atmospheric CO_2[1]). Strictly speaking the mineral found in the vertebrate mineralized tissues is a stoichiometrically imperfect, carbonate-containing HAP analogue with a composition approximating to $Ca_{10}(PO_4)_6(OH)_2$. This mineral phase, which can be referred to as bioapatite, also includes traces of other anionic and cationic species that variously adsorb on crystal surfaces or substitute for ions in the crystal lattice (Turner-Walker 2008). The bioapatite in bone and dentine occupies approximately 70% by weight and 50% by volume (Turner-Walker, unpublished data) whereas in tooth enamel, which is effectively anorganic, bioapatite represents almost 100% of the tissue. The tensile strength and toughness in bone, antler and dentine are provided by the fibrous protein collagen, which comprises around 90% of the organic matter. The remaining organic components are osteocalcin, non-collagenous proteins and proteoglycans. The third major component of bone tissue is tightly-bound water which makes up 7-8% and which persists even when bone is heated to 105 °C (Ortner and Turner-Walker 2003, Turner-Walker 2009).

The intimate chemical and structural relationships between collagen and HAP are responsible for the long term post-mortem stability of the mineralized vertebrate tissues. This protein-mineral bond is mutually protective, with the insoluble collagen insulating the mineral phase from dissolution and, in return, being protected from rapid degradation by micro-organisms because microbial enzymes are too large to penetrate the extremely small spaces between the HAP crystallites. The mineral phase also affords the collagen some protection against thermal and chemical hydrolysis because it is effectively stabilized or "straight-jacketed" by being tightly confined by the surrounding mineral. Nevertheless, the mineralized tissues are susceptible to microbial and chemical degradation over archaeological timescales and the severity of the deterioration is determined by the nature of the burial environment. Luckily, over the past two decades enormous advances have been made in the understanding of how burial environment influences the deterioration of bony tissues (Nielsen-Marsh and Hedges 2000, Hedges 2002, Jans et al. 2004). Various degradation pathways leave very well characterized microstructural changes in the mineralized tissues that can be used to identify different "diagenetic trajectories" – to the extent that preservation of excavated bone can sometimes be used to shed light on different environmental conditions acting on skeletal remains over centuries of burial (Turner-Walker and Jans 2008). This current research documents the very early stages of diagenesis in experimentally buried bones and the use of characteristic diagenetic changes to elucidate the taphonomic and environmental histories of archaeological sites representing a wide range of wet or waterlogged contexts. The aim of the work is to demonstrate the contribution of diagenetic studies to wider archaeological problems and their interpretations.

2. Materials and Methods
2.1. Specimens
This work presents the results of a histological examination of bone from three experimental "burials" in which the aim was to elucidate the very early stages of diagenesis in different burial environments. Diagnostic histological features seen in these bones were attributed to different causal agents and

50

then compared with bones from cemetery sites where we can generally assume that we understand how the bodies were buried and estimate the post-mortem interval within which the corpse was laid in the ground – i.e. the *taphonomy* of how the bones entered the archaeological record. Then we examined specimens of bone, dentine and antler from three very different wet environments: a marine shipwreck site, a Late Neolithic Swiss lake settlement and a Quaternary fossil site. These were interpreted with reference to the specimens excavated from the experimentally buried bovine bone specimens in addition to the well-characterized archaeological contexts to draw conclusions about the speed and manner of burial of the wet finds. The specimens examined and their provenances are summarized in Table 1 and described in further detail below.

Table 1: Summary of samples examined in this study

Site	Sample Type	Provenance	Environment Type	Age/Date
Experimentally buried bones				
Yuntech	Bovine bone	Taiwan University Campus	Dry, aerated loess	13 months
Yuntech	Bovine bone		Wet, anoxic loess	13 months
Yuntech	Bovine bone		Freshwater stream	6 months
Known inhumation bones				
Wharram Percy	Human bone	Yorkshire, UK	Medieval burial: Aerated alkaline soil	c. 800-600 bp
Trondheim	Human bone	Mid-Norway	Medieval burial: Anoxic neutral soil	c. 900-400 bp
Specimens excavated from possibly changing environments				
Mary Rose	Human rib	Solent, of Isle of Wight, UK	Shipwreck: Marine silts	19 July 1545
Mary Rose	Human tooth			
Lake Biel	Antler	Jura Mountains, Switzerland	Late Neolithic lake dwelling	5800-5200 bp
Lake Biel	Antler			
WRFWB	Bone	North Norfolk Coast	Fossil-bearing estuarine muds	6-700,000 bp
WRFWB	Ivory			

Yuntech Campus

The experimentally buried samples presented here all come from the university campus of National Yunlin University of Science and Technology (NYUST) in Taiwan. This site was chosen because of the high annual temperatures and the very rapid decay of a wide range of archaeological materials. The campus of NYUST lies just north of the Tropic of Cancer at 23° 41' North; 120° 32' East in central Taiwan. Bone samples were buried at a depth of 120 cm in two nearby locations: One in dry, compact loess or silt approximately 2 m above a small stream; the other at the stream bank in wet, anoxic mud. Temperatures at 120 cm are being monitored and range from 27.8-20.0 °C. Chemical analyses of the soil and soil water remain to be completed. A third bone sample was exposed above the muddy bottom of a shallow pool into which the stream drained. The water depth was approximately 50 cm and air temperatures in the location ranged from 36.4-2.5 °C. It can be assumed that the water temperature was close to the mean daily temperatures in the range 17-29 °C.

Wharram Percy

Wharram Percy in the UK is a deserted Medieval village that was the subject of extensive research excavations in the 1960s. The burials date mainly to the medieval period (11th to 16th century AD), and largely represent ordinary peasants who lived at Wharram Percy or elsewhere in the parish. The cemetery lies on chalk geology and in spite of low collagen yields the macroscopic preservation of all the skeletons was good. The samples included in this study came from the diaphyses of femora.

Trondheim

The skeletal material for the present study comes from a series of excavations carried out in central Trondheim, Norway during the 1970s and 1980s, principally on the churchyard of St. Olav's church (Anderson and Göthberg, 1986). The skeletons date to the period 1100-1600 AD. Trondheim is situated in Central Norway on Trondheimsfjord where the mean annual temperature is approximately 5 °C. There is an average of 122 days per year with a minimum temperature below 0 °C (data from Norwegian Meteorological Institute, 2005). The deep urban deposits in Trondheim are predominantly waterlogged and the graves were cut into a mixture of organic rich loams and clays, close to or below the water table. The wooden coffins or boards in many graves survived and some contained preserved wood shavings. The majority of the skeletons were in an excellent state of preservation and there was limited soft tissue preservation (brains, hair, etc.). Many of the bones are stained a dark brown color but skeletons varied in color from white to almost black. The samples included in this study were also taken from the diaphyses of femora.

Mary Rose

The Mary Rose was a warship of the English navy during the reign of King Henry VIII. After serving for 33 years she saw her final action on 19 July 1545 while leading the attack on ships a French invasion fleet. The vessel sank in the straits north of the Isle of Wight for reasons that remain contentious. The most common explanation for her sinking is that a strong gust of wind hit the sails as she came about and instability related to the additional weight of recently installed, larger guns caused seawater to flood into the open gunports. After lying on the bed of the Solent for nearly 450 years the wreck of the Mary Rose was rediscovered after a search by divers in 1971 and excavated between 1978 and 1982 by the Mary Rose Trust (Marsden 2003). The bones of a total of 179 individuals were found during these excavations, including 92 almost complete skeletons. osteological evidence showed that the crew were mostly young adult males – some no more than 11–13 years old.

Lake Biel

Lake Biel lies to the northwest of the Swiss capital Bern. The remains of several lake villages built on piles have been found close to the shores of the lake in the once densely populated area of Sutz-Lattrigen. The site from which the samples were recovered was excavated by divers in a rescue excavation at Neue Station in 2008. However, the area had been the focus of several archaeological investigations since 1988. The site of Sutz-Lattringen, Neue Station is dated to 3800-3200 BC based on dendrochronological analyses of timbers from piled dwellings found in 2008. The antler finds came from sediments on the lake bed and earlier analyses on the lake waters showed them to by slightly alkaline in the range 8.40-7.54 with the pH decreasing slightly with increasing depth. Oxygen content also decreased (10.5-2.0 mg l^{-1}) with increasing depth and dissolved sulfate increased (25.0-27.2 mgl^{-1}). Temperatures at the lake bed ranged from 4.2-5.6 °C (Gau 2009).

West Runton Freshwater Bed (WRFWB)

The West Runton Freshwater Bed (WRFWB) in the UK is part of the Cromer Forest Bed formation and forms the type site for the Cromerian interglacial

(Pleistocene stage of the Quaternary). The site lies on the north coast of Norfolk in (SE England) and the sediments, which are exposed at the base of steep gravel cliffs, are approximately 600,000-700,000 years old. During 1995 the skeleton of a steppe mammoth (*Mammuthus trogontherii*) was excavated by the Norfolk Archaeological Unit and the Castle Museum, Norwich (Ashwin and Stuart 1996; Stuart 1996). The WFRWB is comprised of a layer of organic rich detrital silt, approximately one meter thick, overlain by a 19 meter sequence of marine and freshwater sands and silts that make up the cliffs. Preservation of fossil material is exceptionally good with survival of large mammals and well as amphibians, fish and mollusk shells, beetle remains and woody plant material. The specimens examined were a fragment of skull from a large mammal (possibly a juvenile elephant) and a small fragment of ivory tusk recovered from the upper 30cm of the WRFWB during the excavations.

2.2. Experimental Methods

Bones selected for microscopic analysis had small samples removed using a hand-held circular saw and were subsequently vacuum-dried and embedded in low-viscosity epoxy resin (Araldite 20:20) under vacuum. The embedded thick sections were hand-ground and polished to an optically flat surface, then carbon coated for SEM examination. Two microscopes were used in this study. Samples from the Mary Rose, Lake Biel and Trondheim were examined using a Hitachi S-3500N SEM fitted with a four quadrant backscattered electron (BSE) detector. The instrument parameters were as follows; accelerating voltage 20 kV, working distance 15-16 mm and emission current approximately 60 mA. The West Runton and Wharram Percy specimens were examined using a LEO Stereoscan 440i, also fitted with a four quadrant BSE detector and operating at 20 kV with similar instrument parameters. All images were captured and stored in standard electronic format (bmp or tiff files). In BSE-SEM images different grey tone values represent different backscatter intensities, which in turn represent variations in atomic weight density within the specimen. In bone, areas of high mineral density appear bright and the embedding resin appears dark. Holes appear black unless filled with resin. In addition to the histological analyses some specimens were subject to compositional analyses. Both SEMs used in this work were equipped with energy dispersive X-ray spectrometers (EDS or EDX) which could be used to detect the elemental compositions of areas of interest in the SEM images.

The antler samples from Lake Biel were also assayed for their protein content as follows. Residual collagen content may be measured directly by weight loss following total protein removal following a modified procedure based on the method published by Termine *et al.* (1973). This method employs hydrazine hydrate ($NH_2.NH_2.H_2O$) a free flowing liquid and strong reducing agent, which breaks the peptide bonds binding amino acids in proteins, a process known as hydrazinolysis. This effectively breaks the long chain collagen molecules into short segments which are then solubilized in the supernatant hydrazine. The inorganic component is effectively unchanged except for slight dehydration of loosely bound water. Hydrazine is miscible with alcohols and the deproteinized bone may be readily rinsed of excess reagent without washing in water so that the remaining mineral component and other diagenetic minerals are effectively unchanged. This method has also been used by other researchers in the field of bone diagenesis, notably Nielsen-Marsh and Hedges (Nielsen-Marsh & Hedges 2000). Samples of antler were oven dried overnight at 105 °C and weighed on an electronic balance to four decimal places. The dried samples were then placed in glass vials and 20 ml of hydrazine hydrate added by pipette. The vials were then sealed with a plastic screw cap and placed in an oven at 70 °C for a total of 100 hours. The vials were shaken daily and the supernatant was exchanged for fresh hydrazine after approximately 75 hours. Finally the hydrazine was drained from the samples and two changes of 20 ml absolute ethanol at 70 °C were used to rinse off excess hydrazine/peptide residues. The samples were then reweighed and the mass loss expressed as a percentage of the original weight.

3. Results and Discussion

3.1 Experimentally buried bones

Looking at the experimentally buried specimens provides an overview of the very early stages of bone diagenesis in different environments. Figure 1A shows a BSEM image of polished section of bone buried in dry, aerated soil for 13 months. Attack by tunneling bacteria is restricted to the outermost 100-200 μm of the bone tissues and is represented by both demineralized zones and hypermineralized zones (Figure 1B), often in close association (Turner-Walker et al. 2002, Jans 2008).

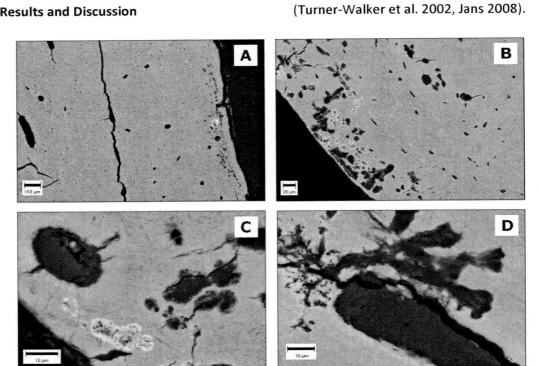

Figure 1. BSEM images of bone buried in dry, aerated loess for 13 months. Attack by tunneling bacteria is restricted to the outermost 100-200 μm.

Although bacterial attack is concentrated close to the outer surface of the bone there is no evidence for tunnels beginning at the surface and progressing into the bone's interior (Figure 1C).

There is However evidence that bacterial colonies became established within the natural pores in the bones before penetrating the bone tissues (Figure 1D). In places demineralization of the bone tissues has progressed so far that only a series of ragged open tunnels with lobe-like ends remain (upper central area of Figure 1D). In

the case of the bone buried in waterlogged mud these tunnels are completely absent, although there is considerable cracking within the sample as a result of a weakening of the bone tissue (Figure 2A). At higher magnifications it is evident that this weakening results from a slight demineralization of the bone tissue and an increase in its microporosity (Figure 2B). Figure 2B also shows a bright, electron-dense feature adhering to the surface of the bone. An EDX analysis

(Figure 3A) of this feature is indicative of the iron phosphate mineral vivianite $(Fe_3(PO_4)_2.8H_2O)$. A single spherical, electron-dense feature was found in a Haversian canal (Figure 2C) and appeared to be composed of numerous smaller particles (Figure 2D). This feature was also analyzed by EDX (Figure 3B and Table 2) and tentatively identified as an iron oxide with a composition approximating to Fe_2O_3. This is almost certainly an iron oxide precursor to a pyrite framboid. Iron oxides and sulfides are minerals whose formation is known to be mediated by microbial biomineralization (Turner-Walker 1998a; 1998b). Pyrite framboids are generally considered to be associated with the sulfate-reducing bacteria that live in anoxic sediments (Turner-Walker 1998b), although there is some evidence that they can form abiotically.

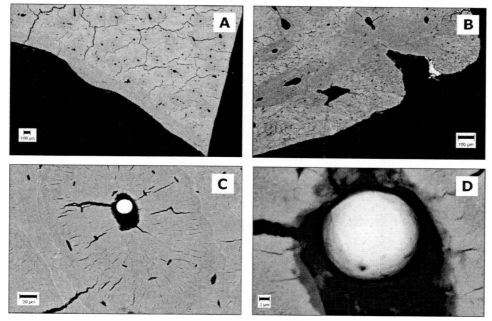

Figure 2. BSEM images of bone buried in waterlogged mud of for 13 months. Tunneling by soil bacteria is absent but the specimen is encrusted with vivianite and contains at least one iron oxide framboid precursor

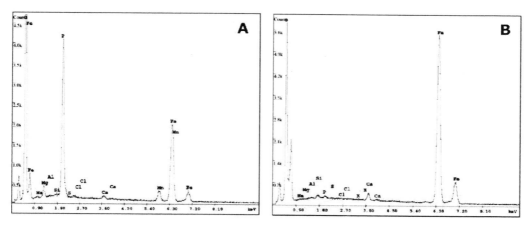

Figure 3. EDX spectra for vivianite (A) and framboid precursor (B) seen in Figure 2.

Table 2. Results of EXD analyses on features seen in bone buried in wet anoxic loess

Sample	O	Na	Mg	Al	Si	P	S	Ca	Mn	Fe

Vivianite									
Weight %	40.20	0.18	0.70	0.32	0.72	16.87	0.10	1.81	3.16	35.61
Atomic %	64.70	0.20	0.74	0.30	0.66	14.02	0.08	1.16	1.48	16.42
Iron Oxide Sphere									
Weight %	27.12	0.13	0.00	0.16	0.40	0.22	0.00	1.03	n.d.	70.81
Atomic %	56.03	0.19	0.00	0.19	0.47	0.23	0.00	0.85	n.d.	41.92

In contrast to the bone buried in waterlogged anoxic loess the bone specimen submerged on the stream bed for 6 months showed no evidence of demineralization. However, the bone surface was extensively tunneled in places (Figure 4A). This tunneling was easily distinguished from that produced by soil bacteria in that it is considerably larger (approximately 10 μm wide) and is closely clustered together with only a thin wall separating adjacent tunnels. The micro-organisms responsible for these tunnels clearly derive some protection from the external environment by leaving a thin layer of intact bone un-attacked on the immediate surface of the bone (Figure 4B). Within each tunnel can be seen dense, mineralized beads approximately 0.5 μm in diameter (Figures 4C-D). This type of destruction is frequently described as Wedl tunneling and is often ascribed to fungal attack but here clearly arises from the action of cyanobacteria – also known as blue-green algae. Cyanobacteria can live in any aqueous environment whether freshwater, saltwater or brackish. Because they are photosynthesisers they are limited to the depth of water they inhabit. Cyanobacteria are known to be responsible for bioerosion of mollusk shells and coral reefs and here too the depth of tunneling is limited to how far light can penetrate below the surface of the shell.

Can any of the features described above be identified in archaeological bone specimens? Figure 5A shows an image of the human bone specimen from Wharram Percy. It illustrates the almost complete destruction of bone by the microfocal destruction and characteristic spongiform porosity attributed to bacterial attack.

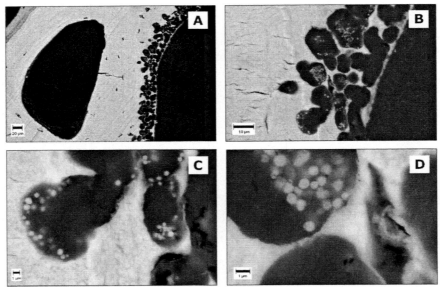

Figure 4. BSEM images of bone specimen submerged on the stream bed for 6 months. The surface is extensively tunneled by cyanobacteria. The tunnels are filled with numerous small electron-bright beads – possibly of re-precipitated HAP.

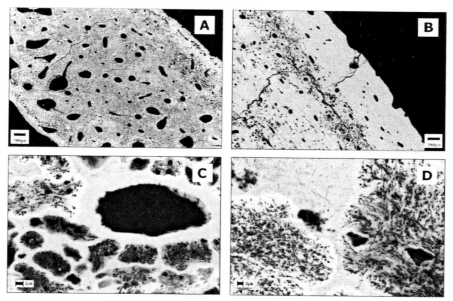

Figure 5. BSEM images of human bone specimen from Medieval Wharram Percy. It shows almost complete destruction of bone by characteristic spongiform porosity attributed to soil bacterial.

Once again the affected bone is restricted to the interior of the bone tissue with a thin layer of un-degraded bone close to the surface (Figure 5B). Figure 5C shows zones of demineralized tissue perforated by circular holes and zones of increased mineral loading with clear meandering tunnels. There is frequently a hypermineralized border or "cuff" at the limit of the affected area (Turner-Walker et al. 2002). Bone in direct contact with the soil water appears to be protected from attack, suggesting that some inhibiting factor is present in the burial environment. The border of the osteocyte lacuna is the only part of Figure 5C that has not been tunneled and a similar pattern is seen in Figure 5D. The microstructural patterns of diagenesis visible in the Wharram Percy skeletons are consistent with burial in aerated, neutral to slightly alkaline soil. The absence of any framboidal pyrite or oxidised framboids indicates that the graves were never waterlogged at any point in their history.

Figure 6 shows a section of human bone from Medieval Trondheim. There is no evidence for bacterial tunneling and apart from some slight shrinkage and cracking caused in the high vacuum of the SEM (Figure 6A) there is almost nothing to distinguish it from fresh human bone (Figure 6B). The Haversian canals however contain numerous bright circular features that are obvious pyrite framboids (Figure 6C). At higher magnification their granular texture is quite clear (Figure 6D). None of the Trondheim inhumations examined to date shows any evidence for the characteristic destruction by soil bacteria but almost all show well-formed pyrite framboids. This is consistent with burial in soils that were always anoxic or partially waterlogged. It is also possible that the low average soil temperatures in Mid-Norway were an additional inhibiting factor that prevented colonization of the bone tissues by bone degrading bacteria. In the rural area south of Trondheim average annual air temperature is 3.30 °C while average temperature at a depth of one meter is 4.22 °C (Turner-Walker and Peacock 2008)

.

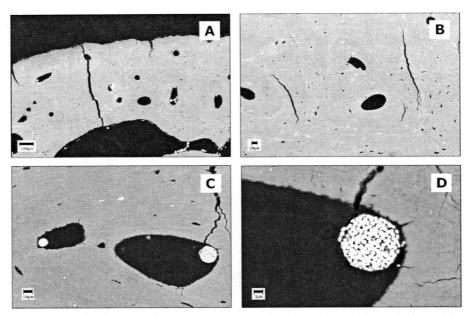

Figure 6. BSEM images of human bone from Medieval Trondheim. There is no evidence for bacterial tunnelling its microstructure looks similar to fresh human bone. The Haversian canals contain numerous bright, circular pyrite framboids.

Looking at a section of the bones from the wreck of the Mary Rose the first obvious feature is that the outer layers of the rib have been extensively tunneled (Figure 7A) and this tunneling is limited to a depth of about 700 μm from the original bone surface. The tunneling is very closely packed, with only a thin wall between adjacent tunnels, and the increase in porosity is such that the tissues have lost approximately 50-60% of their substance (Figure 7B). This pattern is characteristic of colonization by cyanobacteria. Figure 7C shows that discrete pyrite framboids lie clustered on the surface of the bone but also within the tunnels, i.e. colonization by sulfate reducing bacteria post-dates the attack by cyanobacteria. Figure 7D shows the dentine in a tooth from the Mary Rose. There is some enlargement of the dentinal tubules but also obvious tunneling by cyanobacteria and the outer layers of the tooth have fallen away. This shows that cyanobacteria can also degrade dentine and leave the same characteristic meandering tunnels as those seen in bone.

The results above suggest that the skeletonized remains of at least some of the crewmembers of the Mary Rose sat on the sea bed with access to light for enough time to allow cyanobacteria to colonize the bone surfaces, and were subsequently buried in anoxic muds which provided a suitable environment for sulfate-reducing bacteria.

Looking at a specimen of antler from Lake Biel it is clear that the gross anatomy is very different to that of bone, having a much more open and porous structure (Figure 8A). There is some variation in the mineral loading of the tissues (visible as differences in grey tone in the image) but it is unclear whether this is a natural consequence of being exposed to the elements during the animal's life or arises from diagenetic processes. The electron dense areas do not have an appreciably larger calcium or phosphorus content but do have higher values for sodium, magnesium, aluminum, silicon and sulfur (Table 3).

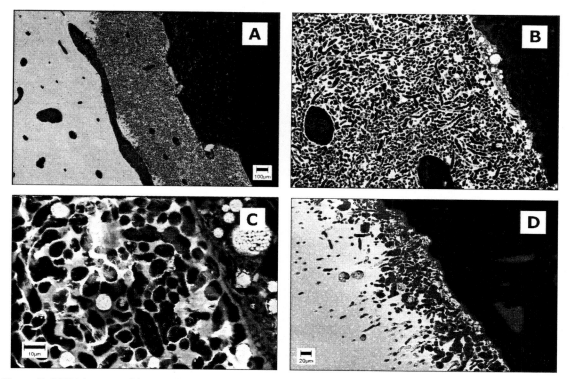

Figure 7. BSEM images of human bone specimen (A-C) and a tooth (D) from the wreck of the Mary Rose. Both specimens exhibit tunneling by cyanobacteria, which clearly predates the growth of pyrite framboids.

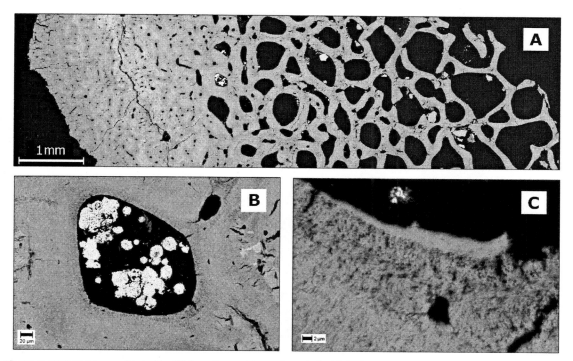

Figure 8. BSEM images of Late Neolithic antler specimen from Lake Biel. The tissues show marked demineralization and the voids contain scattered pyrite framboids.

59

Table 3. *Results of EXD analyses on Lake Biel antler*

Sample	O	Na	Mg	Al	Si	P	S	Ca	Mn	Fe
Pyrite framboid										
Weight %	21.85	0.05	0.15	0.03	0.28	0.05	27.14	0.31	n.d.	50.14
Atomic %	43.51	0.07	0.20	0.03	0.32	0.05	26.97	0.25	n.d.	28.61
High electron density (bright) tissues										
Weight %	34.67	1.10	0.89	0.70	0.88	18.63	1.08	40.11	n.d.	0.96
Atomic %	54.33	1.20	0.92	0.65	0.79	15.08	0.84	25.09	n.d.	0.43
Low electron density (darker) tissues										
Weight %	38.30	0.58	0.23	0.12	0.19	18.66	0.18	40.35	n.d.	0.96
Atomic %	58.62	0.61	0.23	0.11	0.17	14,76	0.14	24.65	n.d.	0.42

There is no evidence for tunneling by soil bacteria in any part of the section. The larger pore spaces are filled with detritus but it is also possible to distinguish discrete pyrite framboids in many of the voids (Figure 8B). There is certainly clear evidence of partial demineralization of the bony tissues (Figure 8C) but this is consistent with burial in a wet environment for several thousand years. The presence of iron pyrite was confirmed by EDX (Figure 9 and Table 3). The results suggest that the iron sulfide is in the form of mackinawite (FeS_{1-x}). The low values of iron seen in the bone tissues and the small number of framboids is consistent with an iron depleted environment with elevated pH values.

The collagen contents for the two samples of Lake Biel antler analyzed are given in Table 4. The original weight percentage of collagen in dry, fresh bone is in the range 23-24% whereas values for antler quoted in the literature are slightly higher and depend on the exact location in the antler from which the sample is taken. From Table 4 it is clear that 093782 has lost a considerable amount of its original organic matter compared to 092829. It is worth adding a caveat here. The sample 092829 comprised several small flakes which may have come from the outer skin of the antler, and this may have originally been collagen rich. Thus, 092829 could have given a slightly higher collagen value than may have been obtained for a larger, more representative sample.

Figure 10 shows bone and ivory specimens from the West Runton Freshwater Bed site. The section of bone in Figure 10A shows mostly normal histology with no evidence for tunneling by soil bacteria. However, there is clear evidence for limited cyanobacterial tunneling close to the surface of the bone. Also in evidence are masses of framboidal pyrite filling the natural porosity of the bone. This pyrite also fills the tunnels made by cyanobacteria (Figure 10B). Although the tusk specimen clearly shows iron pyrite filling the dentinal tubules of the dentine and encrusting the surface, there is no evidence of cyanobacteria having eroded the surface. One interpretation might be that being heavy and dense the tusks quickly broke away from the skull and became buried in muddy sediment whereas the skull, being larger and more buoyant, projected above the sediment into the water of the estuary in which the skeleton became entombed.

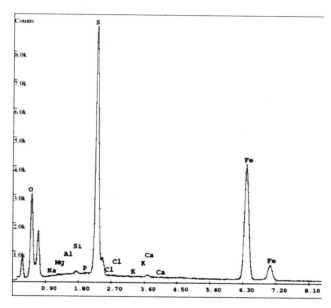

Figure 9. *EDX spectrum of pyrite framboid grain in the Lake Biel antler.*

Table 4: *Residual collagen content for the two samples analyzed*

Sample	Original wt. (g)	Deproteinated wt. (g)	Protein (%)
093782	1.0146	0.9656	4.85
092829	0.6442	0.5254	18.44

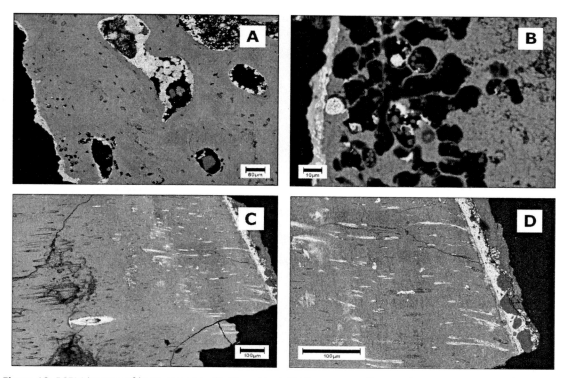

Figure 10: *BSEM images of bone specimen (A-B) and tusk (D) from excavations at the West Runton Freshwater Bed. The bone shows limited tunneling by cyanobacteria but massive clusters of framboids. Note that framboids can be found inside the bacterial tunneling. The tusk shows no evidence of cyanobacteria and presumably suffered rapid burial in sediment.*

4. Conclusions

The skeletal tissues, bone antler and dentine can act as useful proxies for environmental monitors or markers when considering the states of preservation of archaeological finds. Diagnostic features in the microstructure of these long-lasting organic-inorganic composites can reveal the sequence of changes that a depositional environment may have undergone over the lifetime of an archaeological site. An understanding of the various environments experienced by a complex site – such as a shipwreck – may also help inform conservation and curation strategies for recovered artifacts. For example, the presence of framboidal pyrite in bone specimens may act as a proxy for analyses of sediment samples if the latter were not collected and archived at the time of excavation. Since this finely divided pyrite is readily oxidized with the resulting release of sulfuric acid its presence may flag up future conservation problems in other materials.

Notes

[1] Solubility for calcium carbonate was interpolated from data at the following website:
http://www.chem.usu.edu/~sbialkow/Classes/3600/alpha/alpha3.html

References

Anderson T. & Göthberg H. 1986. Olavskirchens Kirkegård. Humanosteologisk analyse og faseinndeling. Fortiden I Trondheim bygrunn: folkebibliotekstomten. Meddelelser nr. 1. Trondheim: Riksantikvaren, Utgravningskontoret for Trondheim. Trondheim.

Ashwin T. & Stuart A.J. 1996. The West Runton elephant. *Current Archaeology* 149, 164-168.

Gau K. (2009) Trocknungsmethoden für wassergelagerte Geweihobjekte an Beispiel einer neolitischen Geweihaxt mit Holzrest aus dem Bielersee. (unpublished diploma thesis, Hochschule für Technik und Wirtschaft Berlin)

Hedges R.E.M. (2002) Bone diagenesis: an overview of processes. Archaeometry 44(3): 319-328.

Jans M.M.E. (2008) Microbial bioerosion of bone – a review. In *Current Developments in Bioerosion* (M. Wisshak & L. Tapanila eds). Erlangen Earth Conference Series, Springer-Verlag, Berlin: 397-414.

Jans M.M.E., Nielsen-Marsh C.N., Smith C.I., Collins M.J., Kars H. (2004) Characterisation of microbial attack on archaeological bone. *Journal of Archaeological Science* 31(1): 87-95.

Marsden P. (2003) Sealed by Time: *The Loss and Recovery of the Mary Rose. The Archaeology of the Mary Rose, Volume 1.* The Mary Rose Trust, Portsmouth.

Nielsen-Marsh C.M. & Hedges R.E.M. (2000) Patterns of diagenesis in bone I: The effects of site environments, *Journal of Archaeological Science*, 27, (12): 1139-1150.

Ortner D.J. & Turner-Walker G. (2003) The biology of skeletal tissues. in *Identification of Pathological Conditions in Human Skeletal Remains - 2nd Edition.* (Donald J. Ortner ed.) Academic Press.

Stuart A.J. (1996) Vertebrate faunas from the Early Middle Pleistocene of East Anglia. In *The Early Middle Pleistocene in Europe* (ed. C. Turner). Balkema, Rotterdam, 9-24.

Termine J.D., Eanes E.D., Greenfield D.S., Nylen M.U. & Harper R.A. (1973) Hydrazine-deproteinated bone mineral: physical and chemical properties. *Calcified Tissue Research* 12, 73-90.

Turner-Walker G. (1998a) The West Runton fossil elephant: a pre-conservation evaluation of its condition, chemistry and burial environment. *The Conservator* 22, 26-35.

Turner-Walker G. (1998b) Pyrite and bone diagenesis in terrestrial sediments: Evidence from the West Runton Fresh Water Bed. *Bulletin of the Geological Society of Norfolk*.48: 3-26. (published 1999)

Turner-Walker G. (2008) The chemical and microbial degradation of bones and teeth. In *Advances in Human Palaeopathology*. (Ron Pinhasi and Simon Mays eds) Wiley, Chichester, England: 3-30.

Turner-Walker G. (2009) Degradation pathways and conservation strategies for ancient bone from wet, anoxic sites. *Proceedings of the 10th Triennial Meeting of the ICOM-CC Working Group for Wet Organic Archaeological Materials.* (H.D.J. Huisman K. Strætkvern eds.) *10-15th September 2007:* 659-675.

Turner-Walker G. & Jans M. (2008) Reconstructing taphonomic histories using histological analyses. *Palaeogeography, Palaeoclimatology Palaeoecology:* 266: 227-235.

Turner-Walker G. Nielsen-Marsh C. M. Syversen U., Kars H., Collins M. J. (2002) Sub-micron spongiform porosity is the major ultra-structural alteration occurring in archaeological bone, *International Journal of Osteoarchaeology* 12: 407–414

Turner-Walker G. & Peacock E.E. (2008) Preliminary results of bone diagenesis in Scandinavian bogs. *Palaeogeography, Palaeoclimatology Palaeoecology:* 266: 151-159.

Questions and answers

Suzanne Grieve: You mentioned that you saw some bone recrystallization. What was causing that? The bacteria?

Gordon Turner Walker: The nature of the concept is that the bacterial enzymes will not actually fit between the crystallites of bone mineral. The cells that are involved in the removal of (living) bone tissue have to de-mineralize (that tissue first), but the difference being that in the burial environment, unless there is a very dynamic hydrology in which water is passing through the pore structure of the bone, the mineral, the dissolved mineral, doesn't move very far. It's very insoluble so it just moves from one area of tunneling to another area of tunneling... It seems that its rates of re-precipitating... it has to re-precipitate in a region of bone that has the volume to accommodate it. So it's going into a previously degraded area. It seems that all the organisms, certainly the bacteria, do this.

Suzanne Grieve: Is that pulling structure strength back into the bone?

Gordon Turner Walker: What you end up with is like a honeycomb structure. Only at the very, very terminal stages of this process where the bone is, this is in the soil, where it's completely riddled with tunnels, the only things surviving are these hypermineralized sort of pockets. They are the last thing to go and also the bone specimen from the Mary Rose. It's about half a millimeter to a millimeter at the outside. I'd say 90-95% of the volume of the bone is gone. So it does impart some additional strength. Otherwise, it wouldn't be there at all but that outer sort of skin often falls off and it's quite limited because it's limited to how far light can penetrate. I mean the cyanobacteria have different species and some of them are very creative in how they make a living. But basically, they require some sunlight so there's a limited depth. So if you are excavating bone from an underwater site I would recommend that you are actually quite careful how you bring it up and move it around because you're going to lose that surface and that's the surface that you may well be interested in. I don't know if that answers your question.

2.2

Studying and Manipulating Bacterial Wood Decay – Results of Laboratory Experiments

Jana Gelbrich*
German Maritime Museum, Bremerhaven,
Germany
E-mail: gelbrich@dsm.museum

Ev I. Kretschmar
Section Biocides IV 1.2, Federal
Environment Agency, Germany

Norbert Lamersdorf
Department of Soil Science of Temperate
and Boreal Ecosystems, University of
Goettingen, Germany

Holger Militz
Department of Wood Biology and Wood
Products, University of Goettingen,
Germany

1. Abstract

A microcosm experiment was set up to establish, monitor and manipulate bacterial wood decay. Sound pine sticks were placed in water saturated sediment from a heavily decayed pine pile foundation site in Amsterdam. In order to investigate the role of oxygen in the bacterial degradation process of wood, microcosm head space were aerated with air, air + O_2 or N_2. As a fourth treatment the air aeration was combined with a vertical water circulation. After 150 days, samples of all these treatments showed degradation pattern of erosion bacteria, evaluated by light microscopy. The fastest and most intense rate of decay was found in the circulated treatment.

In a second experiment it was investigated if the decay process is influenced by the chemical sediment composition. The sediments were supplied with NO_3^-, NH_4^+, PO_4^{3-} and SO_4^{2-}. All kinds of chemical additions resulted in a reduced intensity of bacterial wood degradation compared to the reference after 155 days.

Such an experimental design will be a good base for testing preservations strategies with the view to the impact on the environment.

2. Introduction

Most timbers, except for the most durable heartwood, are rapidly degraded if exposed to optimal conditions of microbial decay, characterized by optimal levels of moisture and adequate supply of oxygen. This explains why most archaeological wood comes from dry or waterlogged sites (Nilsson 1998). Archaeological wood from wet or soaked conditions is affected by biotic decay caused by bacteria and fungi in particular. As a consequence of this decay, archaeological wood often undergoes significant physical-mechanical modifications such as decreased density and changes in EMC (Equilibrium Moisture Content). Soaked archaeological wood may reach MWC (Maximum Water Content) values up to 800 – 1.000 % increasing with the decay intensity (Schniewind 1990). To protect and conserve such fragile wooden archaeological objects, specific conservation treatments were developed to remove the water but retain the original sample sizes.

Due to the lack of funding for excavation and conservation treatments and to protect archaeological wet wood non-destructively and non-intrusively, *in situ* and reburial preservation of underwater archaeological sites represents a new field of interest. These approaches seek to reproduce or rather emulate a pre-excavation (*in situ*) environment that has benefited the long-term preservation of archaeological remains (Nyström Godfrey et al. 2009).

Different methods of in situ and reburial preservation have been trialed in order to minimize further degradation (Pournou 1999, Björdal and Nilsson 1999, Gregory 1999, Hogan et al. 2002, Gregory et al. 2002, Nyström Godfrey et al. 2009) but wood degradation by erosion bacteria, the main wood degrader under waterlogged conditions (Nilsson and Björdal, 2008) could not be inhibited completely, up to now. Therefore a usable preservation strategy against further bacterial degradation is highly relevant.

For development of preservation strategies it is indispensable to understand the ecology and the mechanisms of wood degradation by bacteria. Several test standards exist to simulate fungal wood degradation in laboratory experiments. For simulation of bacterial attack under laboratory conditions no standard exist. All previous investigations using pure cultures of bacteria, isolated from already attacked wood, did not provide any wood degradation in fresh wood up to now. Therefore, a main objective of the EU-project BACPOLES (ECK4-CT-2001-00043) was to find a method for simulation of bacterial wood degradation with reproducible conditions. This method based on the simulation of the living conditions by using soil and water from an infected sample site as well as infected wood in order to establish bacterial wood decay in fresh wood, comparable to the soft rot test (ENV 807).

This study sets out to reduce the knowledge gap between field experiments, with no records of prevailing physical-chemical factors, and controlled laboratory experiments, which can provide good documentation of the governing factors. A microcosm (MC) experiment was set up in which fresh wood was buried in waterlogged sediments in order to establish bacterial wood decay by naturally occurring bacteria consortia. To examine if the presence of oxygen or a certain oxygen concentration is a prerequisite for bacterial wood decay, the availability of oxygen was varied in this study. In a second experiment it was investigated if the decay process is influenced by the chemical sediment composition. The sediments were supplied with NO_3^-, NH_4^+, PO_4^{3-} and SO_4^{2-}.

Such a MC experiment offers the potential to understand the processes of deterioration of archaeological wood in underwater and waterlogged environments but more importantly it offers the possibility to find methods of counteracting these degradation processes and to develop alternative storage options for the preservation of underwater and / or waterlogged archaeological heritage.

3. Materials and Methods
3.1 *Microcosm set up*
Acrylic glass cylinders were filled with sediment and water from a heavily decayed pine pile foundation site in the south of Amsterdam (NL). As a supplementary bacteria source, a moderately decayed pine sapwood stick (7x7x200 mm3), originating from a foundation pile extracted in Koog an de Zaan (NL) was placed in the middle of each Microcosm (MC). 40 sound pine sapwood sticks (10x5x100 mm3) were included as decay controls in each MC. These were arranged in two layers (top and bottom) and every layer consisted of two circles around the decayed wood stick in the middle. The wood samples were inserted during filling the MCs with sediment. To minimize the introduction of air / oxygen to the system, the wood samples were first water saturated. Finally, the packed MCs were filled with ground water from the sediment sample site until the sediment column was overlain by water thereby creating a completely water saturated system. For basic chemical composition of sediment, water, sound and infected wood used in the experiment, see Table 1.

Each MC has a gas inflow and outflow where CO_2, N_2O and CH_4 were continuously monitored using a GC-ECD and FID (Shimadzu, Tokyo, Japan) described in Loftfield et al. (1997). Selected MCs were equipped with oxygen optodes to measure the oxygen concentration in different depths of the MCs during the experiment as described in Kretschmar (2007) and Kretschmar et al. (2008). A scheme of a completely installed MC is shown in Figure 2. The MCs were incubated in the dark at 20 °C.

Figure 1. Distribution of the samples of one layer in a Microcosm

Table 1. Chemical characteristics of sediment, infected wood, sound wood and water incorporated in the microcosms (MCs) (Kretschmar et al. 2008).

	C_{org}	N_t	P_t	S_t	pH
Sediment [mg/g]	3.5	0.1	0.2	0.2	8.3
Wood$_{infected}$ [mg/g]	452	1.3	0.053	1.8	
Wood$_{sound}$ [mg/g]	485	1.2	0.033	0.034	
	DOC	N_t	PO_4^{3-}	SO_4^{2-}	pH
Water [mg/l]	56.5	3.6	0.5	21.6	8.1

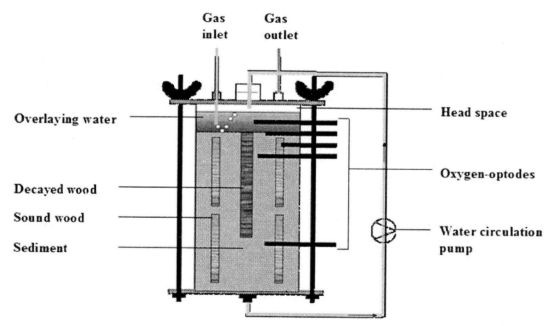

Figure 2. Microcosm scheme with gas supply, oxygen optodes and water circulation.

3.2 Experimental design

To investigate the influence of oxygen availability to bacterial wood degradation, four treatments were used to alter the gas supply in the MC by flowing gases or gas mixtures into the overlaying water layer. So that the gassing efficiency is maximized by circumventing the gas to liquid diffusion barrier.

The different gas inflows were:

1. Air   (A)   21 % vol. O_2

2. Air and Oxygen   (A+O_2) 50 % vol. O_2

3. Nitrogen   (N_2)   0 % vol. O_2

4. In the fourth treatment variant, air (A) inflow was combined with water circulation by pumping the extracted water from the bottom to the top of the sediment column. The sign of abbreviation of this treatment is (A+C) and in the text it is called the "circulated treatment".

MCs were examined after 120, 150, 195, 350 and 400 days, using a glove box with a nitrogen atmosphere and extracting the formerly sound wood together with sediment and water samples.

3.3 Microscopic investigations

From each MC two wood samples of each, the inner and the outer, circle in both layers were investigated using light microscopy. These 8 samples were examined at three heights (top, middle and bottom) with thin transverse and tangential sections cut by hand using a razor blade. Sections were stained with either 1 % w/v safranin in ethanol to highlight the micromorphology of the wood, or 0.1 % w/v aniline blue in 50 % lactic acid to stain fungal hyphae and bacteria. Polarized light was used to demonstrate the remains of crystalline cellulose.

It was checked that three cutting levels were sufficient for precise assignment of bacterial wood decay degrees by investigating eight wood samples from one MC per treatment in ten, one centimeter high layers. The microscopic examinations were conducted by one person only with unknown sample identities to ensure unbiased observations.

3.4 Oxygen measurements

The oxygen concentration in selected microcosms was measured with oxygen optodes (PreSense, Regensburg, Germany) during the experiment. The Optode principle is the dynamic quenching of luminescence measuring the luminescence lifetime of a luminophore immobilized in a sensor foil (Klimant et al. 1995). A circle of 3 mm diameter of the sensor foil (PSt3-PSUP-YOP) is attached with silicone to the outer site of a closed plane end of a glass rod. The so prepared glass rod is inserted into the microcosms with silicone rubber tubing as gasket. For measurements a polymer optical fiber connected to the measurement device (Fibox 2-AOT) is held from the outside of the glass rod against the sensor foil which is inside the microcosm. Before installation, the optodes were calibrated using water saturated air as 100% and water saturated N_2 as 0%. Long-term stability was checked by re-calibrating a spare optode kept in the same room at similar conditions (Kretschmar et al. 2008).

3.5 Variation of sediment composition

In a second experiment the treatment with air inflow into the overlaying water was used in a smaller experimental set up (described in Kretschmar 2007, Kretschmar et al. 2008 and Gelbrich 2009) to investigate if the decay process was influenced by the chemical composition of the interstitial pore water of the sediment. Therefore, on the one side, the sediment nutrient concentration was lowered by "dilution" with silica sand (treatment M for

68

mixture) or pure silica sand (SS) was used. On the other side nitrate (S+N), ammonia (S+A), phosphorus (S+P) or sulfate (S+Su) were added to change the sediment composition. Table 2 shows the different chemical compositions of the sediments in the treatments. For each treatment and each control of the treatment, 4 replicates were used. For all MCs, the pH of the sediment was determined at the beginning and the end of the experiment.

Results and Discussion
4.1 Evaluation of low intensities of bacterial wood degradation
Initial erosion bacteria attack was found in three of the four treatments (absent in the oxygen enriched treatment (A+O$_2$)) after 120 days incubation time. After 150 days, samples of all treatments showed bacterial degradation patterns. For comparison of the different treatments it was (now) necessary to find a way to classify the bacterial attack.

Table 2. Different treatments, their abbreviations (abbrev.), chemicals added and their aimed concentrations in the sediment (Kretschmar et al. 2008), * = calculated values (based on mixture), dl. = detection limit (0.1 mg/g).

Abbrev	Treatment	Addition	Concentration [mg/g]		
			N	P	S
S	Sediment (pure)	-	0.1	0.15	0.25
M	Mixture of 50 % sediment and 50 % silica sand	-	0.05*	0.075*	0.125*
SS	Silica sand	-	< dl.		
S+A	Sediment with ammonium addition	NH$_4$Cl	1 mg N/g		
S+N	Sediment with nitrate addition	KNO$_3$	1 mg N/g		
S+P	Sediment with phosphorous addition	K$_3$PO$_4$	0.5 mg P/g		
S+Su	Sediment with sulphate addition	K$_2$SO$_4$	0.5 mg S/g		

Due to the inhomogeneous distribution of decay along the tracheids (Blanchette et al. 1990, Grinda 1997, Björdal et al. 2005) the evaluation of bacterial attack is based on comparison of different samples and even different sections of one sample. The assignment of the degree of bacterial attack was conducted following the questions listed in Table 3. The pictures of examples in Figure 3 should improve understanding of the scheme.

Using crosses to indicate attack it can be shown in which MC a higher or lower degree of bacterial degradation exists. A classification by numbers would feign a higher accuracy. It is important to mention that the differences between the classes are not always the same. However for data analyses numerical values are needed, therefore the number of crosses were

transformed into digits ("+" = 1, "(+)" = 0.5).

Many studies about wood degradation by bacteria using microscopy mostly characterize the degradation pattern (e.g., Harmsen and Nissen 1965, Boutelje and Bravery 1968, Kohlmeyer 1978, Daniel and Nilsson 1986, Singh 1989, Kim and Singh 1993, Singh et al. 1994) but classifications of the degree of bacterial attack by microscopy are rare. Paajanen and Viitanen (1988), Grinda (1997) and Klaassen (2008) classified the degree of wood degradation by bacteria. These authors used five degree classes for evaluation of bacterial attack ranging between no attack (sound wood) and total disintegration of the cell wall structure. But these classification schemes were too coarse for evaluating differences of bacterial decay intensities of the different MC treatments which were all in the initial stage. In Table 4 the different evaluation scales of Paajanen and Viitanen (1988), Grinda (1997) and Klaassen (2008) are shown and the interval in which the results of the MC experiment could be found. All decay found was in the initial stage of wood degradation by bacteria which is not surprising given the relatively short experimental duration of 400 days.

4.2 Bacterial decay intensity

In all treatments, bacterial wood attack was found. Figure 4 shows the different decay intensities per treatment and incubation time. The data does not allow a statistical evaluation but some trends can be formulated.

In the first half of the experiment, bacteria colonized and opened up the wood. In this stage the decay intensity increased slightly with incubation time. From 195 days onwards the bacterial degradation seems to be stagnated or slowed down in all treatments except the circulated one.

At the end of the experiment the three non circulated treatments showed all comparable decay intensities independent of the gas supply. At all samplings the highest observed bacterial decay intensity was found in the circulated treatment. The

bacterial degradation intensity increased clearly in this variant up to 400 days.

The degree of wood degradation by bacteria was assigned after inspection of samples from different locations in the MCs. The investigation showed no differences in the degradation intensities between samples of the inner and outer circle (not shown). Nevertheless, some differences between the upper and the lower layer could be observed in all treatments. In these cases the degree of attack was always higher in the upper layer than in the lower one. Björdal et al. (2000) found a depth gradient in degree of bacterial wood degradation in archaeological poles and related it to small differences in oxygen concentration associated with the depth of burial in the ground. It seems that exchanges of surrounding material support the bacterial wood degradation process. This assumption is supported by the observation that the differences in the degradation intensities between upper and lower layer decreased in the circulated treatment with incubation time, whereas in all other treatments

Table 3. *Steps for evaluating intensities of initial bacterial wood degradation*

Transverse section	Longitudinal section
• **Is there a positive attack?**	• **Is there a positive attack?**
• **What is attacked?**	• **What is attacked?**
− rays only (Figure 3 a)	− only cell parts (Figure 3 d)
− cell parts (Figure 3 b)	− whole cells (Figure 3e)
− whole cells (Figure 3 c)	
	• **How many cells are attacked? (only an estimation in none, some, middle, many or all cells)**
	• **In all sections is the result similar?**

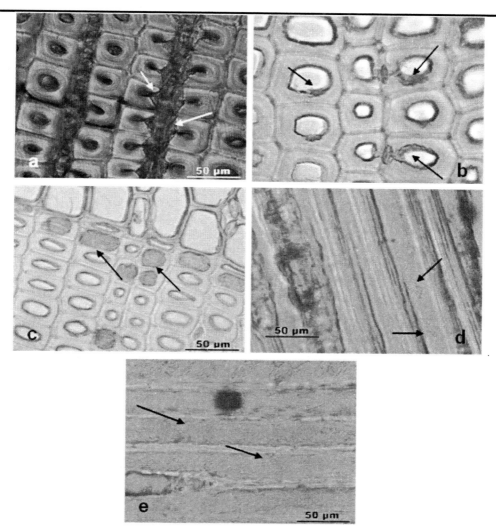

Figure 3 a-e. *Different stages of bacterial degradation in transverse and tangential sections. **a)** The first sign of bacterial attack is a degradation of the rays. The bacteria move through the rays into the wood and start the degradation of the cell walls. **b)** Progress of the initial attack; the bacteria are in cells and start cell wall degradation from the lumen (1:630). **c)** Advanced level of decay creates a typical pattern of apparently sound tracheids adjacent to heavily degraded cells. **d)** Characteristic local decay pattern of initial decay in longitudinal sections. **e)** The decay pattern in progressed attack shows orientation with the microfibrils.*

Table 4. *Survey about different published scales to evaluate the degree of wood degradation by bacteria and the integration of results of MC experiment in these scales.*

Paajanen and Viitanen	Grinda	Klaassen	MC experiment
Sound wood	Sound wood	Sound wood	-
Some indications of degradation	Isolated	Weak degradation	+ - ++
Light degradation	Slight		++ - +++
Moderate degradation	Moderate	Moderate	+++(+)
Heavy degradation, wood softened	Heavy	Severer	
		Total disintegration cell wall structure	

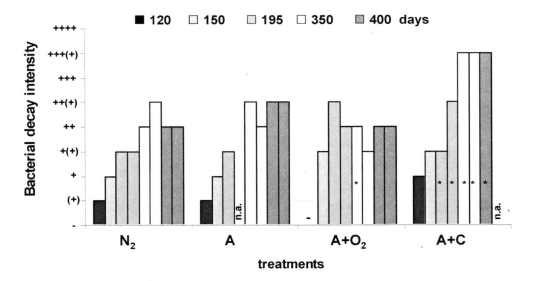

Figure 4. *Intensity of bacterial decay (number of crosses) in the four MC treatments after different incubation times (in days), n.a. = not analyzed, * = additional soft rot decay, - no bacterial decay.*

The degree of wood degradation by bacteria was assigned after inspection of samples from different locations in the MCs. The investigation showed no differences in the degradation intensities between samples of the inner and outer circle (not shown). Nevertheless, some differences between the upper and the lower layer could be observed in all treatments. In these cases the degree of attack was always higher in the upper layer than in the lower one. Björdal et al. (2000) found a depth gradient in degree of bacterial wood degradation in archaeological poles and related it to small differences in oxygen concentration associated with the depth of burial in the ground. It seems that exchanges of surrounding material support the bacterial wood degradation process. This assumption is supported by the observation that the differences in the degradation intensities between upper and lower layer decreased in the circulated treatment with incubation time, whereas in all other treatments the differences prevailed (not shown). It can be concluded, the environments with fluctuating conditions, leading to cycling of various elements, may lead to higher decay rates compared to environments with stable conditions. This is confirmed by Klaassen (2008), who investigated the water flow trough wooden foundation piles: "However, if wooden piles are enclosed in water saturated soils with no water-pressure gradient along the piles and hence no water flow through the stem, bacterial wood degradation should be (almost) inactive."

4.3 Oxygen profile in the different MC treatments

During the experiment the oxygen concentration in selected microcosms was measured with oxygen optodes (Kretschmar 2007) shows the oxygen profile in the MCs resulting from the different gas supply treatments.

In the nitrogen treatment, no oxygen was detectable at any depth. For the other treatments a steep gradient at the sediment water interface from oxygen concentrations corresponding to the solubility of oxygen in the overlaying water to zero at 1 to 2 cm depth in the sediment were measured. The circulation of water in one treatment (A+C) resulted in oxygen being measured further down in the sediment. Even at 6 cm depth in the sediment about 1 mg L^{-1} oxygen occurred.

It is expected that, at the beginning of the experiment, easy degradable organic matter breakdown utilized oxygen and prevented deeper oxygen penetration into the sediment. Upon depletion of easy degradable substrate, the organic matter breakdown slowed down and less oxygen was needed in the upper sediment horizons. Oxygen was obviously transported via diffusion into deeper sediment layers and was measurable in one centimeter depth in the A+C treatment after approximately 100 days (Kretschmar et al. 2008).

The oxygen concentration in one centimeter depth of the sediment rose in the circulated treatment (A+C) after 100 to 120 days to 1 to 2 mg L^{-1} oxygen thus enabling soft rot growth. Oxygen levels of less than 0.03 mmol L^{-1} (0.48 mg L^{-1}) were reported to prevent fungal growth under laboratory conditions (Kohlmeyer and Kohlmeyer 1979). In spite of a sufficient oxygen level not soft rot but bacteria were the first and in this stage the main wood degraders. After 350 days incubation, soft rot patterns were detected (see Figure 4) without any signs of erosion bacteria decay patterns. Because soft rot fungi are faster

wood degraders than erosion bacteria it is supposed that the erosion bacteria were out competed by the soft rot fungi or more likely that bacterial erosion patterns were obscured by soft rot decay patterns.

The soft rot decay was observed in the surface layers of the samples only. It seems that the soft rot decay could not proceed deeper into the wood, because lower levels of oxygen were available there (Björdal et al. 1999). Erosion bacteria degrade efficiently under these conditions, whereas soft rot require higher oxygen concentrations for growth (Björdal et al. 1999).

In spite of the different intensity of available oxygen in the four used treatments, only differences in the velocity of bacterial wood decay were observed, resulting in differences of decay intensity. Under the investigated conditions no differences in the general occurrence of wood degradation by bacteria were evident. From the findings it can be concluded, that bacterial wood decay can proceed without free oxygen present but it happens intensely if oxygen is available.

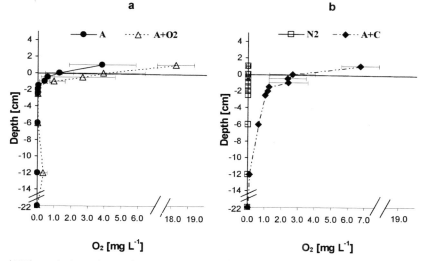

Figure 5. Mean (±SE) vertical gradient of oxygen concentration in the MCs over 400 days a) A = Air, A+O = Air enriched with oxygen, b) N2 = Nitrogen, A+C = Air and water circulation. Positive values are within the overlaying water, negative values within the sediment core, n = 4 for depth +1.0, 0, -0.5, -1.0, -12.0 cm and n = 1 for depth -1.5, -2.0, -2.5, -6.0, -22.0 cm. Note: The O₂ value in the overlaying water for A+O is 18.32 mg L-1 and the last measured depth is -2.0 cm (Kretschmar et al., 2008).

4.4 Influence of the chemical composition of sediment interstitial pore water to the degree of degradation

All decay found was in the early initiation stage of wood degradation by bacteria. This is not surprising given the short experimental duration of 155 days. Based on the aerated treatments with unchanged sediment, bacterial decay intensities of this second MC experiment were comparable with the degree of degradation of the first MC experiment after 150 days.

Treatments with pure sediment (S), silica sand (SS) or their mixture (M) show very slight bacterial wood decay in most of the samples. Furthermore, treatments in which nitrate (NO_3) and sulphur (SO_4) was added to the sediment, did not show any sign of attack after 155 days. However in one single MC of the S+P (added PO_4) and the S+A (added NH_4) treatments some slight

signs of bacterial attack were observed. Table 5 shows the degradation results of this second experiment.

Bacterial wood decay intensity in this experiment appears to be highest at a sediment pH range from 7 to 8.3 in the treatments without chemical addition to the sediment (see Figure 7). The "optimal" pH range found in the experiment is supported by literature reports by Boutelje and Göransson (1975) which measured ground water pH values of 7.2 - 8.0 surrounding bacterial decayed wooden foundation piles in Stockholm. Ground water in contact with bacterial decayed archaeological wood and wooden foundation pilings showed a pH range of 7.0 to 8.5 with two values lower as 7.0 and one values higher as 8.5 (Huisman et al.2008, Kretschmar et al.2008a).

Table 5. *Intensity of bacterial decay after 155 days in different treatments (S = sediment, M = mixture from sediment and silica sand (SS), S+A = sediment with ammonium addition, S+N = sediment and nitrate addition, S+P = phosphate addition, S+Su = sulfate addition) in the second MC experiment, - = no signs of bacterial wood decay found, (+) = very slight decay, + = slight decay.*

Treatment	S	M	SS	S+A	S+N	S+P	S+Su
1	(+)	(+)	(+)	(+)	-	(+)	-
2	(+)	(+)	(+)	-	-	-	-
3	(+)	(+)	(+)	-	-	-	-
4	(+)	(+)	+	-	-	-	-

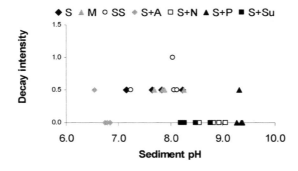

Figure 7: *Bacterial wood decay intensity versus sediment pH at the end of the experiment. (Kretschmar et al. 2008), for treatment abbreviations see Table 5*

The addition of chemicals to the sediment did affect the sediment pH and it can therefore not be distinguished between the pH effect and the chemical effect of the addition. It seems that the sediment pH limit bacterial wood decay intensity when it is outside the "optimal" range. Nevertheless two outliers exist out of four parallels with decay detected at low (6.5) and high (9.4) pH values. As a general rule, bacterial activity is highly influenced by the pH of the growth medium and it is likely that bacterial wood decay intensity was affected by pH together with variations in nitrogen and phosphorus concentrations in the sediment. Conclusions related to the sediment pH are based on values measured at the end of the experiment.

There are indications that a negative relationship exists between bacterial wood decay intensity and sediment nitrogen concentration (Table 6) if it is presumed that sediment pH obscured, but did not totally govern bacterial wood decay intensity.

This might indicate that in sediments with a very high C/N ratio or a generally very low carbon and nitrogen concentration, the C/N ratio of wood is still "interesting" for the bacteria as a food source. Moreover, bacterially decayed wood was reported to have high N concentrations (Boutelje and Göransson 1975, Gregory, 1999, Gelbrich, 2009).

Thus the following conclusion, confirmed by Gregory (1999), as a basis for further research is suggested. Wood surrounded by water saturated sediment with low nitrogen content is more likely to be affected by bacterial wood decay than wood in sediments with medium to high nitrogen contents. This conclusion is drawn from the finding that nitrate addition to the sediment resulted in no bacterial decay in the wood samples. However, this might not in all cases be true as sediment samples with higher total N concentrations

have been found surrounding quite intense bacterially decayed wooden pilings (Boutelje and Göransson 1975).

In addition, sulfate supplements to the sediment seemed to prevent bacterial decay in wooden samples (see Table 5). These results were supported by another MC experiment of 4 weeks, in which the combined addition of glucose and sulfate prevent attack to lignocellulose material (Kretschmar, 2007, Gelbrich 2009). Therefore we concluded that the potential toxicity of sulfate towards erosion bacteria may be the base for a potential method of inhibition of degradation.

5. Conclusion

The performed investigations provided a starting point for understanding the ecology and physiology of erosion bacteria. All results presented are based on sandy sediment. Particularly better knowledge on the conditions suitable for causing attack on wood is gained. Further investigation especially long term experiments are necessary to understand the complex interaction of the bacterial wood degradation. Continuing research is needed to test and clarify

- the effect of strictly anoxic conditions
- the influence of water flow to the degradation process
- the impacts of nutrient additions to the surrounding
- the pH effect

for long term periods and for different sediment types.

The influences and impacts to the environment as well as to the archaeological wood of preservation ideas are not assessable. Therefore, it is important to test preservation strategies in the laboratory before using it in "real" environments, which will be possible with such an experimental design.

Table 6. *Intensity of bacterial decay in different treatments after 155 days and total n content in sediment at the beginning of the experiment.*

Treatment	S	M	SS	S+A	S+N
1	(+)	(+)	(+)	(+)	-
2	(+)	(+)	(+)	-	-
3	(+)	(+)	(+)	-	-
4	(+)	(+)	+	-	-
N (mg/g DW)	<0.1	<0.1	0.11	0.62	0.96

Increasing sediment nitrogen condition

→

Decreasing intensity of wood degradation by bacteria

6. Acknowledgement

The results of this study are parts of two PhD theses of University of Goettingen with a special thank to the team at the Institute of Wood Biology and Wooden Products and the staff at the Institute of Soil Science and Forest Nutrition.

We'd like to give our special thanks to the partners of the project. Thomas Nilsson and Charlotte Björdal who shared a lot of their knowledge of bacterial wood decay with us, especially during the experimental design and the microscopic decay classification. We are grateful to Rene Klaassen from the wood research institute SHR who helped as well with the microscopically decay classification. We'd also like to thank the staff of Fugro Ingenieursbureuau Amsterdam, especially Herman Keijer and Christiaan van Stigt, who organized and conducted the sediment retrieval in Amsterdam. Last, but not least, we appreciate the financial support of the Bacpoles project from the European commission which funded it under the Key Action 4: City of tomorrow and cultural heritage (EVK4-CT-2001-00043).

7. References

Björdal, C. and Nilsson, T., (1999), Laboratory reburial experiments, In Hoffmann et al. (eds.), Proceedings of the. 7th ICOM-CC Working Group on Wet Organic Archaeological Materials Conference 1998, Grenoble, France, pp 71-77

Björdal, C., Nilsson, T. and Daniel, G., (1999), Microbial decay of waterlogged archaeological wood found in Sweden, International Biodeterioration and Biodegradation 43, pp 63-71

Björdal, C., Daniel, G., Nilsson, T., (2000), Depth of burial, an important factor in controlling bacterial decay of waterlogged archaeological poles, International Biodeterioration and Biodegradation 45, 15-26

Björdal, C., Nilsson, T. and Bardage, S., (2005), Three-dimensional visualization of bacterial decay in individual tracheids of *Pinus sylvestris*, Holzforschung 59, pp 178-182

Blanchette, R. A., Nilsson, T., Daniel, G. E., Abad, A., (1990), Biological degradation of wood, In Rowell, R.M. and Barbour, R.J. (eds.) Archaeological wood: properties, chemistry, and preservation, Adv. Chem. Ser. No. 225, Amer. Chem. Soc. Washington D. C., pp 141-174

Boutelje, J.B. and Bravery, A.F., (1968), Observations on the bacterial attack of piles supporting a Stockholm building, Journal of the Institute of Wood Science 20, pp 47-57

Boutelje, J.B., Göransson, B., (1975), Decay in wood constructions below the ground water table, Swedish Journal of Agricultural Research 5, pp 113-123

Daniel, G.F. and Nilsson, T., (1986), Ultrastructural observations on wood degrading erosions bacteria, IRG/WP/1283, The International Research Group on Wood Preservation, Stockholm

ENV 807:2001: Wood preservatives - Determination of the effectiveness against soft rotting micro-fungi and other soil inhabiting micro-organisms.

Gelbrich, J., (2009), Bacterial wood degradation - A study of chemical changes in wood and growth conditions of bacteria, PhD thesis, Georg-August-University, Göttingen, Germany

Gregory, D., (1999), Re-burial of ship timbers in the marine environment as a method of in situ preservation, In Hoffmann et al. (eds.), Proceedings of the. 7th ICOM-CC Working Group on Wet Organic Archaeological Materials Conference 1998, Grenoble, France, pp 78-84

Gregory, D., Matthiesen, H., Björdal C., (2002), In situ preservation of artifacts in Nydam Mose: Studies into environmental monitoring and the deterioration of wooden artifacts, In Hoffmann et al. (eds.), Proceedings of the 8th ICOM-CC Working Group on Wet Organic Archaeological Materials Conference 2001, Stockholm, Sweden, pp 213-223

Grinda, M., (1997), Some experiences with attack of microorganisms on wooden constructions supporting foundations of houses and bridges, IRG/WP/ 97-10232, The International Research Group on Wood Preservation, Stockholm

Harmsen, L. und Nissen, T.V. (1965), Der Bakterienangriff auf Holz, Holz als Roh- und Werkstoff 23, pp 389-393

Hogan, D.V., Simpson, P., Jones, A.M., Maltby E., (2002), Development of a protocol for the reburial of organic archaeological remains, In Hoffmann et al. (eds.), Proceedings of the 8th ICOM-CC Working Group on Wet Organic Archaeological Materials Conference 2001, Stockholm, Sweden, pp 187-212

Huisman, D.J., Manders, M.R., Kretschmar, E.I., Klaassen, R., Lamersdorf, N., (2008), Burial conditions and wood degradation on archaeological sites in the Netherlands, International Biodeterioration and Biodegradation 61 (1), pp 33-44

Kim, Y.S. and Singh, A.P., (1993), Ultrastructural aspects of bacterial attacks on an archaeological wood, IRG/WP/93-1000, The International Research Group on Wood Preservation, Stockholm

Klaassen, R., (2008), Bacterial decay in wooden foundation piles: patterns and causes - A study on historical pile foundations out of pine, spruce, fir, and oak in the Netherlands, International Biodeterioration and Biodegradation 61 (1), pp 45-60

Klimant I., Meyer V., Kühl M., (1995), Fiber-optic oxygen microsensors, a new tool in aquatic biology, Limnology and Oceanography 40, pp 1159-1165

Kohlmeyer, J. (1978), Bacterial attack on wood and cellophane in the deep sea. In Qxleyet al. (eds), Biodeterioration, proceedings of the fourth international symposium, Berlin Pitman publishing Ltd. London and the biodeterioration society, pp. 187-192

Kohlmeyer, J., Kohlmeyer, E., (1979), Marine Ecology: The higher fungi, Academic Press, New York, p. 690.

Kretschmar, E.I., (2007), Anoxic sediments and their potential to favor bacterial wood decay, PhD thesis, Georg-August-University, Göttingen, Germany

Kretschmar, E.I., Gelbrich, J., Militz, H. and Lamersdorf, N., (2008), Studying bacterial wood decay under low oxygen conditions – results of microcosm experiments, International Biodeterioration and Biodegradation 61 (1), pp 69-84.

Kretschmar, E.I., Huisman, D.J., Lamersdorf, N., (2008a), Characterizing physicochemical sediment conditions at selected bacterial decayed wooden pile foundation sites in the Netherlands, Germany, and Italy, International Biodeterioration and Biodegradation 61 (1), pp. 117-125

Loftfield, N., Flessa, H., Augustin, J., Beese, F., (1997), Automated gas chromatographic system for rapid analysis of the atmospheric trace gases methane, carbon dioxide, and nitrus oxide, Journal of Environmental Quality 26, pp 560-564

Nilsson, T., (1998), Microbial degradation of wood – an overview with special emphasis on waterlogged wood, In Hoffmann et al. (eds.), Proceedings of the 7th ICOM-CC Working Group on Wet Organic Archaeological Materials Conference, Grenoble, France, pp 65-71

Nilsson, T. and Björdal, C. G., (2008), Culturing wood degrading erosion-bacteria, International Biodeterioration and Biodegradation 61 (1), pp 3-10.

Nyström Godfrey, I.., Bergstrand, T., Gjelstrup Björdal, C,. Nilsson, T., Bohm, C., Christensson E., Gregory, D., Peacok, E.E., Richards, V., MacLeod, I., 2009; Reburial and analyses of archaeological remains - The RAAR project. Project status and cultural heritage management implications based on the first preliminary results, In Strætkvern et al. (eds.) Proceedings of the 10th ICOM-CC Working Group on Wet Organic Archaeological Materials Conference 2007, Amsterdam, Netherlands, pp 169-196

Paajanen, L. and Viitanen, H. (1988): Microbiological degradation of wooden piles in building foundations, IRW/WP/1370, The International Research Group on Wood Preservation, Stockholm

Pournou, A., Jones, M.A., Moss, S.T., (1998), *In situ* protection of the Zakynthos wreck, In Hoffmann et al. (eds.), Proceedings of the. 7th ICOM-CC Working Group on Wet Organic Archaeological Materials Conference 1998, Grenoble, France, pp 58-64

Schniewind, A. P., (1990), Physical and mechanical properties of archaeological wood, In Rowell, R.M. and Barbour, R.J. (eds.), Archaeological wood: properties, chemistry, and preservation, Adv. Chem. Ser. No. 225, Amer. Chem. Soc. Washington D. C., pp 87-109

Singh, A.P., Nilsson, T. and Daniel, G.F., (1994), Microbial decay of an archaeological wood, IRG/WP/94-10053, The International Research Group on Wood Preservation, Stockholm

Singh, A.P., (1989), Certain aspects of bacterial degradation of Pinus radiata wood, IAWA Bulletin n.s., Vol.10 (4), pp 405-415

Environmental Scanning Electron Microscopy (Esem): An Effective Analytical Tool for Comparing Reagents used in the Conservation of Waterlogged Wood

Catherine Marie Sincich
Nautical Archaeology Program, Department of Anthropology,Texas A&M University, 4352 TAMU, College Station, TX 77843-4352, USA
E-mail: csincich@neo.tamu.edu

Abstract

The purpose of this study was to utilize Environmental Scanning Electron Microscopy (ESEM) to effectively visualize waterlogged wood following treatments with different conservation reagents for comparison of cellular structures involved, degree of penetration, bulking, etc. ESEM differs from Scanning Electron Microscopy (SEM) in that samples can be imaged wet, sputter coating is optional and extremely low vacuum pressures are not required (reducing the chance for specimen distortion, often associated with traditional SEM).

A variety of conservation reagents encompassing a diverse set of chemical compounds (PEG 600, PEG 1500, PEG 3250, silicone polymer, rosin, white sugar, camphor) were applied to waterlogged tongue depressors. Results show that imaging with ESEM was clearly effective at defining the localization of each reagent and the cellular structures involved. It is concluded that ESEM has proven to be an effective analytical tool for conservators to compare reagents used in the conservation of waterlogged wood

Questions and answers

Ian Godfrey: Just a question for Catherine regarding the environmental SEM. I was just wondering a couple of things. I could see quite clearly that you could detect the consolidants in the tracheids but I was just wondering about consolidation within the cell walls of the wood itself and also the other issue of just the sampling. If you're going to monitor the effectiveness of treatment it would seem to me that there's a potential problem in getting to that level to determine how effective the treatment has been. Just wondering if you could comment on those aspects?

Catherine Sincich: Right, well a lot of those samples that you saw today, initially would have been in a standard SEM because we really do want to look at exactly what is going on because it's been reported that with the silicone polymers what you get is structural support rather than bulk so if it's actually lining those tracheids or those vessels, the bulking aspect that you see with PEG that's adding weight, and isn't really there. And with SEM with EDS you can actually look at that. Once we know and have done several samples, then we can go and do the ESEM because we know it's there. The problem with our program is that there are a lot of people doing small little experiments and there's not really one person doing a comprehensive aspect. So I can't really answer your question about long-term stability. It hasn't really been taken all the way. There've been some small studies by this person, this person, this person, but it hasn't really been that comprehensive. When I came to the program, I was really planning to use silicone oils and even though I had lots of equipment it's just a matter of doing lots of samples and how many times can you look at tongue depressor and not look at archaeological samples. Enough samples to actually say what's going on so I think in a roundabout answer, we know it's there, I didn't present any data for it but it's been looked at many many times. It's been repeated many many times, but the long-term stability, we haven't really looked at to see what's going on. For a lot of the materials what you want to do is some hardness testing, some tensile strength testing that hasn't really been done comprehensively. There's a lot of work we need to do to really be able to say comprehensively "After 20 years, after 30 years, this is what's going on." We know in the short-term that there is support but we should be checking that because we've done enough samples. That's all I can think of to say about that.

Vicki Richards: I just want to know how wet is wet because we use what they call an environmental SEM but it's got EDX on it but it's not wet. I put samples in there that I thought were dry and it didn't work so I just want to know how wet is wet?

Catherine Sincich: You can have it as wet as you want. What you actually see is when you are imaging it you get a real time look on the monitor. What I didn't mention with the ESEM is you actually do hydration studies. You can manipulate the pressure, you can manipulate the temperature and actually see crystals solubilize and then recrystallize. You can measure them as they are crystallizing. A lot of the architectural students have come down and done studies with the Getty, so they'll actually look at what's going on with structural stone because they've got magnesium sulfate that will do harm and you can do temperature studies so you can do crystallization studies and a bunch of those kinds of things so you can manipulate a lot of samples using ESEM. As you're looking at it if you put in something that's just saturated in a puddle of water you do have an environment where there's just a little vacuum, so that water will go into vapor and as you watch, you'll start seeing it dry out and there's actually a button that you push and there's a little flask in the back of the instrument that's full of water and it just injects more water vapor. So you can keep it wet even if you

want to image it over a five hour period or if you're going to do a temperature study. Like I say, you're looking at it on the monitor so you can maintain...you're looking at the pressure so as the pressure changes, you can tweak it a bit. You can do a lot with it. So it can be as wet as you want. Don't be afraid with water in the ESEM. Water is your friend in the ESEM. It's the complete opposite if you are going to do the SEM – it needs to be absolutely dry, sputter coated and you don't want any charging. It has to be under extremely high vacuum pressures and the sample has to be very small. In the ESEM, a lot of those aren't issues.

Vicki Richards: We use one that is obviously in the middle. We can put things in that are about as wet as a leaf. So you can have a sample that's "wet", it's not wet, it's dampish. And we can do EDAX analysis and we don't have to sputter coat anything.

Catherine Sincich: The one thing I will caution people who are thinking about using this is generally you will be using someone else's machine, so anything that will go into vapor can go up into the gun and generally if you don't have polymers, polymerized and you don't have something that's going to stay put, it can go up into the gun and then you have a $600,000 paperweight and that's happened...in the past... not since I've been there. But they caution you and there're a lot of people in nanobiology and hydrogels, membranes and stuff, who are doing all kinds of things with polymers as well. They are really looking at a lot of things and they don't want things really hard so they don't polymerize the stuff and then they put it in the ESEM and you can actually see these things coat around it. There is a pressure limiting aperture, two of them, so the gun itself is under high vacuum but then the chamber isn't and things can migrate up through there. So it's not a foolproof technique but if you have really good microscopy staff they will bend over backwards to get your experiments to work. You can do a lot with the ESEM and, like I said, water is your friend so you can do a lot of fun things with it.

John Kenney: Thank you very much for your wonderful pictures with the environmental SEM. I've done a lot of SEM before and we have an environmental SEM actually here in the biology department, and it's also fitted out with an electron news and X-ray fluorescence detection, so one can do elemental analysis even with environmental SEM. But I also have a question. You mentioned something about the differential pumping with the new aperture, what pressure can you get? It looks like your instrument was from the 1970's.

Catherine Sincich: It was purchased in the 1970's and the one problem with this model is there's not a lot of them working

so the staff really make sure that it's maintained properly and that people who come in to use it, use it properly. Because when it does go down, the guy who's in charge of it has to call all over the United States and he's got his contacts and people have stuff in their garage and all that. But I think this machine can go anywhere from 0.4 torr to 50 torr.

John Kenney: Oh, that's not atmosphere...

Catherine Sincich: I don't know how low it <u>will</u> go, but generally, when I ran these samples... it's actually on these pictures. All the parameters are on the bottom. The vapor pressure it is just a little bit of vacuum, not much at all when I was doing the samples. I just don't remember off hand.

John Kenney: Yes, I see, thank you.

Evaluating Long-Term Stability of Waterlogged Archaeological Wooden Objects through Determination of Moisture Sorption Isotherms and Conductance in Conserved Objects and Impregnation Agents

Poul Jensen[*]
The National Museum of Denmark, Department of Conservation, I.C. Modewegs Vej, Brede, DK-2800 Kgs. Lyngby, Denmark.
E-mail*: poul.jensen@natmus.dk

Anne Christine Helms
Ministry of Food, Agriculture and Fisheries, The Danish Plant Directorate, Skovbrynet 20, 2800 Kgs. Lyngby, Denmark

Mikkel Christensen
Museum of Cultural History, University of Oslo, Postboks 6762 St. Olavs plass, N-0130 Oslo, Norway

Abstract

The relative humidity (RH) of the air is a key factor in relation to the long term stability of conserved archaeological artifacts. It controls the amount of moisture sorbed by both the material of the objects and the impregnation agents, and thereby influences the ion mobility and chemical processes with a potential to degrade the objects. The National Museum of Denmark therefore started a research scheme, in which already conserved wooden archaeological objects were analyzed, in order to determine if conservation methods and agents, inappropriate for standard museum climate (20°C, 50% RH), were in use or had been applied in the past. The ion mobility was determined indirectly by measuring the electrical conductance of both conserved objects and aqueous solutions of impregnation agents.

16 impregnation agents and 13 groups of already conserved wooden objects were exposed to air with a relative humidity (RH) ranging from 23% to 95%. The equilibrium moisture content (EMC) for the impregnation agents and objects was determined. The conductance in the conserved objects was measured by inserting two stainless steel screws in the objects at a distance of approximately 2 cm and measuring the electrical conductance by alternating current, when the objects had reached the EMC.

The research resulted in moisture sorption isotherms and deliquescent point for all examined impregnation agents. For the already conserved objects, moisture sorption isotherms and curves for conductance as a function of RH were established. Especially the low sorption rate for pure mannitol and alum are of interest, as it can affect the way we choose to store artifacts treated with these impregnation agents. The research also showed that the moisture sorbed by the wooden structure itself only increased the conductance slightly, whereas the water sorbed in PEG 200 to PEG 600, glycerol and sorbitol increased the conductance in the objects, even at an RH below 50%, indicating that a normal museum climate might not be sufficient to arrest chemical and transport processes. Additional analysis of pH, conductivity and viscosity for aqueous solutions of PEG were conducted, showing that ions are dissociated and highly mobile in the water sorbed by PEG, even at water contents below 10% w/w.

The National Museum will use the method of determination of moisture sorption isotherm and electrical conductance to assess existing and future impregnation agents and conservation methods, as well as for establishing demands for climate conditions in exhibitions and storerooms.

Keywords: impregnation agents, archaeological wood, stability, sorbed water, conductivity, conductance, ion mobility, moisture sorption isotherm, deliquescent point.

1. Introduction

One of the main tasks of he National Museum is to preserve accessioned objects for the future. For waterlogged wood several strategies have been pursued since 1860 (Christensen 1970), but nearly all applied methods have been as reversible as possible, so eventually threatened objects could be saved through re-conservation.

Investigations on conserved objects at the National Museum and the project on the stability of Vasa, the Swedish regal ship (http://www.vasamuseet.se/sitecore/content/ Vasamuseet/Skeppet/Forskning_bevarande. aspx), show problems with salt precipitations, acids, iron, sulfur etc. These findings have raised the question if the objects at the National Museum are stabile over long periods of time or if they will slowly degrade and lose their value as a source of information on our cultural history? Therefore, it was desirable to start research, which could clarify if it was necessary to change conditions for storage and exhibitions or re-conserve objects in order to prevent degrading processes and insure long term stability.

As it is of paramount importance that the conserved archaeological wooden objects in principle can be kept forever, it was important to clarify if there are ongoing degrading processes in the wooden artifacts and which parameters govern or limit them. In a normal museum climate with a relative humidity (RH) below 50%, it is expected that the microbiological processes (Brock & Madigan 1991) (Salisbury & Ross 1969) are arrested and any possible degrading processes have an abiotic chemical nature. The results of chemical processes are difficult to measure directly, therefore an indirect method, determination of the electrical conductance in objects and impregnation solutions, was selected, as it reflects the presence of ions and their mobility (both parameters which are

necessary for a chemical process to take place).

Also the amounts of water sorbed by wooden objects and impregnation agents are of importance, as it is assumed that a certain amount of sorbed water is necessary for non-charged molecules and ions to diffuse in the objects. The deliquescent point, defined as the relative humidity (water activity) at which solid impregnation agents has sorbed enough water to liquefy, is a key factor in relation to museum climate, as presence of aqueous solutions in conserved artifacts can lead to collapse, softening, precipitations and other unwanted phenomena. Both pH, conductivity and viscosity of aqueous solutions of low molecular mass PEG are interesting as they reflect at which water contents and water activities ions are dissociated and mobile.

In 2008 the National Museum started a research scheme supported by *the Danish Agency for Science, Technology and Innovation, Ministry of Science, Technology and Innovation*, where above parameters were determined in order to investigate the stability of conserved wooden objects.

2. Experimental Work

2.1 Determination of moisture sorption isotherms for water soluble impregnation agents and conserved wooden artifacts

The moisture sorption isotherms were determined by placing samples of impregnation agents and small wooden samples in a climate chamber (Weiss, WK III, 180). The temperature was set to 20°C ±0.1deg, and the relative humidity was varied from 35 to 90% in steps of 5% with an accuracy of ±0.2% (see Figure 1A). Each step was held until the equilibrium moisture content (EMC) was established for all samples. In average, it took 4 to 8 days for reaching the EMC. The mass of sorbed water was found by taking the samples out of the climate chamber and weighing the samples on a 4 decimal balance within half a minute to avoid loss or uptake of moisture from the air.

Supplementary determinations were made at 23% and 95% RH for all samples by equilibrating them over salt solutions (CH_3COOK and K_2SO_4) (Rockland, 1960) in desiccator at 20°C ±0.5deg. The equilibrium time was 14 days for each RH level. The EMC in the desiccator was determined with an electronic moisture meter (Vaisala MH70) mounted with a humidity and temperature probe (HMP76).

For selected agents, supplementary determinations of RH over aqueous solutions were made at RH between 95 and 99%. The RH (water activities) over the solutions were determined with an electronic moisture meter (Vaisala MH70) mounted with a humidity and temperature probe (HMP76). The solutions were poured into aluminum humidity calibrators (HMK 15) to a height of 4 mm. The aluminum calibrator was placed in a thermos jar to minimize temperature fluctuations. The temperature was 20°C ±0.5deg. The water activity was determined with an accuracy of ±1%. It took 5 to 10 hours to obtain stable relative humidities over the solutions.

The samples of the impregnation agents (between 0.3 and 0.8 g) were placed in aluminum weighing boats (50 mm in diameter, 10 mm high). The impregnation agents included water free: *tetra* ethylene glycol (TEG), Polyethylene glycol (PEG) 200, 400, 600, 1000, 1500, 2000, 4000, 6000 and 10000, plus mannitol, sorbitol, glucose, sucrose and alum. All samples were in duplicates.

For PEG 2000, additional water activities were measured over solutions of PEG with a water content of 0.10, 0.15, 0.20, 0.25, 0.30 and 0.35 w/w. The water activity was measured as for the solutions in section 3.2 and the phases of the PEG (solid/liquid) were determined in order to document if PEG 2000 can sorb a certain amount of water and still be solid.

The conserved wooden samples from storerooms were selected according to type of wood, impregnation agent and drying method. The samples included: oak (Quercus sp.), pine (Pinus sylvéstris), unspecified broad leaved and coniferous woods and samples from the Vasa and the Skuldelev ships, which are on display in Stockholm, Sweden, and Roskilde, Denmark, respectively. The impregnation agents encompass PEG 200 to 4000 plus alum and glycerol, in concentrations from 0 to 100% saturation. The samples had been air and freeze-dried. See Appendix 1 for exact specification. The samples were relative small with dimensions between 2 and 5 cm in order to reach EMC at the same speed as the pure impregnation agents in the aluminum weighing boats. All samples were in triplicates.

2.2 Determination of deliquescent point for impregnation agents

The deliquescent points were determined for the earlier mentioned impregnation agents, which were solid at room temperature (20°C, 50% RH): PEG 1500, 2000, 4000, 6000 and 10,000 plus glucose, sucrose and alum. Saturated solutions were made in 100 mL glass bottles with approximately 25 mL of each solution. The bottles were closed with vapor tight caps and left at room temperature for 14 days to insure equilibrium. The RH (water activities) over the solutions were determined with an electronic moisture meter (Vaisala MH70) with a humidity and temperature probe (HMP76) fitted vapor tight to a bottle cap. The glass bottle mounted with the sensor cap was placed in a thermos jar to minimize temperature fluctuations. The temperature was 22±0.5°C. The water activity was determined with an accuracy of ±1%. It took 5 to 25 hours to obtain stable relative humidities over the solutions. The water content of the saturated solutions (22±0.5°C) were determined by measuring the mass loss on a 3 decimal balance of 1 to 4 mL solution samples when dehydrated, first at 22°C and 50 RH, followed by vacuum drying at 20°C, with a water vapor pressure 0.2 Pa.

2.3 Determination of electrical conductivity in aqueous solution of glycerol saturated with alum

Aqueous solutions of glycerol with the concentration between 0 and 1 w/w were made in 100 mL bottles, 40 mL of each solution. Alum, $KAl(SO_4)_2 \cdot 12H_2O$, was added under vigorous mixing for 1 hour to an amount where alum crystals were present at the bottom of the solution. The bottles were fitted with vapor tight caps and left at 20°C±0.2 deg for three days to insure saturation. The electrical conductivity in the solutions was determined by an AC conductivity meter (Radiometer MD3) connected to an electrical conductivity sensor (Microelectrodes, MI-905) and the temperature measured with a type-K thermocouple connected to a data logger (Pico Technology). The amount of alum in the saturated solutions was determined by transferring 2 to 4 mL of the solutions into aluminum weighing boats with a pipette, and measuring the mass of alum when water and glycerol had evaporated. The evaporation was performed in a Heto SIC freeze-dryer with temperature controlled shelves, where the water was sublimed at -60° at a pressure of 0.007 Pa and the remaining glycerol at +115°C in a heating cabinet. Water was added to the oven dried alum and the alum was left to dry at room temperature (20°C, 50% RH). The procedure was used in order to ensure 12 mol of crystal water per alum molecule.

The theoretical electrical conductivity, $\sigma_{wattheo}$, in the water in the alum saturated aqueous solutions of glycerol, corrected for the actual volume of water, viscosity and concentration, was calculated by Equation 1. The corrected values give an idea of how the amount of sorbed water influences the activity and mobility of the dissolved ions. Data for viscosity were taken from (Weast 1965) and (Weast 1987). Equation 2 gives a possibility to estimate the conductivity by means of the conductivity for the salt in pure aqueous solution and the viscosity for aqueous solution.

$$\sigma_{wattheo} = \frac{V_{sample}}{V_{wat}} \cdot \frac{\eta_{sample}}{\eta_{wat}} \cdot \sigma_{sample} \qquad S \cdot cm^{-1} \qquad (1)$$

$$\sigma_{sampletheo} = \sigma_{wat} \cdot \frac{V_{wat}}{V_{sample}} \cdot \frac{\eta_{wat}}{\eta_{sample}} \qquad S \cdot cm^{-1} \qquad (2)$$

where :

σ_{sample} = electrical conductivity saturated with alum

$\sigma_{sampletheo}$ = electrical theoretical conductivity saturated with alum

σ_{wat} = electrical conductivity in water saturated with alum

$\sigma_{wattheo}$ = electrical theoretical conductivity in water saturated with alum calculated by means of volume fraction of water, viscosity and concentration of alum

V_{sample} = volume of sample

V_{wat} = volume of water in sample with dissolved salt

η_{sample} = viscosity of sample

η_{wat} = viscosity of water

2.4 Determination of electrical conductivity in aqueous solutions of PEG 200 and 600

The electrical conductivity in aqueous solutions of PEG 200 and PEG 600 was determined by placing an electrical conductivity sensor (Microelectrodes, MI-905) connected to an AC conductivity meter (Radiometer MD3) sensor and a type-K thermocouple connected to a data logger (Pico Technology) in a three neck 500 mL flask. 100 g of deionized water was dripped into the flask trough the free neck. PEG was dripped into the flask with a syringe, approximately 1 g a time. The syringe was weighed on a three decimal balance after each adding of PEG to determine the amount added. The solution was mixed with a magnetic stirrer continuously. The temperature was controlled by a surrounding water bath (20°C±0.2 deg). When equilibrium (temperature and mixing) was established, the electrical conductivity was measured (accuracy ±1%) and the measurements were continued by dripping another 1 g into the solution until 115 g was added. The procedure was repeated with PEG in the flask at the beginning and water dripped into the flask. Measurements were made for both PEG 200 and PEG 600.

The theoretical electrical conductivity, $\sigma_{wattheo}$, in the water in the aqueous PEG solution with KCl, corrected for the actual volume of water and viscosity, can be calculated by Equation 1 and 2, where glycerol and alum are exchanged with PEG and KCl.

2.5 Determination of viscosity in aqueous solutions of PEG 200 and 600

The viscosities of aqueous solutions, with the concentrations between 0 and 1 w/w were measured with a rotation viscosimeter (Rheology International, RI:1:L) and a low viscosity adapter (V.L.) placed in a water bath with a temperature of 20°C ±0.2 deg.

2.6 Determination of electrical conductance in wooden artifacts

For determination of the electrical conductance in the wooden samples, two stainless screws were mounted in each sample with a distance of approximately 20 mm, see Figure 1B. The electrical conductance was measured with an AC conductivity meter (Radiometer MD3), when the samples had reached EMC for the selected RH, see section 3.1. The conductance was determined with an average accuracy of ±1%. It was not possible to determine the conductivity from the measured conductance. All samples were in triplicates.

Figure 1A. A view into the open climate chamber with wooden samples on the top shelf and aluminum beakers with impregnation agents on the lower shelf.

Figure 1B. A wooden sample mounted with two stainless screws for measuring the electrical conductance.

3. Results and Discussion

3.1 Moisture sorption isotherms for water soluble impregnation agents and conserved wooden artifacts

Figure 2 shows the moisture sorption isotherm for selected low and high molecular mass PEGs. The moisture sorption isotherms are in close agreement with (Clariant 1998) and (Nini *et al.* 1999).

At water activities close 0.50, the low molecular mass PEGs only have a slightly higher moisture content than that of wood (Stamm 1964) (Boye 1969) and are such not highly hygroscopic (although this is often postulated). At water contents above 0.55 w/w (water activities above 0.95) the sorption isotherms for high molecular mass PEGs are nearly identical, although small differences exist as presented by Nini *et al.* (1999). Below this water activity the sorption isotherms differ. Especially the water activity at which the PEGs start sorbing moisture and the deliquescent points diverge. Seen in relation to conserved wooden objects the deliquescent point is of paramount importance, as the PEG at this water activity liquefies and the objects start to be instable. Figure 3 shows the sorbed water content at standard museum climate (20°C, RH 50%). If the amount of sorbed water is considered as a potential for chemical and physical transfer processes, it is clear that PEGs with molecular masses below 1500 should be avoided.

Figure 4 shows the moisture sorption isotherms for glucose and sucrose. Above the deliquescent points both agents behave in accordance with their molecular mass and their hydroxyl groups. Sucrose already starts to sorb small amounts of water at a water activity of 0.70 and is fully dissolved at a water activity of 0.84. Glucose first starts to sorb water at a water activity of 0.85 and is fully dissolved at a water activity 0.87. The deliquescent points are not on the curves for the sorption isotherm as the sorption isotherm was made by going from lower towards higher water activities. The deliquescent point represent the point on the moisture sorption isotherm, which can be achieved by making the sorption isotherm from higher towards lower water activities.

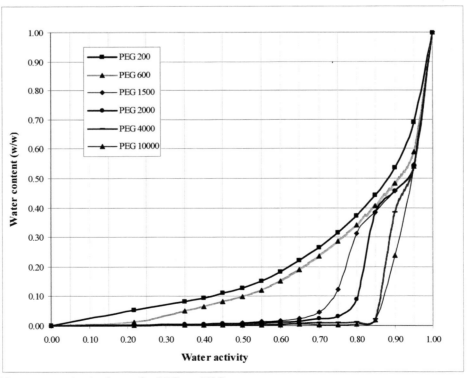

Figure 2. Moisture sorption isotherms for PEGs at 20°C.

88

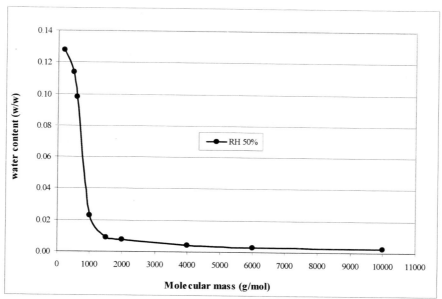

Figure 3. Sorbed water as a function of the molecular mass of PEGs at standard museum climate (20°C, RH 50%).

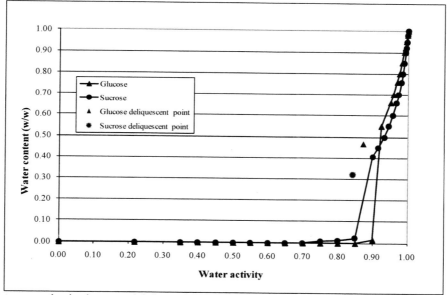

Figure 4. Moisture sorption isotherms and deliquescent points for glucose and sucrose at 20°C.

The difference in moisture content for the same water activity is caused by the different amount of water sorbed to the solid agent under the two conditions. The precipitated glucose or sucrose at the bottom of a saturated solution has a higher amount of sorbed water than the solid agent on aluminum weighing boats in equilibrium with the air in the climate chamber.

Figure 5 shows the sorption isotherm for Mannitol(D) and Sorbitol(D). Although the molecular structures of the molecules are equal except for the spatial orientation of the hydroxyl groups, the ability to sorb water vapor from moist air is very different. Sorbitol starts to sorb water already at a relative humidity of the air of 70% and has a water content of 0.19 w/w at the deliquescent point. Contrary, mannitol first starts to sorb water at a relative humidity of

90% and the water content at the deliquescent point is 0.83 w/w, indication that mannitol is much more stable, due to its low hygroscopicity. The difference between the two impregnation agents is also reflected in the phase diagrams and in the eutectic points (Bjerregaard & Jensen forthcoming). As for glucose and sucrose it is seen that the deliquescent points have higher water contents than the moisture sorption isotherm for the same water activity.

The sorption isotherms for glycerol and alum are shown in Figure 6. Pure alum, $KAl(SO_4)_2 \cdot 12H_2O$, only starts to sorb water at a relative humidity of 90%, making it very stable in respect to changes in relative humidity in the surrounding air at normal museum conditions. The high amount of sorbed water in glycerol has the ability to dissolve alum if mixed (see Section 4.3) and can cause problems with migration of the dissolved ions and cause unwanted chemical processes.

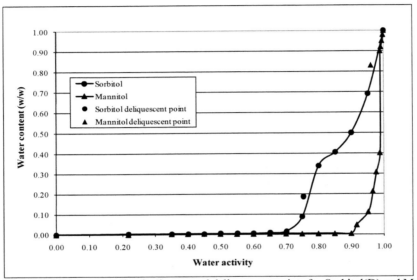

Figure 5. Moisture sorption isotherms and deliquescent points for Sorbitol(D) and Mannitol(D) at 20°C.

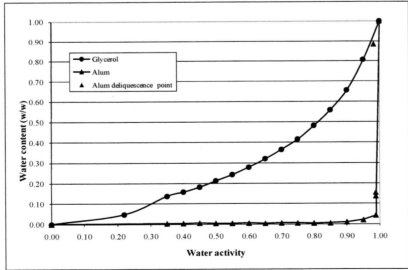

Figure 6. Moisture sorption isotherms for glycerol and alum at 20°C.

90

3.2 Deliquescent point for impregnation agents

Figure 7 shows the water activity at the deliquescent point as function of molecular mass for PEGs, which are normally solid at standard museum climate (20°C, RH 50%). The uneven curves are due to the distribution of the molecular masses within PEGs with a specified molecular mass. The mass distribution can be screw and the average a bit off in relation to the specified average value. As PEGs can be separated in molecular sizes during impregnation (chromatographic effect) plus PEGs can be cleaved by maltreatment (heating, microbial degradation), it looks as if a relative humidity of 75% is the highest which should be accepted for solid PEGs (PEGs with a molecular mass above 1500 g/mol) in museums. PEGs with molecular masses below 1500 are potentially dangerous due to the high amount of sorbed water and thus the ability to dissolve salts (see section 4.4).

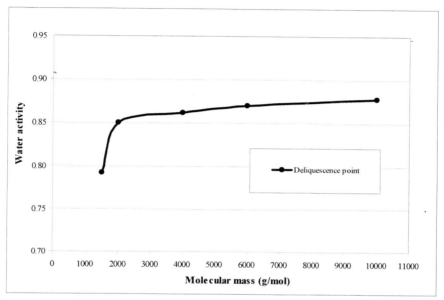

Figure 7. The water activity at the deliquescent point for solid PEGs as a function of molecular mass at 22°C.

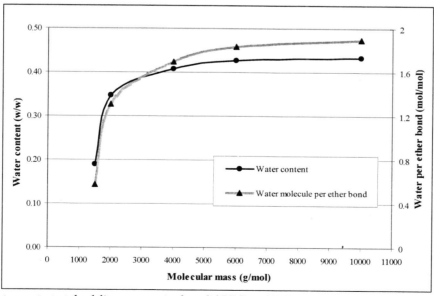

Figure 8. Water content at the deliquescent point for solid PEGs at 22°C as a function of molecular mass.

Figure 8 shows the water content in the aqueous solutions at the deliquescent point as a function of the molecular mass for solid PEGs. Although solid at standard museum climate, PEG 1500 sorbs water at a low relative humidity and forms saturated solutions with a low water content. Only 0.5 water molecule per ether bond is necessary, whereas PEGs with a molecular mass higher than 2000 needs more than 1. For PEGs with molecular masses higher than 10000, 2 water molecules per ether bond are necessary to form saturated solutions.

Table 1 shows the deliquescent points for solid impregnation agents.

3.3 Electrical conductivity in aqueous solution of Glycerol saturated with Alum

Measurements over time of electrical conductivity in aqueous solutions of glycerol saturated with alum (with a surplus of alum at the bottom of the solutions), as presented in Table 2, shows that the dissolution of alum and the time to reach saturation was very long. Additionally it was discovered that the end-concentration of dissolved alum was dependent on the surplus amount of alum, due to the crystal water in alum, which to some extent was removed from the alum salt at the lower water activities. Moreover, the method for determination of the amount of alum in the aqueous solutions of glycerol saturated with alum as described in section 3.3 was not fully satisfactory.

Therefore it was decided to make aqueous solutions of glycerol in the range between 0 to 1 w/w, where the pure water was exchanged with 0.1 w/w aqueous solutions of alum. The 0.1 w/w concentration was selected since a saturated solution of alum at 19°C has a concentration of 0.102 w/w and the divergence to the glycerol solutions saturated with alum would be minimal. Table 3 shows the conductivity and the water activity in the aqueous solution of glycerol with 0.09 w/w alum in the water used for the solution. Finally a 0.09 w/w concentration was used in order to avoid precipitation of alum, if the glycerol sorbed the water molecule so

Table 1. *Water content and water activity for solid impregnation agents at the deliquescent point at 20°C.*

Impregnation agent	Molecular mass	Water content	Water activity
	g/mol	w/w	
Sucrose	342	0.32	0.84
Glucose	142	0.47	0.87
Mannitol	180	0.83	0.96
Sorbitol	180	0.18	0.75
Alum	474	0.87	0.98

Table 2. *Electrical conductivity at 20°C of aqueous solutions of glycerol under saturation with alum measured over time.*

Day		1	14	28
Solution		Electrical conductivity		
	w/w	μS•cm^{-1}	μS•cm^{-1}	μS•cm^{-1}
Glycerol + alum	0.02	1	6	10
Glycerol, RH 35 + alum	0.07	3	10	11
Glycerol, RH 40 + alum	0.17	34	63	60
Glycerol, RH 50 + alum	0.22	90	160	160
Glycerol, RH 75 + alum	0.42	820	940	1050
Glycerol, RH 85 + alum	0.56	1930	1600	2500
Water + alum	1.00	7200	29100	29300

Table 3. *Electrical conductivity of aqueous solutions of glycerol at 20°C, where the pure water has been replaced with 0.09 w/w aqueous solution of alum (KAl(SO₄)₂·12H₂O.*

0.09 w/w alum	Water activity	Electrical conductivity
w/w		$\mu S \cdot cm^{-1}$
1.000	0.980	28300
0.894	0.967	19500
0.797	0.944	13200
0.704	0.918	8800
0.604	0.875	5000
0.504	0.811	2800
0.405	0.726	1250
0.304	0.610	480
0.212	0.474	120
0.107	0.278	15
0.059	0.168	4
0.009	0.037	0.03

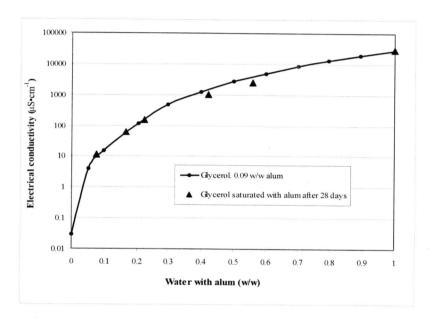

Figure 9. *Electrical conductivity in aqueous solutions of glycerol, where the water has been replaced with 0.09 w/w aqueous solutions of alum, KAl(SO₄)₂·12H₂O, at 20°C, and aqueous glycerol solution saturated with alum.*

hard, that the water could not dissolve the alum. Figure 9 shows the close agreement between the conductivity as a function of the water content in the saturated alum solution and in the 0.09 w/w solution. This justifies using the method with replacement of the saturated solution with the 0.09 w/w alum solution for measuring the conductivity in aqueous glycerol solutions.

Figure 10 shows the conductivity in the aqueous solution of glycerol as a function of the water activity in the aqueous solution of glycerol with 0.09 w/w alum in the water used for preparing the solution. At first glance it looks as if the conductivity at water activities below 0.5 are very low (see graph B), due to the exponential character

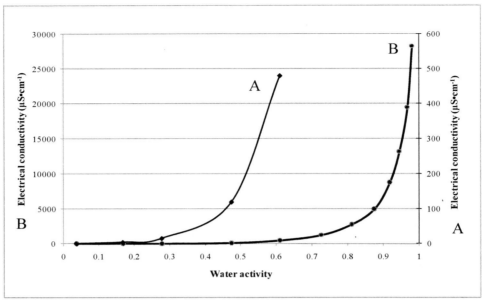

Figure 10. *Electrical conductivity in aqueous solutions of glycerol, where the water has been replaced with 0.09 w/w aqueous solutions of alum, $KAl(SO_4)_2 \cdot H_2O$, at 20°C as a function of water activity.*

of the conductivity as a function of the water activity, but although low, the conductivity increases with the amount of sorbed water already at water activities just above 0 (see graph A). The ions dissolved in the sorbed water enables transfer processes and chemical processes at all water activities, which means that the else stable alum (deliquescent point at 98% RH) is, by adding glycerol, transformed into an impregnation agent which is very sensitive to the surrounding moisture in the air and thereby inherently unstable.

Figure 11 shows the theoretical conductivity in the aqueous solution of glycerol, as a function of the water content in the aqueous solution of glycerol with 0.09 w/w alum in the water used for preparing the solution, corrected for the actual volume of water and viscosity as shown in Equation 1 and 2. The figure also shows the theoretical electrical conductivity in the sample calculated by the conductivity in water with alum and the viscosity for the

aqueous glycerol solution as a function of the water content.

The good agreement between measured and theoretical calculated conductivities for aqueous glycerol solutions with alum, shows that Equation 1 and 2 provide theoretical sound explanations (models) for moving ions in glycerol. The good agreement is due to the small molecular mass of glycerol and the nearly spherical shape of the glycerol molecule when dissolved in water, which brings the system in agreement with the Einstein /Sutherland equation for moving spherical objects in liquid (Einstein 1905a , b) (Sutherland 1904). It also means that dissociation of the ions of the alum salt is not affected by the glycerol (the ions are surrounded by water molecules held by hydrogen bonds) (Capuano *et al.* 2003, 2007) (Graber *et al.* 2004) (Branca *et al.* 2003) and that the viscosity measured by viscosity meter is equal to the *micro viscosity* experienced by the moving ions (Stojilkovic *et al.* 2003).

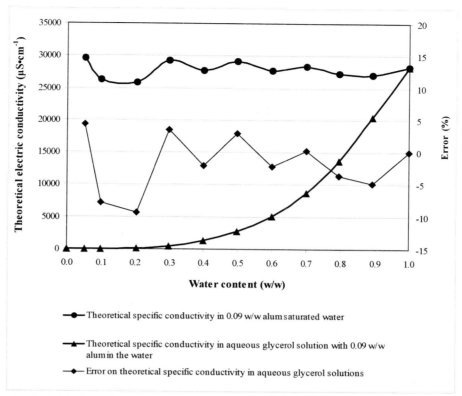

Figure 11. *Theoretical electrical conductivities in aqueous solutions of glycerol, where the water has been replaced with 0.09 w/w aqueous solutions of alum, KAl(SO₄)₂·12H₂O, at 20°C, as a function of the water content.*

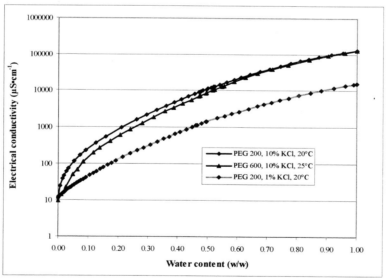

Figure 12. *Electrical conductivity in aqueous solutions of PEG 200 and 600, where the water has been replaced with 0.01 and 0.1 w/w KCl at 20°C as a function of the water content.*

3.4 Electrical conductivity in aqueous solutions of PEG 200 and 600

The electrical conductivity was measured in aqueous solutions of PEG 200 and 600 for the concentrations between 0 and 1 w/w, where the pure water had been replaced with either 0.01 w/w or 0.1 w/w aqueous solutions of potassium chloride (KCl). Figure 12 shows the conductivities measured for PEG 200 (0.010 w/w, 0.091 w/w, 20°C) and PEG 600 (0.095 w/w, 25°C) converted to 20°C, 0.01 and 0.1 w/w in order to make them comparable. The conductivity of PEG 200 is, with the same amount of water and of dissolved KCl, higher than that of PEG 600, due to the lover viscosity, see Figure 16.

Figure 13 shows the conductivity for aqueous solutions of PEG 200 and PEG 600 where the water has been replaced with 0.1 w/w aqueous solutions of KCl as a function of the water activity.

Like for alum in aqueous solutions of glycerol, the conductivity in aqueous PEG 200 and PEG 600 solutions, with 0.1 w/w KCl in the water, is determined by the presence of sorbed water, which has the ability to contain dissociated ions. As low molecular mass PEGs sorbs water at all water activities (RHs), and KCl can dissolve in the sorbed water, one must expect that other ions as well can be dissolved in the sorbed water, making mass transfer and chemical reactions possible at all water activities. Objects impregnated with low molecular mass PEGs must therefore be considered as inherently unstable if moisture is present in the surrounding air, which it always is in relation to displayed museum objects.

Figure 14 shows the theoretical conductivity in the aqueous solution of PEG 600, as a function of the water content

in the aqueous solution of glycerol, with 0.1 w/w KCl in the water used for preparing the solution, corrected for the actual volume of water and the viscosity as shown in Equation 1 and 2. The agreement theoretical calculated values is much poorer than that for alum and glycerol, mainly due to a difference between the measured viscosity and the *micro viscosity* (Stojilkovic *et al.* 2003). The water activity might also affect the activity of the dissociated ions (Capuano *et al.* 2007) (Silva *et al.* 2001) and thereby the conductivity.

The theoretical electrical conductivity for aqueous solutions KCl 0.095 w/w is not constant for solutions with varying water content, which indicate that Equation 1 is not a suitable model for moving ions in aqueous PEG solutions. The main problem is that the measured viscosities differ from the *micro viscosities* for the moving ions due to the elongated shape of the PEG molecules. The PEG molecules also appear to be surrounded by water molecules (Branca *et al.* 2003), at least 2 per ether atom. This can explain the maximum theoretical electrical conductivity in the range from 0.35 to 0.55 w/w aqueous KCl solution, where the PEG might have "borrowed" 1 to 2 water molecules per oxygen in the PEG molecule, see Figure 15.

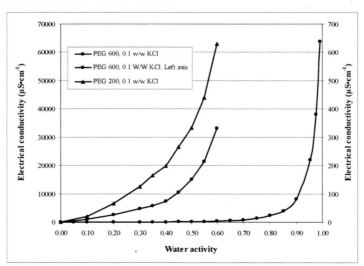

Figure 13. *Electrical conductivity in aqueous solutions of PEG 200 and 600, where the water has been replaced with 0.1 w/w KCl at 20°C as a function of the water activity. For low water activities use the left axis.*

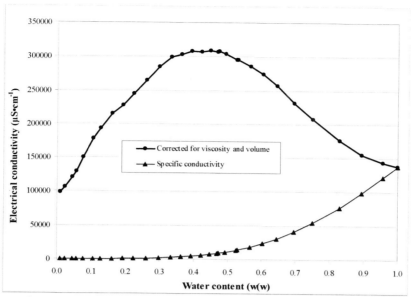

Figure 14. *Electrical conductivities in aqueous solutions of PEG 600, where the water has been replaced with 0.095 w/w aqueous solutions of potassium chloride (KCl) 20°C, as a function of the water content. Upper graph is the theoretical calculated value, the lower graph is the actual conductivity.*

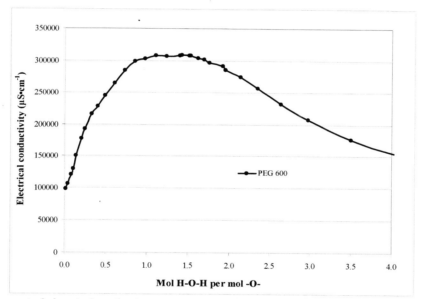

Figure 15. *Theoretical electrical conductivities in aqueous solutions of PEG 600, where the water has been replaced with 0.095 w/w aqueous solutions of potassium chloride (KCl) 20°C, as a function of the water molecule per oxygen atom in the PEG molecule.*

3.5 Viscosity in aqueous solutions of PEG 200 and 600

The viscosity in aqueous solutions of PEG 200 and PEG 600 were determined in order to calculate the theoretical electrical conductivity in the aqueous solutions (see Equation 1) for PEG and 600, where 0.095 w/w of potassium chloride (KCl) has been added to the water making the aqueous solutions. Figure 16 shows the viscosities for PEG 200 and 600 as a function of temperature. The viscosity is a factor of 100 higher in pure liquid PEG than in water. The viscosities are in agreement with the literature (Graber *et al.* 2004) (Branca *et al.* 2003) (Stojilkovic *et al.* 2003) (Kirincic & Klofutar).

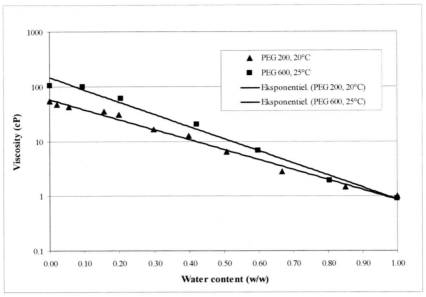

Figure 16. Viscosity of aqueous solutions of PEG 200 and 600 as a function of the water content.

3.6. Moisture sorption isotherms and conductance for wood

The moisture contents in wooden samples are calculated with a EMC at a relative humidity at 0% used as reference for 0% water content. As the PEG content and bulk densities for the wooden samples have not been determined exactly, the values for the moisture content have to be interpreted when compared. The conductance is measured between two stainless steel screws in the samples placed with equal distance. The conductances are not fully comparable, as they can be influenced by the geometry of the samples, but experience with electrical moisture meter, for example the Delmhorst moisture meter with two metal prongs which are pressed into the wood (Stamm 1930) (Jensen *et al.* 2005) show that comparison is possible and especially the tendency in changes as a function of the moisture content is reliable.

The wooden samples are divided into three groups for comparison: PEG treated samples, Vasa wood and alum treated samples.

PEG treated wood

The PEG treated samples included PEG 200, PEG 400, PEG 600, PEG 2000 and PEG 4000 and samples with densities from 100 to 600 kg·m^{-3} and samples both freeze dried and air dried. The moisture sorption isotherms for the different samples do not differ much for relative humilities between 0 and 50%, although the low molecular mass PEGs have slightly higher moisture contents. The differences are due to differences in bulk densities for the woods and the PEG contents. For higher RH, the samples with low molecular mass PEG (200, 400 and 600) start to sorb moisture at a lower relative humidity than the samples with only high molecular mass PEG (2000 and 4000). Figure 17 shows the moisture sorption isotherms for wooden samples where the PEG content is classified as low or high molecular PEG.

Figure 18 shows the conductance as a function of relative humidity for selected samples conserved with PEG. For the high molecular mass PEGs, the sudden increase in conductance is in accordance with the deliquescent point (see Figure 7)

In the samples with low molecular PEGs, the conductance starts at lower relative humidities both as a function of molecular mass and PEG content.

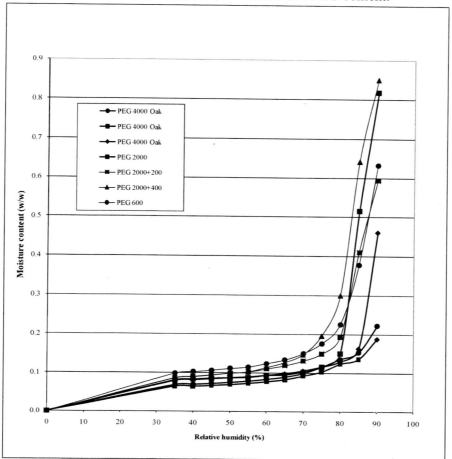

Figure 17. Moisture sorption isotherms at 20°C for wooden samples impregnated with different types of PEG.

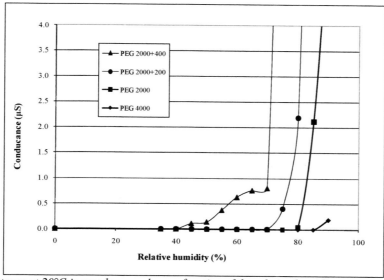

Figure 18. Conductance at 20°C in wooden sample as a function of the relative humidity.

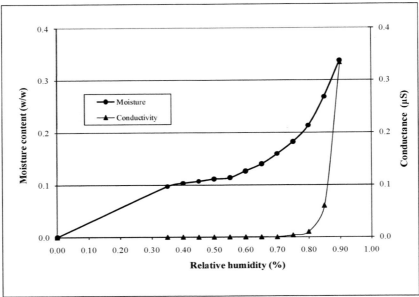

Figure 19. *Moisture content and conductance at 20°C in wooden treated with PEG 600, sample as a function of the relative humidity.*

Figure 19 shows the moisture sorption isotherm and conductance for a freeze-dried sample with 0.1 w/w PEG 600. The relatively low conductance can be explained by the low PEG content and a temperature of 20°C, just below the melting point of PEG 600 (Clariant 1998). Also, it is seen that the increase in conductance starts at 70% RH, which is lower than that of high molecular mass PEGs.

Vasa wood
The hull of the Regal Ship Vasa has been treated with several different types of PEG (PEG 600, 1500 and 4000) (Håfors 2001). In the interior PEG 600 is primarily found, which, due to the low molecular mass, has the ability to penetrate into more well preserved wood. In the outer layers until a depth of 1 to 2 cm, PEG 1500 is found. At the surface, PEG 4000 can be found. Wooden objects, which were not conserved together with the hull, were often impregnated with 100% PEG 4000, although sometimes a smaller amount of low molecular mass PEG 600 was added. Figure 20 shows the moisture sorption isotherm and the conductance for 3 Vasa samples. The moisture sorption isotherms

are quite similar, whereas the conductances start to increase at very different relative humidities.

Sample, Pine 65511A, starts to sorb moisture already at 40% RH, which will say that the impregnated wood has the ability to dissolve ions in the sorbed water at the present climate (RH 52%) (Hocker, Internal papers) in the Vasa Museum. The wood can therefore not be considered inherently stable, as transfer and chemical processes can to occur.

Sample, Oak 65551, starts to sorb moisture at 50% RH and has a low but measurable conductance at the present climate. Just a small increase in the RH of the hall can lead to activity in the wood.

Sample, Oak 65555, first starts to sorb humidity at 70% RH, and should as such be stable at the present climate. The climate in the hall reached 70% RH in the summer 2000 (Sandström 2001), and sample 65555 could during that period have sorbed moisture making transfer and chemical processes possibly.

100

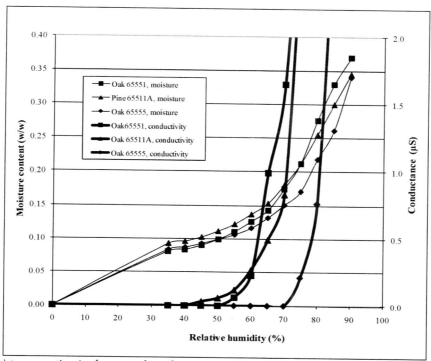

Figure 20. *Moisture sorption isotherms and conductances at 20°C for 3 samples of Vasa wood, as a function of the relative humidity.*

Alum conserved wood

Figure 21 shows moisture sorption isotherms and conductance for two wooden samples. One conserved with alum and one with alum plus glycerol. The sample conserved with alum and glycerol shows higher moisture content at the same relative humidity than the sample conserved with pure alum. This is probably due to the high hygroscopicity of glycerol (see Figure 6).

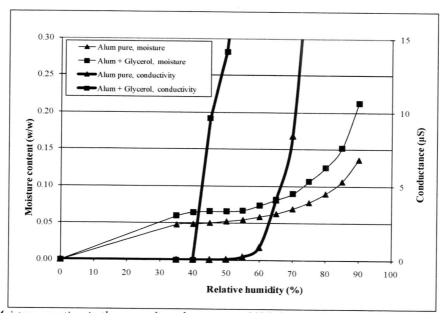

Figure 21. *Moisture sorption isotherms and conductances at 20°C for samples of alum impregnated wood, as a function of the relative humidity.*

101

The conductance starts to increase at relative humidities of about 40%, which means that there is enough sorbed water to dissolve alum and form dissociated ions with a surrounding shell of water molecules and thus ion transfer and chemical processes are possible. The conductance in the sample is at 50% RH (standard museum climate) much higher than of all other measured samples. The wooden sample conserved with pure alum starts to sorb moisture already at 50% RH, much lower than what should be expected from the moisture sorption isotherm and deliquescence point for pure alum (RH 98%). The explanation can be that the alum used for the conservation process in not pure $KAl(SO_4)_2 \cdot 12H_2O$, but a mixture of unspecified sulfates. During the impregnation process other salts can have been formed by precipitation of $Al(OH)_3$. A third explanation can be that the water sorbed to the wooden cell wall can act as a medium for dissolving alum, but that has to be verified.

4. Conclusion

The moisture sorption isotherms for pure impregnation agents clearly show the difference between liquid and solid impregnation agents. The low molecular mass liquid impregnation agents start to sorb water at low relative humidities, as soon as there is any moisture in the surrounding air. The moisture sorption isotherms are continuous and the slopes increase with increasing water activity. The solid impregnation agents only sorb minute amounts of moisture (0 to 0.02 w/w) at low relative humidities. At a certain relative humidity, the deliquescence point, they start to sorb water until they form aqueous solutions.

The deliquescence point is a function of the molecular mass, the molecular structure and the functional groups like –OH and –O- . Solid impregnation agents like PEGs, sucrose, glucose and mannitol can sorb small amounts of water and form a new solid phase with water incorporated between the impregnation molecules. PEG 2000 e.g. can sorb nearly 0.2 w/w water,

equal to 0.5 water molecules per ether bond, and still be solid. For solid PEGs, the deliquescent point is a function of the molecular mass of the polymer. The higher the molecular mass, the higher the relative humidity at which they start to sorb water and the higher the water content. Although the molecular structure of mannitol and sorbitol are nearly equal, mannitol only starts to sorb moisture at a RH of 90% and must be considered a very stable impregnation agent with the potential to be used in connection with freeze-drying. Also alum, which is often postulated to be very sensitive to moisture, does not start to sorb water until a relative humidity of 90%, and is as such stable unless mixed with glycerol.

The moisture sorption isotherms for wooden objects treated with different impregnation agents is a function of the type of wood, the bulk density and the type and the amount of impregnation agent used. The greatest difference between the sorption isotherms is that objects with liquid impregnation agents sorb moisture at all humidities, whereas the high molecular mass solid impregnation agents do not sorb moisture at relative humidities below 75 to 80%, indicating that they are physical stable and support the wooden objects under normal climatic conditions.

The sorption isotherms only show the amount of sorbed water. They do not show the quality of the water and the strength of the impregnation agents. Therefore they cannot stand alone in the aim of finding indications of instability in the treated objects. Analysis with Raman and IR spectroscopy as well as NMR (Silva *et al.* 2001) (Christensen *et al.* 2004) (Christensen *et al.* 2006) have proven to give valuable information, but as these methods of analysis are not always available (and do not directly give information on ion mobility), conductance in impregnated wooden samples and conductivities of aqueous solutions has been introduced as a proxy indicator for transfer and chemical processes.

The conductivities in aqueous solutions of glycerol saturated with alum and aqueous solutions of PEG 200 and 600 with 0.1 w/w potassium chloride demonstrate that salts can be dissolved and the ions solvated in the bound water at all water activities. This indicates that ions can be present even at low water activities and make it possible for chemical processes to take place and degrade the objects at normal museum climate.

Measurements of the conductance in conserved wooden objects also show that the conductance is highest in objects treated with liquid impregnation agents and that ions are formed and movable in the sorbed water.

The research shows that the conductance in conserved wooden objects can be considered to be a good parameter to determine, as the conductance reflects the ion mobility and thereby the potential for chemical reactions and possible degradation as many ions catalyse degradation processes. The methods for determining conductance will therefore be developed further, so they can be used to analyse the stability of conserved objects in storerooms and on display. The conductivity combined with moisture sorption isotherms will also be used to asses future impregnation agents.

6. Future work

The research on moisture sorption isotherms and conductance in archaeological wood is still in progress and will be used to evaluate the stability of existing and future impregnation agents and conservation methods as well as storage and exhibition conditions. The ability to dissolve salts and transport ions in the water bound to conservation agents like PEG 600 and the wooden cell wall at water activities less than 1 will be examined further. Especially salts like those found in the wood of the Vasa, the Mary Rose and the Skuldelev Ships will be investigated. The method of using conductance as a proxy indicator for chemical and physical transport processes will be used in the ongoing project, *Degradation speeds and*

strength relations for conserved wood, and it is a hoped that the conductance measurements in the future can serve as a means of monitoring large conservation projects.

Acknowledgements
The authors greatly acknowledge the Danish Agency for Science, Technology and Innovation, Ministry of Science, Technology and Innovation for sponsoring the project: *Sikring af arkæologiske genstandes stabilitet via måling af vandsorption og ledningsevne i konserverede genstande (Safeguarding archaeological objects stability through determination of water sorption isotherms and conductance in conserved objects). Project No.: 273-08-0127,* as well as The Vasa Museum and The Danish National Museum for providing wooden samples for determination of moisture sorption isotherms and electrical conductance.

References
Brock, T.D. & Madigan, T.M. (1991): *Biology of Microorganisms.* Prentice-Hall International, Inc. USA.

Boye, C. & Baumbach, L.C. (1969): *Trætørring.* Teknologisk Instituts Forlag. København, 1969.

Bjerregaard, N. & Jensen, P. (forthcoming): Mannitol(D) as an impregnation agent or waterlogged wood.

Branca, C., Magazú, S. Migliardo, F. and Romeo, G. (2003): Water poly(ethylene glycol) coordination by rheology and acoustic data. *Journal of Molecular Liquids*, 103-104, pp. 181-185, 2003.

Capuano, F., Mangiapia, G., Ortona, O., d´Errico, G. and Sartorio, R. (2007): Sodium Chloride Molar Conductance in Different Poly(ethylene glycol)-Water Mixed Solvents. *Journal of Solution Chemistry*, 36, pp. 617-629, 2007.

Capuano F., Vergara, A., Paduano, L., Annunzia, O. and Sartorio, R. (2003): Electrostatic and Excluded Volume Effects on Transport of Electrolytes in Poly(ethylene glycol)-Water "Mixed Solvents". *Journal of Physical Chemistry*, 107, pp. 12363-12369, 2003.

Christensen, B.B. (1970): *The Conservation of Waterlogged Wood in the National Museum of Denmark. With a report on the methods chosen for the stabilization of the timbers of the Viking ships from Roskilde Fjord, and a report on experiments carried out in order to improve these methods.* Studies in Museum Technology, no. 1. The National Museum of Denmark. Copenhagen. 118 pp.

Christensen, M, Nielsen, O.F, Jensen, P. and Schnell, U. (2005): Water structure in polyethylene glycols for preservation of wooden artifacts. A NIR-FT-Raman spectroscopic investigation. *Journal of Molecular Structure*, 735–736 , pp. 267–270, 2005

Christensen, M. Frosch, M., P. Jensen, Schnell, U., Shashoua, Y. and Nielsen, O.F. (2006): Waterlogged archaeological wood – chemical changes by conservation and degradation. *Journal of Raman Spectroscopy*, 37, pp. 1171–1178, 2006.

Clariant (1998): *Polyethylenglykole. Produkt-Information. Eigenschaften und Anwendungsgebiete.* Clariant Gmbh. Werk Gendorf, Division Surfactants, Research and Development.

Einstein, A. (1905a): Über die von den molekularkinetischen Theorie der Warme geforderte Bewegung von in ruhenden Flüssigkeiten suspendierender Teilchen. *Annalen der Physik.* 4 (17). 549-560, 1905.

Einstein, A. (1905b): Zur Elektrodynamik bewegter Körper. *Annalen der Physik.* 4 (17). 891-921, 1905.

Hocker, E. (2009): Graphs for the climate in the Vasa Museum. The Maritime Museums, The Vasa Museum.

Håfors, B., (2001). *Conservation of the Swedish warship Vasa from 1628.* Report, The Vasa Museum, Stockholm, 185 pp.

Graber, T.A., Galleguillos, R.H., Céspedes, C. and Taboada, M.E. (2004): Density, Refractive Index, Viscosity, and Electrical Conductivity in Na_2CO_3 + Poly(ethylene glycol) + H_2O Systems form (293.15 to 308.15) K. *Journal of Chemical Engineering*, 49, pp. 1254-1257, 2004.

Jensen, P., Gregory, D. and Strætkvern, K. (2005): The use of conductivity and compression strength to assess the state of preservation of waterlogged archaeological wood. *Preprints of the 14th Triennial Meeting ICOM The Hague 12-16 September 2005.* pp. 1056-1063, 2005.

Kirincic, S. & Klofutar, C. (1999): Viscosity of aqueous solutions of poly(ethylene glycol)s at 298.15 K. *Fluid Phase Equilibria*, 155, pp. 311-325, 1999.

Ninni, L., Camargo, M.S. and Meirelles, A.J.A. (1999): Water activity in poly(ethylene glycol) aqueous solutions. *Thermochimica Acta*, 328, pp. 169-176, 1999.

http://www.vasamuseet.se/sitecore/content/ Vasamuseet/Skeppet/Forskning_bevarande. aspx The home page of the Vasa Museum. Visited 2010 01 04.

Rockland, L.B. (1960): Saturated salt Solutions for Static Control of Relative Humidity between 5° and 40°C. *Analytical Chemistry*, 32, (1960), p. 1375, 1960.

Salisbury, F.B. & Ross, C. (1969): *Plant Physiology.* Wadsworth Publishing Company, Inc. Belmont, California. 1969.

Sandström, M., Jalilehvand, F., Persson, I., Gelius, U., Frank, P., (2001): *Acidity and Salt Precipitation on the Vasa; The Sulfur Problem;* Proceedings of the 8th ICOM Group on Wet Organic Archaeological Materials Conference, Stockholm, 2001, Eds. Per Hoffmann, James A. Spriggs, Tara Grant, [et al.], Bremerhaven: ICOM

Committee for Conservation Working Group on Wet Organic Archaeological Materials, 2002. - 624 pp., pp. 67-89.

Silva, R.A., Silva, G.G. and Pimenta, M.A. (2001): Micro Raman study of poly(ethylene glycol) electrolytes near phase segregation compositions. *Electrochimica Acta*, 46, pp. 1687 1694, 2001.

Stamm, J.A. (1930): An Electrical Conductivity Method for Determining the Moisture Content of Wood. Industrial and Engineering Chemistry, Vol. 2, No.3 pp. 240- 244, 1930.

Stamm, J.A. (1964): *Wood and Cellulose Science*. The Ronald Press Company, New York, 1964.

Stojilkovic, K.S., Berezhkovskii, A.M., Zitserman, V.Y. and Berzsukov, S.M. (2003): Conductivity and microviscosity of electrolyte solutions containing polyethylene glycols. *Journal of Chemical Physics*, 229, 13, pp.6973-6977, 2003.

Sutherland, W. (1905): A dynamic theory of diffusion for non-electrolytes and the molecular mass of albumin. *Philosophic. Magazine*, (6) 9, pp. 781-785, 1905.

Weast, R.C. (1966): *Handbook of Chemistry and Physics, 46th edition*. CRC Press, Inc. Ohio, 1965 - 1966.

Weast, R.C. (1987): *Handbook of Chemistry and Physics, 67th edition*. CRC Press. Inc. Boca Raton, Florida, 1986 - 1987.

Appendix 1
Wooden samples

Sample no.	Museum number	Material	Impregnation agent	Proviniens
01A	6897A	Broad leave	PEG 600	Gilleleje
01B	6897A	Broad leave	PEG 600	Gilleleje
01C	6897A	Broad leave	PEG 600	Gilleleje
02A	P007	Wood	PEG 600 (freeze-dried)	Nydam
02B	P022	Wood	PEG 600 (freeze-dried)	Nydam
02C	P033	Wood	PEG 600 (freeze-dried)	Nydam
03A	217x9129	Wood	PEG 2000	Nydam
03B	217x9129	Wood	PEG 2000	Nydam
03C	217x9129	Wood	PEG 2000	Nydam
04A	217x4530	Wood	PEG 2000+400	Nydam
04B	217x4530	Wood	PEG 2000+400	Nydam
04C	217x4530	Wood	PEG 2000+400	Nydam
05A	459x89 (81)	Wood	PEG 2000 (40%) + 200 (3%)	Gislinge
05B	459x89 (81)	Wood	PEG 2000 (40%) + 200 (3%)	Gislinge
05C	459x89 (81)	Wood	PEG 2000 (40%) + 200 (3%)	Gislinge
06A	A23326	Wood	PEG 4000 (tert.butanol)	Broksø
06B	A23326	Wood	PEG 4000 (tert.butanol)	Broksø
06C	A23326	Wood	PEG 4000 (tert.butanol)	Broksø
07A	JL80	Wood	Alum	Jelling
07B	JL80	Wood	Alum	Jelling
07C	JL80	Wood	Alum	Jelling
08A		Wood	Alum + glycerol	Hjortspring
08B		Wood	Alum + glycerol	Hjortspring
08C		Wood	Alum + glycerol	Hjortspring
09A		Wood	PEG (100%)	?
09B		Wood	PEG (100%)	?
09C		Wood	PEG (100%)	?
10A	27610 (prov 65551)	Oak	PEG	Vasa
10B	27610 (prov 65551)	Oak	PEG	Vasa
10C	27610 (prov 65551)	Oak	PEG	Vasa
11A	22716 (65555)	Oak	PEG	Vasa
11B	22716 (65555)	Oak	PEG	Vasa
11C	22716 (65555)	Oak	PEG	Vasa
12A	(65511A)	Pine	PEG	Vasa
12B	(65511A)	Pine	PEG	Vasa
12C	xx(65511A)	Pine	PEG	Vasa
13A	D183/83	Pine	PEG 4000 (100%)	Skuldelev
13B	D183/83	Pine	PEG 4000 (100%)	Skuldelev
13C	D183/83	Pine	PEG 4000 (100%)	Skuldelev

Questions and answers

Michel Vorenhout: Was your sample size only one?

Mikkel Christensen: Yes, one. I was pressed for time.

Magnus Olofsson: What kind of temperatures?

Mikkel Christensen: The temperature is described in the article from ICOM 1990 on the Hjortspring boat.

Magnus Olofsson: That was 80 degrees centigrade. Lower temperatures could do it.

Cliff Cook: Fifty degrees will do it. It may take a little longer but it will degrade. Take the lid off your barrel sometime and what do you smell? Pure PEG? It will smell like acetic or formic acid.

Sarah Watkins Kenney: Just a comment, and I had one question for Mikkel; in all your graphs, I think I spotted one where you seemed to have something different going on with pine and oak in terms of the point at which they skyrocketed and I just wondered whether that was just those samples you had or whether you think pine and oak and different woods are behaving differently?

Mikkel Christensen: As far as I remember from the data, there is a small but significant, consistent difference between pine and oak that is not necessarily something that would completely change the overall picture of how we should try to store and treat these objects, but usually you do see a small difference, yes.

Lars Andersen: I have a question for Mikkel, I thought about your conductivity measurements and the way that you said that they represented that something is happening and I wondered what you think about the possibility of using conductivity measurements to try to find out if something is happening? You are very fond of the repeatability of these measurements so will you be using these measurements in the future?

Mikkel Christenson: Excellent question! Which of course means, I don't know but I 'm fond of reproducible measurements of course, because it means that you can go and do one or two measurements instead of doing 50 and then an average and you will have a fairly good idea of what the actual state of the object is. Whether this can be developed into something that gives you an easy result – you go, your take your measurements, you consult your chart and then you know how this object should be stored, that's a different question, because it is so preliminary that we have not gone that far yet. I think its promising in theory, but reality may still come crashing down upon our heads.

Lars Andersen: But it's a measurement that you can do…you don't have to run this thing into changing the humidity and things like that, you can just measure how much it is just now.

Mikkel Christensen: You can. Right now of course, that's done by inserting screws into the object… in the long run we'd rather not but there are… it gets very theoretical from here so I'm not going to try to quote specifics, I've seen one or two ideas for how you might be able to do it without damaging the object too much. But of course it's a problem with electrical current. Where does that actually go? Does it go through the object or does it run on the surface if you don't have those screws in there? But even if you do have to have the screws for these initial measurements it could be important in the long run because you could compare it to something else and now you know about mobility so now if its related to Relative Humidity for instance, it would give you a general rule of thumb for any archaeological object without actually measuring the conductivity of that specific artifact.

Anthony Kennedy: Just to follow up on that when you were talking about when you were measuring the conductivity on the surface or within the wood I think, it doesn't necessarily matter how far in the screws are or where the screws are placed because the change is going to find the easiest route through the material regardless.

John Kenney: Just a comment on the physics of it as well. I was wondering has anyone ever tried to do a non-invasive technique? Like an inductive type experiment where you look at the motion of free charges carriers by applying an AC magnetic field event and seeing how much inductance the material would have and therefore being able to estimate perhaps how much free charge carriers.

Mikkel Christensen: By complete accident, I actually was involved with something, that was for the food industry though, so it wasn't on archaeological wood, but it was to see if you were using some kind of gravy or mayonnaise and you mixed up your bottles (and it would be very easy to do exactly that by the way) whether you could sort them out. It turned out to be quite tricky to implement because anyway with the simple system that I worked on it was difficult to get results that were consistent enough that you could do just a few measurements. You needed very many measurements in an average. So, I think it would be... it's simple to try so it would be a good idea to try it but I'm not so sure if you would easily get your results at a reliable level.

Henning Matthiesen: Just a follow up to Lars, one of the things that we are working on, together with Paul Jensen is using the same samples where they already measured the conductivity and its relation to the relative humidity and the same samples to measure the oxygen consumption at the same relative humidities to see if there is a connection because in our heads in order for a chemical reaction to take place there needs to be some kind of ion mobility. We cannot promise that there's an interlink to the oxygen consumption but we're trying... it's next WOAM!

Lars Andersen: That was what I constructed... something's happening and the system is not stable. There is no such thing as a stable system. Jim Spriggs just said at the break here that that's what conservation is all about... to deal with these unstable systems and I think that's why I felt that there was something special in these conductivity measurements. So I'm glad to hear that you will try to broaden it out.

Jim Spriggs: David, you described how the shipworm tunneled through the wood and it laid down a sort of carbonate layer in the holes it inhabits. How is that going to affect the conservation of wood that's affected by shipworm? You've got these carbonate tunnels.

David Gregory: I think Kristiane is a better one to answer that.

Kristiane Straetkvern: We are so fortunate that the PEG solutions are acidic and, in our workshop at least, the pieces remain in PEG baths for years and years and years so hopefully the lining will dissolve in these tunnels. We don't wash out the wood or pre-treat in any particular ways. The only problem is the smell.

Jim Spriggs: So what you're saying is that the carbonate in the shipworm tunnels is helping to buffer your PEG solutions.

Kristiane Straetkvern: In fact it's very rare that we could receive these objects for conservation. We have very few that are attacked by shipworm but I guess that's how we would deal with it.

Vicki Richards: Well, in Australia we have lots of timbers with lots of calcium carbonate in it and we don't wash it out either, Jim, we just put it in our baths and leave it there and freeze dry it and then what tends to happen is it sort of crumbles away and that's what we do. And our PEG solutions are also revolting and acidic as well.

John Kenney: Mikkel, I was looking at your PEG conductivity when you were doing the comparisons of PEGs was that by weight concentration or molar concentrations – I couldn't remember exactly, because I was wondering if that might be causing...

Mikkel Christensen: I think I would have to go back and consult the individual slides because I know that I've done it initially both by volume and by molar concentration.

John Kenney: So you are saying with two different PEGs with the same molar concentration, you still noticed the same conductivity difference?

Mikkel Christensen: Oh, the conductivity shift you mean. I confused myself. Yes that seems to be related to... when you get up to a certain water content where you can saturate all the oxygen atoms in the PEG chamber so it seems to be directly related to molar concentrations.

2.5 (Sc PR)

Formic Acid as a Marker Molecule for Polyethylene Glycol Degradation in Conserved Archaeological Wood – a Radiocarbon Study

Martin Nordvig Mortensen*
The National Museum of Denmark, Department of Conservation, P. O. Box 260, DK-2800, Lyngby, Denmark.
*E-mail: martin.mortensen@natmus.dk,

Helge Egsgaard
Technical University of Denmark, Risø National Laboratory for Sustainable Energy, Biosystems Division, P.O. Box 49, DK 4000, Roskilde, Denmark.,

Jens Glastrup
The National Museum of Denmark, Department of Conservation, P. O. Box 260, DK-2800, Lyngby, Denmark.

Søren Hvilsted
Technical University of Denmark, Department of Chemical and Biochemical Engineering, Danish Polymer Centre, Building 423, DK 2800, Lyngby, Denmark

Abstract

A novel procedure for isolating formic acid from polyethylene glycol (PEG) impregnated archaeological wood was developed and successfully validated with respect to selectivity for formic acid and to recovery, which was 69 % for the entire work-up. It was shown using accelerator mass spectrometry (AMS) that PEG left over from the impregnation of the *Vasa* was ^{14}C-depleted and thus petrochemical. AMS analysis also showed that the cleaned wood components from the *Vasa* had a ^{14}C-content in agreement with the theoretical ^{14}C-contents of these timbers. The ^{14}C-content of formic acid isolated from the *Vasa* indicated that this was mostly petrochemical and thus mostly a product of PEG. This demonstrates that PEG degradation has taken place in the *Vasa* to some extent at some point since the onset of conservation.

Keywords: PEG, degradation, formic acid, radiocarbon, marker molecule, *Vasa*.

Introduction

PEG (polyethylene glycol) impregnation is the method of choice for dimensionally stabilizing waterlogged archaeological wooden objects today and it has been since the sixties (Morén and Centerwall 1960, Seborg and Inverari 1962). Thus, many waterlogged archaeological wooden shipwrecks that have received such treatment, are exhibited on museums around the world today. A few examples include the Swedish warship *Vasa* (Håfors 1990, Håfors 1999, Håfors 2001), the Danish Skuldelev Viking ships (Jensen *et al.* 2002) the German Bremen cog (Clariant 2000, Hoffmann *et al.* 2004) and the *Batavia* in Australia (Unger and Schniewind 2001). The *Mary Rose* in England is currently being impregnated with PEG (Sandström *et al.* 2005). Thus PEG stability concerns many important artifacts.

The stability of PEG and its degradation mechanism have been studied extensively in a large variety of accelerated ageing experiments (Madorsky and Straus 1959, Mcgary 1960, Lloyd 1963, Dulog 1967, Goglev and Neiman 1967, Decker and Marchal 1970, Geymayer *et al.* 1991, Scheirs *et al.* 1991, Costa *et al.* 1992, Bilz *et al.* 1994, Han *et al.* 1995, Glastrup 1996, Yang *et al.* 1996, Han *et al.* 1997, Mkhatresh and Heatly 2002, Glastrup 2003, Mikhal'chuk *et al.* 2004, Mkhatresh and Heatly 2004). In general the experiments agree that the PEG chains break down which results in a lowering of the molecular weight. One study that is relevant to wooden shipwrecks is a study of the re-impregnation of the Danish Hjortspring boat in the sixties. Here surplus PEG was melted from the wood surface at 80°C after impregnation. It was clearly shown that severe PEG degradation had taken place during this treatment (Padfield *et al.* 1990).

The number of experiments aimed at detecting PEG degradation directly in conserved archaeological wood in a museum climate, are limited. The reaction is likely to be very slow and the change in chemical composition that follow, accordingly small and thus difficult to detect. Determining a small change in PEG molecular weight caused by a slow degradation process over some decades in a museum is often made difficult by the lack of PEG starting material for comparison of molecular weight. In one such attempt the PEG molecular weights were analyzed by mass spectrometry in samples from the *Vasa* and the Skuldelev Viking ships. Except for a single sample, the PEG molecular weights and molecular weight distributions seemed normal and thus, without any PEG reference material for comparing molecular weights, no general pattern of degradation could be established using this approach (Mortensen *et al.* 2007). Formic acid has been described as a product of PEG degradation in accelerated ageing experiments e.g. by Glastrup (1996). Formic acid has also been detected in PEG impregnated wooden shipwrecks (Glastrup *et al.* 2006, Almkvist and Persson 2008). If the formic acid in the conserved wooden objects originates from PEG and not from the wood then formic acid would be a useful marker for PEG degradation in PEG impregnated wooden objects.

The present work focuses on the possibilities of using formic acid as a marker molecule for PEG degradation directly in conserved wood. To do this it must be shown to what extent formic acid originates from PEG or wood. A procedure was developed by the authors, through a large number of trials and errors, for isolating formic acid from conserved archaeological wood. The isolated formic acid was oxidized to carbon dioxide and analyzed by accelerator mass spectrometry (AMS) by a procedure adapted from Glasius *et al.* (2000) to find the ^{14}C content. ^{14}C is a radioactive isotope that decays with

a half life of 5730 years. The natural content in *Vasa* wood (from 1628) is therefore relatively high compared to the content in PEG which is a petrochemical (millions of years old plant material) and thus totally ^{14}C depleted. The strategy is to compare the ^{14}C content of the isolated formic acid with the ^{14}C content of wood components and PEG in a sample from the *Vasa*.

The ^{14}C content of plant material measured by AMS is often expressed as pmC (percent modern carbon) or RCA (radiocarbon age). 100 pmC (RCA=0 BP) corresponds to the atmospheric ^{14}C level in 1950 and 0 pmC means that the sample contains no ^{14}C (RCA close to 60000 BP which is the limit of AMS). BP means "before present" where 1950 is taken to be present. These quantities are in accordance with the definitions given by Stuiver and Polach (1977). The present experiment concerns the *Vasa* and for that reason a scale is defined specifically for the *Vasa* by the authors, it is called the percent petrochemical (PP). It reads 0 PP if formic acid isolated from a *Vasa* sample contains the same amount of ^{14}C as the *Vasa* wood components and 100 PP if it contains an amount of ^{14}C equal to that of PEG in the *Vasa* (PP = (-100/96.06)*pmC + (9618/96.06)).

Experimental
Concentration and ratio of $H^{12}COO^-$/$D^{13}COO^-$ and $^{12/13}CO_2$
The analysis of formic acid concentration in wood by SPME GC-MS (solid phase micro extraction gas chromatography-mass spectrometry) was carried out according to the procedure described by Glastrup *et al.* (2006). This procedure was also used as a headspace analysis for formic acid concentrations in aqueous solutions. In this case 100.0 µl of the sample solution was added to a 2 ml autosampler vial and mixed with 0.5000 ml of an aqueous 1 mol/l sulfuric acid solution containing 5.000 µl/l d-acetic acid (CD$_3$COOD with 99.5% D, from Cambridge Isotope Laboratories). A series of standards were analyzed with every set of samples; 100.0 µl of each of

the solutions A to E (A: 0.246 g HCOOH/l, B: 0.187 g HCOOH/l, C: 0.123 g HCOOH/l, D: 0.0615 g HCOOH/l and E: 0 g HCOOH/l) was added to a 2 ml autosampler vial and mixed with 0.500 ml aqueous 1 mol/l sulfuric acid solution containing 5.000 µl/l d-acetic acid.

This procedure was also applied for analyzing the ratio between $D^{13}COOH$ and $H^{12}COOH$. However, in this case, a series of formic acid standard solutions containing a mixture of non-labeled and isotopically-labeled formic acid were measured. The non-labeled formic acid was 98 % from J.T.BAKER, the isotope composition (natural composition) is; ^{12}C: 98.90 %, ^{13}C: 1.10 %, ^{1}H: 99.985 %, D: 0.015 %, ^{16}O: 99.762 %, ^{17}O: 0.038% and ^{18}O: 0.0200 % (Lide 1997). The labeled formate salt used was $D^{13}COONa$ from ISOTEC containing; minimum 99 atom % ^{13}C and minimum 98 atom % D. Non-labeled and labeled formic acid solutions were mixed, using Gilson pipettes, to give solutions where the ^{12}C-fractions ($[^{12}C]/([^{12}C]+[^{13}C])$) were; 0.9890, 0.8897, 0.7907, 0.6920, 0.5937, 0.4956, 0.3979, 0.3004, 0.2033, 0.1065 and 0.0100 respectively (corrected for the 1.1 % natural ^{13}C content present in natural formic acid and for the 1% ^{12}C that is in the $D^{13}COONa$ isotope). The total formate concentration was almost identical in all the solutions (average 5.388 mmol/l, σ=0.026996 mmol/l). The ^{12}C-fractions in unknown formic acid samples were calculated using the relation:

$$^{12}C - fraction = \frac{[^{12}C]}{[^{12}C]+[^{13}C]} = \frac{A_{(47)} + A_{(48)}}{A_{(47)} + A_{(48)} + A_{(49)} + A_{(50)}}$$

where $A_{(m/z)}$ is the area of the peak in the chromatogram plot of the given m/z. This formula correlates to the standard curve with a squared correlation coefficient of R^2=0.9958 (data not shown).

^{12}C-fractions in CO_2 were determined using a Varian 3400 GC interfaced to a Saturn II ion trap MS. The GC-MS transfer line was 250 °C and the MS manifold was 200 °C. The injector temperature was 100 °C

isothermal and the column temperature was 50 °C isothermal. The column was a 25 m, 0.32 mm O.D. fused silica column coated with poraplot U (10 µm). It was operated with helium 99.9995 % as carrier gas with a 15 psi head-pressure on the column. The sample CO_2 was allowed to expand into a 125 ml gas pipette that had been evacuated first on a vacuum line, until the pressure reached approximately 10-20 mbar. The gas pipette was topped off with helium. A 500 µl Hamilton syringe was charged with sample gas from the pipette and 30 µl was injected directly on the GC. The retention time for CO_2 is 1.99 minutes, the peak was integrated with respect to the individual ions at m/z 44 and 45 which then gives the $^{12/13}CO_2$-fraction as:

$$^{12}C - fraction = \frac{A_{(44)}}{A_{(44)} + A_{(45)}}$$

$A_{(m/z)}$ is the area of the peak in the chromatogram plot of the given m/z, here m/z=44 corresponds to the cation of $^{12}CO_2$ and m/z=45 to the cation of $^{13}CO_2$.

Procedure for isolating formic acid from wood

The procedure for isolating formic acid from wood consists of a series of individual steps (extraction, vacuum distillation, ion exchange, a second vacuum distillation and an oxidation step) described below.

Extraction

Wood shavings were planed off from a sample fixed in a vice until approximately 100 g was collected. The shavings were placed in a powerful 1½ l kitchen blender with approximately 300 ml ice made from HPLC-grade (High Pressure Liquid Chromatography) water and blended into cold slurry (the low temperature is to prevent thermal degradation processes). The water (mostly thawed) was decanted from the wood powder and centrifuged for 2 hours at 5400 revolutions per minute. The supernatant, about 150 ml, was collected and the wood chips placed in a Petri dish and left to dry.

Vacuum distillation (VD1)

The equipment used for vacuum distillation consisted of a 100 ml round-bottomed flask connected to a cold trap (35 cm long) which was connected to a second cold trap (25 cm long). Both traps are placed in cylindrical Dewar flasks containing liquid nitrogen. A water bath with cold tap water allowed gentle heating of the round-bottomed flask. The last trap is connected to a two stage Edwards high vacuum oil pump equipped with an alumina foreline-trap to filter oil-mist away. The purpose of the last cold trap is to protect the sample in the first trap from oil-mist from the pump escaping the foreline-trap. 30 ml of the aqueous wood-extract and 20 ml, 2 mol/l H_3PO_4 (57.5 g of 85 % H_3PO_4 in a 250 ml volumetric flask topped off with HPLC-grade water) was added to a 100 ml round-bottomed flask. The round-bottomed flask with contents was frozen and then mounted on the setup for vacuum distillation and the vacuum applied. The distillation was complete when the round-bottomed flask no longer got cold due to evaporation when the water bath was removed (ca. 2-4 hours). The distillate in the first trap was thawed and collected. Solutions with formic acid contents between 0 and 0.15 g/l have been processed successfully. Since no more than 30 ml of extract can be distilled at one time, extracts with low formic acid contents may require several distillations in order to isolate sufficient formic acid.

Ion exchange (IE)

The ion exchange column was a L45 mm, Ø12 mm column packed with PSA (Primary Secondary Amine) bonded silica from Supelco. The column was fitted on a vacuum chamber that allows for collection of the liquid eluting from the column. A 50 ml reservoir was mounted before the ion exchange column for addition of sample and mobile phase. The column was conditioned by applying 15 ml HPLC-grade water. The vacuum was adjusted to give a flow of approximately one drop per second. 10 ml, 2 mol/l aqueous NH_3 solution was applied and finally HPLC-grade water until neutral pH was obtained in the liquid eluting from the column (after approximately 150 ml water). The sample solution was applied, then a 10 ml portion of HPLC-grade water, followed by a 50 ml portion of HPLC-grade water. The container in the vacuum chamber was emptied at this stage then 10 ml, 2 mol/l NH_3 solution was passed through the column followed by a 10 ml portion of HPLC-grade water and finally a 20 ml portion of HPLC-grade water. A solution containing the sample formic acid was collected from the container in the vacuum chamber.

Second vacuum distillation (VD2)

The sample collected after ion exchange was distilled by the procedure described in the first vacuum distillation (VD1).

Oxidation (OX)

Sample formic acid from the second vacuum distillation was oxidized to carbon dioxide according to the reaction:

$$2HgCl_{2(aq)} + HCOOH_{(aq)} \rightarrow CO_{2(g)} + Hg_2Cl_{2(s)} + 2HCl_{(aq)}$$

The reaction flask was charged with a magnetic stirrer bar, the solution containing the sample formic acid, 25 µl 37 % HCl (pH of the solution is 2), 0.5 g $AgClO_4 \cdot H_2O$ (99 %) and 1.0 g $HgCl_2$ (99.5 %).

Figure 1 illustrates the special setup required to isolate the CO_2 produced in the reaction. The chemical reaction occurs in a round-bottomed flask placed in a thermostat-controlled oil-bath with magnetic stirring. Helium (99.9995 %) was constantly bubbled through the contents of the reaction flask. The flask was closed to the atmosphere but connected to a vacuum-line through a reflux condenser with a temperature between 1 and 5 °C, which kept the water from escaping the flask. The temperature of the reflux condenser was maintained by a thermostatic cooler that pumped antifreeze liquid through the reflux condenser. The reflux condenser was connected to a U-tube that could be cooled by liquid nitrogen or mixtures of dry ice and ethanol, in a Dewar flask. The U-tube was connected to a vacuum-line fitted with pressure gauges and several valve-operated compartments for manipulating gas samples. On one valve it was possible to fit an ampoule (L app. 22 cm when sealed, OD 8mm, ID 5.2 mm) using a "Cajon union" O-ring system. The vacuum line was connected to an oil vacuum pump through a cold trap. In order to determine the yield of CO_2, the volume with the attached pressure gauge must be known (V_C in Figure 1). This volume was calibrated using a flask with a precisely known volume (V_A). Gas at a certain pressure, P_1 in V_A was allowed to expand into the evacuated volume of V_B and V_C resulting in a new pressure P_2, which is related to the volume by $P_1V_A=P_2(V_A+V_B+V_C)$. Allowing V_C to expand into V_B enables the calculation of V_C using the relation $P_1V_C=P_2(V_C+V_B)$.

Before a reaction was initiated, helium was passed through the U-tube and into V_B, which was closed to the rest of the vacuum-line (valves 2, 3 and 4 open, valve 1 and 5 closed in Figure 1). The gas leaves the setup through valve 4 and the flask V_A is not on the vacuum-line while the reaction is proceeding. The flow was adjusted to approximately 80 ml/minute, measured at the exit of the vacuum line through valve 4 (atmospheric pressure). Helium was allowed to flow through the system for 5-10 minutes in order to flush before liquid nitrogen was poured into the Dewar flask under the U-tube and the temperature was raised to 100 °C in the oil bath. The reaction then proceeded for three hours after the temperature had reached 100 °C.

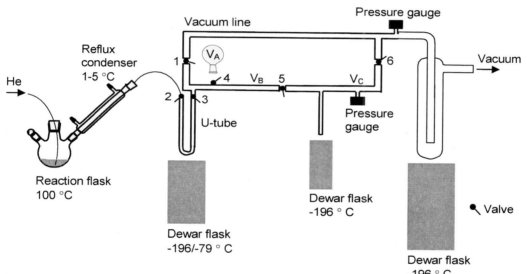

Figure 1. *Schematic diagram of the setup used in the oxidation of formic acid to carbon dioxide. Carbon dioxide is produced in the reaction flask. A flow of helium takes the carbon dioxide to the U-tube (-196 °C) where it condenses. After the reaction has finished the carbon dioxide in the U-tube is distilled from the U-tube (now -79 °C) into the test tube (-196 °C) in V_C. Thawing the carbon dioxide allows the determination of the yield by reading the pressure in the known volume of V_C. The carbon dioxide is transferred to a glass ampoule (not shown) on V_B at –196 °C, which is sealed by melting using a ring burner. The valves are numbered from 1 to 6.*

The CO_2 produced in the reaction passed through the reflux condenser and condensed in the U-tube. The temperature in the U-tube was -196 °C, cold enough to freeze the produced CO_2 (condenses at –79 °C), but not the excess helium (bp –272 °C). When the reaction was finished, the U-tube was closed to the condenser and reaction flask

(valve 2 closed), the helium was turned off, and valves 1, 4 and 6 were closed and valve 5 was opened. Then vacuum was applied (valve 6 was opened) to remove helium (the frozen CO_2 stayed in the U-tube). Valve 6 was closed when the pressure indicated that all the helium was removed. The Dewar flask containing liquid nitrogen around the

113

U-tube was then replaced by a Dewar flask containing a mixture of dry ice and ethanol (-79 °C). In this way, the trapped CO_2 distils from the U-tube into V_B and V_C, which have both been evacuated. The pressure increased as the CO_2 evaporated. When the pressure stopped increasing, the distillation was finished. Then liquid nitrogen was placed under the test tube in V_C and the CO_2 condensed here while the pressure dropped. When the pressure gauge read zero, all the CO_2 was trapped in the test tube. Then valve 5 was closed and the test tube was thawed. The pressure in V_C increased and, since the volume of V_C was known, the yield of CO_2 could be calculated. The U-tube was taken off the vacuum line and replaced by a glass ampoule using a "Cajon union" O-ring system on valve 3. V_B, including the ampoule, was evacuated (by opening valve 1 and closing it again when the pressure gauge read zero). Valve 5 was then opened, the ampoule was cooled with liquid nitrogen trapping the CO_2 in the ampoule. The ampoule containing frozen CO_2 in the bottom was then melted/softened on the middle using a gas/air ring burner. While the glass wall was still soft the ampoule was pulled away from the vacuum-line. Since there was almost vacuum in the ampoule, the soft sides of the tube joined and it was sealed without getting into contact with the atmosphere. The sealed ampoule was transported to the facility for accelerator mass spectrometric (AMS) analysis.

Accelerator mass spectrometry (AMS)
All AMS analysis and related sample preparations were carried out by the staff at Leibniz-Labor für Altersbestimmung und Isotopenforschung at Christian-Albrechts-Universität zu Kiel in Germany. When measuring pure formic acid, pure PEG or purified components from wood, the sample material was combusted to CO_2 in a closed quartz tube together with CuO and silver wool at 900 °C. Both CO_2 samples produced this way and CO_2 samples from formic acid oxidation were graphitized with hydrogen and iron powder as a catalyst at 600°C, the resulting carbon/iron mixture

was pressed into a pellet in the target holder and measured on the AMS. The ^{14}C concentration of the sample was measured by comparing the simultaneously collected ^{14}C, ^{13}C, and ^{12}C beams of each sample with those of oxalic acid standard background material. The percent modern carbon (pmC) was calculated according to Stuiver and Polach (1977) with a $\delta^{13}C$ correction for isotopic fractionation based on the $^{13}C/^{12}C$ ratio measured by the AMS-system simultaneously with the $^{14}C/^{12}C$ ratio.

Samples of PEG-impregnated archaeological wood were extracted (Table 2) to remove organic contaminants, such as PEG. The samples were first extracted 3 times with hot water (85°C) and then subjected to a soxhlet-type serial extraction to remove additional nonpolar to polar organic contaminants. In sequence, they were extracted three times each with boiling tetrahydrofuran (THF), chloroform, petroleum-ether, acetone, and methanol and then rinsed with demineralized water (this step corresponds to the samples called SPAN1 in Table 2). Then the sample material was extracted with hot water 3 times at 100 °C in a soxhlet and subsequently extracted with 1 % HCl, 1 % NaOH at 60 °C and again 1 % HCl (this step corresponds to the samples called SPAN2 in Table 2). Then another 5 extractions with water at 85 °C were performed (this step corresponds to the samples called SPAN3 in Table 2). The cleaned sample material was combusted and measured on the AMS as described above.

Results and discussion
Validation of procedure for isolating formic acid
The procedure for isolating formic acid from conserved archaeological wood includes aqueous extraction of the wood sample followed by vacuum distillation (referred to as VD1), then ion exchange (referred to as IE) followed by a second vacuum distillation (referred to as VD2). These procedures were designed for the purpose of present experiment and

validated by GC-MS techniques that were also developed for that specific purpose by the authors. The product from VD2 is oxidized (referred to as OX) to carbon dioxide in a reaction described in the literature (Johnson 1988, Glasius *et al.* 2000):

$$2HgCl_{2(aq)} + HCOOH_{(aq)} \rightarrow CO_{2(g)} + Hg_2Cl_{2(s)} + 2HCl_{(aq)}$$

The produced CO_2 is trapped, using a procedure adapted from Glasius *et al.* (2000), and analysed.

A test was set up to evaluate the procedure. Formic acid was extracted from a sample of *Vasa* wood and the concentration in the extract determined by GC-MS. An amount of $D^{13}COONa$, approximately equal to the amount of natural formic acid in the extract was added. The resulting solution is referred to as SPIKED and the theoretical ^{12}C-fraction was 0.45 (total formate concentration 0.00921 mol/l). It was divided into three sub-samples each was subjected to the processes from VD1 to OX. The yield and the ^{12}C-fraction were measured after each step in the purification procedure using the relevant GC-MS methods, except for OX where the recovery is based on the pressure of CO_2 in the vacuum-line. The results are illustrated in Figure 2. The top graph shows the average recovery over the triplicate (solid bars) and the corresponding standard deviations, σ (chequered bars). It is seen that the three unprocessed extracts with the added isotope, called SPIKED in Figure 2, have an average recovery of 112 % ($\sigma=12$). This number refers to the measured formic acid content in the solution relative to the theoretical formic acid content, which depends on the measurement of formic acid content in SPIKED before $D^{13}COONa$ was added. After the first vacuum distillation,

the recoveries averaged 74% ($\sigma=3.1$), 105% ($\sigma=5.6$) after the ion exchange, 99% ($\sigma=10$) after the second vacuum distillation and 90% ($\sigma=6.2$) after the oxidation. These

recoveries are all quite high and the standard deviations within the three measurements no higher than 12. Thus the four steps in the isolation procedure are reasonably effective. The total recovery over all the steps from the theoretical SPIKED (100%) to OX is 69 \%.

The ^{12}C-fractions are shown in the lower part of Figure 2 (hatched bars). They are between 0.56 (OX) and 0.47 (VD1), the standard deviations are no higher than $\sigma=0.012$. The ^{12}C-fractions are almost constant after every step except maybe for the oxidation step (OX) where an increase of 0.04 is observed. If this change is not just inaccurate measurements then it is a minor change only. An increase in the ^{12}C content, the natural carbon isotope, could be due to contamination with natural carbon. The most likely source is probably the sample matrix. The difference could also be due to the use of a different apparatus and calibration for measuring the ^{12}C-fraction for CO_2 after the oxidation step (OX).

In summary, it cannot be ruled out that the increase in ^{12}C-fraction over the oxidation step is an indication that a small amount of foreign carbon has entered the sample here. However, if this is the case then the contamination is small. The ^{12}C-fractions are generally not affected by the five steps in the isolation procedure as seen in Figure 2 bottom. This shows that the isolation procedure is selective for formic acid in the matrix investigated.

Radiocarbon analysis
In order to be able to use formic acid as a marker molecule for PEG degradation in conserved archaeological wood, the source of the PEG must be petrochemical in nature. For that reason three samples of PEG, left over from the conservation of the *Vasa*, were analysed by AMS. Table 1 summarizes AMS measurements on a batch of PEG 1500 and PEG 4000 supplied by the manufacturer "Mo & Domsjö" and a batch of PEG 4000 supplied by "Berol AB". The pmC values are between 0.06 and 0.17 corresponding to almost total ^{14}C-depletion.

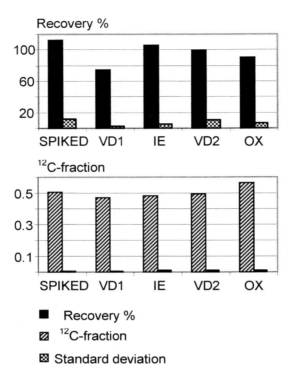

Figure 2. *Top: Solid bars represent the recovery of formic acid over the four steps in the purification (average over three samples); vacuum distillation (VD1), ion exchange (IE), second vacuum distillation (VD2) and oxidation to CO₂ (OX), SPIKED is the name of the initial formic acid extract with D¹³COONa added. Bottom: Hatched bars represent ¹²C-fractions in the purification steps (average over three samples). The standard deviation is shown as chequered bars.*

The corresponding radiocarbon ages (RCA) are all higher than 50000 BP in good agreement with the PEG samples being almost completely petrochemical. The average of these three measurements was used to set the PP scale to 100.

Wood components and isolated formic acid were analyzed by AMS in two samples from the *Vasa* called samples A and B. The wood shavings left after formic acid had been extracted, were washed until the ¹⁴C content was stable. This is shown in Table 2, where the shavings from sample A are called A_SPAN. It is seen that the corrected pmC ends up at 93.56 for sample A_SPAN3 and 96.18 for sample B_SPAN3 after the three extraction series (SPAN1 to 3). These values correspond to 535 BP and 315 BP respectively which is fairly close to the theoretical value for the *Vasa* (322 BP counting from 1628). It should be mentioned that the wood chips of sample A had some wood chips from sample B added

by accident. Sample B, however, is still pure. The pmC's do not seem to stabilize completely in the case of sample B which indicates that the extractions may not be 100% complete. However the increase is only two pmC from the first to the last extraction and for the purpose of estimating the origin of formic acid this is acceptable.

The formic acid isolated from these wood samples was oxidized to CO₂ and measured by AMS (Table 2, A_OX and B_OX). The measurement of sample A_OX shows a corrected pmC of 91.51 which is almost as high as the pmC for the wood in that sample. The result from sample B_OX, however, reveals that something is wrong. The pmC for sample B_OX is 164.10, but the maximum value on the pmC scale is 100 'corresponding to the natural atmospheric ¹⁴C content in 1950. This sample, however, contains more than that and not even a post-bomb calibration (1950 to 2009) can convincingly explain a pmC

116

this high. The conclusion is that the equipment or facilities must be contaminated with something enriched in ^{14}C.

"Hot samples" is a phenomenon that is well known by AMS laboratories. The natural level of ^{14}C is very low (^{14}C:^{12}C ratio; 1:10^{12}), which means that it takes very little ^{14}C to contaminate a sample. One common cause of ^{14}C-contamination in a laboratory is that experiments have been carried out with ^{14}C-labelled substances, for example $^{14}CO_2$ (from $^{14}CO_3^{2-}$) to investigate the rate of photosynthesis in plants. The ^{14}C results obtained for formic acid, shown in Table 2, were measured on samples purified in a former plant research department. Thus, suspicion fell on these facilities. For this reason most of the formic acid isolation procedure was moved to other facilities. Furthermore, new chemicals were bought for the entire isolation procedure and delivered directly to the new address. The glassware that had to be moved was cleaned in a bath made up of concentrated sulfuric acid and hydrogen peroxide (30 %) for several days. No change was made to the isolation procedure itself. The only step that was still performed at the first location after this relocation was the oxidation of formic acid to carbon dioxide and the isolation thereof in glass ampoules. It should be mentioned that the wood samples, A and B_SPAN, shown in Table 2 have not been in contact with the possibly contaminated facilities.

After this cleaning, a control experiment was performed to find out if the problem with contamination had been solved. The results are shown in Table 3. A new bottle of 98 % formic acid was bought and analyzed directly by AMS (C_HCOOH). Another sample from the same bottle was subjected to the entire series of steps in the isolation procedure (VD1, IE, VD2 and OX) and then analyzed as CO_2 by AMS (named C_OX)

It is seen that the formic acid (C_HCOOH) is 99.26 PP (corrected pmC=0.83), which is

in good agreement with the product being petrochemical. The CO_2 that came out of the purification of this formic acid (C_OX), is 86.65 PP (pmC=12.94). Thus the carbon went from being 99.26 PP to 86.65 PP after isolation indicating that a contamination corresponding to 12.61 PP (99.26 PP – 86.65 PP=12.61 PP) has appeared during the isolation procedure. The contamination has been reduced significantly from the first situation in which a pmC of 164 was measured for sample B_OX (at least 64 pmC too high). Even though the situation is far from ideal it was decided to analyze a real *Vasa* sample using this procedure. Formic acid was isolated from a *Vasa* sample and converted to CO_2, which was then analyzed by AMS (D_OX in Table 3). The analysis showed that the sample is 87.95 percent petrochemical (11.70 pmC). If contamination is assumed to be fairly constant from the control experiment (C_OX) to the real *Vasa* sample (D_OX), then all of the ^{14}C in D_OX would come from the contamination and the formic acid would really be 100 PP. In this interpretation, all of the formic acid is a product of PEG degradation. Another way of viewing the result is by assuming that the ^{14}C contamination is not constant and that the sample from the *Vasa* (D_OX) has not been contaminated at all. In this scenario, formic acid would have a PP of 87.95, i.e. 87.95 percent of the formic acid in the sample comes from PEG degradation and the rest from the *Vasa* wood components. The two scenarios considered here define the upper and lower limits of the ^{14}C content that is really in the sample. If the sample has not been contaminated then the formic acid in D_OX is 100 PP, whereas if all the ^{14}C in the sample comes from contamination then the PP is 87.95 PP. Thus the PP of formic acid isolated from D_OX is between 87.95 PP and 100 PP. If this is expressed as 100>PP≥87.95 (i.e. PP not equal to 100), then the fact that some formic acid has been detected in non-impregnated wood, is acknowledged (Glastrup *et al.* 2006).

.

117

Table 1. *Carbon isotope analysis of PEG*

	Sample Description	Corrected pmC†	RCA	PP*
PEG1	PEG 1500 from Mo & Domsjö AB	0.06±0.04	> 52670 BP	100.06
PEG2	PEG 4000 from Berol AB	0.13±0.04	53160 (+3050 / -2210) BP	99.99
PEG3	PEG 4000 from Mo & Domsjö AB	0.17±0.05	51120 (+2600 / -1960) BP	99.95

†"Corrected pmC" indicates the percent of modern (1950) carbon, corrected for fractionation using the ^{13}C measurement.

*The average of these three measurements was used to set the PP scale to 100 (PP = (-100/96.06)*pmC + (9618/96.06)).

Table 2. *Carbon isotope analysis of wood and formic acid from the* Vasa

Name	Description	Corrected pmC†	RCA	PP
A_SPAN1	Wood chips extracted with organic solvents	93.35±0.23	550±20 BP	2.95
A_SPAN2	Wood chips extracted with organic solvents and with an acid-alkali-acid series.	94.41±0.32	460±25 BP	1.84
A_SPAN3	Wood chips extracted with organic solvents and with an acid-alkali-acid series and a series of hot water extractions.	93.56±0.29	535±25 BP	2.73
B_SPAN1	Wood chips extracted with organic solvents	94.50±0.23	455±20 BP	1.75
B_SPAN2	Wood chips extracted with organic solvents and with an acid-alkali-acid series.	95.38±0.24	380±20 BP	0.83
B_SPAN3	Wood chips extracted with organic solvents and with an acid-alkali-acid series and a series of hot water extractions.	96.18±0.26	315±20 BP	0.00*
A_OX	CO_2 from purified HCOOH	91.51±0.25	715 ± 20 BP	4.86
B_OX	CO_2 from purified HCOOH	164.10±0.38	-	-

†"Corrected pmC" indicates the percent of modern (1950) carbon, corrected for fractionation using the ^{13}C measurement.

*This value was used to set the PP scale to zero because it is the most accurate representation of the Vasa wood ^{14}C content available
(PP = (-100/96.06)*pmC + (9618/96.06)). This sample is pure (not mixed with A) and it has the highest pmC (it has been extracted the most times).

Table 3. *Carbon isotope analysis of formic acid from the* Vasa *and control experiments*

	Sample Description	Corrected pmC†	RCA	PP
C_HCOOH	98 % formic acid	0.83±0.10	38460+1070/ -950 BP	99.26
C_OX	CO_2 from formic acid	12.94±0.21	16420±130 BP	86.65
D_OX	Wood from the Vasa	11.70±0.12	17230±80 BP	87.95

†"Corrected pmC" indicates the percent of modern (1950) carbon, corrected for fractionation using the ^{13}C measurement.

In summary, it seems likely that PEG in the *Vasa* is petrochemical based on the measurements given in Table 1; the average of the three pmC values given here was used to set the PP scale for 100. The radiocarbon measurement on wood (Table 2) showed that the pmC was 96.18 for B_SPAN and this was used to set the zero on the PP scale. Control experiments revealed a small ^{14}C contamination due to the isolation procedure in spite of the efforts made to avoid this. The sample that was measured from the *Vasa* (D_OX) contained formic acid with a PP of 87.95. This measurement in combination with the control experiment, allows us to conclude that 100>PP≥87.95 for formic acid isolated from the *Vasa* (D_OX). Thus most of the formic acid in this *Vasa* sample is petrochemical and hence originates from PEG. Some formic acid may originate from wood components, but most of it is petrochemical and that can only be explained by PEG degradation. Thus PEG degradation has taken place and formic acid can be used as a marker molecule for PEG degradation.

If evaporation of formic acid from the wood surface is ignored then the extent of PEG degradation can be estimated. If it is assumed that the average formic acid concentration is 0.03 % $^w/_w$ as reported by Glastrup *et al.* (2006), that 25 % of the ship consists of a 1:1 mixture of PEG 600 and PEG 1500, that the stoichiometry between formic acid and degraded ethylene glycol monomeric units is 2:1, and that 46 years have elapsed since the onset of conservation, then a lifetime of 76000 years is predicted for PEG in the ship, 86000 years if PP=87.95 is taken into account. Thus in such an interpretation very little PEG degradation has taken place since the onset of conservation. The degradation could also have taken place during the conservation treatment e.g. during the PEG spray treatment of the ship or during melting off the surplus PEG from the wood surface. Taking formic acid evaporation from the wood into account is interesting in light of the finding that 100>PP≥87.95.

Continuous evaporation of formic acid with a PP lower than 100, would require constant formation of both PEG-based and wood-based formic acid. This would suggest that a wood degrading reaction takes place along with PEG degradation. So either PEG degradation is taking place like this, continually, possibly along with a wood degrading reaction, or only very little PEG degradation has taken place since the onset of conservation 46 years ago.

Conclusions

A technique for isolating formic acid from PEG impregnated archaeological wood was successfully validated with respect to selectivity for formic acid and with respect to recovery which was 69 % overall.

The radiocarbon measurements done by AMS showed that three samples of PEG left over from the conservation of the *Vasa* were all totally ^{14}C-depleted in agreement with the PEG being petrochemical in nature. The *Vasa* wood components had a ^{14}C content of 96.18 pmC, which is in agreement with the theoretical ^{14}C content of the timbers.

Formic acid was isolated from a sample from the *Vasa* and analyzed using AMS. It could be concluded that the formic acid was between 87.95 and 100 percent petrochemical (100>PP≥87.95), which means that it is mostly a degradation product of PEG. This demonstrates that PEG degradation has taken place in the *Vasa* to some extent since the onset of conservation. However, the exact extent of degradation is not revealed by the present experiment.

Acknowledgements
This project is funded by the National Maritime Museums of Sweden research project "Save the VASA" sponsored by The Bank of Sweden Tercentenary Foundation, The Swedish National Heritage Board, The Swedish Foundation for Strategic Research (SSF), The Swedish Research Council for Environment, Agricultural Sciences and Spatial Planning (FORMAS) and The Swedish Agency for Innovation Systems

(Vinnova). The Danish Ministry of Culture and the Danish National Museum are also kindly acknowledged for funding.

References

Almkvist G. and Persson I., (2008), Analysis of acids and degradation products related to iron and sulfur in the Swedish warship Vasa, Holzforschung, 62, 6, pp 694–703.

Bilz M., Dean L., Grattan D.W., McCawley J.C. and McMillen L., (1994), A study of the thermal breakdown of polyethylene glycol, in Hoffmann, P., Daley, T., and Grant, T. (editors), Proceedings of the 5th ICOM Group on Wet Organic Archaeological Materials Conference Portland/Maine 1993, Bremerhaven, International Council of Muesums (ICOM), Committee for Conservation Working Group on Wet Organic Archaeological Materials, pp 167-197.

Clariant, (2000), A very fine preserve. Clariant and the Hanse project, Brochure Clariant.

Costa L., Gad A.M., Camino G., Cameron G.G. and Qureshi M.Y., (1992), Thermal and thermooxidative degradation of poly(ethylene oxide)-metal salt complexes, Macromolecules, 25, 20, pp 5512-5518.

Decker C. and Marchal J., (1970), Use of oxygen-18 in study of mechanism of oxidative degradation of polyoxyethylene at 25 degrees C, Comptes Rendus Hebdomadaires des Seances de l Academie des Sciences Serie C, 270, 11, pp 990.

Dulog L., (1967), Autoxidation of polyeposides, Angewandte Chemie-International Edition, 6, 2, pp 182.

Geymayer P., Glass B. and Leidl E., (1991), Oxidative degradation of polyethyleneglycols, in Hoffmann P. (editor), Proceedings of the 4th ICOM Group on Wet Organic Archaeological Materials Conference Bremerhaven 1990, Bremerhaven, The international Council of Museums (ICOM), Committee for Conservation Working Group on Wet Organic Archaeological Materials, pp 83-89.

Glasius M., Wessel S., Christensen C. S., Jacobsen J. K., Jørgensen H. E., Klitgaard K. C., Petersen L., Rasmussen J. K., Hansen T. S., Lohse C., Boaretto E. and Heinemeier J., (2000), Sources to formic acid studied by carbon isotopic analysis and air mass characterization, Atmospheric Environment, 34, 15, pp 2471-2479.

Glastrup J., (1996), Degradation of polyethylene glycol. A study of the reaction mechanism in a model molecule: tetraethylene glycol, Polym. Degrad. Stab., 52, 3, pp 217-222.

Glastrup J., (2003), Stabilization of polyethylene and polypropylene glycol through inhibition of a beta-positioned hydroxyl group relative to an ether group. A study of modified triethylene and tripropylene glycols, Polym. Degrad. Stab., 81, 2, pp 273-278.

Glastrup J., Shashoua Y., Egsgaard H. and Mortensen M.N., (2006), Formic and acetic acids in archaeological wood. A comparison between the Vasa Warship, the Bremen Cog, the Oberländer Boat and the Danish Viking ships, Holzforschung, 60, 3, pp 259-264.

Goglev R.S. and Neiman M.B., (1967), Thermal-oxidative degradation of simpler polyalkyleneoxides, Polym. Sci. USSR., 9, 10, pp 2351-2364.

Han S., Kim C. and Kwon D., (1995), Thermal-degradation of poly(ethyleneglycol), Polym. Degrad. Stab., 47, 2, pp 203-208.

Han S., Kim C. and Kwon D., (1997), Thermal/oxidative degradation and stabilization of polyethylene glycol, Polymer, 38, 2, pp 317-323.

Hoffmann P., Singh A., Kim Y.S., Wi S.G., Kim I.-J. and Schmitt U., (2004), The Bremen Cog of 1380 - an electron microscopic study of its degraded wood before and after stabilization with PEG, Holzforschung, 58, 3, pp 211-218.

Håfors B., (1990), The role of the Wasa in the development of the polyethylene-glycol preservation method, in Rowell R. and Barbour J. (editors), Archaeological Wood: Properties, Chemistry, and Preservation, Washington DC, American Chemical Society, pp 195-216.

Håfors B., (1999), Procedures in selecting and evaluating the conservation liquid for the Vasa wooden material, in Hoffmann P., Bonnot C., Hiron X. and Tran Q. K. (editors), Proceedings of the 7th ICOM-CC Working Group on Wet Organic Archaeological Materials Conference Grenoble 1998, Bremerhaven, ARC-Nucléart for the International Council of Museums (ICOM), Committee for Conservation Working Group on Wet Organic Archaeological Materials, pp 87-94.

Håfors B., (2001), Conservation of the Swedish warship Vasa from 1628, Stockholm, The Vasa Museum, Stockholm.

Jensen P., Petersen A. H. and Strætkvern K., (2002), Conservation, in Crumlin-Pedersen O. and Olsen O. (editors), The Skuldelev Ships I. Roskilde, The Viking Ship Museum in Roskilde, pp 70-81.

Johnson B. J., (1988), The carbon-13 content of atmospheric formaldehyde. Ph.D. thesis, The University of Arizona.

Lide D. R. (editor), (1997), CRC Handbook of Chemistry and Physics. 78th ed. CRC Press LLC Boca Raton.
Lloyd W.G., (1963), Influence of transition metal salts in polyglycol autoxidations, J. Polym. Sci. Pt. A-Gen. Pap., 1, 8, pp 2551-2563.

Madorsky S.L. and Straus S., (1959), Thermal degradation of polyethylene oxide and polypropylene oxide, J. Polym. Sci., 36, 130, pp 183-194.

Mcgary C.W., (1960), Degradation of poly(ethylene oxide), J. Polym. Sci., 46, 147, pp 51-57.

Mikhal'chuk V.M., Kryuk T.V., Petrenko L.V., Nelepova O.A. and Nikolaevskii A.N., (2004), Antioxidative stabilization of polyethylene glycol in aqueous solutions with herb phenols, Russian Journal of Applied Chemistry, 77, 1, pp 131-135.

Mkhatresh O.A. and Heatley F., (2002), A C-13 NMR study of the products and mechanism of the thermal oxidative degradation of poly(ethylene oxide), Macromol. Chem. Phys., 203, 16, pp 2273-2280.

Mkhatresh O.A. and Heatley F., (2004), A study of the products and mechanism of the thermal oxidative degradation of poly(ethylene oxide) using H-1 and C-13 1-D and 2-D NMR, Polym. Int., 53, 9, pp 1336-1342.

Morén R. and Centerwall B., (1960), The use of polyglycols in the stabilizing and preservation of wood, Meddelande från Lunds Universitet Historiska Museum, pp 176-196.

Mortensen M.N., Egsgaard H., Hvilsted S., Shashoua Y. and Glastrup J., (2007), Characterisation of the polyethylene glycol impregnation of the Swedish warship Vasa and one of the Danish Skuldelev Viking ships, Journal of Archaeological Science, 34, 8, pp 1211-1218.

Padfield T., Winsløw J., Pedersen W.B. and Glastrup J., (1990), Decomposition of polyethylene glycol (PEG) on heating, in Grimstad K. (editor), 9th Triennial Meeting Dresden, German Democratic Republic 26-31 August 1990. ICOM Committee for Conservation, United States of America, pp 243-245.

Sandström M., Jalilehvand F., Damian E., Fors Y., Gelius U., Jones M. and Salome M., (2005), Sulfur accumulation in the timbers of King Henry VIII's warship Mary

Rose: A pathway in the sulfur cycle of conservation concern, Proceedings of the National Academy of Sciences of the United States of America, 102, 40, pp 14165-14170.

Scheirs J., Bigger S.W. and Delatycki O., (1991), Characterizing the solid-state thermal-oxidation of poly(ethylene oxide) powder, Polymer, 32, 11, pp 2014-2019.

Seborg R.M. and Inverari R.B., (1962), Preservation of old, waterlogged wood by treatment with polyethylene glycol, Science, 136, 3516, pp 649-650.
Stuiver M. and Polach H. A., (1977), Reporting of C-14 data – discussion, Radiocarbon, 19, 3, pp 355-363.

Unger A. and Schniewind A.P., (2001), Conservation of wood artifacts: A handbook, Springer, pp 412.

Yang L., Heatley F., Blease T.G. and Thompson R.I.G., (1996), A study of the mechanism of the oxidative thermal degradation of poly(ethylene oxide) and poly(propylene oxide) using H-1- and C-13-NMR, Eur. Polym. J., 32, 5, p.

2.6 (Sc PR)

Oxygen Measurements in Conserved Archaeological Wood

Henning Matthiesen
Department of Conservation, National Museum of Denmark, IC Modewegsvej, DK-2800 Lyngby, Denmark
E-mail: henning.matthiesen@natmus.dk;

Martin Nordvig Mortensen
Department of Conservation, National Museum of Denmark, IC Modewegsvej, DK-2800 Lyngby, Denmark
E-mail: martin.mortensen@natmus.dk

Abstract
Oxygen is a key factor in many of the recent studies of instability of conserved archaeological wood, for instance on the Vasa and the Batavia, as it may oxidize different components in the wood. This paper evaluates new methods developed to elucidate the oxygen dynamics: Oxygen consumption is measured non-destructively and without accelerated ageing using optical oxygen sensors and heat sealable bags of oxygen barrier film. Oxygen concentration inside wood is measured by oxygen sensors installed in small holes drilled into the wood samples. Diffusion properties are elucidated by changing the outer atmosphere from atmospheric air to nitrogen and measuring the reaction time for the sensors installed at different depths.

The methods have been tested on 30 samples of conserved archaeological wood and fresh wood showing that: all wood pieces consumed oxygen (typical rates of 0.5-5 µg/g wood/day at 50% RH); the oxygen concentration inside large pieces of wood was significantly lower than in the surrounding air (typically 10-90% saturation); and the diffusion properties of the conserved wood varied significantly (diffusion constants varied over 4 orders of magnitude). The developed methods have a great potential for investigating and controlling oxidative processes in wood.

Keywords: archaeological wood, oxidation, non-destructive, respirometry, oxygen diffusion, oxygen concentration,

Introduction
Ideally the conservation of archaeological wood should make the material completely stable and allow it to be displayed or stored for an indefinite time without any decay or changes. However, there are several examples were the conserved wood has turned out to be unstable, for instance the Batavia (Ghisalberti et al. 2002) and the Vasa (Fors & Sandström 2006). The exact processes are still under investigation, but most of the suggested mechanisms involve oxygen that oxidizes different components (such as iron, sulfur, PEG or cellulose) in the wood. Despite its importance, very few studies have focused on the oxygen dynamics in archaeological wood, possibly due to a lack of adequate measuring methods. During the recent years new (optical) methods for oxygen measurements have become available and this study explores their potential for investigating the consumption, concentration, and diffusion of oxygen in wood:

If an object consumes oxygen it indicates that a biological or chemical reaction is taking place in the material, and measurement of the oxygen consumption rate (respirometry) can be used to quantify this reaction. Respirometry is commonly used to study the degradation of different polymers due to its high sensitivity: Scheirs et al. (1995) give a review of more than 100 studies, where one of them focuses on PEG-degradation (Lloyd 1961, studying oxidation at high temperatures). It has also been used in a few conservation studies (Dufour & Havermans 2001, Grattan 1993, More et al. 2003). As for wood, Stusek et al. (2000) suggested the use of respirometry to detect the activity of wood boring insects. Recently Skinner & Jones (2009) used it to measure the oxidation rate of marine archaeological wood, studying the effect of treating the wood with calcium phytate. They used small wood samples that were freeze dried and ground in a mill to increase the surface area and oxidation rate. They suggested that the effect of grinding should be further investigated, as the physical damage to polymer fibers may cause a production of free radicals (Urbanski 1971), which itself can increase the oxygen consumption. In this study we measure on whole wood samples instead, using a non-destructive method developed for museum objects (Matthiesen 2007).

The actual oxygen concentration may influence the oxidation process and -rate, and obviously the process will cease if there is no oxygen available at all. However, no studies have been found describing measurements of oxygen concentration inside archaeological wood samples. For living trees and fresh wood there are some studies of oxygen in sapwood, for instance del Hierro et al. (2002) who studied daily variations in the oxygen concentration with optical oxygen sensors drilled into living trees. Hicks & Harmon (2002) measured yearly variation in the oxygen concentration in woody debris (decaying wood logs) and tried to correlate to the water content and oxygen diffusion rates. Sorz & Hietz (2008) have measured the concentrations in wood stems and compared the results with model calculations based on measured diffusion constants and respiration rates. Here we try to modify the methods to be used on dry conserved wood.

The diffusion of oxygen into the wood is important as it controls the supply, i.e. how much oxygen can pass through the wood layers and cause decay in the inner part of the wood. Sorz & Hietz (2006) have measured diffusion constants for 6 different wood species at different water contents, and presented the results in a numerical diffusion model. Hicks & Harmon (2002) have also measured the diffusion of oxygen through decaying wood. No studies of the diffusion of oxygen through PEG conserved wood have been found, but Mexal et al.

(1975) and Ju & Ho (1986) have measured oxygen diffusion in aqueous PEG-solutions - both studies show that the diffusion in PEG solutions is slower than in pure water. The normal procedure for measuring diffusion properties of wood would imply drilling out cylinders from the sample, but here we test a less destructive method as it shall be used for archaeological artifacts.

All three parameters: consumption, concentration and diffusion are interrelated, as shown in Figure 1. If the diffusion is fast and the consumption low, the oxygen concentration inside the wood will be high (Figure 1a). If on the other hand the diffusion is slow and the consumption high, anoxic conditions may be found inside the wood (Figure 1b). It is possible to use Ficks law of diffusion and the depth specific consumption to calculate a theoretical steady state oxygen concentration at different depths. Sorz & Hietz (2006) have presented a numerical model to describe these relations in a homogeneous piece of wood (Figure 1c). The data shown in Figure 1c were calculated from their model, using an oxygen consumption of 1 $\mu g/g/day$ throughout the wood, an air content in the wood of 34% vol and a water content of 9% vol. The diffusion constant D (in m^2/s) is a material specific parameter that depends on the wood species, the direction (axial or radial), the water and air content, and probably also the degradation and the conservation treatment of the wood. The axis "–log D" is the negative logarithm of D; here it ranges from 8 (D = 10^{-8} m^2/s) that gives a fast diffusion and deep oxygen penetration to 12 (D = 10^{-12} m^2/s) (as in Figure 1a) that gives a slow diffusion and little oxygen penetration (as in Figure 1b).

Methodology
All oxygen measurements are made with an optical method using a Fibox3LCD oxygen meter from PreSens (www.PreSens.de), along with their sensor foil SF-PSt3-NAU-YOP. It is based on luminescence in which molecules are excited with light at one wavelength and emit the energy at another (Figure 2a).

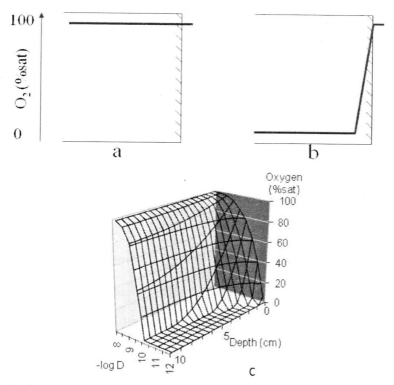

Figure 1. *Correlation between oxygen consumption, diffusion and concentration inside porous materials such as wood. The outer surface is shown to the right (hatched) and the drawings are simplified by assuming a homogenous material and oxygen supply from one side only. Oxygen concentration is given as % saturation, where atmospheric air (and solutions in equilibrium with atmospheric air) is assigned 100%. a) Fast diffusion and low consumption give high oxygen concentrations inside the material. b) Slow diffusion and high consumption give low oxygen concentrations inside. c) Theoretical model of the oxygen concentrations in the outer 10 cm of a homogeneous oxygen consuming piece of wood, depending on the diffusion constant D - see text for details.*

Different oxygen sensitive molecules have been developed, where the presence of oxygen quenches the emission of light, and the oxygen concentration can be determined from the luminescence decay time of the emitted light. The optical sensors do not consume any oxygen in the measurement, unlike for instance traditional Clark electrodes. Another advantage of an optical system is that it works through transparent materials such as glass or (some) plastics. This means that if the object under study and the oxygen sensitive compound are encapsulated in a transparent container, the oxygen concentration can be measured through the container wall (Figure 2b). There is no need to lead an electrode or tube through the chamber wall, which reduces the risk of leakage. The response of the oxygen sensor depends on the temperature, for which the Fibox3LCD compensates automatically via a built in temperature sensor. The accuracy of the oxygen measurement is given as ±1% at 100% saturation. Figure 3 shows the different experimental designs tested in this study.

Oxygen consumption: The oxygen consumption was measured non-destructively on whole wood samples by enclosing them in a transparent bag of Escal™ film along with an oxygen sensor spot (seen as a small circle in Figure 3a). Escal™ is an oxygen barrier film used in conservation and it has been tested that a bag filled with nitrogen is oxygen tight for at least a year and that the Escal™ film does not consume oxygen itself (Matthiesen 2007). The bag is flexible, which allows us to use it for wood samples of different size and shape and to reduce the volume of air around the samples.

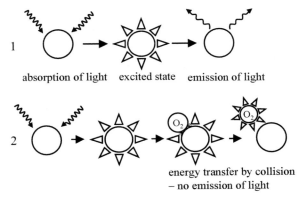

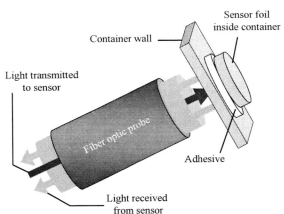

Figure 2a. Principle behind optical oxygen measurements. A luminescent dye is used which is exited by light at one wavelength and emits light at another wavelength (1). When oxygen is present, the energy of the exited molecule is transferred by collision with oxygen instead of emission of light (2). The oxygen concentration correlates to the luminescence decay time.

Figure 2b. Light is transferred via an optical fiber. Here the sensor foil with the oxygen sensitive dye is placed inside a transparent container, and light is transferred and measured through the transparent container wall. In other experimental designs the oxygen sensor is glued directly to the end of the optical fiber (not shown).

Work is still in progress of characterizing each sample in terms of iron and sulfur content, exact conservation treatment and state of preservation. Most of the samples were conditioned in a climate chamber to a given relative humidity (for instance 50% RH) before being placed in Escal™ bags. The bags were heat sealed and the oxygen concentration inside the bags was measured at intervals for a couple of months. The samples were kept in the laboratory at room temperature during this period. In order to convert concentration curves to oxygen consumption rates it was necessary to know the amount of air inside the bags; this included both the air that was "visible" in the bag (external air volume) and air trapped in pores inside the wood (internal air volume). The external air volume was measured by buoyancy in water, by measuring first the volume of the wood sample itself (protected from the water by a thin flexible PE-film) and afterwards of the wood sample in the Escal™ bag. The internal air volume was calculated as the outer volume of the wood sample minus the volume of cell wall material and adsorbed

water (which were found from the weight of the wood sample, the estimated water content and the densities of water (1 g/cm^3) and cell wall material (1.5 g/cm^3)). The exact PEG content of the samples was not known so the density of PEG (1.2 g/cm^3) was ignored in the first estimation of the internal air volume.

In order to test the possible effect of physical rupture (grinding) as suggested by Skinner & Jones (2009), coarse wood powder was made from one of the wood samples by planning perpendicular to the fiber direction, and the oxygen consumption of the powder was measured in glass vials closed with an airtight lid.

Oxygen concentration inside wood: The oxygen concentration inside wood samples was measured by drilling small holes into the wood for oxygen sensors. Two different designs were developed: For measurements at shallow depths the oxygen sensor spot was glued directly on the end of an optical fiber (Ø = 3 mm) and the fiber was placed in a 4 mm hole (as shown in Figure 3b).

Figure 3. Different experimental designs used in this study. a) shows non-destructive measurement of oxygen consumption of a wood sample in an airtight bag of Escal^{TM} film, the arrow points towards the round oxygen sensor; b) shows method for measuring oxygen concentration inside wood, where optical fibers (Ø = 3 mm) with an oxygen sensor glued to the end are installed in holes drilled into the wood ; c) shows a diffusion experiment where a wood piece with oxygen sensors at different depths is placed in a plastic bag, and where the oxygen concentration inside the wood is continuously logged while flushing the bag with nitrogen.

The free space between the fiber and the side of the hole was filled with epoxy, to avoid a "shortcut" for gas diffusion from the outside to the tip of the sensor. For measurements at greater depths a more rigid setup was needed: Here a 5 mm glass tube was sealed at one end (by melting), the end was ground flat and polished and an oxygen sensor spot adhered to the outside. The tube was placed in a 6 mm hole and again the free space between the side of the hole and the glass tube was filled with epoxy. Measurements could be made with an optical fiber inside the glass tube; this fiber could be removed in between the measurements. For wet samples an expanding, moisture curing polyurethane glue was used instead of epoxy.

Measurements were made at different depths in three large samples of conserved wood, installing a total of 21 sensors. Sensors were also installed in samples of waterlogged wood from the Roskilde ships (Gøthche 2006) that are still under conservation – here it is planned to follow the oxygen concentration inside the wood during the whole conservation process.

Oxygen diffusion in wood: Diffusion through wood is often measured by drilling out a cylindrical wood plug that is sealed on the round surface while the two ends are connected to two compartments – the

diffusion through the wood is then measured by changing the environment in one compartment and seeing how long time it takes before the other compartment is influenced (Sorz & Hietz, 2006). This setup gives a well defined geometry, i.e. the area and diffusion path is well known and the cylinder is drilled out in either the radial or axial direction. However, it is also quite destructive, as cylinders of several cm^3 need to be cut out from the wood samples, and it does not necessarily represent the full complexity of the samples, where diffusion may take place in all directions. For these reasons we tested an alternative setup: Oxygen sensors were installed at different depths in whole wood samples as described above. The samples were placed in plastic bags while logging the oxygen concentration continuously. At a given time the air in the bag was exchanged (and continuously flushed) by nitrogen gas and it was registered how and when the sensors at the different depths reacted to the changed atmosphere. Diffusion experiments were made for all three wood samples with oxygen sensors inside (above).

Results

Oxygen consumption: Figure 4 shows how the oxygen concentration decreased over time for four archaeological wood samples (A-D) placed in airtight Escal^{TM} bags. For these four (and the other 26 wood samples) it was possible to get a good measure of the oxygen consumption in 80 days or less. The curves in Figure 4 are only meant as typical examples of oxygen consumption curves, and will not be discussed in detail.

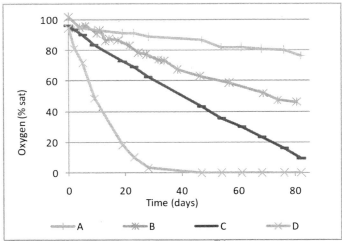

Figure 4. *Examples of decreasing oxygen concentration in Escal^{TM} bags with four different samples of conserved archaeological wood (A-D). The slope of the different curves cannot be compared directly as the amount of air inside the bags may vary.*

The oxygen consumption rate was found from the slope of the oxygen curves:

$$Oxygen\ consumption\ rate\ [\mu g/g/day] = \frac{V \cdot C \cdot \Delta O_2/\Delta t}{m \cdot 100} \qquad \text{(Eq. 1)}$$

where V is the total volume of air in the bag (cm^3), C is the concentration of oxygen at 100% saturation (276 $\mu g/cm^3$ in atmospheric air at 1 atm pressure and 23°C), $\Delta O_2/\Delta t$ is the slope of the oxygen curve (%sat/day), m is the weight of the sample (g), and the constant 100(%) is included to convert the number to $\mu g/g/day$. The slope of the oxygen curves was estimated using linear regression - for non-linear curves only the first part of the curve (down to approximately 80% saturation) was used in the regression. Results for the different samples are compiled in Table 1.

To study the effect of sample preparation wood powder was made from one of the samples (sample "B" in Figure 4) where the whole sample had a consumption of 1 $\mu g/g/day$. The oxygen consumption of the powder was measured in triplicate in closed glass vials (Figure 5). It showed a strong curvature and the oxygen consumption was as high as 36-47 $\mu g/g/day$ during the first 2 days. It decreased to 3-5 $\mu g/g/day$ within a few days, and after 200 days the curves became almost linear with a constant oxygen consumption rate, 0.7-0.8 $\mu g/g/day$, which is close to the rate found for the whole wood sample.

Table 1. *Oxygen consumption rates measured for whole wood samples and PEG 600, all at 50% relative humidity.*

Source	# samples	Oxygen consumption: Range ($\mu g/g/day$)
Conserved archaeological wood	26	0.4 - 5
Fresh wood (oak, pine), un-conserved	4	0.3-1
PEG 600	2	0.006-0.007

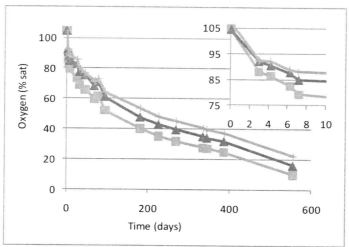

Figure 5. *Measurement of oxygen consumption of wood powder, made from sample "B" in* **Figure 4.** *The small inset shows the first 10 days of the concentration curve.*

Oxygen concentration: Figure 6 shows an example of oxygen concentrations measured inside a large sample of archaeological oak wood. Figure 6a shows a radiograph of the sample, where the oxygen sensors (glass tubes) inside the wood are visible. After installation of the sensors it took 1-2 months before the concentration measurements were stable, which is probably due to the disturbance cause by drilling holes for the sensors. The concentrations measured after 57 days are shown in Figure 6b.

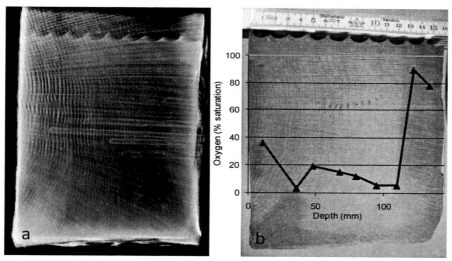

Figure 6. *Large sample of archaeological oak wood (20x20x15 cm) with oxygen sensors installed at nine different depths. a) shows a radiograph of the sample where the oxygen sensors (glass tubes) are visible as horizontal lines. b) shows a photo of the sample along with a curve of the concentrations measured after 57 days where the oxygen levels had stabilized. Depths are given relative to the left side of the sample, but the oxygen sensors have been installed from the right side. The distance from the sensors to the other 4 surfaces is approximately 10 cm.*

Figure 7 shows results from another wood block, where 3 sensors were installed at 1 cm depth and 3 sensors at 3 cm depth to investigate the repeatability of the measurements. Sensors installed 1 cm or more into waterlogged samples (from the Roskilde ships) all showed 0% oxygen (not shown).

129

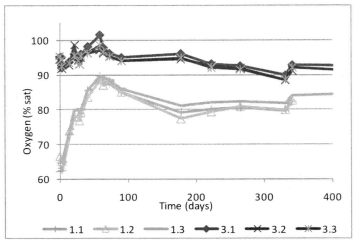

Figure 7. Repeatability of oxygen measurements: results from 6 oxygen sensors in a sample of conserved archaeological pine wood (14x8x8 cm) 3 sensors at 1 cm depth and 3 sensors at 3 cm depth. The oxygen concentration was followed for more than a year where the sample was stored in the laboratory (no control on relative humidity).

Oxygen diffusion: Figure 8 shows how five of the oxygen sensors from Figure 6 react when the surrounding atmosphere is changed to nitrogen, and (after 187 h) back to atmospheric air again. Similar experiments have been made for all 21 oxygen sensors installed in different wood samples.

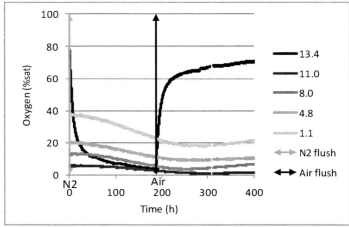

Figure 8. Oxygen concentrations measured at different depths in the sample from Figure 6 after the outer atmosphere is changed from air to nitrogen and back to atmospheric air. The names of the curves refer to their depth as shown in Figure 6. Sensor 1.1 is placed 1.1 cm from the left side, and sensor 13.4 is placed 13.4 cm for the left side (and 1.1 cm from the right side) in Figure 6.

Discussion

Oxygen consumption: The experimental design using Escal™ bags for measuring oxygen consumption of whole wood samples was successful: It was possible to quantify the oxygen consumption for all the tested wood samples non-destructively and without accelerated ageing – this took a few days for the most reactive samples, and up to 2-3 months for the more inactive samples (Figure 4). At room temperature and 50% RH the oxygen consumption for all 26 pieces of conserved wood was in the range 0.4-5 µg/g/day, with most values around 1 µg/g/day (Table 1). Fresh pine showed a similar oxygen consumption (1 µg/g/day), but the consumption for fresh oak was slightly lower (0.3 µg/g/day). PEG 600 showed a very low oxygen consumption of only 0.006 μg/g/day.

In order to convert these oxygen consumption rates into decay rates for the wood, it is necessary to know more about what the oxygen is used for. This will be discussed in future papers as it requires detailed knowledge of the individual wood samples, a knowledge that is not available yet. However, a desktop calculation may put the numbers into perspective: 1 μg/g/day corresponds to approximately 1 mg oxygen per g wood in 3 years time. At this rate it would take as much as 3000 years to oxidize organic material (with the gross formula CH_2O) all the way to CO_2, but still the oxygen measurements are sufficiently sensitive to follow it in real-time. Of course other oxygen consuming processes are also possible as for instance partial oxidation of wood components or oxidation of Fe and S compounds in the wood. If it is found out exactly which processes the oxygen is used for, measurement of the oxygen consumption rate makes it possible to study these decay processes without having to use accelerated ageing. This would allow good estimates of "real" decay rates, which makes the method very promising for studying for instance the effect of different treatments or storage conditions.

As for the accuracy of the method, the oxygen concentration inside the bags may be measured with an accuracy of approximately ±1%. However, the oxygen consumption rate calculated from Equation 1 is less accurate as it is difficult to measure the volume of air inside the bag, especially the air trapped inside the wood. At this stage the external air volume is measured through buoyancy and the internal air volume inside the wood is calculated from the weight and volume of the sample, using estimated contents and densities of cell wall material, water and PEG in the sample, as described in the Method section. Furthermore it is assumed that the oxygen concentration decreases at the same rate in the internal and the external air volume. The accuracy of the oxygen consumption

rate calculated in this way is estimated to be no better than ±25%. This is not ideal, and work is ongoing to find better methods for calculating the oxygen consumption rate from the decrease in concentration.

The oxygen consumption of wood powder was significantly higher than for whole pieces of wood, especially right after the powder was made (Figure 5). The first few days the powder had an oxygen consumption of 36-47 μg/g/day, while the whole sample had a consumption of only 1 μg/g/day. At this stage we cannot be sure whether this is simply due to an increased surface area of the powder or whether the physical rupture actually introduces new oxygen consuming reactions that do not take place in the whole wood piece, for instance caused by the formation of free radicals when the polymers are physically broken (Urbanski 1971). Skinner & Jones (2009) measured oxygen consumption of 40-120 μg/g/day at 75% RH for ground samples of archaeological wood from HMS Dartmouth, but it is difficult to say to which extent these high rates are due to the reactivity of the archaeological samples, the high relative humidity, or the grinding process itself. It is thus suggested, that measurements of the oxygen consumption of whole wood samples give a more realistic estimate of the "real" rate of oxidative decay, despite the in-accuracies of the current method.

The oxygen consumption curves for most of the archaeological samples from this study were (almost) linear, as shown for curve A, B, and C in Figure 4. A linear curve implies that the oxygen consumption rate is independent of the actual oxygen concentration, i.e. the process is equally fast at 20% and at 100% oxygen saturation. Curve D in Figure 4 is an exception: it is clearly curved, which implies that the consumption rate is lower at low oxygen concentrations. Plotting these data in a log (dc/dt) versus log [O_2] plot gives a straight line with a slope of 0.37, corresponding to the reaction order with respect to oxygen. This could indicate that the oxygen consuming process in that particular sample is different from the others, which have reaction orders close to zero. In that way the shape of the curves may help elucidate the oxygen consuming processes. For comparison the oxidation of for instance pyrite in moist air has a reaction order of 0.5 with respect to oxygen (Jerz & Rimstidt 2004).

Oxygen concentration inside wood: The experimental design with optical fibers or glass tubes drilled into the wood works well. It takes 1-2 months before the measurements are stable, which may be explained by the disturbance caused by the drilling: On the one hand fresh air is introduced into the hole until it is sealed by epoxy, and on the other hand the physical destruction made by the drill probably initiates the same increased oxygen consumption as seen for the wood powder. The repeatability of the method is good as indicated by the good correspondence between triplicate measurements in Figure 7. It is difficult to check the accuracy of the measurements (as there are no alternative methods to compare to) but the fact that less than 100% oxygen saturation is measured indicates that it is possible to seal the hole around the glass tubes sufficiently with the epoxy used.

The curve in Figure 6 demonstrates that the oxygen concentration varies significantly through a block of wood, from almost 100% saturation in the outer part to less than 20% saturation in the middle. Completely anoxic conditions have not been found, so oxidation processes can probably take place at all depths in this wood sample. If the wood was completely homogenous we would expect that the concentration decreased evenly towards the middle of the sample. Obviously this is not the case – the oxygen curve is more complex showing both decreasing and increasing concentrations with depth. This is due to the heterogeneity of the wood, and also the fact that oxygen transport may take place in all 3 directions, for instance through the wood vessels that are perpendicular to the profile shown in Figure 6. This is also the case for the sample in

Figure 7, where higher oxygen concentrations are found at 3 cm depth than at 1 cm depth, implying that the oxygen supply is faster and/or the consumption is lower at 3 cm. The waterlogged samples from the Roskilde ships were anoxic inside, as the oxygen supply through water is very slow. Such anoxic conditions have also been a prerequisite for their preservation in situ for more than a thousand years.

Oxygen diffusion: Figure 8 shows that the oxygen concentration inside the wood does not respond immediately when the outer atmosphere is changed to nitrogen, and even after 150 hours oxygen is still found at all the depths shown here. Also when the atmosphere is changed back to atmospheric air there is a long lag phase before the oxygen concentration starts to increase again.

The response time at a given depth will depend both on the distance to the surface, the concentration gradient, and the diffusion constant for the wood. It is described as $\partial c/\partial t = D \cdot \partial^2 c/\partial x^2$, in Ficks 2nd law for diffusion, where c is the concentration, t is the time, x is the distance and D is the diffusion constant. For dynamic diffusion in a half-open system the differential equation may be solved as $x^2 = 2Dt$, where t is the time it takes before the initial oxygen concentration has decreased by 32% (Alberty 1987). The formula is exact for one-directional diffusion of a non-reactive gas into a homogenous medium. In our case the system is far from homogenous, the oxygen gas is reactive, and diffusion may occur in all directions. Still, if we use this formula on the data in Figure 8 and define x as the linear distance to the closest surface, apparent diffusion constants that vary between $1*10^{-10}$ m^2/s and $4*10^{-9}$ m^2/s are obtained. Measurements at other depths and in two other samples of conserved wood gave apparent diffusion constants between $1*10^{-10}$ m^2/s and $3*10^{-6}$ m^2/s i.e. a variation over 4 orders of magnitude. It must be emphasized that these estimates are very rough and it is necessary to compare them to more traditional (destructive) measurements using wood plugs. Even so they give a semi-quantitative understanding of the diffusion and the method will allow studies of for instance the effect of different surface treatments. For comparison Sorz & Hietz (2006) find diffusion constants from 10^{-11} m^2/s (moist wood with 0% air volume) to 10^{-6} m^2/s (dry wood with 50-60% air volume) using wood plugs from different wood species and different directions.

Conclusion and Future Work

Overall the methods have proven very useful for studying the oxygen dynamics in wood: The oxygen consumption measurements in Escal^{TM} bags are completely non-destructive and sufficiently sensitive to allow real-time, non-accelerated studies of decay, which is very difficult by any other method. The future work includes studies of the reaction mechanisms to find out exactly which process consumes the oxygen. Further studies also include measurements in different environments (especially different relative humidities) in order to investigate their influence on the oxygen consumption and find out if there are any environments, where the oxygen consumption of artifacts from a given find increases or decreases. The method can in principle be used to screen wood samples from any find in order to choose the optimal storage conditions for that find.

The measurements of oxygen concentration inside wood have given interesting results: for all the samples investigated until now the oxygen concentration was lower than 100% saturation at all depths, but completely anoxic conditions were not found anywhere at 50% relative humidity. Only the waterlogged samples (from the Roskilde ships) were anoxic inside. The future studies include measurements at other relative humidities, installation of sensors directly in the hull of conserved ships, and continued measurements of wood samples from the Roskilde ships through the whole conservation process.

Finally the measurements of oxygen diffusion: these have only begun recently and the future work includes comparison to more traditional diffusion measurements.

They can be used to investigate the effect of different treatments to find out if it for instance is possible to decrease the oxygen flux into (and the oxygen consumption inside) a wooden artifact by using different surface treatments.

Acknowledgements

The work on the Vasa wood samples has been commissioned by the Vasa museum and they are gratefully thanked for their financial support. Also thank to the other participants in the project "A future for Vasa" for discussion of results. The work on other wood samples has been supported by the Danish Ministry of Culture, ref no TAKT 2008-039. The instruments for oxygen measurements have been financed by the Danish Directorate for Cultural Heritage, ref no 2003-3321/10101-0039. Two anonymous referees and Dr. Poul Jensen and Dr. David Gregory from the National Museum of Denmark are thanked for their input to this manuscript.

References

Alberty, R.A. (1987). *Physical chemistry. 7th edition.* New York: Wiley.

Cederlund, C.O., Hafström, G., Hocker, F. & Wendel, P. (2006). *Vasa I. The archaeology of a Swedish warship of 1628.* Stockholm: National Maritime Museums of Sweden.

Crumlin-Pedersen, O. & Olsen, O. (eds) (2002). The Skuldelev ships I, in Ships and boats of the north, 4.1.Roskilde: Vikingeskibsmuseet & Nationalmuseet

del Hierro, A.M., Kronberger, W., Hietz, P., Offenthaler, I. & Richter, H. (2002). A new method to determine the oxygen concentration inside the sapwood of trees. *Journal of Experimental Botany* **53**, 559-563.

Dufour, J. & Havermans, J.B.G.A. (2001). Study of the photo-oxidation of mass-deacified papers. *Restaurator* **22**, 20-40.

133

Fors, Y. & Sandström, M. (2006). Sulfur and iron in shipwrecks cause conservation concerns. *Chemical Society Reviews* **35**, 399-415.

Ghisalberti, E., Godfrey, I., Kilminster, K., Richards, V. & Williams, E. (2002). The analysis of acid affected Batavia timbers. In (P. Hoffmann, J.A. Spriggs, T. Grant, C. Cook, & A. Recht, Eds) *Proceedings of the 8th ICOM Group on Wet Organic Archaeological Materials Conference, Stockholm, 11-15 June 2001.* Bremerhaven: ICOM. pp. 281-305.

Gøthche, M. (2006). The Roskilde ships. In (L. Blue, F. Hocker, & A. Englert, Eds) *Connected by the Sea. Proceedings of the Tenth International Symposium on Boat and Ship Archaeology Roskilde 2003.* Oxford: Oxbow Books, pp. 252-258.

Grattan, D.W. (1993). Degradation rates for some historic polymers and the potential of various conservation measures for minimizing oxidative degradation. In (D.W. Grattan, Ed) *Saving the twentieth century: The conservation of modern materials. Proceedings of a conference symposium 1991.* Ottawa, Canada: Canadian Conservation Institute. pp. 351-361.

Hicks, W.T. & Harmon, M.E. (2002). Diffusion and seasonal dynamics of O2 in wood debris from the Pacific Northwest, USA. *Plant and Soil* **243**, 67-79.

Jerz, J.K. & Rimstidt, J.D. (2004). Pyrite oxidation in moist air. *Geochimica et Cosmochimica Acta* **68**, 701-714.

Jørgensen, L., Storgaard, B., Thomsen, L.G. (eds) (2003). *The spoils of victory. The North in the shadow of the Roman Empire.* Copenhagen: National Museum of Denmark.

Ju, L.-K. & Ho, C.S. (1986). The measurement of oxygen diffusion coefficients in polymeric solutions. *Chemical Engineering Science* **41**, 579-589.

Lloyd, W.G. (1961). Inhibition of polyglycol autoxidation. *Journal of chemical and engineering data* **6**, 541-547.

Matthiesen, H. (2007). A novel method to determine oxidation rates of heritage materials in vitro and in situ. *Studies in Conservation* **52**, 271-280.

Mexal, J., Fisher, J.T., Osteryoung, J. & Reid, C.P.P. (1975). Oxygen availability in polyethylene glycol solutions and its implications in plant-water relations. *Plant Physiol.* **55**, 20-24.

More, N., Smith, G., Te Kanawa, R. & Miller, I. (2003). Iron-sensitized degradation of black-dyed Maori textiles. *Dyes in history and archaeology* **19**, 144-148.

Scheirs, J., Bigger, S.W. & Billingham, N. (1995). A review of oxygen uptake techniques for measuring polyolefin oxidation. *Polymer Testing* **14**, 211-214.

Skinner, T. & Jones, M. (2009). Respirometry: a technique to assess the stability of archaeological wood and other materials containing sulfur compounds. In (K. Strætkvern & H. Huisman, Eds) *Proceedings from the 10th ICOM Group on Wet Organic Archaeological Materials Conference, Amsterdam 2007.* Amersfoort Nederlandse Archeologische Rapporten 37. pp. 517-524.

Sorz, J. & Hietz, P. (2006). Gas diffusion through wood: implications for oxygen supply. *Trees* **20**, 34-41.

Sorz, J. & Hietz, P. (2008). Is oxygen involved in beech (Fagus sylvatica) red heartwood formation? *Trees* **22**, 175-185.

Stusek, P., Pohleven, F. & Capl, D. (2000). Detection of wood boring insects by measurement of oxygen consumption. *International Biodeterioration and Biodegradation* **46**, 293-298.

Urbanski, T. (1971). Degradation of amber and formation of free radicals by mechanical action. *Proc.R.Soc.Lond.A.* **325**, 377-381.

2.A

Waterlogged Wood from the Miocene Forest of Bükkábrány: A Preliminary Investigation of Material Morphology and Chemistry.

Maria Petrou*
Department of Conservation of Antiquities and Works of Art, Technological Educational Institute of Athens, Ag. Spyridonos, Aegaleo, 12210 Athens, Greece
E-mail*:petroumar@yahoo.gr

Glen McConnachie .
The Mary Rose Trust, College Road, H M Naval Base, Portsmouth, PO1 3LX, U.K.

Anastasia Pournou
Department of Conservation of Antiquities and Works of Art, Technological Educational Institute of Athens, Ag. Spyridonos, Aegaleo, 12210 Athens, Greece.

Abstract

The oldest standing palaeo-forest in the world, preserved as waterlogged wood, is located at Bükkábrány, Hungary. A sudden rise in the water level of Lake Pannon, some 7 million years ago and the rapid sedimentation of sands from a prograding delta that followed, covered the landscape and produced a waterlogged anoxic burial environment, preserving the un-mineralized trunks to the present day.

Samples from tree stumps were examined to identify their morphology at the cellular level and their chemical composition. Characterization of waterlogged paleontological wood is of paramount importance in understanding the long term effects of the burial environment on the degradation processes that took place from the Miocene to the present day, as well as facilitating the development of conservation strategies. The preliminary approach of the investigations included light microscopy, SEM-EDAX, and FTIR analyses. Comparisons were made with samples of the closest modern equivalents (*Sequoia sempervirens* and *Sequoiadendron giganteum*), in order to highlight morphological changes in the structure of the wood, as well as the modification of wood chemical components.

Preliminary data obtained showed the abundance of inorganic inclusions in the wood structure. Additionally, alterations were observed in micro-morphology associated with microbial activity, as well as qualitative and quantitative alterations to the wood chemical composition.

1 Introduction

The oldest standing palaeo-forest in the world was exposed during excavation works at the lignite mine of the Bükkábrány in Hungary (Császár et al 2009, Erdei et al 2009, Hámor-Vidó et al 2010). The lignite seams formed during the Late Miocene extend to 10 m and are overlain by sand layers of up to 60 m. At that time Lake Pannon covered the Inner Carpathian region and forests flourishing on the delta plain provided a great amount of organic matter which accumulated and was buried by sediments. The fossil forest of Bükkábrány comprises one of the thickest non-marine Late Neogene sedimentary sequences in Europe (Rasser & Harzhauser 2008, Császár et al 2009).

Bükkábrány forest trunks are considered and described as fossil wood; however their macroscopic appearance does not indicate signs of fossilization (Császár et al 2009). The material was wet / waterlogged and mostly preserved as soft tissue, creating a challenge for its preservation.

Even though this unique material is being studied by several scientists to reveal information related to palaeobotany (Erdei et al 2009) to the site palaeoenvironment (Hamor-Vido 2010), to stratigraphy, hydrogeology, geology etc (Kazmer 2008, Császár et al 2009), in order to design an appropriate conservation approach for preserving this material, a series of targeted studies towards its preservation state appeared essential.

Thus, this study aimed at a preliminary investigation of the material in order to highlight morphological changes in the structure of the wood, as well as the modification of wood chemical components, specifically since plans for its conservation are in place (Kazmer 2008, Császár et al 2009). Additionally the results aimed to contribute to the understanding of the long term effects of the burial environment on the degradation processes that took place from the Miocene to the present day.

2 Materials and Methods
2.1 Wood samples
Excavation material was provided by the Hermann Ottó Museum. Nine samples examined in this study correspond to three different levels (top, middle and bottom) of trunks10, 12 and 13. These trunks have been identified as *Taxodioxylon germanicum* (Greguss) Van der Burgh, related to modern *Sequoia gigantea* (Lindley) Decaisne [1] and *Sequoia sempervirens* (D. Don) Endlicher, (Erdei 2009). Therefore for FTIR analysis samples of *Sequoia sempervirens* (D. Don) Endlicher and *Sequoiadendron giganteum* (Lindley) J.Buchholz, have been examined, kindly provided by the Johann Heinrich von Thünen-Institut (vTI).

2.2 Light microscopy
Hand cut longitudinal and transverse sections were mounted in 50% v/v aqueous solution of glycerine and were examined using an OLYMPUS CX 41 microscope equipped with an OLYMPUS C-5050 zoom digital camera system.

2.2 Scanning electron microscopy
Material was cut using a double-edged razor blade, dehydrated through an ethanol series and then left to air dry in a desiccator for 72 hours. It was then mounted on aluminum stubs using carbon glue, coated with palladium/gold in a POLARON SC7640, QUORUM sputter coater and examined using a JEOL JSM-5310 scanning electron microscope at 15 kV.

2.3 Energy dispersive X-ray analysis
Energy dispersive X-ray analysis (EDX) was performed with a JEOL JSM-5310 scanning electron microscope equipped with a Pentafet 6587 EDX-detector (INCA analysis system, Oxford Instruments). EDX was performed at an acceleration voltage of 15 kV.

2.4 Fourier transform infrared spectroscopy
ATR-FTIR spectra were acquired using a Perkin Elmer 'Spectrum One' spectrophotometer in the absorbance range 4000 to 650cm-1. For each sample run, 32 scans were averaged at a resolution of $4cm^{-1}$, after which spectra were baseline corrected and normalized to the highest peak at around $1030cm^{-1}$. Three runs were averaged for each individual sample and further averaging was performed on collective spectra from each fossil trunk.

3 Results and Discussion
3.1 Light microscopy
Light microscopy showed extensive degradation of all nine samples examined. The earlywood was severely distorted compared to latewood which occasionally retained the cell anatomy (see Figure 1a, b).

More specifically, severe biodeterioration was observed, caused by both fungi and bacteria. Abundant fungal hyphae in all cell lumina and active penetration of tracheid cell walls were frequently detected (see Figure 1c, d), which can be attributed to both soft rot and staining fungi (Eaton and   Hale 1993).

Figure 1. (a), (b) Severe distortion of earlywood compared to latewood. (c) Fungal hyphae in cell lumens. (d) Active penetration of tracheids cell walls

Bacterial decay patterns were also recorded, most commonly appearing as narrow erosion zones extending from one bordered pit to the other, parallel to the cell axis. These zones appeared to widen and cover the entire tracheid wall as decay progressed (see Figure 2a). In addition, V and X-shaped nicks were also observed, either on the cell wall layer (see Figure 2b) or centered on pit cavities (see Figure 2c), as well as occasional 'stripes', running parallel to the cellulose microfibrils (see Figure 2d), or in a circular direction around the pit cavity or border. The abovementioned patterns appeared to be associated with erosion bacteria attack (Holt 1981, Holt 1983, Daniel and Nilsson 1986, Singh and Butcher 1991, Björdal Nilsson and Daniel, 1999, Björdal and Nilsson 2008).

Furthermore, patterns which could be attributed to cavitation bacteria (Nilsson and Singh 1984; Singh and Butcher 1991) were also present, in the form of angular cavities surrounding the pit borders (see Figure 3a). Finally tunnels spreading in all directions and including the ML (see Figure 3b), were observed, indicating tunneling bacteria attack (Nilsson and Daniel 1983, Daniel and Nilsson 1985, Singh, Nilsson and Daniel 1990, Singh and Kim 1997). The bacterial decay patterns described were seen separately but quite often coexisted on the same cell wall (see Figure 3c).

Light microscopy also revealed some mineral inclusions (large prismatic crystals), which seemed to be of exogenous origin (see Figure 3d).

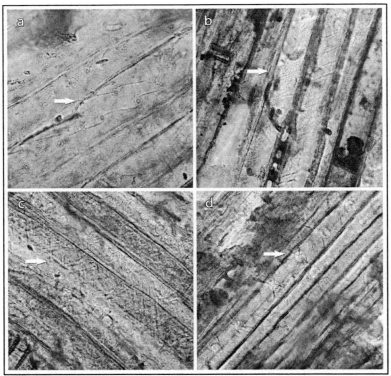

Figure 2: *(a) Narrow erosion zones forming wider zones as decay progressed. (b) V and X-shaped nicks on the cell wall layer. (c) X-shaped nicks centered on the pit cavity (d) Erosion stripes parallel to cellulose microfibrils.*

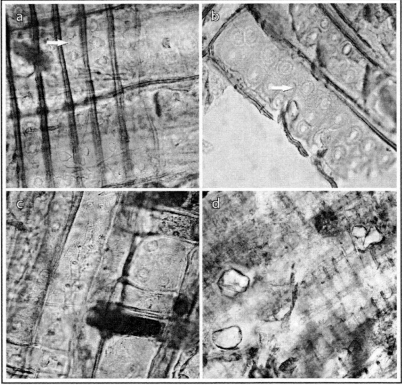

Figure 3: (a) Patterns in the form of angular cavities surrounding the pit borders. (b) Tunnels spreading in all possible directions. (c) The bacterial decay patterns quite often coexist on the same cell wall. (d) Mineral inclusion (large prismatic crystal).

3.2 Scanning electron microscopy

Scanning electron microscopy confirmed light microscopy results concerning the extensive biodeterioration of the material (see Figure 4a) and the severe distortion of the wood tissue. The separation of the compound middle lamellae from the secondary wall was also observed (see Figure 4b). Even though abundant fungal hyphae were detected inside the cell lumina, enzymatic dissolution of the wood cell wall layers was not apparent.

Regarding the bacterial attack, the V or X-shaped 'nicks' on the cell wall layer (see Figure 4c) were clearly defined, indicating that their orientation was determined by the crossed arrangement of the cellulose microfibrils (Tsoumis 1991) of the S_1 or S_3 cell wall layers. Stripes at an angle of 30 to 40° to the cell wall axis were also recorded in the S_2 layer (see Figure 4d).

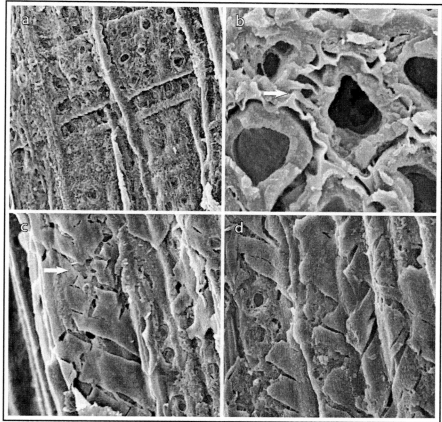

Figure 4: *(a) Extended biodeterioration of the material examined. (b) Separation of the compound middle lamellae from the secondary wall. (c) V or X-shaped nicks on the cell wall layer. (d) Stripes along the cell axis.*

Concerning the patterns of decay appearing as zones, it appears that they have initiated as minute holes in the wood cell wall layer which coalesced (see Figure 5a), forming both narrow and wide erosion zones from pit to pit, or around the pit border (see Figure 5b, c).

Tunneling and cavitation bacteria patterns of decay were not clearly demonstrated; either because the samples examined did not present this pattern of decay, or the light microscopy results were ambiguously interpreted.

Finally, crystals of exogenous origin of various morphologies were detected. The two morphologies most commonly found were needle shaped, 'star' forming crystals and rectangular, densely packed ones forming various patterns (see Figure 5d).

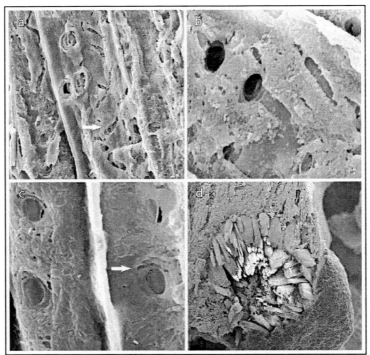

Figure 5: (a) Erosion zones initiated as minute holes which progressively coalesced. (b) Narrow and wide erosion zones extending from pit to pit. (c) Erosion around the pit border. (d) Rectangular densely packed crystal.

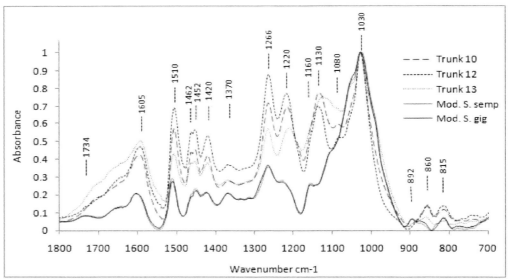

Figure 6. Baseline corrected, normalized and averaged ATR-FTIR spectra of modern Sequoia sempervirens, modern Sequoiadendron giganteum and wood from three fossil trunks (excluding samples known to contain phloem).

3.3 Energy dispersive X-ray analysis

Regardless of the different crystal morphology revealed with the SEM, the use of EDX showed that all of them consisted mainly of similar elements, such as calcium, sulfur and small amounts of iron. These elements most likely originated from the burial environment.

3.4 Fourier transformed infrared spectroscopy

The most prominent feature of the wood samples was a dramatic increase in their lignin character (see Figure 6). Peaks at 1605cm[-1], 1510cm[-1], 1420cm[-1] and 1267cm[-1] are related to aromatic vibrations in lignin (Faix 1991, Obst et al 1991, Ucar et al 1996,

142

Pandey and Pitman 2003) and show significant increases in relation to modern samples. Well resolved peaks also appear at 1220cm^{-1} and 1130cm^{-1}, which are lignin related (Pandey and Pitman 2003).

In contrast, carbohydrate peaks at 1734cm^{-1}, associated with hemicelluloses (Macleod and Richards 1997; Pandey and Pitman 2003), at 1160cm^{-1} with holocellulose (Macleod and Richards 1997, Pandey and Pitman 2003) and at 892cm^{-1} with cellulose (Pandey and Pitman 2003), disappear in the miocene wood spectra. The carbohydrate character of the samples does persist however in the peaks at 1030cm^{-1} and at 1370cm^{-1}, assigned to holocellulose (Macleod and Richards 1997, Pandey and Pitman 2003). Hamor-Vido et al (2010) also confirm the persistence of cellulose in samples of other trunks from the same site. Both the lignin and carbohydrate character of samples is consistent with previous studies of degraded palaeontological waterlogged softwoods (Obst et al 1991, Ucar et al 1996).

Based on relative lignin peak absorbance values (see Table 1), some variation in the degree of degradation of samples could also be ascertained from the spectra. Trunk 13 showed the smallest increases in lignin absorbance values, suggesting a lower degree of deterioration, while trunk 12 showed the highest. Some variation could also be seen for samples taken from different heights of individual trunks. Trunk 10 showed highest lignin absorbance values for the top of the trunk, intermediate for the middle and lowest for the bottom. Relationships were not so clear for trunks 12 and 13 however.

Table 1. Key peaks and absorbance values obtained from averaged spectra normalized to 1.0 at 1030cm^{-1}.

	Absorbance			
	1510cm^{-1}	1420cm^{-1}	1268cm^{-1}	1370cm^{-1}
Modern *Sequoia sempervirens*	0.303	0.213	0.345	0.202
Modern *Sequoiadendron giganteum*	0.265	0.19	0.34	0.181
Fossil Trunk 10	0.523	0.364	0.671	0.207
Fossil Trunk 12	0.621	0.454	0.823	0.29
Fossil Trunk 13	0.349	0.29	0.496	0.185

4 Conclusions

Light microscopy illustrated clearly the extensive degree of biodeterioration in all samples examined. Since fungi, tunneling, erosion and cavitation bacteria decay patterns were all recorded; it is probable that the wood has been exposed to different burial environments relating to oxygen concentration. The selective removal of carbohydrates versus lignin shown by FTIR spectra is consistent with the extensive microbial deterioration revealed by light and electron microscopy observations. Unfortunately, it was not possible to safely correlate differences in preservation state between the two sets of data.

Based on this preliminary analysis, the conservation approach should be designed towards a lumen filling impregnation treatment that would maintain the cell size and shape and prevent collapse during drying, rather than a cell wall bulking approach, since limited cellulose is likely to remain.

However, in order to make final decisions concerning the preservation of this material, more investigation is essential that would provide information on material physical properties and fossilization processes.

Acknowledgments

The authors wish to thank Dr. Veres János the supervising archaeologist of the Bükkábrány excavation and Dr.Veres László Director of the Borsod-Abaúj-Zemplén County Museum (Hermann Ottó Museum) for permitting study of the material, Dr. Gerald Koch, Institute of Wood Technology and Wood Biology, Johann Heinrich von Thünen-Institut (vTI) for providing the fresh samples of *Sequoia spp.* and A. Karabotsos, TEI of Athens, for the technical assistance with the SEM.

Note

[1] Equivalent to: *Sequoiadendron giganteum* (Lindley) J.Buchholz 1939; *Wellingtonia gigantea* Lindley 1853 (Earle 2010)

References

Björdal C. G., Nilsson T., & Daniel G., (1999), Microbial decay of waterlogged archaeological wood found in Sweden Applicable to archaeology and conservation, International Biodeterioration & Biodegradation 43(1-2): 63-73.

Björdal C. G. & Nilsson T., 2008, Reburial of shipwrecks in marine sediments: a long-term study on wood degradation, Journal of Archaeological Science, **35**(4): 862-872.

Császár G., Kázmér M., Erdei B., & Magyar I., (2009), A possible Late Miocene fossil forest PaleoPark in Hungary, in Lipps J. H. & Granier B. R.C. (editors), PaleoParks - The Protection and Conservation of Fossil Sites World-Wide, International Palaeontological Association Berkeley, USA.

Daniel G. F. & Nilsson T., (1985), Ultrastructural and TEM·EDAX studies on the degradation of CCA-treated radiata pine by tunnelling bacteria. The International Research Group on Wood preservation. Document, IRG/WP 1260.

Daniel G. & Nilsson T., (1986), Ultrastructural observations on wood-degrading erosion bacteria. Working Group Ia, Biological Problems (Flora), The International Research Group on Wood Preservation. Stockholm

Earle C. J. (ed), (2010), The Gymnosperm Database, available online at http://www.conifers.org/cu/se2/index.htm accessed 15/4/2010

Eaton R. A. & Hale M. D., (1993), Wood. Decay, pests and protection. Chapman & Hall. London, New York.

Erdei B., Dolezych M. & Hably L. (2009), The buried Miocene forest at Bükkábrány, Hungary.- Review of Palaeobotany and Palynology, Amsterdam, vol. 155, n° 1-2, p. 69-79.

Faix O., (1991), Classification of lignins from different botanical origins by FTIR Spectroscopy. Holzforschung Volume 45, 21-27.

Hámor-Vidó M., Hofmann T., & Albert L. (2010), In situ preservation and paleoenvironmental assessment of Taxodiacea fossil trees in the Bükkalja Lignite Formation, Bükkábrány open cast mine, Hungary, International Journal of Coal Geology Volume 81, Issue 4, 1 April 2010, Pages 203-210.

Holt D. M., (1981), Bacterial breakdown of timber in aquatic habitats and their relationship with wood degrading fungi, Ph.D thesis, Portsmouth Polytechnic.

Holt D.M., (1983), Bacterial degradation of lignified wood cell walls in anaerobic aquatic habitats: decay patterns and mechanisms proposed to account for their formation, J. Inst. Wood Science, Vol 9, pp 212-223.

Kázmér M. (2008), The Miocene Bükkábrány Fossil Forest in Hungary - field observations and project outline. Hantkeniana, Budapest, vol. 6, p. 229-244.

Macleod I.D. & Richards V.L. (1997), Wood degradation on historic shipwreck sites: The use of FT-IR Spectroscopy to study the loss of hemicelluloses. In: Proceedings of the 6th ICOM group on wet organic archaeological materials conference, York, 1996.P. Hoffmann, T. Grant, J.A. Spriggs & T. Daley (eds.), ICOM, Bremerhaven.

Nilsson T. & Singh A.P., (1984), Cavitation bacteria. Document, The International Research Group on Wood Preservation, Document No: 1235.

Nilsson T. & Daniel G., (1983), Tunneling bacteria. Stockholm: The International Research Group on Wood Preservation, Document No: 1186.

Obst J.R., Mcmillan, N.J., Blanchette, R.A., Christensen, D.J., Faix, O., Han, J.S., Kuster, T.A., Landucci, L.L., Newman, R.H., Pettersen, R.C., Schwandt, V.H. & Wesolowski, M.F. (1991), Characterization of Canadian Arctic Fossil Woods. In: Tertiary Fossil Forests of the Geodetic Hills, Axel Heiberg Island, Arctic Archipelago. R.L. Christie & N.J. Mcmillan (eds.): Geological Survey of Canada, Bulletin 403, p. 123-146.

Pandey K.K. & Pitman, A.J. (2003), FTIR studies of the changes in wood chemistry following decay by brown-rot and white-rot fungi. International Biodeterioration & Biodegradation Volume 52, 151-160.

Rasser M.W. & Harzhauser M., (2008), Palaeogene and Neogene of Central Europe. In: McCann T. (ed.), The Geology of Central Europe. vol. 2: Mesozoic and Cenozoic.- Geological Society, London, p. 1031-1140.

Singh A. P. & Butcher J. A., (1991), Bacterial degradation of wood cell walls: a review of degradation patterns. Journal of the Institute of Wood Science, Vol 12, No 3, pp 143-157.

Singh A. P., Nilsson T. & Daniel G. F., (1990), Bacterial attack of Pinus sylvestris wood under near anaerobic conditions. Journal of the Institute of Wood Science, Vol 11, No 6, pp 237-249.

2.B

The *Stirling Castle* Wood Recording Project: A Pilot Project to Compare and Evaluate Traditional and Innovative Recording Techniques for Waterlogged Wood

Angela Karsten*

English Heritage, Fort Cumberland, Fort Cumberland Road, Eastney, Portsmouth, PO4 9LD, UK
E-mail*:angela.karsten@english-heritage.org.uk

Graeme Earl

Archaeological Computing Research Group, University of Southampton, Avenue Campus, Highfield, Southampton, SO17 1BF, UK

Abstract

This project compares traditional and innovative recording techniques for waterlogged wood. A number of graphic, visualization and digital methods were investigated and evaluated using parameters such as access to/ availability of, accuracy, time required and product. The digital techniques incorporate an analytical element which was applied to track how fine surface details on wood change during the process of conservation. The findings confirm that some change is taking place, although this in minimal.

Introduction

This project was jointly carried out between English Heritage (Archaeological Conservation and Technology Team) and the University of Southampton (Archaeological Computing Research Group).

The recording of wooden remains, where tool marks, constructional and natural features are documented, has long played an important role in archaeology (Morris 1990, Allen 1994, Brunning 1996, Sands 1997). The study of tool marks on waterlogged timbers can answer a variety of questions from wood conversion over to the production of the artifact, to the actual tools used.

So far the recording techniques used either photography, hand drawings and in some cases the use of molding materials. Lately the application of digital recording techniques and their use in archaeology is becoming increasingly common. Some projects use digital recording equipment as their first and prime technique (Jones 2009).

The *Stirling Castle* Wood Recording Project is designed as a trial to compare and evaluate traditional and innovative recording techniques. The potential to document fine surface details and constructional features of wooden objects is being investigated using traditional techniques such as photography, illustration, X-radiography, silicone rubber moulds, and newer digital techniques such as laser scanning and Polynomial Texture Mapping (PTM). Some of these techniques are being used as a monitoring tool to track how fine surface details change during the conservation process and how well some techniques capture surface details. All techniques are being evaluated in terms of accuracy, availability, time and costs.

Aim of the project

The overall aim of the project is to compare and evaluate traditional and more innovative recording techniques for waterlogged wood.
To achieve this, the project has the following objectives:

- To compare traditional and innovative recording techniques for wooden remains.

- To establish the effect of conservation treatments on fine surface details.
- To establish the accuracy when using molding and casting techniques.

Study material

The piece of waterlogged wood used in this study was recovered from the protected wreck of the *Stirling Castle* in 2006 by Wessex Archaeology, who undertook an investigation of the site on behalf of English Heritage.

One barrel fragment was selected to carry out the recording project using the techniques described below (see Figure 1). This piece was chosen for its small size, tool marks and constructional features. It is either a base or a head piece of a barrel (in the accompanying documentation it is referred to as a head piece, although this must remain unsure as it was a stray find). It is part of a composite base, as two dowels are present at the timber's flat edge. It is 40cm long, 9cm wide and the diameter can be reconstructed to 56.5cm.

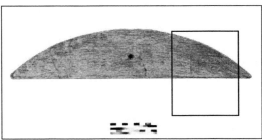

Figure 1. Head Piece 2255 after conservation (the box indicates the area for close examination, see Figure 2)

The site

The wreck of the *Stirling Castle* was discovered in 1979. It is a post-medieval ship, built in 1699 and lost during the great storm of 1703 on the Goodwin Sands, off Kent, United Kingdom (Dunkley 2007). The wreck has been protected under the Protection of Wrecks Act since 1980.

The recovered artifacts and the remaining hull timbers in situ are very well preserved and the archaeological potential of the assemblage is high. The site of the Goodwin Sands is subject to sediment movements, which cover and expose the wreck at intervals. This poses a threat to the stability of the wreck. Furthermore, the remains are vulnerable to fishing activity.

Figure 2. Area for close examination

Methodology

A variety of techniques were employed in this study (see Table 1). To compare and evaluate the methods, the following parameters were chosen:
- Access to/ Availability of
- Skills required
- Time
- Product
- Accuracy
- Ease of using data

Analysis of the dataset retrieved from laser scanning and polynomial texture mapping focused on comparison between the pre-treatment timber, the mould, the cast produced from the mould and the post-conservation timber [1]. These comparisons took three forms: visual examination of the laser scan and PTM datasets, and metric comparison of the laser scan data.

The pre-conservation state of the head piece is considered to be the original in this study and gives the baseline against which all findings are compared. An area containing tool marks was chosen for close examination (see Figure 2)

.

Table 1. Overview of recording techniques used

Traditional Recording Techniques	Innovative Recording Techniques
Sketch Hand drawing Illustration Photography X-radiography Silicone rubber mould and plaster cast	Laser Scanning Polynomial Texture Mapping

The pilot study

The traditional recording techniques are well established and need no further explanation, with the exception of X-radiography. Brief introductions to the innovative recording techniques are given here, but for more details please refer to the forthcoming report (Karsten and Earl, 2010 forthcoming).

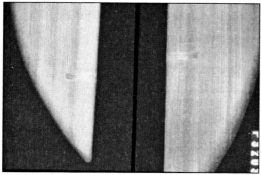

Figure 3: X-radiograph of dowels within Head Piece 2255

X-Radiography is a visualization technique not commonly used for organic materials, although it is becoming more recognized (O'Connor and Brooks 2007). When Earwood notes that some constructional details such as dowels can only be observed if wooden vessels are being dismantled (1993, 175), no consideration was given to non-destructive investigative techniques such as X-radiography. In this study X-radiography was used to examine the wooden dowels inside the head piece (see Figure 3).

Laser scanning or non-contact digitizing is becoming an increasingly common tool for conservation recording and analysis. The value of such techniques for cultural heritage visualization was recognized almost as soon as the technology was developed. Implementations include work as diverse as the Stanford Digital Michelangelo project (Levoy et al. 2000), the unwrapping of cuneiform (Anderson and Levoy 2002) and recording of mosaics (Maino 2009).

The non-contact digitizer employed for this study was a Konica Minolta vi910 triangulation laser scanner. All captures in this study used the telephoto lens with a focal length of 25mm. The measurement range was set at a constant 0.6m, which provides the maximum possible density of points for this instrument. Each capture produced a maximum of 307,000 individual points with a quoted accuracy in the x of ±0.22mm, y of ±0.16mm and z of ±0.10mm. All instrument settings were set to the highest possible capture quality for this study.

Polynomial Texture Mapping was invented by Hewlett Packard Labs in 2000 (Malzbender et al. 2000). This technique employs a fixed position digital SLR camera and records multiple frames with varying light source directions and has seen application in a broad range of archaeological and other contexts (e.g. Earl et al. 2010, Mudge et al. 2005, Padfield et al. 2005). The technique is analogous to the raking light photography commonly employed in the recording of archaeological artifacts (see Figure 10). However, its automated implementation has a number of benefits. First, it employs many more light directions and therefore provides a good coverage of the likely best shadow and light configurations for viewing subtle surface details. The best location of light for identification of surface detail can be defined automatically in software, in addition to trial and error approaches. Second, the Polynomial Texture Map (PTM) format enables interactive movement of the light source, including artificial reduction of the grazing angle to enhance very low relief details. Thirdly, the digital record can be subjected to a range of image processing algorithms in order to enhance surface details and to derive accurate true three-dimensional data. Fourthly, variations in surface form can be extracted and then used to provide metric comparisons. Finally, the PTM file can be used to provide relighting of the object, using multiple light sources, in order to produce idealized photographs for publication.

Results

All traditional recording techniques require some understanding of wood conversion and technology. The graphical techniques (see Figure 4 – 6) will most likely result in a selection or interpretation as the drawing is created. Drawing conventions are a way

of bringing conformity into the wide field of personal styles (Clarke at al. 1993). Close collaboration between archaeologists, wood technologists, conservators and the illustrator are essential. Imaging techniques such as photography, X-radiography, laser scanning and PTM do not make a selection and it depends on the knowledge and the skills of the operator to record surface details. Laser scanning and PTM also offer the added benefit of an analytical element that allows for measurements or distortion analysis to be undertaken. Molding is a technique that captures all surface details regardless of their nature and the skills of the operator (see Figure 7) (provided that mould and cast are produced correctly and to a high standard).

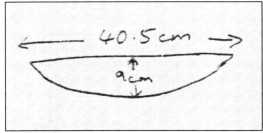

Figure 4. Sketch of Head Piece 2255

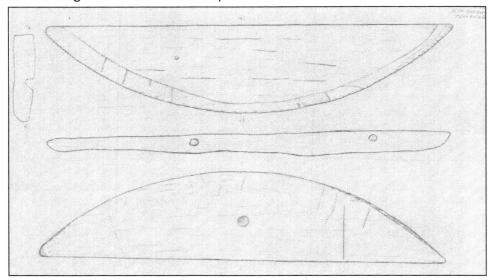

Figure 5. Hand drawing of Head Piece 2255 (scale 1:1)

150

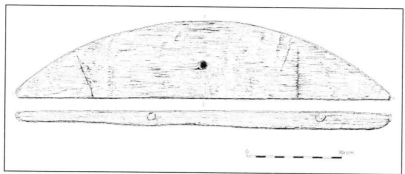

Figure 6. *Illustration of Head Piece 2255 (scale 1:1)*

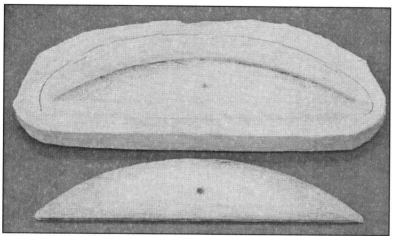

Figure 7. *Silicone mold and Plaster of Paris cast*

Table 2. *Evaluation of recording techniques*

	Accuracy	Availability	Time	Costs
Sketch	not very accurate	readily available	minimal	minimal
Hand Drawing	accurate	readily available	medium	minimal
Illustration	accurate	available	medium	minimal
Photography	accurate	readily available	medium	minimal
X-radiography	accurate	specialist equipment required	medium	medium
Silicone mould and cast	very accurate	specialist equipment required	medium	medium
Laser scanning	very accurate	specialist equipment required	high	high
PTM	very accurate	possible with readily available equipment	medium	medium

Photography, sketching and hand drawing are the techniques most commonly carried out during field work and at later stages. No special equipment is needed and with some practice good results can be achieved in relatively short time. Archaeological illustration, X-radiography and molding require slightly more time (see Figure 12). These techniques are carried out by personnel trained or qualified in these areas and more specialist equipment is needed.

Laser scanning and PTM are not routinely carried out and their application is often triggered by a research question. However, the low price of capture equipment, relatively simple implementation, and the free availability of the necessary software required for polynomial texture mapping mean that it could rapidly become a regularly employed technique.

Laser scanning and PTM are useful techniques to evaluate the effect of conservation treatment on fine surface details, such as tool marks. The analysis showed that there is some change between the pre-conservation and post-

conservation timber (see Figures 8 and 9). It is however difficult to quantify this change. First, it would appear that the volume lost is close to the tolerance of the laser. Second, comparison of laser scan datasets requires an accurate registration of the scans. As the processes studied themselves distort the surface there is a direct, inverse relationship between the quality of match between the scans and the accuracy of the measured difference between them.

Figure 8. *Illustration of where cross section analysis (see Figure 9) through the timber was carried out*

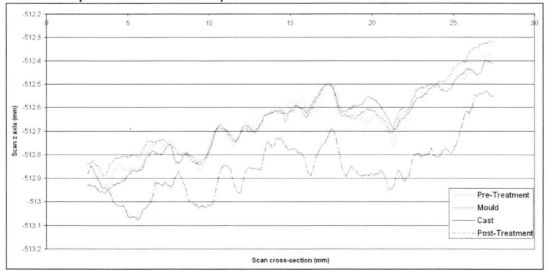

Figure 9. *Cross section through the timber illustrates how the post-treatment timber (bottom graph) differs from the mould, cast and pre-treatment timber (top three graphs). Note however that although the profile is roughly similar the low quality of match between the pre- and post-conservation scan datasets prohibits direct use of the quantitative values e.g. difference in volume*

152

Visual analysis of the scans indicated that the more the process of capturing surface details moves away from the original (which we consider to be the pre-conservation wood), the less accurate the maintenance of fine surface details between processes becomes (see Figure 11). So wet wood and silicone mould are fairly similar with a little loss of detail at the edges, the silicone mould and the plaster cast are again fairly similar, with the greatest difference seen between the pre- and post-treatment wood. The loss of fine surface details from pre-conservation wood to plaster cast is a little bigger than the other two, as this is an accumulation of the surface detail loss experienced during the other two stages.

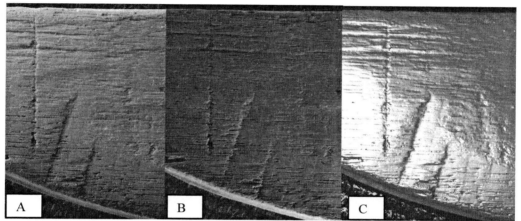

Figure 10. PTM of plaster cast illustrating the impact of differently angled lighting (A and B) and specular enhancement (C)

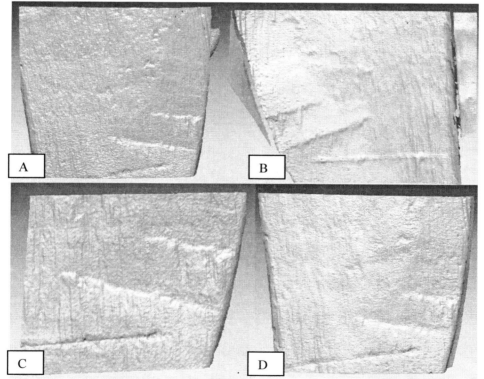

Figure 11. Visual comparison of the scans confirms a progressive softening of the sharpened edges present in the pre-treatment timber (A: pre-treatment timber, B: silicone mould, C: plaster cast, D: post-treatment timber)

Conclusion

The pilot study has demonstrated that various recording techniques are available, which can be utilized depending on the nature of an object or the overall project. Each method has its own benefits and shortcomings (see Table 2 and Figure 12) and an informed decision has to be taken when choosing one recording technique over another. Often a combination of two or more techniques will prove useful.

In order to evaluate the effect of conservation treatment on fine surface details and to establish the accuracy when using molding and casting techniques, the innovative techniques are more suitable than the traditional ones, as they allow the user to carry out analysis.

The findings support our expectations and reiterate that recording should be carried out on the wet timber. Some surface changes take place during conservation. And even though detailed study of fine surface details is not impossible after conservation, better results will probably be achieved when examining the wet timber before conservation.

Figure 12. Rating of recording techniques with regards to accuracy and time/ costs

Acknowledgment

We would like to thank Chris Evans (English Heritage) for producing the illustration of the timber, Tom Malzbender at Hewlett Packard Labs Palo Alto, and Carla Schroer and Mark Mudge from Cultural Heritage Imaging for help and advice on PTM. The capture equipment used by Graeme Earl is funded by the AHRC via the Portus Project and the DEDEFI program.

Notes

[1]   The head piece was conserved using 20% PEG400 followed by 20% PEG4000 and freeze drying. No volumetric measurements to record the dimensional changes were made.

References

Allen S., (1994), The illustration of wooden artifacts: An introduction and guide to the depiction of wooden objects, Technical Paper No. 11, Oxford: Association of Archaeological Illustrators and Surveyors

Anderson S. and Levoy M., (2002), Unwrapping and visualizing cuneiform tablet, IEEE computer graphics and applications *22:6*, 2002, pp 82-88,

Brunning R., (1996), Waterlogged wood: Guidelines on the recording, sampling, conservation and curation, London: English Heritage

Clarke R., Dean M., Hutchinson G., McGrail S., Squirrel J., (1993), Recent work on the R. Hamble wreck near Bursledon, Hampshire, The International Journal of Nautical Archaeology, 22.1, pp 21-44

Dunkley M., (2007), *Stirling Castle* Goodwin Sands off Kent: Conservation statement and management plan. English Heritage

154

Earwood C., (1993), Domestic wooden artifacts in Britain and Ireland from Neolithic to Viking times, Exeter: University of Exeter Press

Earl G.P., Martinez K. and Malzbender T. (2010) (forthcoming), Archaeological Applications of Polynomial Texture Mapping: Analysis, Conservation and Representation, Journal of Archaeological Science, forthcoming

Jones T., (2009), Three-Dimensional Recording and Digital Modeling of the Newport Medieval Ship, A.C.U.A. Underwater Archaeology Conference Proceedings, 2009, pp111-116

Karsten A. and Earl G.P., (2010) (forthcoming), The *Stirling Castle* wood recording project: A pilot project to compare and evaluate traditional and innovative recording techniques for waterlogged wood, English Heritage Research Department Research Series, Portsmouth: English Heritage

Levoy M., Pulli K., Curless B., Rusinkiewicz S., Koller D., Pereira L., Ginzton M., Anderson S., Davis J., Ginsberg J., Shade J., Fulk D., (2000), The digital Michelangelo project: 3D scanning of large statues, in Brown J.S. and Akeley K. (eds) Proceedings of the 27th annual conference on computer graphics and interactive techniques, ACM Press, pp 131-144

Maino G. (2009), Advanced techniques for the studies of stones and paintings on walls: State of the art and open problems, in Remondino F., El-Hakim S., Gonzo L. (eds), Proceedings of the 3rd ISPRS International Workshop 3D-ARCH 2009: "3D Virtual Reconstruction and Visualization of Complex Architectures" Trento, Italy, 25-28 February 2009

Malzbender T., Gelb D., Wolters H., Zuckerman B., (2000), Enhancement of shape perception by surface reflectance transformation, Technical Report HPL-2000-38R1, Hewlett-Packard Laboratories, Palo Alto, California

Morris C.A., (1990), Recording ancient timbers: The technologist's view, in Coles J.M., Coles B.J., Dobson M. J. (eds), Waterlogged Wood: The recording, sampling, conservation and curation of structural wood. Proceedings of a conference sponsored by WARP and English Heritage on 15 January 1990, WARP Occasional Paper 3, pp 9-15

Mudge M., Voutaz J.P., Schroer C., Lum M., (2005), Reflection transformation imaging and virtual representations of coins from the hospice of the Grand St. Bernard, in Mudge M., Ryan N., Scopigno R. (eds), Proceedings of 6th International Symposium on Virtual Reality, Archaeology and Cultural Heritage (VAST2005), Eurographics Association, pp 29–39

O'Connor S. and Brooks M.M., (2007), *X-Radiography of textiles, dress and related objects*. Oxford: Elsevier

Padfield J., Saunders D., Malzbender T., (2005), Polynomial texture mapping: A new tool for examining the surface of paintings, in Verger I. (editor), ICOM Committee for Conservation: 14th Triennial meeting, The Hague, 12-16 September 2005,Vol I, pp 504-510

Sands R., (1997), Prehistoric Woodworking: The analysis and interpretation of bronze and Iron Age toolmarks. London: Archetype

155

2.C

Measurement of Responses in Archaeological Wood to Ambient Temperature and Relative Humidity – Case Study - The Oseberg Ship

Maria Jensen[*]
Museum of Cultural History, University of Oslo, Department of Conservation, PO Box 6762 St. Olavs plass, 0130 Oslo, Norway.
E-mail*: maria.jensen@khm.uio.no

Bjarte Aarseth, Jan Bill, Susan Braovac, Guro Hjulstad, Ragnar Løchen and Elin Storbekk,
Museum of Cultural History, University of Oslo, Department of Conservation, PO Box 6762 St. Olavs plass, 0130 Oslo, Norway

Paolo Dionisi Vici
IVALSA_CNR, San Michele all'Adige (TN), Italy.

Abstract

The dimensional response of archaeological oak from the Oseberg ship to seasonal variation in the ambient environment is being monitored using transducers. Each measurement device consists of two transducers installed at a fixed distance and connected to a data logger. Four sets are installed: two locations monitoring restrained wood and two locations monitoring wood free from physical restraint. Of the unrestrained wood, one sample is of new, sound oak, and one sample is a loose fragment from the ship. As expected, results show the response in the unrestrained samples is higher than the restrained samples. Sound oak is the most reactive. The lowest dimensional response was recorded in the restrained sample under greatest loading. This indicates the absorption of stresses in restrained wood since they are prevented from moving. Further work must evaluate whether the absorbed stresses are damaging to the wood. The aim is to find out which RH range is considered "safe" for the object, while taking into account energy efficiency.

Keywords: environmental conditions, relative humidity, dimensional change, oak, wood, transducers, restrained, unrestrained, Gnumeric, Oseberg ship.

1. Introduction

Recommendations for temperature (T) and relative humidity (RH) are suggested for museum objects to ensure minimal physical damage, but these recommendations do not distinguish archaeological wood from wood which has undergone natural aging without burial (Thomson, 1978). This study aims to measure the response of oak wood from the Oseberg ship, subjected to seasonal variations in the ambient environment, in an attempt to understand its effect on the dimensional changes in the wood and the potential stresses involved. As of today we have not seen any signs of damage that can be ascribed to fluctuations in RH however this is difficult to ascertain in an object of variable condition. A long-term goal of this project is to establish an allowable range of environmental conditions to ensure the future preservation of the ship.

Excavated in 1904, the Oseberg ship, dated from 800 AD, is one of the most important discoveries of the Viking age period in Norway. The fact that the ship consists of 90 % of the original material makes it a unique find with no comparison elsewhere in the world. The ship is 24 meters long and 5 meters at its' widest, and it is built with radially cut 3 cm thick oak planks. In 1907 the waterlogged wood was conserved with linseed oil and creosote and the surface exterior was then lacquered. Over 2000 pieces were used for the reconstruction of the ship. Both original nails and modern screws were used together with adhesive.

The Oseberg ship, displayed at the Viking Ship Museum in Oslo, has been subjected to an uncontrolled environment since 1926, with only heating in winter. The display area is therefore influenced by seasonal changes in relative humidity, which rises above 70% RH in the summer and drops below 30% RH in the winter. Rapid changes over the course of a few hours have also been recorded.

2. Materials and Methods:

This project is a collaboration between the conservation staff at the Museum of Cultural History and Dr. Paolo Dionisi Vici, a wood scientist, who was employed as a researcher at IVALSA-CNR Trees and Timber Institute. The method and setup used in this study was originally developed to measure deformations of panel paintings (Uzielli et al., 1992).

The measuring system consists of two transducers (see figure 1) which convert small linear mechanical displacements in the wood into an electrical signal (volt). Voltage can be converted to millimeters (mm) by a simple calibration step. The transducers are arranged parallel to each other, at pre-set distances. The distance above the wood surface is also pre-set. The transducers are connected to a data logger with four external channels, which is capable of recording the electrical signals from the transducers as well as the ambient T and RH at chosen intervals. This setup measures swelling and shrinkage of the wood, due to its dynamic response to changes in the ambient T and RH. The raw data is accessed through the data logger software program where dimensional changes in the wood are plotted together with changes in RH and T. The geometrical setup of the transducers allows for the measured values to be analyzed using different formulas in a spreadsheet like Gnumeric[1]. We have chosen to observe

% dimensional change in the arc length. (Dionisi Vici, P. et al., 2002)

A total of four separate transducer sets have been used to measure specific points of interest, which focus on both restrained and unrestrained wood. The restrained wood consists of planks in the ship hull held together with iron rivets on each edge. In addition, two unrestrained samples have been chosen as references, to establish the behavior of wood free from physical restraint. All measurements are taken on radial sections and record movement across the grain. The planks chosen do not, as far as possible, contain cracks or breaks. The end grains of the two unrestrained samples were sealed with aluminum foil so that only movement due to penetration of water across the grain is measured. The unrestrained samples were placed in the ship.

The four measurement points include:
- an oak plank in the upper part of the hull, under low stress ('upper ship')
- an oak plank in the lower part, under high stress due to the accumulated weight from the overlying planks ('lower ship') (Hørte, T. et al., 2005)
- an oak sample previously cut from the ship for dendrochronological dating ('dendro oak')
- a modern oak sample with the same thickness as the above sample ('fresh oak').

3. Preliminary Results

The unrestrained samples show the greatest response to the variations in RH and T (see figure 2). The fresh oak reacts more rapidly than the dendro oak sample, however the span of movement is approximately the same: fresh oak has up to 0,5% dimensional change in arc length while the dendro oak sample has about 0,4-0,45% dimensional change. The delayed and slightly lower response to moisture of the dendro oak sample in relation to the fresh oak sample is possibly due to the presence of linseed oil and creosote on its surface.

The restrained wood from the lower part of the ship's hull is the least responsive but it still follows the general trend of varying with RH. The response of the plank from the upper ship's to changes in climate (0.2 % dimensional change) is greater than that observed in the plank from the lower ship's hull (about 0.15% dimensional change).

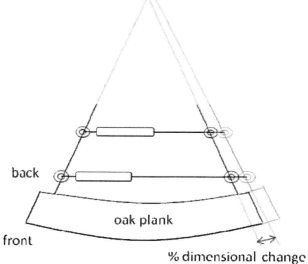

back

oak plank

front

% dimensional change

Figure 1. *The set-up of one transducer for the 'dendro oak' sample and its placement in the Oseberg ship. The diagram (Figure 2) below shows how dimensional change was measured.*

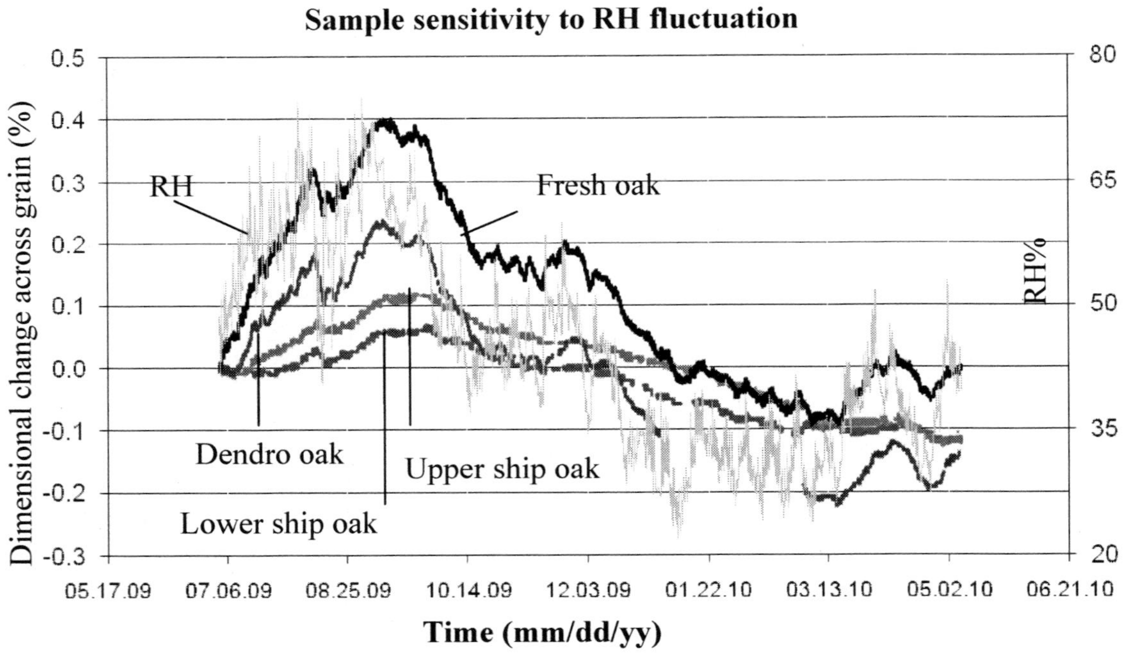

Sample sensitivity to RH fluctuation

Figure 2. Four transducer sets were installed. Two sets, the 'fresh oak' and 'dendro oak' samples are physically unrestrained and are therefore freer to react to changes in RH in the room. Two sets, the 'lower ship oak' and 'upper ship oak' are restrained by rivets used to reconstruct the ship in 1907. In the 'dendro oak' sample, there is a portion of data missing, due to connection problems in the transducer set.

4. Conclusion

Preliminary results show that the fresh wood is slightly more reactive to environmental changes than the archaeological oak treated with linseed oil and creosote. Although all four measuring sites show the same general trend in the wood's dimensional response to changes in RH and T, we found a clear distinction between the unrestrained and restrained samples. The lowest dimensional response was recorded in the wood under greatest loading ('lower ship'). However the measurement site in the upper ship also had significantly lower dimensional response than in the unrestrained samples. This indicates the absorption of stresses in the restrained wood since they are prevented from moving. Further work should be done to evaluate whether the absorbed stresses are a source of damage.

Acknowledgements

The authors would like to thank Professor Luca Uzielli, Department of Forest Environmental Sciences and Technologies, University of Florence, for his advice and interest in this project. We would like to thank COST-Action IE0601, Wood Science for Cultural Heritage, for providing the financial support for our collaboration. Thanks are also extended to the Metropolitan Museum of Art, NYC, for covering the travel costs for one author to present the poster at ICOM-CC's WOAM Triennial meeting, 2010.

NOTES

[1]. Gnumeric is a free-software spreadsheet oriented to scientific analysis, released under the GPL license and freely downloadable at http://projects.gnome.org/gnumeric/

REFERENCES

Dionisi Vici P., Fioravanti M., and L. Uzielli (2002), Monitoring moisture-induced deformations of panel paintings: reasons, requirements and suggested equipment, Art 2002, 7th International Conference on Non-Destructive Testing and Microanalysis for the Diagnostics and Conservation of the

Cultural and Environmental Heritage, Antwerp, June 2002.

Hørte, T., Sund, O., Ronold, K. & H. Rove, (2005), Styrkeanalyse av Osebergskipet, Rapport nr. 2005-1615, revisjon nr. 02, Det Norske Veritas (DNV), internal report delivered to the Museum of Cultural History, UiO.

Thomson, G., (1978), The Museum Environment, London, Butterworth's, pp 118.

Uzielli L., Fioravanti M., Casazza O., and G. Perucca, (1992), A technique for double-sided monitoring of the deformations of the wooden support of panel paintings: the experience of Giotto's Maestà di Ognissanti, Conference Acts Art92, Viterbo, 1992, pp. 501-514.

2D

Mapping PEG Diffusion into Waterlogged Wood Samples

Anthony Kennedy*
East Carolina University, Department of Chemistry, Greenville, NC 27858
*E-mail: kennedyan@ecu.edu

Jessica Bingham, Rohan Patel and Sanjana Vasnani
East Carolina University, Department of Chemistry, Greenville, NC 27858

Sarah Watkins-Kenney and Shanna Daniel
NC Department of Cultural Resources, Underwater Archaeology Branch, Queen Anne's Revenge Conservation Laboratory, ECU West Research Campus, Greenville, NC 27834

Abstract
The overall goal of this research project is to map PEG diffusion into waterlogged wood. The first step in this process was to develop and validate a rapid method for determining PEG concentrations in wood, ideally with little or no sample preparation. We examined a series of PEG / Water infrared spectra to find a suitable absorption band for this purpose. A calibration curve was produced and used to predict the % PEG in waterlogged samples.

Introduction
The most widely used technique currently being used to preserve waterlogged wood involves passive replacement of the water with Polyethylene Glycol. Artifacts may need to be soaked for several years in order to obtain complete diffusion and homogeneous dispersion of the PEG within the wood. The diffusion rate of the PEG is affected by many factors and it is therefore difficult to optimize the process. It may be that a suitable dispersion of PEG within the wood could have been obtained in less time. Our aim is to determine quantitatively the rate of diffusion of PEG within waterlogged wood and develop a series of equations which may be used to determine the optimum soaking time for any given piece. Our initial work was focused on trying to determine a fast and efficient way to determine the PEG concentration deep within the wood. ATR infrared spectroscopy was chosen for this purpose as it is a relatively robust reliable technique requiring little to no sample preparation. Our goal was to develop a method requiring no sample preparation.

ATR Spectroscopy
In ATR infrared spectroscopy a fleeting 'evanescent' wave interacts with a sample which is placed in optical contact with an internal reflection element. The depth of penetration of that wave is dependent upon the refractive index of the crystal and the sample as well as the wavelength. It may be measured using the following equation;

$$d_p = \frac{\lambda}{2\pi \left(n_1^2 sin^2\theta - n_2^2\right)^{\frac{1}{2}}}$$

where dp is the depth of penetration. If a crystal with a large refractive index (n1) is chosen then slight changes in the sample refractive index (n2) should be well tolerated and not result in significant changes in the depth of penetration and hence the path length. One should therefore not have to be concerned with preparing samples with repeatable path lengths and given the right conditions no sample preparation should be necessary. A schematic of an ATR assembly is shown below in Figure 1.

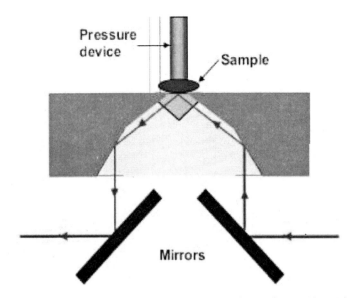

Figure 1. Schematic of ATR Crystal

Methods

A core sample of wood from the hull timbers of the Beaufort Inlet Shipwreck (31CR314), believed to be Queen Anne's Revenge, was examined. The core sample was cut into 10 segments each approximately 1cm long. Each sample was numbered 1 through 10. Samples 1 and 10 therefore represent the outer surface of the wood sample. This surface would be in direct contact with the PEG soaking solution. Samples 5 and 6 would therefore represent the innermost portion of the wood and the samples furthest from the wood surface. It would be reasonable to assume that the samples could be divided into two groups which should have the same PEG concentrations. Samples 6-10 were dried in an oven at 60°C until a constant weight was obtained. The PEG was then extracted from each sample according to a previously reported procedure (Mortensen 2007) again until a constant dry weight was obtained. The extraction typically took 6 hours to complete. The composition of the segment may be determined by simple gravimetric analysis using this method. The data obtained from this approach is shown in Figure 2.

ATR Infrared spectra were then obtained on samples 1-5. No sample preparation was necessary. The segments were simply placed under constant pressure against a diamond internal reflection element (~3mm2 area). Spectra were acquired as the average of 256 scans at 4cm-1 resolution.

A series of PEG / Water standards were then prepared and examined in the same way.

Results and Conclusion

In order to build a suitable calibration curve it was important to find an absorption band in the infrared spectrum of the standards that responded in a clearly measurable manner over a wide range of concentrations. The water bands at ~3500cm-1 and ~ 1600cm-1 cannot be used as the position and shape of this combination band varies significantly due to hydrogen bonding, changes in bound water versus free water, temperature,

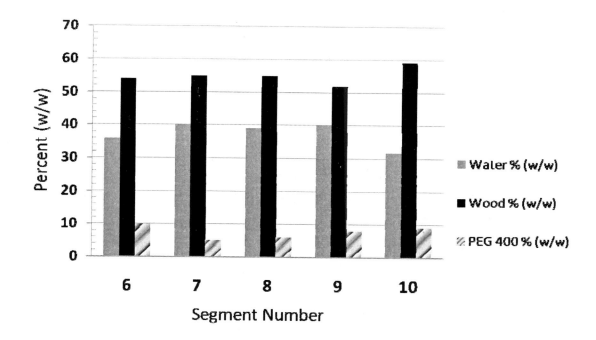

Figure 2. *Gravimetric Analysis Results*

ionic strength and environment. After careful examination of the spectra the band at ~1350cm-1 was chosen. The frequency of maximum absorption of this band varied no more than 0.5cm-1. Furthermore, this band did not appear to change significantly with moderate changes in the ambient room temperature. This band corresponds to the ether C-O-C stretching vibration in PEG. Prior to analysis the spectra were normalized to set the water absorption band at 3500cm-1 to unity. Spectra were then baseline corrected in the spectral window around the ether band (~1295-1400cm-1). The result of these spectra can be seen in Figure 3. The corrected absorbance was then plotted versus the PEG concentration to generate the calibration curve (Figure 4) which was used to determine %v/v PEG in an aqueous environment

Based on the gravimetric analysis it was determined that the %w/w PEG 400 in each segment was ~10%w/w based on the weight of each component. However the % based on the weight of solvents only was 20%w/w. This would indicate that the PEG 400 had diffused completely throughout the wood. Small variations were seen but these can be explained by variations in the porosity and characteristics of the wood.

The PEG / Water spectra showed several promising absorbance bands but the only band that fit the initial criteria was that due to the ether stretching frequency. This band (Figure 3) not only responded in a linear fashion (Figure 4) over a wide concentration range but it also appeared relatively unaffected by small environmental changes.

After analysis of our wood samples we determined using our calibration curve that the %v/v PEG 400 was ~22.5±1.5% w/w which is in good agreement with the gravimetric data indicating that this technique shows promise as a tool for rapid analysis. In theory a very small sample of wood may be analyzed using this technique top accurately determine when the PEG 400 has diffused completely throughout the wood. It is hoped that with

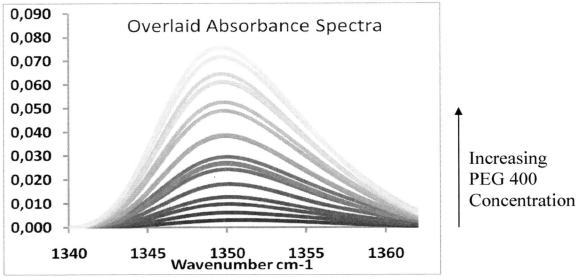

Figure 3. *Infrared Calibration Data*

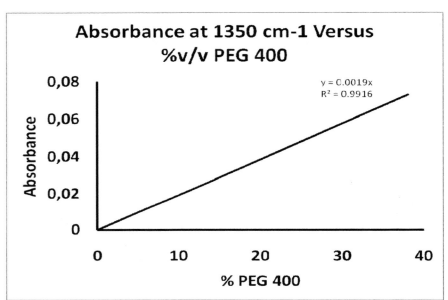

Figure 4. *Infrared Calibration Curve*

some refining and fine tuning one may be able to simply place an optical probe inside the wood and determine the PEG concentration in the wood directly.

Acknowledgements
The authors wish to acknowledge support from ECU in the form of start-up funds. We would also like to thank Dr. Kenney (ECU, Dept. of Physics) for helpful discussion as well as all of the staff working on the QAR conservation project and the NC Department of Cultural Resources.

References:
Martin Nordvig Mortensen, Helge Egsgaard, Søren Hvilsted, Yvonne Shashoua, Jens Glastrup (2007): Characterization of the polyethylene glycol impregnation of the Swedish warship Vasa and one of the Danish Skuldelev Viking ships. Journal of Archaeological Science, Volume 34, Issue 8, August 2007, Pages 1211-1218

3.1

Bacteria/Fungi: A Growing Concern for Waterlogged Wood Storage

Shanna L. Daniel*,

QAR Conservator North Carolina *Queen Anne's Revenge* (QAR) Conservation Lab, NC Department Cultural Resources, Office of State Archaeology, Underwater Archaeology Branch, East Carolina University-West Research Campus, 1157 VOA Site C Road,Greenville, NC 27889
E-mail*: shanna.daniel@ncdcr.gov

James M. Rolston,

QAR Conservator Technician North Carolina *Queen Anne's Revenge* (QAR) Conservation Lab, NC Department Cultural Resources, Office of State Archaeology, Underwater Archaeology Branch, East Carolina University-West Research Campus, 1157 VOA Site C Road, Greenville, NC 27889

Abstract

Bacteria and fungi are a growing concern in wet storage of wood artifacts and ship timbers at the *Queen Anne's Revenge* (QAR) Conservation Lab. The initial strategy of controlling microbial growth in these wet storage tanks was through regular changes of water without any biocides, but this method has proven ineffective. It was decided to investigate the use of a biocide known as Proxel™ BD20, a biocide similar to Kathon° CG. Preliminary tests were conducted to determine the effectiveness of this biocide in preventing microbial growth in various solutions used in waterlogged wood storage. Results indicated that Proxel™ BD20 could be effective in controlling the growth of bacteria and fungi in wet wood storage tanks.

Keywords: waterlogged wood, biocide, wet storage, microbes, Kathon° CG, Proxel™ BD20

1. Introduction

Wood artifacts recovered from wet environments are usually kept wet prior to conservation to prevent any shrinkage and distortion, which is likely to occur if allowed to dry without appropriate treatment [Mouzouras 1987, Ravindra et al. 1980). Conditions in long term wet storage, however, can also be ideal for microbe growth, such as fungi, bacteria, and algae, which can cause further biodeterioration of archaeological wet wood. These organisms attach to the wood's cellular structure causing irreversible effects which weaken the integrity of archaeological wood (Unger et al. 1980).

The QAR Lab is tasked with conserving artifacts recovered from an early 18th century shipwreck, identified as Blackbeard the pirate's flagship *Queen Anne's Revenge*, which sank in Beaufort Inlet, North Carolina in 1718 (Moore 1997, Lawrence et al. 2001). Wood artifacts from the wreck including parts of the ship's hull structure have been recovered and transported to the QAR lab for further archaeological investigations and conservation (Moore, 2001).

After recovery from the wreck site, wood artifacts are stored immersed in either tap water or reverse osmosis (RO) water in large fiberglass tanks or covered Rubbermaid containers (Watkins-Kenney et al. 2005).Most of the large ship timbers are stored in fiberglass tanks located in the QAR lab's warehouse and covered with tarpaulins, while smaller wood artifacts are placed in various size covered containers and stored in a, fridge to deter microbial growth.

In 2003, some of the QAR ship timbers (oak hull planks QAR419.000 and QAR436.000, oak frame QAR427.000, and pine sheathing plank QAR440.000) were examined for bacteria and fungi. All pieces were heavily decomposed with a softened outside layer due to bacteria disintegrating the S2 layer of the wood cell wall but leaving the middle lamellae and tertiary walls intact (Watkins-Kenney et al. 2005). On hull plank QAR436.000, fruiting bodies of ascomycete (*Ceriosporopsis* cfr. *Halima*) and traces of marine fungi were detected (Kohlmeyer 2008).

Until 2008, the lab's strategy to control growth in the storage tanks was through regular changes of the either tap or RO water (Watkins-Kenney et al. 2005). However, visible microbe colonies were still growing in the tanks, and with the recovery of the stern post in 2007 (see Figure 1) it was decided to investigate the feasibility of using a biocide/fungicide.

Figure 1. *Recovery of Sternpost from QAR wreck site. (Photo Courtesy of N.C. Department of Cultural Resources/ Wendy Welsh)*

2. Searching for a Biocide/Fungicide

Conservators have tried various biocides or fungicides, such as adesol, dowicide, entachlorophenate, or borax to deter microbe growth (Bjordal and Nilsson 2001). Many of these biocides or fungicides have a toxic effect on humans and the environment, so conservators are now turning to a more environmentally friendly way to decrease microbial growth while wood is in wet storage.

The *QAR* Lab, located at East Carolina University's (ECU) West Research Campus, is surrounded by a protected wetland environment with no municipal sewer system. This posed a challenge to find a biocide that complied with both United States Environmental Protection Agency (EPA) and the ECU Environment Health and Safety requirements. Many of the biocides commonly used with waterlogged wood were deemed too toxic for use at the *QAR* lab. The primary objective was to find an environmentally friendly biocide/fungicide effective enough to decrease the growth.

Effectiveness, resistance, toxicity, and compatibility are several factors to consider before selecting a biocide (Dawson 1982). One biocide meeting these factors is Kathon[®] CG. Successful use of Kathon[®] CG, an isothiazolin, for conservation purposes has been reported (Morgos et al. 1993, Sakai et al. 1996. Attempts to procure this biocide from Rohm & Haas, for use at the *QAR* Lab, were unsuccessful, as its proposed method and purpose of use were not covered by U.S. EPA regulations (Gordon 2008). Further searching led to an organic biocide commercially known as Proxel[TM] BD20 manufactured by the Arch Chemical Corporation in Atlanta, Georgia, USA. It is similar to Kathon[®] CG but its active site is a benzyl group rather than a chlorine (see Figure 2 and 3). This biocide is an aqueous dispersion solution consisting of 1, 2-benzisothiazolin-3-one and is an efficient microbiostate preservative for any water base solution (Arch Chemical Incorporation, 2004). It will break down into its non-harmful components naturally in 9 months or when it is exposed long-term to Ultra Violet (UV) or sunlight, which is unlike biocides based on heavy metals that never break down (Brown, 2009, 2010).

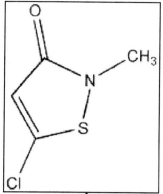

Figure 2. Kathon® CG chemical structure

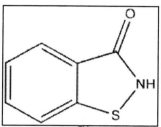

Figure 3. Proxel™ BD20 chemical structure

A previous study examined a 1, 2-benzisothiazolin-3-one biocide on wood in stable wet storage. However, their study did not show a decrease in microbial growth due to the experiment's low concentration of biocide at 0.03% (Sakai et al. 1996). Since there has had limited testing on Proxel™ BD20 with archaeological materials, the *QAR* lab conducted preliminary tests to assess its effectiveness for archaeological waterlogged wood in three different solutions: sea water, tap water and water purified by reverse osmosis treatment (RO). After eight weeks, the preliminary tests were complete and observations were reported. A large scale experiment on Proxel™ BD20 is currently being conducted in wet storage tanks containing *QAR* ship hull structure.

3. Methodology

The experiment consisted of testing Proxel™ BD20's effectiveness, resistance, toxicity, and compatibility in sea water (SW), tap water (TW), and reverse osmosis (RO) water.

For each solution tested there were four variables (see Table 1):
1. Solution
2. Solution + wood sample
3. Solution + biocide (0.1% volume/volume)
4. Solution + wood sample + biocide (0.1% volume/volume)

Wood samples were taken from unprovenienced wood recovered from the *QAR* wreck site. According to Arch Chemical, a concentration within the range of 0.02% – 0.35% is sufficient to protect against bacterial attack (Arch Chemical Incorporation, (2004). A concentration of 0.1% of Proxel™ BD20 was chosen because it was between the ranges stated by Arch Chemical.

3.1 Methodology: Sample and Solution Preparation

Six unprovenienced pieces were cut from a large fragment of wood from the *QAR* wreck site into 1.3 centimeter cubes (cm^3). Photographs, weights (in grams), measurements (in inches) and pin tests were obtained for each wood sample. Pin test is a quick way to evaluate the wood's structural integrity by inserting a straight pin into the wood to see how far it will go before hitting resistance. This test revealed that the structural stability varied slightly among all six wood pieces, but overall the wood was not very deteriorated.

Twelve test tubes were cleaned thoroughly with boiled RO water to ensure a sterile environment. Each test tube received 30 milliliters of solution and was capped with a cotton ball and perforated aluminum foil. All test tubes were weighed (in grams), photographed with a color scale, and pH readings were obtained using Hydrion™ pH paper with a 1 to 12 scale, before the experiment began. The test tubes were placed in an environment similar to conditions found in the wet storage of *QAR* wood to encourage microbial growth by keeping all solution samples in an

Table 1. *Test Tube Contents.*

Sample ID	Sample Solution	Control	Proxel BD20 0.1%
TW1	TW	x	
TW2	TW + Wood	x	
TW3	TW + Biocide		x
TW4	TW + Biocide + Wood		x
SW1	SW	x	
SW2	SW + wood	x	
SW3	SW + Biocide		x
SW4	SW + wood + Biocide		x
RO1	RO Water	x	
RO2	RO water + wood	x	
RO3	RO water + Biocide		x
RO4	RO water + Biocide + wood		x

Key: TW = Tap Water SW = Sea water

environment with ambient temperature and fluctuating relative humidity.

3.2 Methodology: Solution Monitoring

Various aspects were monitored and documented weekly for eight weeks. Weights of the test tubes including the contents (wood and solution), color of solution compared to *The Munsell Plant Tissue Color Chart,* and solution levels (in inches) were recorded. Also, photographs were taken for each test tube group with a color scale to monitor the solution's change in color (see Figure 4). Observation of each solution's appearance was examined and any changes noted, especially when growth appeared.

3.3 Methodology: After Experiment

At the end of the eight week period, all test tube groups were photographed with a color scale. Weights, solution levels, solution's color, and pH were obtained from all test tube samples. Next, each wood sample was removed from the test tube and weights and measurements were recorded for each.

Figure 4. *Test Tube Groups Tap Water, Sea Water, and RO water with a color scale (shown in B&W). (Photo Courtesy of N.C. Department of Cultural Resources/Shanna Daniel and Myron Rolston)*

4. Observations Proxel™ BD20 Experiment

4.1 Tap Water

The following observations were noted with test samples TW1, TW2, TW3, and TW4 after testing was completed.

- Sample containing a wood piece and biocide (TW4) showed a change in the solution color when compared to the control sample (TW2) containing a wood piece with no biocide (see Table 2).
- Sample containing just the biocide (TW3) showed a change in solution color when compared to the control sample containing only tap water (TW1) (see Table 2).
- Samples with no biocide in the solution (TW1 and TW2) showed a decrease in pH after the experiment from 7 to 6.5 (see Figure 5).
- Samples with biocide in the solution (TW3 and TW4) showed an increase in pH after the experiment from 7 to 7.5 (see Figure 5).
- Sample TW2 containing the wood piece without the biocide showed a slight decrease in the wood's weight from 1.77 to 1.70 grams. Sample TW4 containing the wood piece with the biocide showed no weight change in wood weight.
- Wood piece measurements varied only slightly for both the control piece (TW2) and the piece with the biocide (TW4) (see Table 3).
- No visible degradation to the wood was noticed when viewed under a microscope.
- There was no visible microbial growth on all tap water samples during the experiment.

4. 2 Sea Water Results

The following observations were noted with test samples SW1, SW2, SW3, and SW4 after the testing was completed:

- Sample containing a wood piece and biocide (SW4) showed a change in the solution color when compared to the control sample (SW2) containing a wood piece with no biocide (see Table 4).
- Sample containing just the biocide (SW3) showed a change in solution color when compared to the control sample containing only sea water (SW1) (see Table 4).
- Samples with no biocide in the solution (SW1 and SW2) showed a decrease in pH after the experiment from 6.5 to 6 (see Figure 7).
- Samples with biocide in the solution (SW3 and SW4) showed no decrease or increase in pH after the experiment (see Figure 7).
- Sample SW2 containing the wood piece without the biocide showed an increase in the wood's weight from 1.75 to 2.00 grams. Sample SW4 containing the wood piece with the biocide also showed a slight increase change in wood weight from 2.11 to 2.30 grams (see Figure 8)
- Wood piece measurements varied only slightly for both the control piece (TW2) and the piece with the biocide (TW4) (see Table 5).
- No visible degradation to the wood was noticed when viewed under a microscope.
- There was no visible evidence of microbial growth on all sea water samples during the experiment.

4.3 Reverse Osmosis (RO) Water Results

The following observations were noted with test samples RO1, RO2, RO3, and RO4 after testing was completed.

- Sample containing a wood piece and biocide (RO4) showed a change in the solution color when compared to the control sample (RO2) containing a wood piece with no biocide (see Table 6). Unlike in the control samples (TW2 and SW2), there was

171

Table 2. Munsell Plant Tissue Color for tap water samples

Sample ID	Munsell Color - before	Munsell Color - after
TW1	Clear	Clear
TW2	Lighter than 2.5Y 8/2	2.5Y 8/4
TW3	Lighter than 2.5Y 8/2	2.5Y 8/2
TW4	2.5Y 8/4 -8/6	2.5Y 8/4 -8/6

Table 3. Wood piece measurements for tap water samples

Sample ID	Wood measurements before (length x width x thickness) in inches	Wood measurements after (length x width x thickness) in inches
TW 2	0.65" x 0.53" x 0.30"	0.65" x 0.53" x 0.37
TW4	0.65" x 0.57" x 0.44"	0.65" x 0.52" x 0.41"

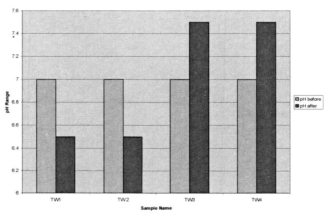

Figure 5. The before and after pH of tap water samples.

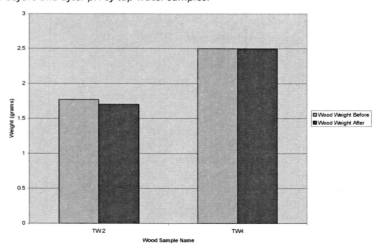

Figure 6. The before and after weight of wood in tap water samples.

172

Table 4. *Munsell Plant Tissue Color for sea water samples*

Sample ID	Munsell Color - before	Munsell Color - after
SW1	Clear	Clear
SW2	Clear	Lighter than 2.5Y 8/2
SW3	Lighter than 2.5Y 8/2	Lighter than 2.5Y 8/2

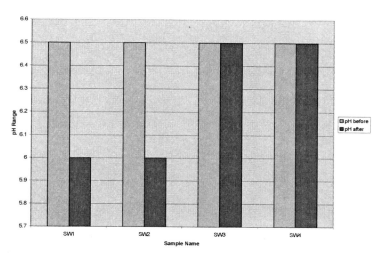

Figure 7. *The before and after pH of sea water samples.*

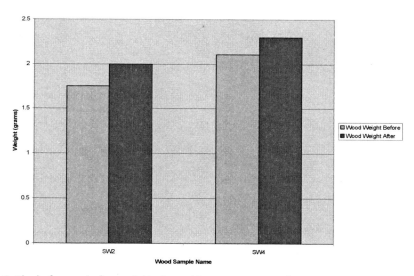

Figure 8. *The before and after weight of wood in sea water samples.*

Table no. 5: *Wood piece measurements for sea water samples.*

Sample ID	Wood measurements before (length x width x thickness) in inches	Wood measurements after (length x width x thickness) in inches
SW2	0.78" x 0.50" x 0.42"	0.73" x 0.52" x 0.43"
SW4	0.58" x 0.58" x 0.50"	0.57" x 0.57" x 0.51"

Table no. 6: *Munsell Plant Tissue Color for RO water samples*

Sample ID	Munsell Color - before	Munsell Color - after
RO1	Clear	Clear
RO2	Lighter than 2.5Y 8/2	Lighter than 2.5Y 8/2
RO3	lighter than 2.5Y 8/2	lighter than 2.5Y 8/2
RO4	2.5Y 8/2 -8/4	25Y 8/4

no change in the sample with a wood piece without biocide (RO2) from the beginning to the end of the experiment.

- Sample containing just the biocide (RO3) showed a change in solution color when compared to the control sample containing only RO water (RO1) (see Table 6).
- Sample with no biocide in the solution (RO1) showed a decrease in pH after the experiment from 6 to 5 (see Figure 9).
- Sample with wood but no biocide in the solution (RO2) showed no increase or decrease in pH unlike samples TW2 and SW2 with a decrease in pH (see Figure 9).
- Sample with biocide in the solution (RO3) showed a decrease in pH after the experiment from 6 to 5, unlike samples TW3 and SW3 which showed either an increase or no change in pH (see Figure 9).
- Sample with biocide and wood (RO4) showed an increase in pH from 6 to 6.5 (see Figure 9).
- Samples RO2 containing the wood piece without the biocide showed a slight increase in the wood's weight from 1.87 to 2.10 grams. Sample RO4 containing the wood piece with the biocide showed a slight decrease in weight from 2.48 to 2.40 grams (see Figure 10).
- Wood piece measurements varied only slightly for both the control

piece (RO2) and the piece with the biocide (RO4) (see Table 7).

- No visible degradation to the wood was noticed when viewed under a microscope.
- There was no visible evidence of microbial growth on any RO water samples during the experiment.

4.4 Overall Results of Proxel™ BD20

Preliminary testing indicated that over eight weeks Proxel™ BD20 could be successful in decreasing the growth of bacteria and fungi in the sample solutions. The following is a summary of the results of Proxel™ BD20 used in tap water, sea water, and RO water.

- This biocide can have an effect on the pH, but does not cause harm to the wood.
- It does affect the color of the solution slightly when compared to the controls (see Tables 2, 4, and 6).
- There was a slight change in the wood's weight to samples containing the biocide (TW4, SW4, RO4,) (see Figures 6, 8, and 10).
- There was a slight change in the wood's measurements before and after the experiment in both the control and test samples.
- No visible degradation of the wood samples with Proxel™ BD20 when viewed under a microscope.

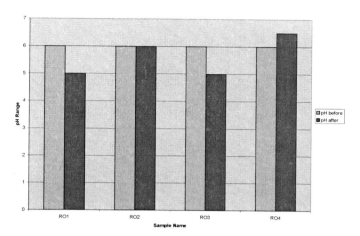

Figure 9. *The before and after pH of RO water samples.*

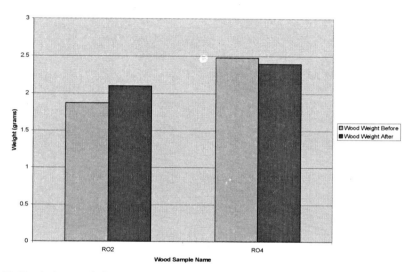

Figure 10. *The before and after weight of wood in RO water samples.*

Table 7. *Wood piece measurements for RO water samples.*

Sample ID	Wood measurements before (length x width x thickness) in inches	Wood measurements after (length x width x thickness) in inches
RO2	0.57" x 0.44" x 0.47"	0.56" x 0.57" x 0.43"
RO4	0.57" x 0.52" x 0.57"	0.57" x 0.56" x 0.54"

5. Proxel™ BD20: Testing in Large Storage Tanks

The results from the small scale test indicated that Proxel™ BD20 could be effective in controlling the growth of bacteria and fungi on wood in large storage tanks. Given this finding, a large scale study using this biocide is being conducted in three of the large wood storage tanks. These tanks contain part of the *QAR*'s ship timbers (see Figure 11), which include the hull planks, sacrificial planks, and stern post (see Figure 12 and 13). In each of these tanks, there have been noticeable fungal hyphae, white fruiting bodies, and biofilm at the liquid/air interface.

175

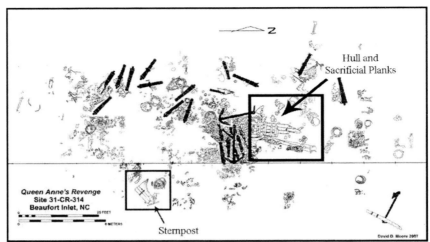

Figure 11. *Illustration showing location of QAR ship timbers in-situ. (Courtesy of N.C. Department of Cultural Resources/David Moore)*

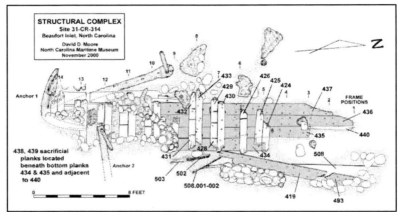

Figure 12. *Illustration showing QAR hull planks and sacrificial planks in-situ. (Courtesy of N.C. Department of Cultural Resource/ David Moore)*

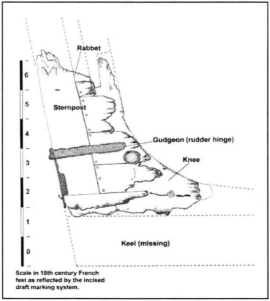

Figure 13: Illustration of QAR stern post. (Courtesy of N.C. Department of Cultural Resources/David Moore)

176

Testing began in the fall of 2008 with a low concentration of 0.02% by volume of Proxel[TM] BD20 in either tap water (sternpost tank) or RO water (hull and sacrificial planks). This concentration was chosen to see how effective the biocide would be on waterlogged archaeological wood at the lowest concentration standard set by Arch Chemical(Arch Chemical Incorporation, (2004). After one month, microbial growth was still visible. The concentration was increased to a 0.2% concentration in the tanks containing the stern post and sacrificial planking. The hull plank tank was left at a 0.02% for comparison. This concentration was suggested by Scott Brown, Arch Chemical BP Technical Group Leader, as a feasible threshold level for microbial degradation. After extensive trials by Arch Chemicals, 0.02% of Proxel[TM] BD20 was found to be the least amount of product needed for protection of pure water from bacterial growth. Larger quantities of the biocide would be necessary if there are nutrients in solution which would foster microbial growth (Brown 2009; Brown 2010)

During a six-month period, observable changes were noted in all three wood storage tanks. The solution's color gradually became a dark brown hue due to the added biocide when compared to tap or RO water's clear hue. The most observable change was with the tank holding the stern post. Fungal hyphae were no longer visible on the wood and no biofilm was present at the liquid/air interface. These observations were only providing results seen visually with the naked eye. The next stage was to see what Proxel[TM] BD20 was doing at the micro-scale.

5.1. Testing Solutions from Large Storage Tanks

Water samples were obtained from all three wood storage tanks and sent to Arch Chemical Laboratory to be analyzed for any bacteria or fungi (see Table 8).

In addition, the lab's tap water was analyzed by the local water supplier, Bell Arthur Water Corporation, for any sign of human pathogenic microbes. The result was 372 Colony Forming Units (CFU). This quantity was within normal parameters for potable water. The limited scope of the Bell Arthur analysis suggests a nutrient level in the water that supports microbe populations, but was unable to identify the species of microbe (Baldree, 2009).

These results were intriguing and brought about a new round of questions for the Arch Chemical's technical team. The main question was why there were considerable quantities of microbes still present in the hull plank and stern post tanks since both contained the biocide (Brown, 2009). The high number of microbes within the hull plank tank was due to the low concentration of biocide at 0.02% used for a seemingly large tank. With a high microbial population within a wet storage

Table 8. *Results for bacteria and fungi in wood storage tanks, which were examined by Arch Chemical, Inc. Laboratory.*

Storage Tank Number	Artifact(s): Ship Timbers	DPC (CFU) TSA*	PDA*	BIT*
Tank 1	Sacrificial Planks	<10	not test	118 ppm
Tank 2	Hull Planks	2.86×10^4	no fungi	11 ppm
Tank 46	Stern Post	2.68×10^4	no fungi	345 ppm

TSA = Trypticase Soy Agar Plates for bacteria growth

PDA = Potato Dextrose Agar Plates for fungi growth

BIT = measurement of active Proxel in parts per million

tank, it can overwhelm the concentration of biocide rendering it useless.

As for the stern post tank, 0.2% of biocide was an effective concentration for this tank, but other variables could have been contributing to the increase in microbial growth. The absence of circulation allowed the water to become stagnant and thus, triggered microbial growth. This is especially a factor if there are any materials rich in nutrients, such as archaeological wood, within the uncirculated tank. This allows colonies of microbes to proliferate over time and break through the Proxel™ BD20 coating allowing more growth to occur without having contact with the biocide. Additionally, tap water could be a factor by providing the nutrients for growth. The Bell Arthur examination showed that water treatment does not remove all microbes and frequent water changes could be adding more microbes to the solution. Reverse osmosis (RO) water with Proxel™ BD20 would be best to use because of its low level of nutrients, which would not support microbial growth even with other materials rich in nutrients.

Figure 9. James Myron Rolston collecting samples from the sternpost for DNA identification analysis. (Courtesy of N.C. Department of Cultural Resources/Shanna Daniel)

5.2 Identifying the Microbes

Research is still in progress to identify the species of bacteria and/or fungi present in the storage tanks. Helms (2004) states "it is essential to know our enemies before we can fight against them and potentially overrule them". To find out which microbes are present that could be detrimental to the archaeological wood, the *QAR* lab has teamed up with Dr. Matthew Schrenk, Assistant Professor of Biology at ECU. Samples have been collected (see Figure 9) and submitted for DNA identification.

6. Recommendations for Improving the Effective use of Proxel

After discussions with colleagues at ECU and Arch Chemicals, a number of ways to improve the effective use of Proxel™ BD20 in controlling microbial growth have been suggested. Ideally, the tanks should be thoroughly cleaned first. At least a 0.2% by volume of the biocide in RO water should be dissolved completely and directly in the tank before wood is added. It is best to keep the tanks covered, so the biocide is not exposed long-term to Ultra Violet (UV) or sunlight. With these procedures in place, this should decrease the amount of microbial growth in tanks without the laborious task of frequently changing out wet storage tanks.

7. Conclusion

Proxel™ BD20 has many positive attributes as a biocide in storage tanks holding wet archaeological wood. The eight-week preliminary study showed Proxel™ BD20 to be effective in controlling microbial growth when using the right concentration. Most importantly, the biocide is environmentally safe because it naturally breaks down in nine months or when exposed long-term to UV or sunlight. For several months, a larger scale study using Proxel™ BD20 in some of the lab's large wet storage tanks containing *QAR* ship timbers has proven partially successful and much has been learned from discussions with colleagues about how to improve its effectiveness in this application. With these new insights into the use of Proxel™ BD20, a few changes will be made to its application on the larger scale and monitoring of its effectiveness will continue.

Acknowledgments

The authors and the *QAR* Conservation Laboratory staff would like to express thanks to Jim Loricchio, Arch Chemical Inc. Account Manager; Scott Brown, Arch Chemical BP Technical Group Leader, Dr. Matthew Schrenk, Assistant Professor of Biology at ECU; and North Carolina Department of Cultural Resources and the North Carolina Underwater Archaeology Branch.

Products

Proxel™ BD20
Arch Chemical Inc.
Corporate Headquarters
501 Merritt 7
PO Box 5204
Norwalk, CT 06856
USA
1-203-229-2900
www.archchemcials.com

Kathon® CG
Rohm and Haas
Dow Chemical Customer Information Group
Dow Ashman Center
4520 Ashman Street
Midland, Michigan 48642
USA
1-800-447-4369
www.rhpersonalcare.com

References

Arch Chemical Incorporation, (2004), Proxel BD20- Technical Information Bulletin, Cheshire, Arch Biocides

Baldree, Ray, (2009), personal communications, Bell Arthur, North Carolina, Bell Arthur Water Corp

Bjordal, G.C and T. Nilsson, (2001), Observation of Microbial Growth during Conservation Treatment of Waterlogged Archaeological Wood, Studies in Conservation, Vol 46, No 3, 2001, pp 211-220

Brown, Scott, (2009), personal communication, New Castle, Delaware, Arch Chemical Corporation

Brown, Scott, (2010), personal communication, New Castle, Delaware, Arch Chemical Corporation

Dawson, John, (1982), Some Considerations in Choosing a Biocide, Proceedings of the ICOM Waterlogged Wood Working Group Conference, Ottawa, International Council of Museums (ICOM), Waterlogged Wood Working Group, 1981, pp 269-277

Gordon, Sam, (2008), personal communication, Philadelphia, Pennsylvania, Rohm and Hoss Company

Helms, Anne Christine, (2004), Chosen Strategies for Identification and Verification of Wood Inhabiting Microorganisms, in Hoffmann and Straetkvern (editors), Proceedings of the 9th ICOM Group on Wet Organic Archaeological Materials Conferences, Copenhagen, International Council of Museums (ICOM), Committee for Conservation Working Group on Wet Organic Archaeological Materials, 2004, pp 119-125

Kohlmeyer, Jan, (2003), Result of Microscopic Examination of Samples from "Queen Anne's Revenge", Institute of Marine Sciences – University of North Carolina Chapel Hill, Morehead City, North Carolina, http://www.qaronline.org/rcorner/envi.htm

Lawrence, Richard W. and Wilde-Ramsing M., (2001), In Search of Blackbeard:

Historical and Archaeological Research of Shipwreck Site 0003BUI, Southeastern Geology, Vol 40, No.1, 2001, pp 1-9.

Moore, David, (1997), Blackbeard the Pirate: Historical Background and the Beaufort Inlet Shipwrecks, Tributaries, No. 7, 1997, pp 31-39.

Moore, David, (2001), Blackbeard's *Queen Anne's Revenge*: Archaeological Interpretation and Research Focused on the Hull Remains and Ship-related Accoutrements Associated with Site 31-CR-314, Tributaries, No. , 2001, pp 49-64.

Morgos A., Strigazzi G., and Preuss H., (1993), Microbicides in Sugar Conservation of Waterlogged Archaeological Wooden Finds: The Use of Isothiazolones, in Hoffmann (editor), Proceedings of the 5th ICOM Group on Wet Organic Archaeological Materials Conference, Portland, International Council of Museums (ICOM), Committee for Conservation Working Group on Wet Organic Archaeological Materials, 1993, pp 463-484

Mouzouras, R., (1987), Problems associated with storage of waterlogged archaeological wood, in Kennedy, J.F, Phillips, G.O., Williams P.A. (editors), Wood and Cellulosics, Chichester, Ellis Horwood Limited, 1987, pp 393-400

Ravindra, R., Dawson, J.E., and Lefontanie, R.H., (1980), The Storage of Untreated Waterlogged Wood, IIC-Canadian Group Journal, Vol 5, No 1, 1980, pp 25-31

Sakai, H., Imazu, S., and Morgos, A., (1996), Protection of waterlogged wooden objects kept in water against decay, in Hoffmann, Daley, and Grant (editors), Proceedings of 6th ICOM Group on Wet Organic Archaeological Materials Conference, York, International Council of Museums (ICOM), Committee for Conservation Working

Group on Wet Organic Archaeological Materials, 1996, pp. 295-316

Unger, A., A.P. Schniewind, and W. Unger, (2001), Conservation of Wood Artifacts: A Handbook. Heidelberg, Germany, Springer-Verlag Berlin

Watkins-Kenney, Sarah, Nordgren, Eric, Welsh, Wendy, and Henry, Nathan, (2005), The *Queen Anne's Revenge* Shipwreck Project: Recovery, examination, and treatment of wood, in Hoffman, P.; Straetkvern, K.; Spriggs, J. (editors), Proceedings of the 9th ICOM Group on Wet Organic Archaeological Materials (WOAM) Conference, Copenhagen, Denmark, 2004, ICOM-CC WOAM, pp 389-402.

Questions and answers

Jim Spriggs: What is the cost of Proxel compared to Kathon?

Shanna Daniel: That's a good question. I do not know the price for Kathon off hand but Proxel is about $300 for 5 gallons but you only use 0.2%. That's very little and we actually have a lot left from that 5 gallons.

Khoi Tran: In the past we used also a biocide based on diozothaline, it is water soluble. And I wonder about your biocide is it water soluble?

Shanna Daniel: Yes it is. It takes a little time to dissolve into the water so you have to wait, but yes it is.

Khoi Tran: I wondered about the coloring of the water in your tank.

Shanna Daniel: The Proxel gives it a brown color but it doesn't affect the wood at all. It's just a brown solution.

Khoi Tran: But I mean it would be better if your tank were circulating.

Shanna Daniels: Yes, that would definitely help out as well. Unfortunately, we don't have that available for us. Although it would even be better for us since we have the availability of RO water that would probably help us out.

Howard Wellman: Shanna, you mentioned that the product breaks down in nine months or in UV or sunlight. Does that mean it breaks down in solution if it's not exposed to sunlight? So it only has a nine month use life?

Shanna Daniel: Yes. It only has a nine month use life.

Howard Wellman: So after nine months is your plan to flush the tank and replace it or go back to fresh water hoping that you've killed the population and don't have to use the product?

Shanna Daniel: That is something we're looking into. Right now what we're doing is just finishing it and reusing the biocide again until we get to that point where we can do conservation.

Jim Spriggs: And along the same vein Shanna, can I ask you have you looked at using it in combination with polyethylene glycol solutions?

Shanna Daniel: I actually have. I didn't want to put it in the scope of this paper and it's still very, very preliminary and we haven't tested it as much as we have with the just regular tap water and water solutions. Visually, the first month or so you can't see bacteria growing but then it will start to come up and I think that it's interacting with the other nutrients within the PEG. So it hasn't been completely safe but it has been tested with both PEG 400 and PEG 4000 and ammonium citrate dibasic.

Cliff Cook: One comment... Jacuzzi filters. They're designed to filter water that you hop into, so you get a lot of crud out of your water and you can circulate at the same time.

Shanna Daniel: What do they cost?

Cliff Cook: I don't know. The filter I'm familiar with we used at Parks years ago. It was, I think, a 50 micron cartridge which had 10 filter packs in it. It was a system we designed and built and it would keep the solution fairly free of slime but it would be colored. So you'd have a colored solution, junk coming out of the wood but there was no particulate matter and very little slime. The other thing you can think about too is I noticed you refrigerate your material if it's small enough. You can insulate your tanks and using a lab chiller you can actually chill your whole tank. We used to keep our 24 foot by 3 foot x 3 foot tanks at about 10° C just sitting in the lab. So you can refrigerate larger quantities of water if you want to invest in the hardware.

Shanna Daniel: If it's feasible for the project...

Cliff Cook: As I say, there's a hardware cost there, and then a power cost to run the chiller. The other question is have you looked at corrosion? I've noticed that since you've started putting your objects in you've still got some metal fastenings I presume?

Shanna Daniel: We've definitely looked at it. It's showing no corrosion effect at all visibly. We'll look into that more definitely.

Cliff Cook: Drop a nail in and see what happens.

Shanna Daniel: Yes... but we're not seeing anything.

Cliff Cook: That's a good thing.

Sarah Watkins Kenney: I just wanted to respond to the comment about trying to circulate the water in order to keep it clearer. We did try that before we looked into Proxel. In '04 and '05, we had circulation going and we were filtering the water, not through Jacuzzi filters, it was suggested to us to try it through insulator material. We found that worked for a couple of years and I think I talked about that in the '04 WOAM conference. But then having said that it seemed to be working in '04, by '06 it didn't seem to be working anymore and we were getting the fungi and the slime coming back, well the bacteria growth on the wood. That was why we then decided "well perhaps we need to step this up and look at something more than just circulating the water." And somebody suggested to us that by circulating the water we might be causing a problem. We might be making it worse because we might be oxygenating the water which would then promote growth etc....I like the chilling idea. We'll try to do something with that... especially here in North Carolina it gets pretty warm in the summer.

Jim Spriggs: We have over the years at WOAM conferences heard about other filtration based techniques for keeping solutions clean. One is ultraviolet radiation. I don't know if anyone's using that still...are they? And the other one was of course the silver ion electrode solution system. Is anybody still using that effectively? We used that in York for many years.

Liz Goodman: We presented in 2004 on displaying wood using a chilled system of water and we found that actually that would work. It was on a small scale... but it seemed to work for us.

Eric Nordgren: Sorry, just on the UV possibility I've heard that that may possibly cause the formation of ozone and I just wanted to ask anyone for their thoughts on whether that's the case or whether that might have any effect on organics or composite artifacts?

Michel Vorenhount: The ozone will help you in disinfecting the water. It's used in drinking water, so that might be a very good thing. And another thought I had is whether there is ever the possibility that you could make the system anoxic, just close it off completely, - that would kill half of your organisms.

Sarah Watkins Kenney: It would be nice...but no. You'll see this evening.

Jim Spriggs: Anoxic isn't always good.

Sarah Watkins Kenney: Well if anyone has suggestions how we might get it anoxic that would be great.

Mikkel Christenson: Just as a thought. The ozone will also be extremely chemically reactive so if you have polymers or anything in there that you plan to impregnate your wood with, it might actually start degrading the polymer very quickly. I mean I know that ozone is poisonous because it's so reactive in a way. So it might be a delicate balance.

Michel Vorenhount: In drinking water they have a system getting rid of the ozone in one area. So it's like a filtration unit that is separate. So that might be an idea but I don't know about cost.

Howard Wellman: A comment about the anoxic tanks. I've had storage tanks where they were not circulated and you got anoxic zones under the timbers and extensive black staining that then had to be removed later. So I think anoxic storage is also a tricky thing to balance.

Cliff Cook: The problem with UV sterilization is you can get a heating effect. John Gross looked at that years ago. He found the water warmed up and then you're self defeating. With warmer temperatures you get increased activity so UV can be a problem. The same kind of problem exists with any kind of mechanical movement of the water. You end up heating the water to some extent. It's going through the pump system and I think Howard said you also get oxygenation too because your turbulence at the pump impellers will result in you ending up with higher levels of O_2 in the water. So that can be a problem also.

A strategy for testing impregnation agents for waterlogged archaeological wood - examination of azelaic acid.

Nanna Bjerregaard Pedersen*
University of Copenhagen; Faculty of Life Science; Forest & Landscape Denmark, Rolighedsvej 23, DK-1958 Frederiksberg C
*E-mail: nape@life.ku.dk

Poul Jensen
National Museum of Denmark; Department of Conservation; Research, Analysis & Consulting, I.C. Modewegsvej, Brede, DK-2800 Kgs. Lyngby

Knud Botfeldt
The Royal Danish Academy of Fine Arts; School of Conservation, Esplanaden 34, DK-1263 Copenhagen K

Abstract

The procedure and methods used in this study to examine the potential of azelaic acid (nonanedioic acid) as an impregnation agent for waterlogged wood has produced reliable results in a relatively fast, low technical and low cost way. The study shows that azelaic acid is not hygroscopic even at a relative humidity above 90%, however the aqueous impregnation solution is very acidic (pH is approximately 2). Impregnation with azelaic acid is fast and it is possible to prevent collapse in heavily degraded wood in combination with air drying. It is however not possible to prevent shrinkage in well preserved waterlogged wood in combination with air drying. In addition the wood material is degraded during impregnation in the hot and acidic solutions. The study shows that azelaic acid cannot be recommended as an impregnation agent for waterlogged wood but the outlined procedure can be applied to test other impregnation agents.

Keywords: Azelaic acid, waterlogged wood, binary phase diagram, pH, hygroscopicity, surface tension, sorption.

1. Introduction

1.1 Examination of azelaic acid as an impregnation agent for waterlogged archaeological wood

Gilles Chaumat and his co-workers from ARC-Nucléart, Grenoble, France (Chaumat et al. 2009) presented preliminary results from a study of azelaic acid as an impregnation agent for waterlogged wood at the ICOM-CC working group conference for waterlogged organic materials in Amsterdam in September 2007. The results looked promising.

The principle of azelaic acid conservation is similar to conservation with alum. The wood is immersed in hot azelaic acid solutions since azelaic acid is water soluble at temperatures about 70-75°C for aqueous solutions in the range of 0.1 w/w and 0.7 w/w. After impregnation the wood is left at room temperature and the azelaic acid will crystallize in the wood within minutes upon cooling. The wood structure is locked in its waterlogged dimensions and the water can evaporate freely without collapse of the cell wall.

1.2 Strategy for testing impregnation agents for waterlogged archaeological wood

When considering a new impregnation agent for waterlogged wood several demands have to be tested before the agent can be put into use (Hoffmann 1985, p. 95; Horie 1987, pp. 4, 15-17, 59-62, 65, 71-73; Andersen 1993, pp. 39, 130). The following five step procedure is suitable for examining the potential of new impregnation agents for waterlogged wood:

1. Determination of physical and chemical properties of the agent.
2. Determination of the swelling and sorption capacity of treated wood material.

3. Conservation experiments on waterlogged archaeological test material.
4. Determination of the degradation potential of the agent in connection to the wood material.
5. Determination of the long term stability of the agent.

The fundamental physical and chemical properties are chemical formula, molecular mass, physical form (melting/boiling point), viscosity, vapor pressure and surface tension. Further properties absolutely necessary to know are solubility in aqueous solutions, pH in aqueous solutions, and hygroscopicity of the agent at a relative humidity between 30% and 80 %. Health and safety must be considered as well as price and availability of the product. Some of these physical and chemical properties are readily available in the literature others have to be determined through experimental work. In this study low technical and low cost methods were used to determine a binary phase diagram, pH, hygroscopicity, and surface tension for azelaic acid.

Determination of the swelling and sorption capacity of recent wood give an indication of the ability of the agent to prevent shrinkage in well preserved waterlogged wood. The preferred test material is waterlogged wood but recent wood is a much more homogeneous test material. For this reason recent beech veneer was used as test material in this study. This made it possible to conduct experiments by simple procedures, which yield readily interpretable data.

Conducting conservation experiments on waterlogged test material is important to determine if the conservation treatment is acceptable in terms of visual appearance, shrinkage and collapse. The more homogeneous test material the easier it is to compare different concentrations of the impregnation solutions and different drying methods. It is also important to use both heavily degraded and well preserved waterlogged wood since the conservation demands of the two types of material are quite different. Test material with a combination of well preserved core and an outer more degraded layer is preferable, since the stress and strain between the two layers often causes splits during drying.

The agent should not degrade the treated wood material further neither during impregnation nor in the solid state when embedded in the wood (Feller 1978, 78/16/4; Horie 1987, pp. 4, 31-39). It is therefore important to examine the degradation potential of the agent. In addition the long term degradation potential of the agent when embedded in the wood and exposed to moisture, heat, photochemical exposure and gaseous pollutants in the indoor museum climate should be examined. In studying azelaic acid only preliminary studies on the degradation potential during impregnation was conducted by ATR-FTIR analysis.

The long term stability of the agent itself must be tested. The agent must be resistant towards thermal, photolytic, oxidative, hydrolytic, microbial, and physical degradation. Studying the long term stability is a time consuming and complex task. Reviewing the literature on possible chemical reactions of the agent can give a first impression if the agent is likely to be chemically inert in an indoor museum climate. In studying azelaic acid it was decided to do a preliminary literature survey and leave the necessary experimental work for later studies if azelaic acid had a potential as an impregnation agent for waterlogged wood.

1.3 Physical and chemical properties of azelaic acid

Azelaic acid is the common name for the dicarboxylic acid nonanedioic acid. Azelaic acid consists of a long un-branched alkyl chain with seven methyl groups and two carboxylic acid functional end-groups (Gunstone *et al.* 1994, N-00054). The structural formula is shown in Figure 1.

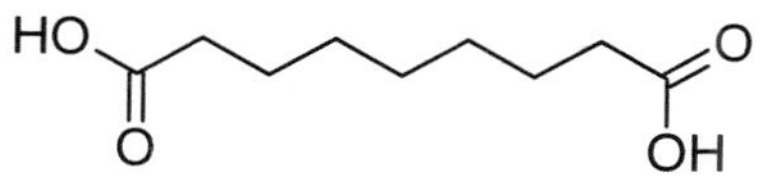

Figure 1. *Structural formula of azelaic acid. After Bond et al. (2001).*

Table 1. *Chemical and physical data for azelaic acid. From Gunstone et al. (1994, N-00054) and Merck (Anon 2006a).*

Chemical formula	$HOOC\text{-}(CH_2)_7\text{-}COOH$
Synonym names	Nonanedioic acid; 1,7-heptanedicarboxylic acid; anchoic acid; lapargylic acid
Cas. no.	[123-99-9]
Physical form	White, odorless crystals
Molecular mass	188.233 g/mol
Melting point	106.5°C
Vapor pressure	< 1 hPa (20°C)
Solubility in water	2.4 g/L (20°C)
Boiling point	237°C (20 hPa)
Thermal decomposition	> 360°C
Flash point	215°C
Density	1.029 g/cm^3 (20°C)
pH value (1 g/L)	3.5
Acid dissociation constants	pK_{a1} = 4.56; pK_{a2} = 5.53 (25°C, 0.1 M KNO_3)

Azelaic acid is a crystalline material arranged in a monoclinic crystal system. The molecules are linked in infinite chains by strong intermolecular hydrogen bonding of the carboxylic acid end-groups. The chains of azelaic acid are arranged in a layered structure with the molecular chains placed parallel to each other and the inter-chain aggregation maintained by hydrophobic interaction between the methylene groups (Thalladi *et al.* 2000, p. 9233; Carey 2008, p. 794). Table 1 shows a summary of physical and chemical data available for azelaic acid.

The azelaic acid used for the experiments in this study was obtained from Merck at a price of approximately 60 EUR per kilo. It is a technical grade for synthesis with a purity of >88%. The rest substance is not disclosed by the manufacturer, but between 1 and 10% is in accordance to the Material Safety Data Sheet (MSDS) suberic acid (octanedioic acid) which is classified as irritant (X_i) (Anon 2006a). Pure azelaic acid (98%) is not harmful in accordance to the MSDS (Anon 2006b), but it is very costly.

2. Experimental work

2.1 Binary phase diagram for aqueous solutions of azelaic acid

Dissolution temperatures were determined by the whisking method (Jensen & Schnell 2005, p. 285). Solutions of azelaic acid (Merck, >88% purity) in de-ionized water were prepared in test tubes (Pyrex, Ø 15 mm, length 160 mm) to a total mass of 10.000 g with concentrations of 0.010 w/w, 0.050 w/w, 0.10 w/w, 0.20 w/w, 0.30 w/w, 0.40 w/w, 0.50 w/w, 0.60 w/w, 0.70 w/w, 0.80 w/w, and 0.90 w/w. Each test tube was heated in a water bath with a temperature between 70°C and 85°C and stirred until dissolution was complete. A platinum resistance thermometer, Pt-100 (offset determined by ice water), coupled to a Gantner IDL 101 data logger, was placed in the test tube and the solution cooled in a water bath to a temperature between 15°C and 25°C. The solution was then again heated slowly in a water bath while the Pt-100 sensor was whisked vigorously and constantly in the solution to ensure an even temperature in the solution. The temperature where the solution became fully dissolved (clear) was registered as the dissolution temperature. This was repeated three times for each solution and the experiment was repeated two or three times for each concentration of azelaic acid.

Precipitation temperatures were determined in thermos flasks. Solutions of azelaic acid (Merck, >88% purity) in de-ionized water were prepared to a total mass of 300.00 g with concentrations of 0.10 w/w, 0.30 w/w, 0.50 w/w, 0.70 w/w, and 1.0 w/w. The solutions were heated in an oven at 110°C for six hours until the azelaic acid was dissolved. Each solution was poured into a preheated thermos flask and closed tightly. A thermocouple thermometer, K-type (offsets determined by ice water), was placed in each thermos flask through a 2 mm hole drilled through the middle of the cap. The thermocouples were coupled to a Pico Technology data logger. The thermos flasks were placed in an expanded polystyrene box closed tightly with duct tape. The box was placed in a freezer at -25°C. The temperature in the thermos flasks was monitored for 137 hours until all the thermocouples had reached -25°C.

2.2 pH in aqueous solutions of azelaic acid at 80°C

Solutions of azelaic acid (Merck, >88% purity) in de-ionized water were prepared to a total mass of 50.00 g with concentrations of 0.10 w/w, 0.20 w/w, 0.30 w/w, 0.40 w/w, 0.50 w/w, 0.60 w/w, 0.70 w/w, and 0.80 w/w. The solutions were heated to 80°C overnight and held in a water bath at $80 \pm 1°C$ one at a time during measurement. The pH was measured three times for each solution with a hand held pH-meter (IQ Scientific Instruments, IQ 150) with an Ion Sensitive Effect Transistor (ISFET) silicon chip sensor (PH37-SS). The sensor was cleaned with hot de-ionized water between each determination and wiped dry. The pH measurements were repeated the following day. Before use the pH meter was calibrated with two buffers, pH 7.00 and pH 4.01, at room temperature. In addition the two buffers were heated in a water bath to $80 \pm 1°C$ and the pH was determined three times in each solution to determine how the pH sensor would react to high temperatures.

2.3 Hygroscopicity

4.000 g pure azelaic acid (Merck, >88% purity), 4.000 g PEG 400 (Merck), and 4.000 g PEG 2000 (INEOS Oxide) were weighed in separate metal trays. To enable duplicate determination this was repeated twice giving a total of six trays. The trays were put in a climatic chamber with desiccated silica gel. The relative humidity and the temperature were measured with a data logger (Tinyview Plus, TinyTag). The silica gel was exchanged with saturated potassium carbonate, then exchanged with saturated sodium bromide, saturated sodium chloride, saturated potassium chloride, and in the end de-ionized water to gain relative humidity steps of 4%, 44%, 59%, 72%, 80%, and 93% in the chamber at room temperature (20°C). Each relative humidity was held constant in the chamber for at least four days and nights to obtain equilibrium before the weight gain of the agents were measured.

2.4 Surface tension

The capillary height method (Harkins 1949, pp. 364-366) was used to estimate the surface tension of a saturated azelaic acid solution at 20°C and a 0.1 w/w solution at 80°C. De-ionized water held in a beaker at room temperature (20°C) was sucked up into a capillary tube (Pyrex, Bie & Berntsen, 1.5-1.8 x 70 mm) by holding the capillary tube vertical in the beaker leaving the upper end of the tube free for air passage. The water level held in the tube was then measured with a digital slide gauge (0.01 mm resolution). This was repeated ten times with ten different capillary tubes. The experiment was repeated with a saturated solution of azelaic acid (Merck, >88% purity) at room temperature, de-ionized water held in a water bath at $80 \pm 1°C$, and a 0.10 w/w azelaic acid solution kept in a water bath at $80 \pm 1°C$. The capillary tubes used for the hot solutions were heated to 80°C in an oven before use.

2.5 Sorption capacity of recent wood material

The amount of azelaic acid and polyethylene glycol (PEG) 400 sorbed within the cell wall of recent beech (*Fagus sylvatica*) veneer after impregnation was determined by the weighing method developed by Jensen (1995, pp. 15-19). The test material was beech spatulas (120 mm x 18 mm x 2 mm) with the width of the spatula corresponding to the tangential direction of the wood. The spatulas were immersed in de-ionized water at 80°C for seven days and nights, dried at 80°C for 24 hours, and cut into four pieces (30 x 18 x 2 mm) each. The samples where dried at 105°C for 24 hours, cooled down in a desiccator, and weighed to three decimal points.

Solutions of azelaic acid (Merck, > 88% pure) in de-ionized water were prepared to a total mass of 50.00 g with concentrations of 0.10 w/w, 0.20 w/w, 0.30 w/w, 0.40 w/w, 0.50 w/w, 0.60 w/w, 0.70 w/w, and 0.80 w/w. Three solutions of 0.50 w/w azelaic acid solution were prepared in order to make a triple determination. All solutions were heated to 80°C (90-100°C for the 0.7 w/w and 0.8 w/w solutions, to avoid precipitation of the azelaic acid) and three dry test pieces were put in each solution. Three test pieces were held in de-ionized water as reference pieces. The test pieces were impregnated for four weeks at 80°C (90-100°C).

Three solutions of PEG 400 (Merck) in de-ionized water were prepared to a total mass of 50.00 g with concentrations of 0.20 w/w, 0.40 w/w, and 0.60 w/w. Three dry test pieces were put in each solution. The solutions were kept at room temperature (19-20°C) for eight weeks.

After impregnation the concentrations in the azelaic acid and PEG 400 solutions were determined threefold by mass determination before and after complete evaporation of water from the solutions. Upon removal from the impregnation solutions the surface of the test pieces were wiped clean and the test pieces were weighed. The test pieces were dried at 105°C, cooled down in a desiccator and weighed again.

2.6 Swelling capacity of recent wood material

The test material used for the experiment was similar to the test material used in the sorption experiment described above. The test pieces were held at room temperature (20°C) in a climate chamber for three days at 43% relative humidity controlled by saturated potassium carbonate. The relative humidity within the chamber was monitored by a data logger (Tinyview Plus, TinyTag). The width of the test pieces were measured with a digital slide gauge. The test pieces were then soaked in de-ionized water at room temperature overnight and the width of the test pieces measured again. The test pieces were impregnated in azelaic acid solutions or PEG 400 solutions as described in the sorption experiment above. The widths of the test pieces were measured after impregnation when still wet and after drying to constant mass in a desiccator controlled to 43% relative humidity by saturated potassium carbonate.

2.7 Conservation experiments on waterlogged archaeological test material

2.7.1 Test material

Two types of waterlogged archaeological test material were used in this study, named Nybro and Nydam wood in the following. Nybro wood is oak (*Quercus sp.*) piles excavated at the location Nybro in Western Jutland, Denmark in 1998. The piles originate from a road or bridge construction from the early Viking age dendrochronologically dated to 741-812 A.D (Frandsen 1999; Ravn 1999). Two well preserved Nybro piles were used as test material. The piles were cut from stems in transverse direction making up triangular piles of about an eighth of the original stem. The inner core of the hardwood was cut off but about 2 cm of pale heavily degraded sapwood was preserved on the opposite side of the piles. In the transverse section the piles had a length of 10-12 cm and a width between 2.5 and 8.5 cm. The heartwood of pile 1 had a narrow edge of 2-3 mm of more degraded heartwood. Twelve pieces of wood from pile 1 and 10 pieces from pile 2 were sawn on a band saw in the transverse direction of the pile, each with a thickness of 19 mm. The Nydam wood originates from Nydam Mose; a bog located in Southern Jutland, Denmark. The location contains several thousand metal and wooden objects from the Iron Age (Rieck *et al.* 1997). The test material used was nine fragments of heavily degraded cylindrical ash (*Fraxinus excelsior*) poles with a length between 5.2 cm and 9.0 cm and a diameter between 1.9 cm and 2.6 cm. The poles were excavated in August 2006 from a depth of 120-130 cm. The poles were divided into three pieces each. One piece was used as air dried reference, one for the conservation experiment, and one piece as untreated waterlogged reference.

To document the degree of degradation of the two types of test material the density (dry weight per wet volume) of the untreated waterlogged test material was determined (Tsoumis 1991, p. 122). In addition the material was examined with transmitted light microscopic (JENAMED-DIC, Carl Zeiss, Jena), scanning electron microscopy (JEOL JSM-5310 LV, 15 kV, 33 Pa, 200x and 350x magnification), and ATR-FTIR analysis (Perkin Elmer Spectrum 1000, 4000 cm^{-1} to 600 cm^{-1}, 10 scans, resolution 4.0 cm^{-1}).

2.7.2 Documentation of impregnation time and reversibility of treatment

Four pieces of Nybro wood were impregnated in 0.50 w/w azelaic acid (Merck, >88% purity) solution at 80°C for four weeks. After one, two, and three weeks one test piece at a time was removed from the solution and air dried. After four weeks the last test piece was removed from the impregnation solution and immersed in de-ionized water at 80°C for four weeks with frequent changes of the water. A slice approximately 0.5 cm wide was cut from each of the four test pieces through the centre of the pieces and used for ATR-FTIR

analysis (Perkin Elmer Spectrum 1000, 4000 cm^{-1} to 600 cm^{-1}, 10 scans, resolution 4.0 cm^{-1}).

2.7.3 Conservation of test material

14 pieces of Nybro wood were impregnated in seven azelaic acid (Merck, > 88% pure) solutions (two pieces in each solution) with concentrations of 0.1 w/w, 0.2 w/w, 0.3 w/w, 0.4 w/w, 0.5 w/w, 0.6 w/w, and 0.7 w/w at 80°C for three weeks. Two test pieces were air dried as references. Eight pieces of Nydam wood were impregnated in seven azelaic acid (Merck, > 88% pure) solutions with concentrations of 0.1 w/w, 0.2 w/w, 0.3 w/w, 0.4 w/w, 0.5 w/w, 0.6 w/w, and 0.7 w/w at 80°C for two weeks. Two pieces were impregnated in the 0.4w/w solution. As reference material two Nybro test pieces and one Nydam test piece were impregnated in PEG 2000 (INEOS Oxide) at room temperature. The impregnation was conducted in steps with four months of impregnation in a 0.1 w/w PEG 2000 solution followed by 0.20 w/w for four months, 0.33 w/w for three months and 0.50 w/w for another three months.

After impregnation all test pieces were removed from the impregnation solutions, cleaned on the surface and the wet mass of the test pieces was determined. The pH was determined in the azelaic acid solutions with a pH-meter (IQ Scientific Instruments, model IQ150, ISFET silicon chip sensor (PH37-SS) as described above.

Half of the test pieces impregnated with azelaic acid were air dried in ambient climate (t = 18-22°C, RH = 30-50%) for at least two weeks and the other half were vacuum freeze-dried between -13°C to -9°C for four days (HETO PowerDry PL9000). The PEG 2000 impregnated test pieces were vacuum freeze-dried in a separate process at -25°C for seven weeks (HETO PowerDry PL9000).

2.7.4 Efficiency of conservation treatments

To document the efficiency of the conservation treatment a number of examinations were conducted. The mass of the test pieces were determined before impregnation, after impregnation and after drying. A profile outline of the test pieces were drawn in scale 1:1 on one side of the transverse section before and after conservation. The percentage shrinkage from waterlogged to conserved condition was determined by measuring the distance between two pins placed in the radial and two pins in the tangential direction of the wood before and after treatment. The visual appearance of the test pieces were described before and after conservation and documented by digital photos, and the conserved test pieces were compared to the air dried reference material and the PEG treated references. After the above mentioned examinations the test pieces were bisectioned in the tangential longitudinal direction to examine the structure of the wood and the precipitation of azelaic acid in the center of the test pieces. The test pieces were in addition examined with transmitted light microscopic (JENAMED-DIC, Carl Zeiss, Jena) and scanning electron microscopy (JEOL JSM-5310 LV, 15 kV, 33 Pa) and compared to untreated dry and wet material.

2.8 Degradation potential of azelaic acid and wood material upon impregnation

ATR-FTIR (Perkin Elmer Spectrum 1000, 4000 cm^{-1} to 600 cm^{-1}, 10 scans, resolution 4.0 cm^{-1}) was used to analyze whether azelaic acid had degraded during heating, and whether recent wood and archaeological wood treated with azelaic acid had degraded during impregnation.

Four types of azelaic acid were analyzed: Azelaic acid as delivered from Merck, a 0.10 w/w and a 0.50 w/w azelaic acid solution heated to 70°C and re-precipitated by cooling to room temperature and a yellowed solution of azelaic acid heated for five days and nights at 120°C and re-precipitated by cooling to room temperature.

Test pieces of recent beech veneer from the sorption experiment; a reference treated in de-ionized water and four test pieces impregnated with azelaic acid concentrations of 0.1 w/w, 0.6 w/w, 0.7 w/w, and 0.8 w/w, were immersed in de-ionized water for four weeks with frequent changes of water to wash the azelaic acid out from the wood structure. The test pieces were air dried and analyzed.

Waterlogged archaeological Nydam wood, a fragment from a shield, was cut into three pieces. Two pieces were impregnated in two separate 0.50 w/w azelaic acid solutions for four weeks at 80°C and 105°C respectively. The two test pieces were then put into hot de-ionized water (80°C) for 24 hours with three changes of the water before they were air dried and analyzed. The third test piece was air dried and used as reference material.

3. Results
3.1 Binary phase diagram for aqueous solutions of azelaic acid
Figure 2 shows the binary phase diagram of azelaic acid/water mixtures based on the dissolution temperatures and precipitation temperatures obtained in the experiment by the whisking method and in the thermos flasks respectively. The values obtained in the thermos flasks are lower than the values obtained by the whisking methods due to sub-cooling in the thermos flasks.

3.2 pH in aqueous solutions of azelaic acid at 80 °C
Table 2 shows the average value of the six pH determinations in each of the eight azelaic acid solutions at 80 ± 1°C. Measurement of pH in a 4.01 buffer solution at 80 ± 1°C showed that the pH-meter used on average measured 0.5 pH units higher than at room temperature. For this reason 0.5 pH units have been subtracted from the pH determinations in Table 2

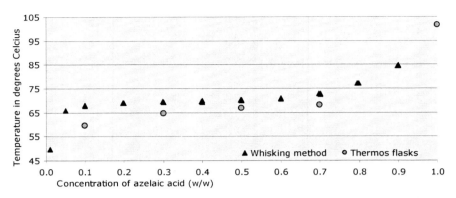

Figure 2. *Binary phase diagram of azelaic acid and water mixtures. The diagram shows the dissolution temperatures determined by the whisking method and the precipitation temperatures determined by the thermos flask experiment.*

Table 2. *Average values of pH measurements in azelaic acid solutions at 80 ℃ and corresponding calculated pH-values.*

Concentration	0.1 w/w	0.2 w/w	0.3 w/w	0.4 w/w	0.5 w/w	0.6 w/w	0.7 w/w	0.8 w/w
pH	2.24	2.09	1.94	1.85	1.66	1.50	1.25	1.15
pH, calculated*	2.42	2.27	2.18	2.11	2.07	2.03	1.99	1.96

*The calculated pH-values are based on the pK_a values for pure azelaic acid.

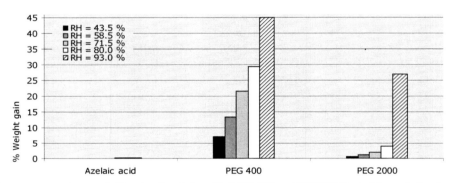

Figure 3. *Average percentage weight gain of azelaic acid, PEG 400 and PEG 2000 at rising relative humidity.*

3.3 Hygroscopicity of azelaic acid

Figure 3 shows the average percentage weight gain of the tested agents at increasing relative humidity.

3.4 Surface tension

Table 3 shows the average values for the liquid columns measured in the capillary tubes and the determined surface tensions for the examined solutions. In addition the table shows the density and surface tension of water and the densities of azelaic acid used in the calculations.

3.5 Sorption capacity of recent wood material

The amount of azelaic acid sorbed in the cell wall of the test material was negative for all test pieces. This was due to degradation of the wood material and the resulting loss of mass during impregnation in hot aqueous solutions. The reference test pieces treated in hot water alone had a mass loss of about 15% due to the treatment. The amount of PEG 400 in the cell wall was as to be expected increasing with increasing concentration of PEG 400. Thus the weighing method cannot be used for examination of treatments in hot aqueous solutions but is applicable for treatments at room temperature where the mass loss of the test material is negligible

192

Table 3. *Measured liquid columns, density and surface tension of water and density of azelaic acid; determined surface tension based on the measured liquid column.*

	Water 20°C	Water 80°C	Azelaic acid, saturated 20°C	0.1 w/w Azelaic acid 80°C
Measured liquid column, h (mm)	23.81	22.28	20.01	16.89
Density, ρ (kg/m^3)	998.2[1]	971.8[1]	998.0[2]	977.5[3]
Surface tension, γ (mN/m)	72.75[1]	62.6[1]	-	-
Determined surface tension, γ (mN/m)	-	-	61.1	47.7

[1]Weast (1977). [2]Estimated density is set equal to water at 20°C. [3]Estimated density is calculated from the density of pure azelaic at 20°C acid and water at 80°C.

3.6 Swelling capacity of recent wood material

The hot aqueous treatment has degraded the test material as described above making the results of the experiment unreliable. It is likely that the test pieces treated in azelaic acid have degraded to at least the same degree as the reference pieces treated in hot water. The actual zero point for the tangential swelling of the test pieces are not known due the degradation, but at least it must be the same as the shrinkage of the reference pieces. If the zero point is set as the average tangential shrinkage of the reference pieces, the results show a small shrinkage for test material treated in 0.1 w/w azelaic acid treated and a swelling between 1% and 7% for test pieces treated in 0.2 w/w to 0.6 w/w azelaic acid solutions. The results of the PEG 400 treatment show about 10% swelling of the wood when treated with 0.4 w/w and 0.6 w/w solutions. This equals the swelling of the test material in waterlogged condition.

3.7 Conservation experiments with waterlogged archaeological test material
3.7.1 Documentation of test material
The density of Nybro heartwood was 280 kg/m^3 for pile 1 and 380 kg/m^3 for pile 2. The density for Nybro sapwood was 61.0 kg/m^3 for pile 1 and 80.0 kg/m^3 for pile 2. The average density of the nine Nydam poles was 105 kg/m^3.

Transmitted light microscopic and SEM analysis of untreated test material confirm that the Nydam wood is oak (*Quercus*). The analysis show heavily degraded sapwood with only the compound middle lamella preserved, and well preserved heartwood with areas of intact wood cells and degraded wood cells randomly distributed in the wood. The analysis confirmed that the Nydam wood is ash (*Fraxinus excelsior*) and that the wood is heavily degraded. All wood fibers are empty and only the compound middle lamella is left throughout the wood.

The ATR-FTIR spectra of the test material confirmed that the Nybro heartwood is well preserved and that Nybro sapwood and Nydam wood is heavily degraded when compared to spectra of recent oak and ash wood (Pavia *et al.* 1996 pp. 32, 35-37, 42, 48, 50-52; MacLeod & Richards 1997, p. 206; Giachi *et al.* 2003; Pandey & Pitman 2003, p. 154; Giachi *et al.* 2009).

3.7.2 Documentation of impregnation time and reversibility
Azelaic acid impregnated wood analyzed with ATR-FTIR show characteristic absorption bands both for hardwood (Pavia *et al.* 1996 pp. 32, 35-37, 42, 48, 50-52; MacLeod & Richards 1997, p. 206; Giachi *et al.* 2003; Pandey & Pitman 2003, p. 154;Giachi *et al.* 2009) and azelaic acid (Corish & Davison 1955, p. 2434-2435; Aggarwal & Srivastava 1967, p. 630; Pavia *et al.* 1996 p. 36-37, 49, 52-56, 62-63). The longer the impregnation time the more dominant the characteristic absorption bands for azelaic acid become. All test pieces were analyzed in three points starting from the surface moving to the centre of the test piece in the radial direction. After one and two weeks of impregnation the spectra of the test pieces

show more dominant absorption bands for azelaic acid at the surface than in the centre of the test pieces. After three weeks of impregnation the spectra from the centre and the surface are identical. The spectra are in addition dominated by azelaic acid after three weeks of impregnation. The ATR-FTIR spectra of the test piece impregnated in azelaic acid for four weeks followed by four weeks of immersion in hot water show identical spectra from the surface to the centre of the test piece. In addition the spectra are almost identical to untreated Nybro heartwood and no characteristic absorption bands from azelaic acid are present in the spectra.

3.7.3 pH in the azelaic acid solutions after impregnation

Table 4 shows the average value of three repeated determinations of the pH value of the impregnation solutions for both Nybro and Nydam wood after impregnation.

Table 4. *The average value of the pH determined at 80 ℃ in the impregnation solutions after impregnation of Nybro and Nydam wood.*

Concentration	0.1 w/w	0.2 w/w	0.3 w/w	0.4 w/w	0.5 w/w	0.6 w/w	0.7 w/w
pH, after imp. (Nybro)	3.42	3.07	2.89	2.76	2.63	n.a.*	n.a.*
pH, after imp. (Nydam)	3.44	3.14	2.94	3.08	3.12	2.83	2.36

* It was not possible to determine the pH value, since both the used sensor and a spare sensor were unable to measure the solutions.

3.7.4 Efficiency of the conservation treatments

The visual inspection, the 1:1 drawings and microscopic analysis (transmitted light microscopy and SEM) show that air drying of untreated heavily degraded wood (Nydam wood and Nybro sapwood) resulted in a considerable collapse. It was possible though to prevent the collapse by freeze-drying alone. The conservation experiment with azelaic acid showed, that it is possible to prevent collapse in heavily degraded waterlogged archaeological wood material. This was the case both for the air dried and the freeze-dried test pieces, and a 0.1 w/w azelaic acid solution was just as effective in avoiding collapse as a 0.7 w/w solution.

The visual inspection of air dried Nybro test pieces showed that the heartwood had shrunk to an extent visible to the naked eye independent of treatment whereas the freeze-dried material was closer to the original waterlogged dimensions. Table 5 shows the determined percentage shrinkage of both Nybro and Nydam test pieces. The percentage shrinkage and the 1:1 drawings show results roughly in agreement with the visual inspection. The dimensions of the conserved Nydam wood are very close to the waterlogged dimensions before conservation ranging from a small swelling and a small shrinkage (Table 5). A few test pieces have a shrinkage/swelling of more than 2% (Table 5). There is no correlation between the shrinkage/swelling of the test pieces and the concentration of the azelaic acid solutions or the drying method. The inconsistency is most likely due to dislocation of the pins in the soft wood during treatment. This is confirmed by the 1:1 drawings where the dimensions of the test pieces are very similar before and after conservation. As expected the PEG/freeze-dried Nydam wood has not shrunk significantly.

The 1:1 drawings and the percentage shrinkage (Table 5) show that the air dried and untreated Nybro heartwood has shrunk significantly without any kind of treatment. The air dried test pieces treated with azelaic acid all have significant shrinkage in the radial direction (7 to 11%).

Table 5. *Determined percentage shrinkage of Nybro and Nydam test pieces after treatment with azelaic acid or PEG 2000 in combination with air or freeze-drying.*

Impregnation	Method of drying	Shrinkage, Nybro		Shrinkage, Nydam	
		Direction parallel to growth rings	Radial direction	Direction parallel to growth rings	Radial direction
-	Air drying	12%	16%	29%[1]	73%[1]
0.5 w/w PEG 2000	Freeze-drying	1.5%	2.9%	0.057%	-1.6%
0.1 w/w azelaic acid	Air drying	6.3%	n.a.	-	-
0.1 w/w azelaic acid	Freeze-drying	3.9%	1.1%	5.7%	-1.1%
0.2 w/w azelaic acid	Air drying	4.9%	11%	-	-
0.2 w/w azelaic acid	Freeze-drying	4.2%	-1.0%	-0.059%	0.3%
0.3 w/w azelaic acid	Air drying	4.6%	11%	-	-
0.3 w/w azelaic acid	Freeze-drying	3.4%	0.91%	2.4%	-3.2%
0.4 w/w azelaic acid	Air drying	5.6%	8.2%	0.91%	3.6%
0.4 w/w azelaic acid	Freeze-drying	1.4%	0.57%	-0.069%	0.82%
0.5 w/w azelaic acid	Air drying	1.8%	6.9%	1.4%	2.7%
0.5 w/w azelaic acid	Freeze-drying	2.4%	n.a.	-	-
0.5 w/w PEG 2000	Freeze-drying	2.1%	5.3%	-	-
0.6 w/w azelaic acid	Air drying	n.a.	n.a.	-3.6%	-2.3%
0.6 w/w azelaic acid	Freeze-drying	n.a.	n.a.	-	-
0.7 w/w azelaic acid	Air drying	n.a.	n.a.	6.1%	-1.7%
0.7 w/w azelaic acid	Freeze-drying	n.a.	n.a.	-	-

[1]Average value for the nine untreated air dried reference pieces. n.a.: The value is not available due loss (corrosion) of the pins placed in the test piece.

In the direction parallel to the growth rings the shrinkage is significant for the test pieces treated in 0.1 w/w to 0.3 w/w whereas the test pieces treated in 0.4 w/w to 0.7 w/w only have a small amount of shrinkage in the direction parallel to the growth rings (about 2%). The freeze-dried test pieces only have significant shrinkage in the direction parallel to the growth rings of the heartwood. This is also the case for a freeze-dried but untreated test piece. The lower level of shrinkage in the radial direction must therefore be due to freeze-drying and not to the azelaic acid treatment. The shrinkage is less than or about 2% in both directions in test pieces treated with the 0.4 w/w azelaic acid solution or higher concentrations when followed by freeze-drying. This is a dimensional stability comparable to or actually better than the test pieces treated with 0.5 w/w PEG 2000 followed by freeze-drying. For all the test pieces the shrinkage is lower in the azelaic acid treated wood than in the air dried reference pieces, meaning that treatment with azelaic acid has some effect.

SEM analysis show that splits are formed in heavily degraded Nydam wood when impregnated with azelaic acid solutions of less than 0.5 w/w independent on drying method. Visual inspection reveals that splits are also formed in heavily degraded Nybro sapwood upon air drying (Figure 4). These splits are independent of the concentration of the azelaic acid solution, and are probably due to stress and strain caused by shrinkage of the heartwood during drying.

The freeze-dried Nybro test pieces all have well preserved sapwood mostly without splits, but instead splits were formed in the heartwood between the well preserved heartwood and the outer 3 mm edge of more degraded heartwood (Figure 5).

The test pieces from pile 2 did not have a thin layer of outer more degraded heartwood. In these test pieces splits were formed along the line between sapwood and heartwood and for air dried test pieces splits were also formed along the rays in the wood. The splits formed in the freeze-dried Nybro heartwood is most likely due to a very low relative humidity in the vacuum chamber during freeze-drying. The PEG treated test piece did not contain any visible splits.

The visual inspection of the treated test pieces show that the PEG treated Nybro wood is dark in color and appears waxy. The heartwood has kept the characteristic black color of waterlogged oak wood. The sapwood has turned dark brown. The reason for the darkening of the sapwood is probably due to discoloring of the impregnation solution from the heartwood. Bi-sectioning showed that the discoloration is only on the surface, not in the internal part of the sapwood.

Figure 4. Nybro test piece before and after impregnation in 0.4 w/w azelaic acid followed by air drying. Splits have formed in the sapwood and the colour of both heartwood and sapwood has changed.

Figure 5. Nybro test piece before and after impregnation in 0.4 w/w azelaic acid followed by freeze-drying. Splits have formed in the heartwood and the color of both heartwood and sapwood has changed.

The azelaic acid treated Nybro heartwood is lighter in color than the PEG treated wood. The characteristic black appearance of the oak wood is replaced by a dark brown color. The wood looks pale and dry compared to the PEG treated wood. The sapwood has turned dark brown on the surface as the PEG treated wood. The color change of both the Nybro sapwood and heartwood form respectively light brown and black to dark brown does not detract vitally from the visual appearance of the wood compared to the PEG treated Nybro wood. The PEG treated Nydam wood is a little bit darker than the azelaic acid treated wood, but the difference is not significant. Both the PEG treated and the azelaic acid treated Nydam wood has a natural looking appearance.

Azelaic acid precipitation within the test pieces was documented by bisection, by determination of the mass, and by microscopic analysis (transmitted light microscopy and SEM). Bisection of both the Nybro test pieces and the Nydam test pieces showed white precipitations throughout the whole test piece for all test pieces. This corresponds well to the determined weight gain of the test pieces. Comparison of the dry weight of the test pieces after conservation with the estimated dry weight in an untreated state show an increasing weight gain with increasing concentration of azelaic acid. Nybro test pieces have a weight gain ranging from 20% to 116% and Nydam test pieces from 75% to 643% when impregnated with solutions between 0.1 w/w and 0.7 w/w.

The transmitted light microscope examinations of the conserved Nybro heartwood show only weak indications of precipitated azelaic acid in the fiber cells but distinct indications of crystalline precipitate of azelaic acid in the early wood vessels. In contrast the SEM analyses show a smooth structure indicating that the fiber cells are filled with azelaic acid.

Transmitted light microscope analysis show that azelaic acid has precipitated within both fiber cells and early wood vessels in

heavily degraded Nybro sapwood and Nydam wood. SEM analysis of Nydam wood clearly show that the fiber cells contain more precipitated azelaic acid the more concentrated the azelaic acid solutions (Figure 6). Nydam wood treated in 0.7 w/w azelaic acid has such a massive amount of precipitated azelaic acid within the wood structure that the outline of the wood structure is very hard to recognize (Figure 6).

3.8 Degradation potential of azelaic acid and wood material upon impregnation

3.8.1 Heated azelaic acid solutions

Comparison of ATR-FTIR spectra of azelaic acid as delivered from Merck (Merck, > 88% purity) and azelaic acid which has been dissolved at 70°C and re-precipitated (0.1 w/w and 0.5 w/w aqueous solutions) show identical spectra. The spectrum of azelaic acid solution heated to 120°C for five days has only two very small deviations from the spectrum of the un-heated azelaic acid even though the azelaic acid had yellowed.

3.8.2 Recent beech wood

The ATR-FTIR spectrum of recent beech wood immersed for eight weeks in water at 80°C is not identical to the spectrum of untreated recent beech wood (Figure 7). The major changes lie in the range from 1770 cm^{-1} to 1500 cm^{-1} indicating changes in the carbonyl groups in the wood structure. The carbonyl absorption band assigned to hemicellulose (1735 cm^{-1}) has almost disappeared. The range from 1650 cm^{-1} to 1507 cm^{-1} has changes from several peaks in the region into two broad absorption bands at 1593 cm^{-1} and 1507 cm^{-1}. This indicates changes in the aromatic ring structure of the wood. The C-H bending vibrations between 1490 cm^{-1} and 1320 cm^{-1} has changed intensity in proportion to each other. The absorptions band assigned to lignin (1457 cm^{-1} and 1420 cm^{-1}) are unchanged though. The C-O stretching vibration assigned to phenols at 1235 cm^{-1} has changed from a single peak to three unresolved bands. The broad absorption band from 1160 cm^{-1} to 900 cm^{-1}

assigned to the glycoside bond in cellulose and hemicellulose has changed. This indicates changes in intensity of the absorption bands in the region. Analysis of recent beech wood treated in hot water for eight weeks show that the hemicellulose has suffered the most but the lignified part of the wood has also been degraded to some extent. This is in agreement with work done by Evans & Banks (1990).

The ATR-FTIR spectrum of the wood immersed in 0.1 w/w azelaic acid for four weeks followed by immersion in water at 80°C for four weeks is not identical to the untreated beech wood or to the wood treated in hot water for eight weeks (Figure 7). The C-H stretching vibration has shifted from 2900 cm^{-1} to 2918 cm^{-1}, a broad carbonyl absorption band with medium intensity at 1718 cm^{-1} has emerged, and the three unresolved C-O stretching vibrations assigned to phenols has changed intensity in proportion to each other. The spectrum is otherwise identical to the test piece immersed in hot water. The ATR-FTIR spectra of the recent beech wood immersed in 0.6 w/w, 0.7 w/w and 0.8 w/w azelaic acid solutions are not identical to the spectrum of the wood treated in 0.1 w/w azelaic acid (Figure 7).

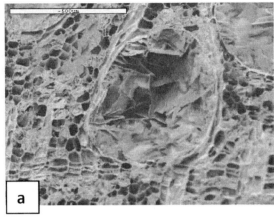
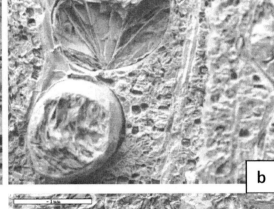
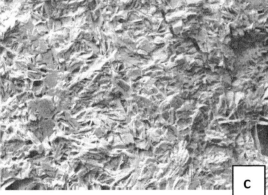

*Figure 6: Transverse section of Nydam wood impregnated in **a.** 0.2 w/w azelaic acid followed by freeze-drying (350x magnifications), **b.** 0.4 w/w azelaic acid followed by freeze-drying (350x magnifications), and **c.** 0.7 w/w azelaic acid followed by air drying (500x magnifications) respectively. When comparing the three images it is evident that the fibre cells contain more precipitated azelaic acid the more concentrated the azelaic acid solution. The outline of the wood structure is very hard to recognize for wood impregnated in 0.7 w/w azelaic acid solution.*

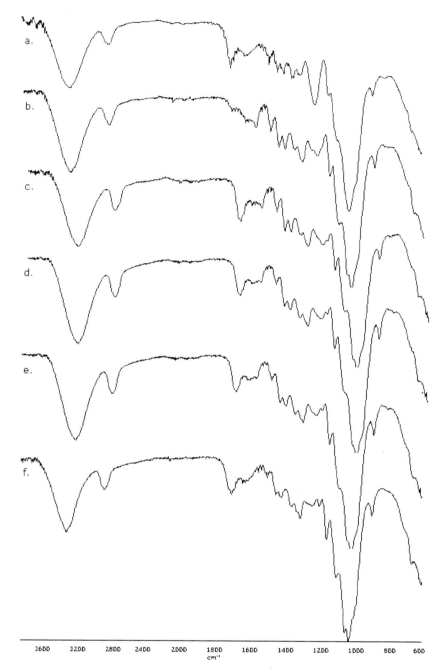

Figure 7. *ATR-FTIR spectra of untreated recent beech wood (a.), beech wood treated in hot water (b.), and beech wood treated in 0.1(c.), 0.6 (d.), 0.7(e.) and 0.8w/w (f.) azelaic acid solutions at 80 °C. When comparing the spectra it is evident that the chemical structure of the wood has changed both when treated in hot water alone and when treated in hot azelaic acid solutions.*

The major changes are the very low intensity of the C=C stretching vibration of the aromatic ring structure assigned to lignin at 1595 cm⁻¹ and 1507 cm⁻¹, and the drop in intensity of the C-H bending at 1460 cm⁻¹ also assigned to lignin. The three unresolved C-O stretching bands at 1270-1215 cm⁻¹ have again changed intensity in proportion to each other. The absorption band at 830 cm⁻¹ assigned to lignin becomes weaker as the concentration of azelaic acid rises. The spectra of recent beech wood impregnated with azelaic acid show that the acidic treatment degraded both the lignin and holocellulose, and that increased concentrations of the azelaic acid increases the degree of degradation.

3.8.3 Waterlogged wood

The ATR-FTIR spectra of Nydam wood immersed for four weeks in azelaic acid solution at 80°C and 105°C show residues of azelaic acid within the wood. The residues of azelaic acid are due to a very short immersion of the test pieces in hot water after treatment. This makes an analysis of the spectra more difficult. The C-O/C-O-C stretching region (between 1200 cm^{-1} and 1000 cm^{-1}) is not influenced by azelaic acid, but it is hard to assign to specific functional groups in the complex wood structure. However the spectra show that the Nydam wood treated in an azelaic acid solution at 80°C differs from the untreated reference. The Nydam wood treated in an azelaic acid solution at 105°C differs both from the untreated reference and the wood treated at 80°C. Comparison of the spectra show a structural change (degradation) in the already heavily degraded wood structure upon treatment with hot azelaic acid solutions which is more pronounced at 105°C than at 80°C.

3.9 Literature survey on the long term stability of azelaic acid

Dicarboxylic acids are not inert chemical components. Like mono-carboxylic acids dicarboxylic acids are weak acids and will obtain equilibrium with water upon dissolution leading to acidification of the solution (Zumdahl 1997, p. 649; Carey 2008, pp. 794-796, 799, 802). In presence of strong bases carboxylic acids and dicarboxylic acids are neutralized and form water soluble carboxylate salts (Carey 2008, pp. 797-798). Dicarboxylic acid are also able to form metal complexes; azelaic acid most likely act as a monodentate ligand (Aggarwal & Srivastava

1967, p. 630). Apart from the acid/basic reactions carboxylic acids may undergo reduction (Gunstone 1996, p. 217; Carey 2008, p. 628), halogenation (Suzuki et al. 1992, p. 171; McMurry 1998, pp. 321-327), esterification (Gunstone 1996, p. 208; Carey 2008, p. 635), decarboxylation (Carey 2008, p. 815), or oxidation (Jin et al. 2006, pp. 80-87; Yang et al. 2008). In addition to the abiotic chemical reactions of carboxylic acids and dicarboxylic acids azelaic acid can be degraded by both bacteria and yeast. The degradation is facilitated by the β-oxidation pathway and the products formed are pimelic acid ($HOOC(CH_2)_5COOH$) and glutaric acid ($HOOC(CH_2)_3COOH$) (Ohsugi et al. 1984, p. 1881; McMurry 1998, pp. 548-549).

The long-term stability of azelaic acid in ambient climate has not been tested. But the possible reactions mentioned above might be crucial for the long term stability. Photo-oxidation of unsaturated fatty acids used as binders in oil paintings form azelaic acid as a degradation product (Ligeza et al. 1987; Schilling & Khanjian 1996; Wouters et al. 2000). This indicates that azelaic acid is chemically inert in an ambient climate. Photo-oxidation of azelaic acid has been shown to take place in the aqueous phase but no testing has been done on azelaic acid in the solid state. Oxidation of azelaic acid is otherwise only found at temperatures above 400°C which indicates stability in a museum climate (Jin et al. 2006, pp. 80-87; Yang et al. 2008).

The acidic reaction of azelaic acid only takes place in the aqueous phase. In the solid state the two acid functional groups of the azelaic acid molecules are held together in infinite long chains and are therefore unable to react. Since the solubility of azelaic acid in water is very low in ambient climate an acid reaction is not expected to occur in the solid state within the wood. Thermal decomposition takes place at temperatures above 360°C and

200

azelaic acid is therefore expected to be stable in ambient climates. Carboxylic acids are exceptionally difficult to reduce and reduction of carboxylic acids to alcohols will not have influence on the stability of azelaic acid in ambient climates (Carey 2008, p. 628). The possibility of halogenation or halogen substitution is not likely either during impregnation or after precipitating within the wood; since halogens are only present in very low concentrations in the wood and in ambient climates. Esters, amides and acid anhydrides are primarily formed from carboxylic acid via acid halides and lack of acid halides prevents formation of these (McMurry 1998, pp. 321, 327). As long as alcohols are not present in the impregnation baths esterification of azelaic acid cannot take place either. Decarboxylation is the last possible abiotic reaction for dicarboxylic acids. The two carboxylic acid groups in azelaic acid are separated by seven methyl groups, and it is likely that decarboxylation is as rare as in mono-carboxylic acids (Carey 2008, p. 815). The literature survey shows that it is not very likely that azelaic acid will react chemically in ambient climates, and it is highly probable that azelaic acid is chemically stable as a conservation agent. Microbial degradation of azelaic acid by bacteria and yeast is the most likely degradation mechanism, but the rate of degradation needs to be tested in a climate comparable to a museum climate. It has not been possible to find literature on photolytic stability and stability toward gaseous pollutions. Further investigation of the stability of azelaic acid should therefore concentrate mainly on microbial and photochemical degradation and on the possible degradation mechanisms of gaseous pollutions common in museum storage and exhibition.

4. Discussion

The five step procedure has made it possible to study the potential of azelaic acid as an impregnation agent for waterlogged wood by low technical and low cost methods. It seems useful to perform the procedure one step at a time and evaluate the results before the next step is preformed.

4.1 Physical and chemical properties of azelaic acid

The physical and chemical properties determined for azelaic acid show that the azelaic acid molecule is small, has a low molecular mass, and is a solid crystalline material at room temperature. The fact that azelaic acid is a crystalline material with high melting point (above 100°C) insures that the agent is hard and solid even in tropical climate zones. In addition the solid azelaic acid will not become soft and sticky at elevated temperature or too brittle at low temperatures as is often the case with amorphous impregnation agents. The low vapor pressure implies that azelaic acid is non-volatile and sublimation of azelaic acid from treated wood is not to be expected. Determination of a binary phase diagram for azelaic acid shows solubility temperatures between 68°C and 73°C for concentrations between 0.1 w/w and 0.7 w/w. This makes it possible to impregnate waterlogged wood with aqueous solutions of azelaic acid at temperatures between 70°C and 75°C. pH measurements in aqueous azelaic acid solutions at 80°C show pH values as low as between 2.2 and 1.2 for solutions between 0.1 w/w and 0.8 w/w. The wood material itself is only slightly acidic and near neutral solutions are as a rule of thumb most appropriate for treatment. The low pH of the azelaic acid solutions can cause some degradation of the wood material. The hygroscopicity of azelaic acid is as expected very low even at a relative humidity above 90%. The low hygroscopicity of azelaic acid in combination with the crystalline structure and high dissolution temperature indicates that there should be no problems with uptake of water, leaking of impregnation agent or softening of the material due to high moisture content or temperatures upon display or storage in a museum climate. In conclusion the examination of the physical and chemical properties of azelaic acid is only of concern in relation to the low pH values of the aqueous solutions.

4.2 Swelling and sorption capacity of azelaic acid on wood

The small molecular size of azelaic acid promotes a fast diffusion within the wood and increases the possibility of azelaic acid entering the cell wall of the wood and not just the cell lumen of the wood. If azelaic acid can enter the cell wall it might have the potential to sorb to the cell wall and replace the bound water and avoid shrinkage of the wood upon drying.

Examination of the swelling and sorption capacity of azelaic acid on recent beech wood was unfortunately inconclusive. The considerable loss of mass of the test pieces during impregnation indicates a considerable degradation of the wood. The reference test pieces treated in water alone had a loss of mass of more than 10%. The sorption isotherm examined by the weighing method could therefore not be determined. The swelling rate of the test pieces showed only a minor if any swelling capacity of azelaic acid in recent beech wood. The methods used are however fully applicable to test materials which are to be treated at room temperature.

Comparison of the results of the shrinkage of the waterlogged archaeological test pieces in the conservation experiment and the rather unreliable results of the swelling capacity of recent wood indicate that azelaic acid only has a slight if any bulking capacity on the cell wall. Azelaic acid is not able to keep the cell wall swollen when the bound water evaporates from the wood structure. The positive results regarding the dimensions of the heavily degraded wood point to the fact

that azelaic acid builds up a physical skeleton that is stronger than the capillary forces of the water within the wood structure. It seems possible that the shrinkage in the Nybro heartwood is due to a lack of exchange of bound water in the cell wall with azelaic acid. As long as water has a stronger binding to the wood structure azelaic acid will not be exchanged with the bound water during impregnation. In the well preserved wood structure the bound water will form a protective film on the cell wall and azelaic acid will precipitate outside this film during cooling. When water evaporates during drying the azelaic acid is already solid and stays in place. The azelaic acid will not fill out the space previously occupied by water, and the wood will shrink. If the physical skeleton is strong enough shrinkage will be lower than in untreated wood.

4.3 Conservation of waterlogged wood with azelaic acid

The conservation experiments showed that the well preserved Nybro wood, cut in slices of 19 mm, were fully impregnated with azelaic acid within three weeks at 80°C. Transmitted light and scanning electron microscopic examinations confirmed that azelaic acid was distributed in the wood structure and filled the empty spaces in both vessels and fibers. The treatment was found to be reversible, as it was possible to wash the azelaic acid out of the wood by immersion in hot water.

The conservation experiments showed that impregnation of heavily degraded waterlogged wood (oak sapwood and ash wood) with azelaic acid solutions at 80°C followed by air drying prevented collapse in the wood structure and the original form and dimensions of the wood was kept at concentrations even as low as 0.1 w/w. Freeze-drying did not yield better results and can be omitted for heavily degraded wood. Microscopic splits were formed in the wood impregnated with azelaic acid solutions below 0.5 w/w and heavily degraded wood should be impregnated in 0.5 w/w solutions or higher. The general appearance of the heavily degraded Nydam wood treated with azelaic acid was satisfactory. The color was a little lighter than the untreated air dried wood but still kept a natural appearance.

Conservation experiments with well preserved waterlogged wood (oak heartwood) showed that azelaic acid concentrations above 0.4 w/w followed by freeze-drying were necessary to avoid pronounced shrinkage of the well preserved heartwood. Under these conditions the dimensions of the conserved wood was actually closer to the original dimensions of the waterlogged wood than the PEG treated reference wood. The visual appearance was also acceptable. Unfortunately the freeze-drying resulted in formation of splits along the line between the more degraded outer zone of heartwood and better preserved inner zone. The formation of cracks might be due to the low relative humidity within the freeze-drying chamber, and it may be possible to avoid splits if the relative humidity can be regulated better during the freeze-drying process. If this is not the case conservation of well preserved waterlogged wood with azelaic acid cannot be recommended.

4.4 Degradation of wood treated with hot aqueous azelaic acid solutions

Examination of the wood structure with ATR-FTIR analysis showed structural changes in recent wood treated in the hot acidic solutions. Treatment in hot water (80°C) alone showed structural changes in the wood material after eight weeks of treatment. Degradation of the wood structure was primarily assigned to hemicellulose and lignin. Treatment in hot azelaic acid solutions for four weeks followed by four weeks in hot water show structural changes in both lignin

and hemicellulose/cellulose. The effect is more pronounced the higher the azelaic acid concentration. ATR-FTIR analysis also showed chemical changes in heavily degraded waterlogged archaeological wood after four weeks of treatment in hot azelaic acid solutions. The degradation was more pronounced in wood kept at 105°C than wood kept at 80°C. The analysis showed that even relatively short treatments in hot acidic solutions are damaging to the wood structure. Further degradation of the archaeological wood material in order to preserve it is completely unacceptable from a conservation point of view. Treatments for small heavily degraded objects might be less than the two weeks used in the conservation experiment. If azelaic acid is to be a serious candidate for impregnation of heavily degraded wood it will be necessary to determine the shortest possible impregnation time and if this treatment is destructive. It is necessary to treat heavily degraded wood with 0.5 w/w azelaic acid solution to avoid splits but no more that 0.50 w/w is needed. The 0.5 w/w solution is soluble at 70° C. For this reason the temperature of the impregnation bath can be set just above 70°C.

4.5 Long term stability of azelaic acid

Literature on the long term stability of azelaic acid in ambient climate was not available, but the possible reactions of carboxylic acids and dicarboxylic acids suggest that it is not likely that azelaic acid will react in ambient climates. Azelaic acid is most likely a chemically stable conservation agent but further investigation on microbial and photochemical degradation and possible degradation mechanisms of gaseous pollutants common in museum storage and exhibition must be conducted.

5. Conclusion

Azelaic acid is a fast and cheap way to conserve heavily degraded waterlogged wood to obtain dimensional stability. The method has a few major drawbacks though. The azelaic acid solutions are hot and very acidic leading to degradation of both lignin and carbohydrate in the already damaged wood structure. In addition azelaic acid only works well on heavily degraded wood. Due to the drawbacks and the fact that the long term stability is not known azelaic acid cannot be recommended as a standard treatment for waterlogged wood. The five step procedure and outlined methods used in this study have produced reliable results in a relatively fast, low technical and low cost way. The procedure and methods are therefore suitable for examining the potential of other impregnation agents for waterlogged wood.

Acknowledgment

The authors wish to thank Lene Frandsen from Museet for Varde By og Omegn and the National Museum of Denmark for donation of test material. Jettie van Lanschot from Royal Danish Academy of Fine Arts, School of Conservation for running the SEM apparatus. David Gregory from the National Museum of Denmark and the whole staff at the wet wood laboratory at the National Museum of Denmark for great help and collaboration during the work included in this study.

References

Aggarwal, R.C. & Srivastava, A.K. (1967): Infrared Spectral Studies of Thallium(III) Complexes of Aliphatic Dicarboxylic Acids. Indian Journal of Chemistry. Vol. 5, pp. 627-631.

Andersen, L.M. (1993): Frysetørring af arkæologisk træ og andre våde organiske materialer. Copenhagen. Konservatorskolen, Det Kongelige Danske Kunstakademi. 256 p.

Anon (2006a): Merck Safety Data Sheet for azelaic acid, technical grade (online). http://www.chemdat.info (search · azelaic acid, catalogue no. 820116). Date of issue: 07.11.2006, date of visit: 06.11.2008.

Anon (2006b): Sigma-Aldrich. Sikkerhedsdatablad for azelaic acid, 98% (online). http://www.sigmaaldrich.com/MSDS/MSDS/ DisplayMSDSPage.do. Last updated 11.02.06, date of visit: 06.11.2008.

Bond, A.D.; Edwards, M.R. & Jones, W. (2001): Azelaic acid. Acta Crystallographica, Section E, organic papers. Vol. E57, pp. O143-144.

Carey, F.A. (2008): Organic Chemistry. Seventh edition. Boston. McGraw-Hill. 1229 p.

Chaumat, G., Blanc, L.; Albino, C. & Miffon, F. (2009): Development of new consolidation treatments from fatty acid resin solutions. In: Strætkvern, K. & Huisman, D.J. (eds.): Proceedings of the 10th ICOM Group on Wet Organic Archaeological Materials Conference, Amsterdam 2007. Nederlandse Archeologische Rapporten 37. Amersfoort. Pp. 291-299.

Corish, P.J & Davison, W.H.T. (1955): Infrared Spectra and Crystallinity. Part II. $\alpha\omega$-Dicarboxylic Acids. Journal of the Chemical Society. 1955, part 3. Pp. 2431-2436.

Evans, P.D. & Banks, W.B. (1990): Degradation of wood surfaces by water. Holz als Roh- und Werkstoff. Vol. 48, pp. 159-163.

Feller, R.L. (1978): Standards in the evaluation of thermoplastic resins. In: The International council of Museums. Committee for conservation. 5th triennial meeting, Zagreb 1978. Preprints, 78/16/4.

Frandsen, L.B. (1999): Nybro – gamle bro – et vejanlæg fra tidlig vikingetid. Mark og

Montre. Årbog for Ribe Amts museer 1999. Ribe Amts Museumsråd. pp. 39-50.

Giachi, G., Bettazi, F.; Chimichi, S. & Staccioli, G. (2003): Chemical characterisation of degraded wood in ships discovered in a recent excavation of the Etruscan and Roman harbour of Pisa. Journal of Cultural Heritage. Vol. 4, pp. 75-83.

Giachi, G., Pizzo, B.; Macchioni, N. & Santoni, I. (2009): A chemical characterisation of the decay of waterlogged archaeological wood. In: Strætkvern, K. & Huisman, D.J. (eds.): Proceedings of the 10th ICOM Group on Wet Organic Archaeological Materials Conference, Amsterdam 2007. Nederlandse Archeologische Rapporten 37. Amersfoort. Pp. 21-33

Gunstone, F.D. (1996): Fatty Acid and Lipid Chemistry. London: Blackie Academic & Professional. 243 p.

Gunstone, F.D., Harwood, J.L. & Padley, F.B. (1994): The Lipid Handbook. London. Chapmann & Hall. 721 p. + Appendix.

Harkins, W.D. (1949): Determination of Surface and Interfacial Tension. In: Weissberger, A. (ed.): Physical Methods of Organic Chemistry. 2nd edition. New York. Interscience Publishers, inc. Pp. 355-426.

Hoffmann, P. (1985): On the stabilization of waterlogged oakwood with PEG. Molecular size versus degree of degradation. In: Waterlogged Wood. Study and conservation. Proceedings of the 2nd ICOM Waterlogged Wood Working Group Conference. Grenoble 1984. Pp. 95-115.

Horie, C.V. (1987): Materials for Conservation. Organic consolidants, adhesives and coatings. Oxford. Butterworth-Heinemann. 281 p.

Jensen, P. (1995): Sorption of water and watersoluble agents in waterlogged wooden cell walls. Ph.D. Thesis. Copenhagen. National Museum of Denmark & Royal Veterinary and Agricultural University. 133 p.

Jensen, P. & Schnell, U. (2005): The implications of using low molecular weight PEG for impregnation of waterlogged archaeological wood prior to freeze drying. In: Hoffmann, P.; Strætkvern, K.; Spriggs, J.A. & Gregory, D. (eds.): Proceedings of the 9th ICOM Group on Wet Organic Archaeological Materials Conference. Copenhagen 2004. Pp. 279-310.

Jin, F., Cao, J.; Enomoto, H. & Moriya, T. (2006): Identification of oxidation products and oxidation pathways of high molecular mass dicarboxylic acids under hydrothermal conditions. Journal of Supercritical Fluids. Pp. 80-88.

Ligeza, M., von Endt, D.W.; Erhardt, W.D.; Olin, J.S. & Cheng, Y.T. (1987): The effect of gamma radiation on the chemical stability of paint media. AIC Preprints of papers at the fifteenth annual meeting. Vancouver. P. 238.

MacLeod, I. D. & Richards, V. L. (1997): Wood Degradation on Historic Shipwreck Sites: The use of FT-IR Spectroscopy to Study the Loss of Hemicellulose. In: Proceedings of the 6th ICOM Group on Wet Organic Archaeological Materials Conference. York 1996. Bremerhaven. Pp. 203-228.

McMurry, J. (1998): Fundamentals of Organic Chemistry. 4th edition. Pacific Grove. Brooks/Cole Publishing Company. 566 p.

Ohsugi, M., Miyauchi, K.; Inoue, Y. (1984): Pimelic Acid as a Degradation Product of

Azelaic Acid by Yeast. Agricultural and Biological Chemistry. Vol. 48(7), pp. 1881-1882.

Pandey, K.K. & Pitman, A.J. (2003): FTIR studies of the changes in wood chemistry following decay by brown-rot and white-rot fungi. International Biodeterioration & Biodegradation. Vol. 52, pp. 151-160.

Pavia, D.L., Lampman, G.M. & Kriz, G.S. (1996): Introduction to spectroscopy. A guide for students of organic chemistry. Second edition. Fort Worth. Harcourt Brace College Publishers. 511 p.

Ravn, M. (1999): Nybro. En trævej fra Kong Godfreds tid. In: Laursen, J. (ed.): KUML 1999. Årbog for Jysk Arkæologisk Selskab. Jysk Arkæologisk Selskab. Pp. 227-257.

Rieck, F., Jørgensen, E.; Petersen, P.V. & Christensen, C. (1997): »…som samlede Ofre fra en talrig Krigerflok«. Status over Nationalmuseets Nydamprojekt 1989-97. Nationalmuseets Arbejdsmark. 1997. Pp. 11-35.

Schilling, M.R & Khanjian, H.P. (1996): Gas chromatographic determination of the fatty acid and glycerol content of lipids: I. The effect on pigments and ageing on the composition of oil paints. I: Bridgland, J. (ed.): ICOM committee for conservation, 11th triennial meeting in Edinburg, Scotland, 1-6 September 1996. Preprints. Pp. 220-227.

Suzuki, Y., Muraishi, K. & Matsuki, K. (1992): Thermal behaviour of dicarboxylic acids. Determination of melting point by DTA. Thermochimica Acta. Vol. 211, pp. 171-180.

Thalladi, V.R., Nüsse, M. & Boese, R. (2000): The Melting Point Alternation in α,ω-Alkandicarboxylic Acids. Journal of the American Chemical Society. Vol. 122, pp. 9227-9236.

Tsoumis, G. (1991): Science and Technology of Wood. Structure, Properties, Utilization. Van Nostrand Reinhold. New York. 494 p.

Weast, R.C. (ed.): Handbook of Chemistry and Physics. A ready-reference book of chemical and physical data. 58th Edition 1977-1978. Cleveland: The Chemical Rubber Company.

Wouters, J., van Bos, M.; Lamens, K. (2000): Baroque stucco marble decorations. II. Composition and degradation of the organic materials in historic samples and implications for their conservation. Studies in Conservation. Vol. 45, pp. 169-179.

Yang, L., Ray, M.B.; Yu, L.E. (2008): Photooxidation of dicarboxylic acids – Part I: Effects of inorganic ions on degradation of azelaic acid. Atmospheric Environment. Vol. 42, pp. 856-867.

Zumdahl, S.S. (1997): Chemistry. Alternate Edition. Boston. Houghton Mifflin Company. 1031 p

Questions and answers

Mikkel Christensen: Nanna, you said at one point that the hemicelluloses were most heavily degraded was that determined by FTIR or what method did you use?

Nanna: FTIR

Mikkel Christensen: Yes, FTIR is a very nice method when it works, but it can be terribly tricky to assign everything.

3.3

Study of the azelaic / palmitic acids association to treat waterlogged archaeological wood

Gilles CHAUMAT*, Lionel BLANC,
Christophe ALBINO
ARC-Nucléart, CEA-Grenoble, 17, rue des Martyrs, Grenoble 38054, France
*E-mail: gilles.chaumat@cea.fr

Abstract

This paper describes two methods using azelaic acid to treat wet wood that give satisfactory results in terms of lack of deformation when compared to an equivalent PEG treatment: azelaic/freeze-drying and azelaic/air-drying. An additional treatment was explored for very degraded wood and composite artifacts. It combines azelaic diacid with palmitic acid (a monocarboxylic acid with 16 carbons) within a three-step treatment: azelaic acid permeation, freeze-drying and "dry" palmitic acid permeation of the porous wood structure. Unlike azelaic acid, palmitic acid is fully hydrophobic and not water-soluble. Although the advantages of palmitic acid compared to azelaic acid are numerous, the main problem with the treatment is the inability of replacing water in the wood with palmitic acid. The use of azelaic acid must be used as a transient method allowing the water to be removed without causing the wood to collapse and shrink. The results are promising enough to continue investigating this method in the future.

Keywords: azelaic diacid, palmitic acid, fatty acids, degraded wood, bulking, freeze-drying.

1. Introduction

ARC-Nucléart has already produced preliminary results concerning the use of azelaic diacid as a substitute for PEG in archaeological impregnation (Chaumat, 2007). This carboxylic diacid is ambivalent in its behavior to water as it is water-soluble at high temperature (< 60°C) but not at room temperature (20°C).

Interesting results have been obtained in terms of:

➢ the permeation kinetics of the resin inside the wood,
➢ the efficiency as a bulking agent, even with resin low contents,
➢ the high chemical stability of azelaic acid in the long term,
➢ the low sensitivity of azelaic acid to relative humidity at room temperature.

Although it is possible to exchange water and azelaic acid, preliminary development has shown there are limitations of the treatment if only highly concentrated azelaic acid (more than 50% wt) is used. In fact, there are at least four problems to solve:

- the exposure of the wood to the acidic solution throughout the treatment,
- the large consumption of azelaic acid (from the economic point of view),
- the mechanical cleaning of the azelaic resin crust from the surface of the wood after treatment which produces irritating azelaic powder dust in the air,
- the possibility of treating composite artifacts (iron, salts).

ARC pursued this study for three years, focusing on several important aspects with a view to improving the use of azelaic acid for treating waterlogged wood in realistic and acceptable conditions. These include controlling the pH of the solution, optimizing the operating parameters (short duration, low temperature, low resin content) and the possibility of easily cleaning the wood after treatment in order to remove excess resin from the surface.

Ways of improving the previous parameters were investigated including using a strong base to balance the acidity and using palmitic acid. Why use palmitic acid? We are convinced that palmitic acid is a better substitute for PEG in waterlogged wood treatment than azelaic diacid because the palmitic resin is very cheap, easily available, health-friendly (fit for human consumption), natural (obtained from vegetable oil), more hydrophobic than azelaic acid, chemically stable and it has a melting point near 60°C (closer to that of PEG). Of greatest interest is its surface-active behavior. This property is potentially useful for the preservation of composite artifacts as a passivation phenomenon is expected for iron and minerals (e.g. sulfide contamination).

2. Palmitic Acid with Azelaic Diacid Permeation Treatments

Palmitic acid is an aliphatic fatty monoacid with 16 carbons. Unlike azelaic acid, it is very hydrophobic and not water-soluble at any temperature. We therefore began a short preliminary study of the ternary phase diagram of the "azelaic diacid + palmitic acid + water" system.

FTIR analysis was used to carry out semi-quantitative measurements. Peaks from a specific spectral region (430 to 1550 cm^{-1}) were used to perform a comparison between azelaic acid and palmitic acid in water. Calibration curves were created with some reference samples at different known concentrations. A Thermo-Fisher Nicolet 380® spectrometer was used in combination with ATR (Attenuated Total Reflectance) for faster results.

The main mixture studied was 45%wt azelaic acid + 45%wt water + 10%wt palmitic acid. Two working temperatures of 70°C and 80°C were considered.

The ternary system appears to be very complex:

- At 70°C, at least 3 phases are noted: a light, thin cap of palmitic and azelaic acid; a thin middle layer consisting of azelaic acid and water; and the largest and heaviest phase at the bottom is a mixture of azelaic acid and water with a very small amount of palmitic acid (see Figure 1 and Table 1).
- At 80°C, the system is simpler. Only two phases are observed: a thin cap of palmitic and azelaic acid and a homogeneous phase of a mixture of azelaic acid and water with a very small amount of palmitic acid (see Figure 1 and Table 2).

According to these initial results, palmitic acid **cannot** be dissolved in significant amounts in a water/azelaic diacid solution. The palmitic acid content is less than 5% wt. The tripahsic layers of the solution at 70°C cannot be used for treatment. The biphasic mixture of water + azelaic acid at 80°C however can be used for impregnating wood as it is quite homogenous throughout the bulk of the liquid. There are no successive stratified layers of azelaic acid and water with different contents which means that the bulk monophasic solution can be used to treat the wood, ensuring the reproducibility of the treatment.

Consequently, the results show that it is not possible to combine azelaic and palimitic acids in the water contained in archaeological wood. Even though these two acids can be mixed, they separate in the presence of water. Azelaic acid is hydrated while palmitic acid remains insoluble in water. The use of palmitic acid will therefore be restricted to that of a simple "liquid stopper" on the aqueous solution of azelaic acid to limit water vaporization during the azelaic acid treatment. For this reason, palmitic acid is unable to participate directly in azelaic acid permeation of wet wood. Palmitic acid impregnation can be considered only during subsequent treatment after the wood has been dried.

Table 1. *Phases from the mixture of 45% wt azelaic acid + 45% wt H₂O + 10% wt palmitic acid at 70°C after stirring.*

Phase	Azelaic acid % wt	H₂O % wt	Palmitic acid % wt
1 Top	29%	0%	71%
2 Middle	31%	69%	0%
3.1 Bottom	53%	46%	1%
3.2 Bottom	61%	37%	2%
3.3 Bottom	62%	36%	2%

Table 2. *Phases from the mixture of 45% wt azelaic acid + 45% wt H₂O + 10% wt palmitic acid at 80°C after stirring.*

Phases	Azelaic acid % wt	H₂O % wt	Palmitic acid % wt
1 Top	30%	4%	66%
3.1 Bottom	50%	46%	4%
3.2 Bottom	50%	46%	4%
3.3 Bottom	50%	46%	4%

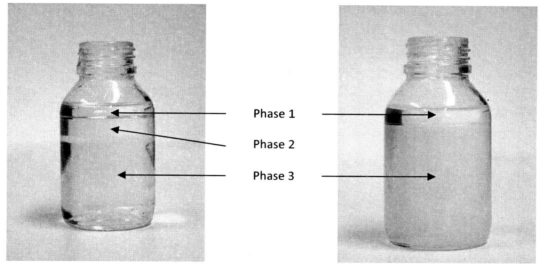

Phase 1

Phase 2

Phase 3

Figure 1. Comparison of phases from the mixture of 45% wt azelaic acid + 45% wt H₂O + 10% wt palmitic acid after stirring between 70°C (left) and 80°C (right).

3. Controlling the Acidity of an Azelaic Solution

Recent studies show that the acidity of azelaic diacid at high temperatures is able to degrade wood quickly (Pedersen 2008). Theoretically, it is possible to obtain a buffer solution by neutralizing an organic acid such as azelaic acid with a strong base. Caustic potash or potassium hydroxide (KOH) was chosen as the buffer. Three buffer concentrations were studied and compared with an un-neutralized reference. The azelaic acid/water content is kept constant at 50 wt%/50 wt%. There is no need for a higher azelaic acid content. It does not improve consolidation, is costly and makes the treatment solution too acidic. Consequently, the entire study was carried out with an azelaic acid concentration of no more than 50 wt%.

The measurement protocol involved a pH-meter (Metrohm 692® pH/ion Meter) with a Solitrode® electrode coupled with a Pt 100 for the temperature measurement. The solutions were stirred and heated to

209

70°C (considered to be the working temperature for wood impregnation). Each measurement point was read after 90 minutes at equilibrium. *Table 3* compares different KOH neutralization rates at 70°C. Complete neutralization of azelaic diacid requires 2 moles of KOH for 1 mole of azelaic diacid.

The first observation is the acidity of the reference solution (without KOH) which is below pH 2(see Figure 2). This level is not acceptable for treating wood, especially already chemically degraded wood such as archaeological artifacts. A 5% KOH mol or 10 KOH% mol neutralization rate is not sufficient to increase the pH above 4. A pH of 4 is an acceptable target and is comparable to the pH of PEG solutions currently used. Satisfactory values were reached above a 20 KOH% mol neutralization rate as we succeeded in raising the pH to 4.5 (see Figure 3). A 20 KOH% mol neutralization rate corresponds

to the following composition of the treatment solution mixture:

azelaic diacid content = 8.4 % mol= 46.5 % wt

water content = 87.4 % mol= 46.5 % wt

KOH content = 4.2 % mol= 7 % wt

It is thus possible to propose a 46.5%-46.5%wt azelaic acid-water solution for treating waterlogged archaeological artifacts if at least 7% wt of KOH is add to partially neutralize the acidity.

Another interesting approach consists in looking at the conductivity of the solution. Azelaic acid dissolution corresponds to the production of carboxylate and proton ions in the solution (electrical signature of azelaic dissolution). Each point is read after 90 minutes to ensure equilibrium (see Figure 4).

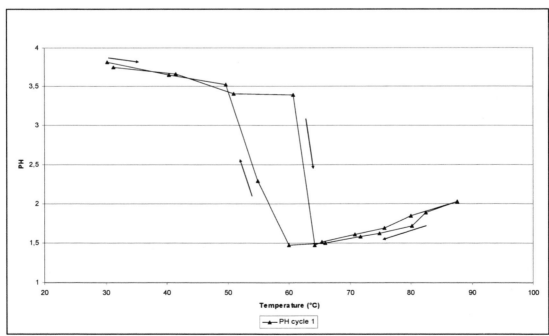

Figure 2. *Change in pH versus temperature of 50% wt azelaic acid + 50% wt water solution without KOH.*

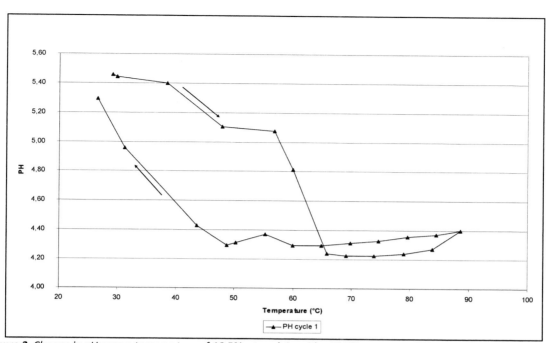

Figure 3. Change in pH versus temperature of 46.5% wt azelaic acid + 46.5% wt water + 7% KOH solution (20% mol KOH neutralization rate).

Table 3. pH of different solutions of 50% wt azelaic acid + 50% wt water with several KOH neutralization rates at 70°C.

KOH neutralization rate (% mol)	0	5	10	20
pH	1.5	3.5	3.8	4.3

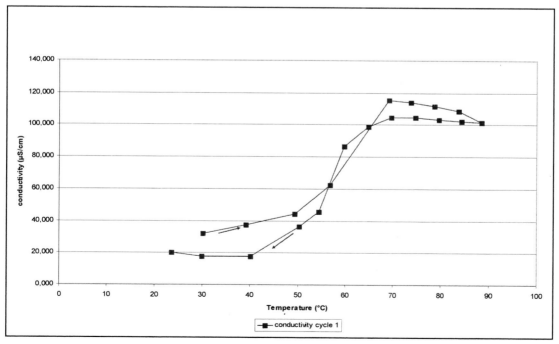

Figure 4. Conductivity curves of a solution containing 50% wt azelaic acid + 50% wt water versus temperature.

Firstly, it can be seen that the conductivity and pH curves are roughly consistent. It is possible to choose one of these two methods for studying the dissolution of azelaic diacid in a water solution. Secondly, it is easy to observe the strong increase in electrical conductivity that gives the threshold temperature area in which dissolution becomes more effective. This domain is close to the 40-65°C range for both pH and conductivity curves

A third approach consisted in measuring the melting point (in fact the plateau just after the supercooling point) obtained by a thermal probe during cooling of the solution. Table 4 and Figures 5 a and b show the change in melting point of a 50%-50%wt azelaic acid-water solution with and without neutralization with various amounts of KOH as well as the effect of the addition of 7% palmitic acid.

Potassium hydroxide lowered the melting point to a point between 58°C and 46°C. The effect of a small amount of palmitic acid dissolved in the mixture is insignificant. The melting point dropped to 58.6°C with palmitic acid instead of 58.8°C without palmitic acid (see Table 4). Lowering the melting point by adding KOH is potentially interesting for the treatment, because it becomes possible to use a lower permeation temperature of 60°C or even 50°C instead of 70°C.

Similar experiments were performed using an aqueous solution with a very low azelaic acid content of 15% wt. This diluted solution will be used in subsequent work associated with freeze-drying. Using a neutralization rate of 20% mol KOH the following composition was obtained: 15% wt azelaic acid + 84% wt H_2O + 1% wt KOH. The melting point of this bath was 46.9°C with a pH near to 4.05 at 70°C. This composition can be considered to be useful as a treatment option for wood as the pH is higher than 4.

4 Developing a Treatment Protocol For Archaeological Wood Using Azelaic Acid

Two approaches were tested: a concentrated azelaic acid treatment followed by air-drying (equivalent of a PEG saturation treatment) and an azelaic acid treatment with lower bulking resin content followed by freeze-drying (equivalent of a PEG/freeze-drying treatment). The treatment used an aqueous azelaic acid solution partially neutralized by KOH at 70°C. At this temperature all the azelaic acid is fully dissolved in water and can permeate the bulk of the wood. After the impregnation step, the wooden artifacts are removed from the solution and immersed in fresh water to crystallize the azelaic diacid into a rigid skeleton in the wood.

Table 4. Melting point of azelaic acid base treatment solution with and without neutralization with KOH and with and without 7% palmitic acid. * Contents given in % wt

KOH neutralization rate % mol	0 without palmitic cap*	0 with palmitic cap*	5 with palmitic cap*	10 with palmitic cap*	20 with palmitic cap*
Melting point	58.8°C	58.6°C	54.8°C	53.5°C	46.3°C

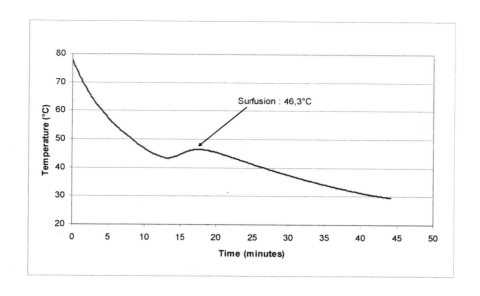

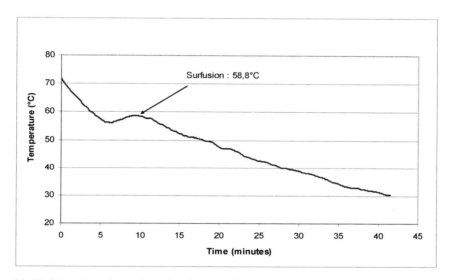

Figures 5 a and b: Melting point of azelaic acid and water solutions with different KOH neutralization rates: 0% mol (4b, bottom), 20% mol (4a, top).

4.1. Treatment with concentrated azelaic acid solution and drying in air (saturation treatment)

In contrast to PEG treatment, there is no need to reach a concentration of 70-80% wt of azelaic acid. Azelaic resin is stronger than PEG and it can be used at 50% wt without the wood collapsing, even if the wood is very degraded. Consequently a solution containing 46.5% wt water + 46.5% wt azelaic acid + 7% wt KOH was prepared at 70°C. Nine samples of archaeological wood of different shapes and different degrees of degradation were selected. The impregnation process lasted 10 days. Permeation ended with simple air-drying for a couple of weeks at 20°C without any humidity control. The sizes of the samples were measured before and after the treatment in order to evaluate a "volume lost" coefficient, as follow (see Table 5):

Volume lost = (final volume – initial volume) / initial volume

Table 5. *Volume lost after treatment with a solution containing 46.5% wt water + 46.5% wt azelaic acid + 7% wt KOH followed by a simple air-drying.*

	Very degraded wood (3 samples of soft wood))	Slightly degraded wood (6 samples of hard wood)
Volume lost (%)	-8, -8, -11	-13, -11, 13, -15, -13, -10

Table 6. *Volume lost after treatment with a solution containing 83% wt water + 15% wt azelaic acid + 2% KOH followed by freeze-drying treatment.*

	Very degraded wood (4 samples of soft wood)	Slightly degraded wood (4 samples of hard wood)
Volume lost (%)	0, -5, 0, -1	-10, -6, -10, -12

4.2. Treatment with low azelaic acid content and vacuum freeze-drying

The first point to check, when freeze-drying, is the melting point (or freezing point) of a "water + azelaic acid" mixture. Using a thermal probe, the plateau just after the supercooling point was measured as the temperature of the mixture rose from -20°C to +20°C. The melting point is 0°C, the same as that for pure water. Unlike PEG, azelaic acid does not have any effect on the freezing point and complete freezing of the water in archaeological wood during freeze-drying treatment can be obtained. We even had successful freeze-drying with a poor vacuum level between 50 to 200 Pa.

A solution containing 15% wt azelaic acid, 83% wt H_2O and 2% wt KOH was chosen for the experiments. Eight samples were permeated for 10 days, followed by freeze-drying for one week in a vacuum of 8 x Pa. The results are summarized in Table 6.

4.3. Discussion

Treatments with azelaic acid and equivalent treatments with PEG 4000 produce comparable results. With slightly degraded wood the volume lost is nearly 10%. The results are not as efficient with slightly degraded wood because freeze-drying and saturation treatments do not prevent any shrinkage of cell walls when the water is removed. The results are more promising in the case of treatment with a low azelaic acid content, especially for degraded wood. Some samples displayed almost no deformation.

The strength of the wood with only 15% wt of resin may be insufficient from a mechanical strength point of view. Moreover, the treatment is not fully suitable for heterogeneous artifacts. The acidity of azelaic acid solution aggravates the corrosion of iron and reactions of other minerals (sulfide, chloride salts). For these two last reasons, it was decided to study a complementary treatment of "dry" impregnation of the freeze-dried wood in a pure liquid palmitic acid bath.

5. Complementary Treatment with Pure Palmitic Acid

5.1. Description of the "dry" palmitic acid treatment

The first and second steps are similar to those of the previous protocol described with freeze-drying. First, impregnation in a solution with 15% wt azelaic acid, 83% wt H_2O and 2% wt KOH. The impregnation phase lasted 10 days at 70°C. At the end of this, the wood was immersed in cold water to prevent it from drying after it was removed from the solution. Secondly, freeze-drying was performed at 8 Pa for one week. The third part of the treatment is optional and can be used for very degraded wood or composite artifacts. In the case of very degraded and brittle artifacts the wood may be consolidated by a final impregnation in a pure liquid palmitic acid bath. This impregnation occurs as a result of capillary forces. It is very short, lasting several hours, and is carried out at 70°C. This last treatment produces artifacts that have better mechanical strength and are insensitive to changing environmental conditions. Figure 6 shows the microstructure of degraded wood after palmitic acid permeation. It can be seen that some of the cell porosity has been kept. Only the cell walls are covered. Only about half the cell lumens are full of palmitic acid. Impregnation is only partial. To prevent corrosion of metals a full impregnation of the wood would likely be needed. A "vacuum/pressure" technique might permit us to reach this target.

5.2. Cleaning of the wood after treatment

It is important to clean the wood by removing excess resin from the surface in order to recover the natural color of wood. It is strongly recommended that the artifact should be drained at 60°C for several minutes to remove all excess palmitic acid resin from the surface. It is possible to increase this "draining" treatment by using an oxygen free environment (e.g. vacuum) to limit the oxidation of the organic resin, especially in humid atmospheres. Figure 7 shows the samples treated with azelaic/palmitic acids before and after cleaning.

6. Conclusion and perspectives

After a 5-year study, ARC-Nucléart has succeeded in defining at least three protocols for treating waterlogged wood using fatty acids instead of PEG:

- An equivalent to a PEG saturation treatment using a solution containing 46.5% wt azelaic acid, 46.5% wt H_2O and 7% wt KOH. This treatment is followed by simple air-drying.

- An equivalent to a PEG/freeze-drying treatment involving 15% wt azelaic acid, 83% wt H_2O and 2% wt KOH.

- A complementary treatment of a "dry" impregnation in pure palmitic acid, applied after an azelaic acid/freeze-drying treatment, for very degraded wood or composite artifacts.

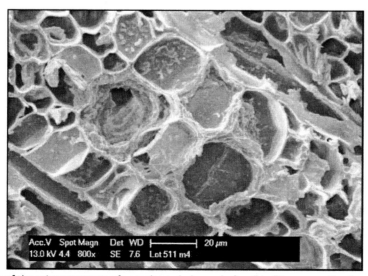

Figure 6. SEM image of the microstructure of very degraded wood after "dry" impregnation by palmitic acid.

Figure 7. Samples after azelaic/palmitc resin permeation with cleaning (top), without cleaning (bottom).

The last protocol constitutes a preliminary phase of the study and more work is required before the treatment can be validated. The results appear to be sufficiently satisfactory to continue with this investigation. Our main efforts must now focus upon the behavior of composite materials with the palmitic treatment. Does the treatment stabilize the corrosion of the iron parts and the salts such as sulfides or chlorides? Investigation also needs to be performed to demonstrate the harmlessness of carboxylic acids on wood tissues during and after treatment *i.e.* the resistance of the material to chemical ageing during long-term exhibition or storage.

References

Chaumat, G., Blanc, L., Albino, C. and F. Miffon (2007): Development of new consolidation treatments from fatty acid resin solutions, Proceedings of the 10th ICOM Group on Wet Organic Archaeological Materials Conference, Amsterdam 2007, pp 291-300.

Pedersen, N.B (2009): Examination of azelaic acid as an impregnation agent for waterlogged archaeological wood, Master Thesis – Konservatorskolen, Det Kongelige Danske Kunstakademi, January 2009.

Questions and answers

Stephanie Crette: I was wondering if you were planning on comparing your study on corrosion and azelaic acid with some of the corrosion inhibitors that are based on fatty acids.

Giles Chaumat: No, because I have been trying to do this. The last tests I did are not in the paper.

Stephanie Crette: I have no idea about France but here in the States, you have some projects on contact corrosion of metal and iron and fatty acids and I was wondering if that would be interesting?

Jim Spriggs: You say in your paper that you started using the palmitic acids to modify the azelaic acids and you ended up by finding that there might be more use for the palmitic acids than the azelaic acid. So is this the last we're going to hear of azelaic acid?

Giles Chaumat: No, I think there is complement between these two materials. I cannot use palmitic acid directly with wet wood but if I find other acids than azelaic acid, that are soluble that would be better.

3.4 (ScPR)

Dimensional Stability and Ultrastructural Features of Waterlogged Wood Reinforced by Pure Feather Keratin

Rie Endo*

Toyo Feather Industry Co. Ltd.and Research Institute for Sustainable Humanosphere, Kyoto University
Address: 2-26-5, Fuchinobe, Chuo Ward, Sagamihara, Kanagawa, 252-0206, Japan.
*E-mail: riendomame@rish.kyoto-u.ac.jp

Junji Sugiyama

Research Institute for Sustainable Humanosphere, Kyoto University

Abstract

Commercially available pure feather keratin powder was investigated for conservation of waterlogged wood. Thin sections of waterlogged wood were used to determine dimensional stability. Feather keratin provided excellent dimensional stability to waterlogged wood. Micromorphological observations showed that middle lamellae became more electron dense than secondary walls. Feather keratin penetrated into the middle lamellae rather than into the secondary walls. The middle lamellae reinforced by feather keratin supported the wood mechanically by providing a honeycomb structure.

Keywords: feather keratin, waterlogged wood, conservation, dimensional stability, middle lamellae.

1. Introduction

In 2004, we presented a novel method for the conservation of waterlogged wood using avian feather keratin (Endo et al. 2004). Avian feather is one of several biomass resources that have been examined as sustainable materials in recent years. Feather is composed mainly of keratin protein and the molecular mass of feather keratin is lower than that of other keratin proteins such as wool or hair keratins. Therefore, feather keratin has various applications; for example, it is used as a substrate for cell culture medium (Poopathi et al. 2008), as material for fiber composites (Bullions et al. 2006) and in the production of enzymes (Azeredo et al. 2006). In our study, feather was hydrolyzed with 1M sodium hydroxide aqueous solution and neutralized with acetic acid. Therefore, the feather hydrolysate contained feather keratin and sodium acetate. The treatment using feather hydrolysate suppressed deformation caused by drying and provided excellent dimensional stability to waterlogged wood (Endo et al. 2008). It also enhanced the physical and mechanical properties of the wood (Endo et al. 2010). However, the process for preparing feather hydrolysate was laborious; it included many steps such as disintegration from bulk, followed by dissolution and concentration of the feather hydrolysate. In addition, the treatment made the wood very hygroscopic because of high amount of sodium acetate contained in feather hydrolysate.

To overcome such disadvantages, we investigated pure feather keratin powder commercially available from the Toyo Feather Industry Co. Ltd. We examined the dimensional stability of wood treated with pure feather keratin. The measurement of dimensional stability was performed using thin sections instead of wood blocks. Microscopic observations of feather keratin-treated wood were performed with scanning electron microscopy and transmission electron microscopy.

2. Materials and Methods
2.1. Wood samples
A waterlogged Chinese soapberry (*Sapindus mukorossi Gaertn*) log was found at an

archaeological site (2800 years old). The saturated moisture content (*Umax*) of the waterlogged wood was calculated as follows:

$$U\max(\%) = \frac{W_u - W_0}{W_0} \times 100$$

Here, W_u is the weight of saturated waterlogged wood specimens immersed in water in a vacuum desiccator for 30 min and W_0 is the oven-dry weight of waterlogged wood specimens at 105°C for 48 h.

Chinese soapberry was cut into 5(Tangential) × 5(Radial) × 10(Longitudinal) mm specimens for evaluation of dimensional stability and cut into 5(T) × 5(R) × 5(L) mm specimens for microscopic observation.

Table 1. *Characteristics of feather keratin, 'Keratide'.*

Appearance	: white yellowish brown
Nitrogen	: > 7%
pH	: 4.5-8.5 (5% aqueous solution)
Heavy metals	: < 20 ppm
Arsenic	: < 2 ppm
Loss of drying	: < 10%
Residue on ignition	: < 12%

2.2 Impregnation

For the evaluation of dimensional stability, sections of Chinese soapberry 100 ☐m in thick were cut from the 5(T) × 5(R) × 10(L) mm specimens with a microtome. Feather keratin powder was provided by the Toyo Feather Industry (Kanagawa, Japan). Table 1 shows the characteristics of the feather keratin *Keratide*. The molecular mass of feather keratin powder was about 750 (instruction leaflet of Toyo Feather Industry 2009). Each Chinese soapberry section was set up in a well of a 24-well microplate and 1-mL of 10 w/v % to 60 w/v% feather keratin aqueous solution was added to the wells. The treatment was performed at 25°C for two days. After the treatment, the solution was removed and the sections were air dried in the wells at 25°C for one day.

For the microscopic observation, the Chinese soapberry specimens were immersed into a 20 w/v% feather keratin aqueous solution at 25°C, and the concentration of the solution was raised every 2 days in steps of 20 w/v%

finally to 60 w/v%. The blocks were air dried at 25°C in 60% relative humidity.

2.3 Measurement of dimensional stability

Dimensional stability was determined as follows. Calculations were made using the distances between two points on the same annual ring for the tangential direction and on the same ray for the radial direction. The photographs of the treated sections before and after drying were taken with a CCD camera (Kodak Megaplus camera model 1.6i). The images (1538 ×1032 pixels) obtained were analysed to measure the dimensional stability using image analysis software (Image J, National Institutes of Health, USA). Shrinkage (☐) and shrinkage in cross-sectional shrinkage (☐$_{cs}$) were calculated as below:

$$\beta(\%) = \frac{l_u - l_t}{l_u} \times 100$$

$$\beta_{cs}(\%) = \left[1 - (1 - \frac{\beta_t}{100})(1 - \frac{\beta_r}{100})\right] \times 100$$

where, l_u and l_t are the distances in saturated wood without treatment and in the wood treated with feather keratin, respectively. Where, $\square_t$ and $\square_r$ are shrinkages in the tangential and in radial directions, respectively. Anti-shrink efficiency (ASE), as an indicator of the dimensional stability of wood, was calculated as follows:

$$ASE = \frac{S_c - S_t}{S_c} \times 100$$

where S_c is shrinkage in the cross section of air-dried wood without treatment and S_t is shrinkage in the cross section of feather keratin-treated wood. The mean values from three similar specimens were calculated.

2.4 Scanning electron microscopy (SEM)

Cross sections cut from freeze-dried, air-dried without treatment and feather keratin-treated Chinese soapberry were coated with platinum (2 nm in thickness). They were observed at 1.5 kV and 20 mA under 10^{-8} Pa by a field-emission SEM (JSM-6700F).

2.5 Transmission electron microscopy (TEM)

Air-dried, untreated and feather keratin-treated Chinese soapberry specimens (5 (T) × 5(R) × 5(L) mm) were fixed with 3% glutaraldehyde for 4 h and washed with distilled water 6 times. The specimens were fixed in 2% osmium tetroxide for 2 h and washed with distilled water 6 times. After the dehydration procedure in an ethanol series, the specimens were embedded in Epon 812. The sections were cut with a Reichert-Jung ULTRACUT *E* ultramicrotome and stained by uranyl acetate and lead citrate. The observation was performed at an acceleration voltage of 100 kV by TEM (JEM-2000EX II).

3. Results and Discussion
3.1. Dimensional stability

Table 2 shows the cross-sectional shrinkage and anti-shrink efficiency of Chinese soapberry. The Umax of Chinese soapberry was about 500%. The dimensional stability of Chinese soapberry improved with increasing concentrations of feather keratin for treatment. Figure. 1 shows the feather keratin-treated sections. The treatment with 60 w/v% feather keratin solution provided excellent stability to the wood. The result shows that pure feather keratin is efficient in the conservation of waterlogged wood. The measurement with thin sections enabled us to prepare sequential and identical specimens easily and determine shrinkage quickly

3.2 Microscopic observation

SEM images of air-dried without treatment, freeze-dried without treatment and feather keratin-treated wood are shown in Figure 2. In the air-dried section, most cells have collapsed. Figure 2b shows the freeze-dried section without treatment. The secondary.

Table 2. Shrinkage and anti-shrink efficiency of Chinese soapberry treated with feather keratin.

Keratin concentration (w/v%)	Cross-sectional shrinkage (%)	Anti-shrink efficiency
0	39.7	
10	15.7	60
20	8.9	77
30	7.4	81
40	6.6	83
50	2.6	93
60	0.9	98

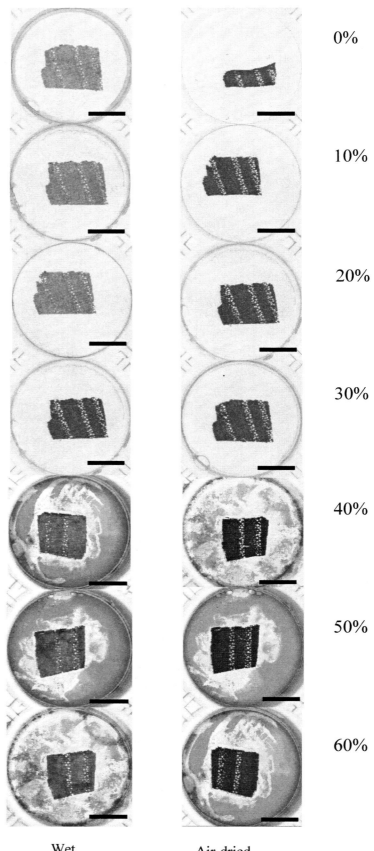

Figure. 1. Wet (left column) and air-dried (right column) waterlogged Chinese soapberry sections treated with feather keratin. Scale bar = 5 mm.

0%

10%

20%

30%

40%

50%

60%

Wet

Air-dried

Figure. *2.* Scanning electron micrographs of cross sections from Chinese soapberry.

(a) Air-dried wood without treatment,

(b) freeze-dried wood without treatment and

(c) feather keratin-treated wood.

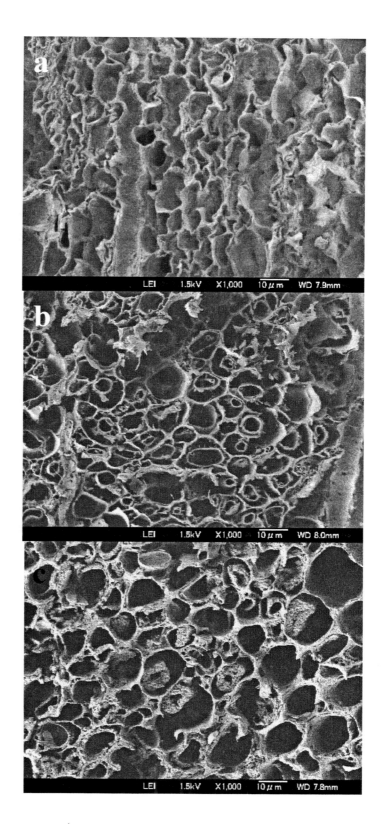

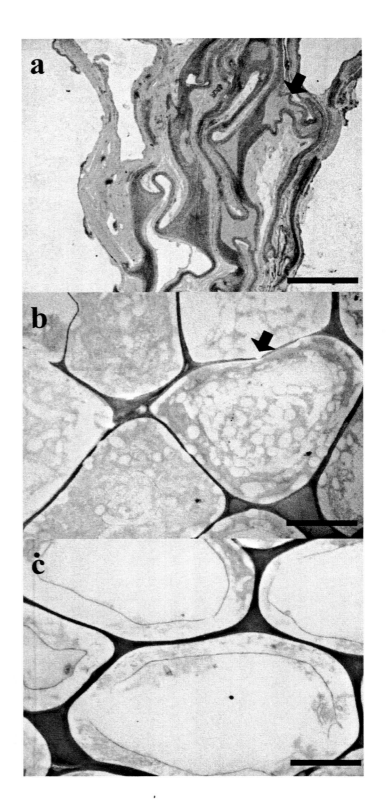

Figure. 3. Transmission electron micrographs of cross sections from Chinese soapberry.

(a) Air-dried wood without treatment,

(b) untreated wood and

(c) feather keratin-treated wood.

Scale bar = 5μm.

walls have almost decayed and remain as tube-like thin walls inside the lumen. However, in the feather keratin-treated section, the middle lamellae retained the contours seen in Figure 2c. At the same time, sponge-like secondary walls were observed 'floating' in the lumen. The result shows that feather keratin penetrated into the middle lamellae as well as into the secondary walls and provided the rigidity to the middle lamellae and some stability to the remnants of the secondary walls.

Figure 3 shows TEM images of air dried without treatment, untreated and feather keratin-treated wood. The cells have been crushed by air drying as shown in Figure 3a. Both secondary walls and middle lamellae were wavy (the arrow in Figure 3a) and had no mechanical strength. It is well known that bacterial attack is primarily responsible for the decay of waterlogged wood (Björdal *et al*. 1999, Blanchette *et al*. 2000, Gelbrich *et al*. 2008). The cell walls in our samples were heavily attacked by erosion bacteria, as shown in Figure 3b. The decay by bacteria was observed not only in the secondary walls but also in a part of the middle lamellae (arrow in Figure 3b). The secondary wall has already departed from the middle lamellae and lost the layer structure. However, in feather keratin-treated wood, the middle lamellae were more electron dense than the secondary walls (Figure 3c). Feather keratin penetrated into the middle lamella and supported the wood mechanically as a rigid honeycomb structure. The results indicated that feather keratin reinforced middle lamellae regions of waterlogged wood.

These micromorphological observations revealed the unique mechanism of conservation with feather keratin. In particular, the accessibility of middle lamellae for feather keratin is an advantage for the conservation of waterlogged wood, because middle lamellae remain comparatively stable compared to the secondary walls in the heavily degraded waterlogged wood.

4. Conclusion

Commercially available feather keratin powder was examined for the conservation of waterlogged wood. The measurement using thin sections of waterlogged wood indicated that feather keratin treatment provided good dimensional stability to the wood. In this study, we used small specimens in order to identify feather keratin's effect. To apply feather keratin to practical conservation of waterlogged wood, experimental data that used bigger specimens should be accumulated. Microscopic observations showed that feather keratin penetrated into the middle lamellae reinforced the cell walls.

Acknowledgement
The study was performed with the support of the Xylarium Database of the Research Institute for Sustainable Humanosphere, Kyoto University. We thank the Kyoto City Archaeological Research Institute for donating experimental wood specimens.

References
Azeredo L. A. I. D., Lima M. B. D., Coelho R. R. R., Freire D. M. G., (2006), A Low-cost Fermentation Medium for Thermophilic Protease Production by *Streptomyces* sp. 594 Using Feather Meal and Corn Steep Liquor. Current Microbiology. 53, 4, 335-339.

Bullions T. A., Hoffman D., Gillespie R. A., Price-O'Brien J., Loos A. C., (2006), Contributions of Feather Fibers and Various Cellulose Fibers to the Mechanical Properties of Polypropylene Matrix Composites. Composites Science and Technology. 66, 1, 102-114.

Björdal C. G., Nilsson T., Daniel G., (1999), Microbial Decay of Waterlogged Archaeological Wood Found in Sweden,

Applicable to Archaeology and Conservation. International Biodeterioration and Biodegradation. 43, 63-73.

Blanchette R. A., (2000), A Review of Microbial Deterioration Found in Archaeological Wood from Different Environments. International Biodeterioration and Biodegradation. 46, 189-204.

Endo R., Kawahara Y., (2004), Research Activities Using Duck Feather Hydrolysate for Archaeological Waterlogged Woods, Proceedings of the 9th International Council of Museums Group on Wet Organic Archaeological Materials Conference, 637-639, Copenhagen/Denmark.

Endo R., Kamei K., Iida I., Kawahara Y., (2008), Dimensional Stability of Waterlogged Wood Treated with Hydrolyzed Feather Keratin. Journal of Archaeological Science. 35, 1240-1246.

Endo R., Kamei K., Yokoyama M., Iida I., Kawahara Y., (2010), Physical and Mechanical Properties of Waterlogged Wood Treated with Hydrolyzed Feather Keratin. Journal of Archaeological Science. 37, 1311-1316.

Gelbrich J., Mai C., Militz H., (2008), Chemical Changes in Wood Degraded by Bacteria. International Biodeterioration and Biodegradation. 61, 24-32.Instruction Leaflet of hydrolyzed keratin from down and feather, (2009), Toyo Feather Industry Co. Ltd. (in Japanese)

Poopathi S., Abidha S., (2008), Biodegradation of Poultry Waste for the Production of Mosquitocidal Toxins. International Biodeterioration and Biodegradation. 62, 4, 479-482.

Questions and answers

Dilys Johns: Did you do any reversibility studies?

Rie Endo: Maybe it was difficult because this is specifically introduced into the middle lamella that is why most of the keratin can be removed but something is happening at the middle lamella that is affecting removal.

Jim Spriggs: It would depend, I suppose, if there is any chemical bonding between the protein and the structure of the middle lamella making it more difficult to remove.

Rie Endo: Yes.

Jim Spriggs: There's a question about whether you can even remove polyethylene glycol from the second order space.

Lars Andersen: Have you tried this method on bigger objects? There is more surface on very small objects and I notice that when you just went a little bit further you got quite a lot of shrinkage and I thought if you're impregnating by 14% maybe its response is confined by osmosis.

Rie Endo: Yes. I wanted to try to save the waterlogged wood - it's difficult to get samples and the results are disappointing because of the terrible shrinkage. Maybe something is wrong – I need more keratin or treatment conditions …..

Keratin as a Bulking and Stabilization Agent for Collapsible Waterlogged Archaeological Wood

Poul Jensen* and Kristiane Strætkvern
The National Museum of Denmark, Department of Conservation, I.C. Modewegs Vej, Brede, DK-2800 Kgs. Lyngby, Denmark, Phone: +45 3347352145 or +33473525
*E-mail: poul.jensen@natmus.dk

Knud Villy Christensen
Institute of Chemical, Biotechnology and Environmental Technology, University of Southern Denmark, Campusvej 55, DK-5230 Odense M, Denmark

Dorte Bak
Tetra PAK Filtration Systems, Søren Nymarksvej 13, DK-8270 Højbjerg, Denmark

Ulrich Schnell
Skovmindevej 12, Øster Alling, 8963 Auning, Denmark

Abstract
Water-soluble keratin made from hydrolyzed duck feathers was tested as a bulking and stabilizing agent for recent beech veneer and low density waterlogged archaeological wood.

The duck feather keratin used was provided by Toyo Feather Company. It is a light yellow powder with a bulk density of approximately 170 $kg \cdot m^{-3}$. The density for the solid keratin substance is 1560 $kg \cdot m^{-3}$, close to that of cell wall material of wood. It does not have a melting point, but starts to decompose at 160°C. At 50% RH it has an equilibrium moisture content below 3% w/w and is as such less hygroscopic than wood. Duck feather keratin reduces the surface tension of aqueous solutions to 45 $mPa \cdot m^{-1}$, and its pH in aqueous solutions is between 7 and 6. Although its reported molecular weight is between 1500 and 2000 $g \cdot mol^{-1}$, it has a high freezing point depression, due to a substantial amount of salts and other impurities present in the powder. Based on freezing point depression and EMC, the keratin has an apparent molecular mass of approximately 185 $g \cdot mol^{-1}$. It does not have well defined collapse or eutectic temperature and is therefore unsuitable as an impregnation agent for objects which are to be freeze-dried.

The keratin molecules are able to enter the cell wall and replace some of the bound water, to swell recent beech veneer beyond that of pure water, and keep swollen dimensions up to 8% over that of pure water after air drying at standard museum climate conditions (20°C, 50% RH). Waterlogged archaeological wooden objects with a density of 100 $kg \cdot m^{-3}$ and a high tendency to collapse, only showed a minor reduction in collapse when air dried, although impregnated with up to 0.40 w/w aqueous keratin solution. The average tangential shrinkage was in the order of 25% at the end of the drying process.

The general conclusion is that the present type of keratin made from hydrolyzed duck feather cannot be used for impregnation of heavily degraded low density waterlogged archaeological wooden artifacts prior to air drying if collapse is to be avoided. Owing to its ability to enter the cell wall, keratin may be used as bulking or stabilizing agents for the surface treatment of non-collapsible archaeological wood, but further research has to be done, including an examination of health and safety aspects of its use.

Keywords: Hydrolyzed duck feather keratin, waterlogged wood, air-drying, collapse, shrinkage, solubility, binary phase diagram, pH, surface tension.

1. Introduction
Endo & Kawahara (2005), Kawahara et al. (2008) describe a conservation method

where water-soluble duck feather hydrolysate is used. Archaeological wood specimens are immersed in 10% w/w aqueous solution of hydrolyzed feather keratin at 60°C. The concentration of the solution is then raised every 3 or 5 days in steps of 10% w/w up to 40% w/w. After the impregnation is finished, the specimens are air-dried at ambient temperature until equilibrium moisture content (EMC) is reached. Their research demonstrated that hydrolyzed keratin could be used as a bulking and stabilizing agent where heavily degraded waterlogged wooden objects could be impregnated and subsequently air-dried without collapse. Investigations at the School of Conservation in Copenhagen (Hansen 2005) gave less positive results.

In 2005, The National Museum, Department of Conservation, set up a research scheme for testing keratin to see if it was suitable for the types of waterlogged wood normally treated by freeze-drying at the National Museum. A pilot project using hydrolyzed keratin from chicken feathers and lambs' wool as impregnation agents prior to air-drying gave inconclusive results. Systematic research was started in collaboration with the South Danish University (SDU), which was working on a project concerning the concentration of water-soluble duck feather keratin hydrolysate (Christensen et al. 2009). SDU provided industrial produced keratin hydrolysate made by Toyo Feather Industry Co. Ltd., Japan, similar to that used by Endo & Kawahara (2005). The Japanese keratin hydrolysate was used for all further experiments.

As keratin is just one of a series of impregnation agents the Conservation Department wants to examine, the research followed a systematic method described by Pedersen (2009), so the results can be part of a broader analysis of the properties of impregnation agents and related conservation methods. The results of the research on keratin are presented in this article.

2. Experimental work

Industrial produced keratin hydrolysate made by Toyo Feather Industry Co. Ltd., Japan was used for all experiments. The standard physical properties given by the manufacturer, see data sheet (Anon. 1) in Appendix 1. All water used for the experiments was de-ionized with a conductivity of less than $4\mu S\ cm^{-1}$.

The experimental work with duck feather keratin was divided in two parts: one part examined the material properties for duck feather keratin while another evaluated conservation treatments.

Determination of material properties for keratin:
- melting point
- bulk density of keratin powder
- density of aqueous solutions and
- density of solid keratin
- pH in aqueous solutions at 20° C
- surface tension of aqueous solutions
- viscosity of aqueous solutions
- binary phase diagram for aqueous solutions
- moisture sorption isotherm
- form stability of aqueous solutions when air dried

Conservation experiments with wood and keratin
- Swelling capacity of recent beech wood veneer
- Conservation experiments on degraded waterlogged archaeological wood

2.1 Determination of decomposition temperature

As dry duck feather keratin does not have a melting point, only the decomposition temperature was determined. The decomposition temperature of the keratin was determined by a melting point apparatus Mettler FP800 equipped with a Hot Stage FP82. Starting at a temperature of 130°C, the temperature was increase by 0.5 deg per minute. An average decomposition temperature was calculated from 3 determinations.

2.2 Determination of bulk density of keratin powder

The bulk density for dry keratin powder (3% moisture) was determined by measuring the weight of keratin powder in a 10 mL glass measuring tube and calculating an average from triplicate measurements.

2.3 Determination of density of aqueous solutions of keratin

The densities of aqueous solutions, with concentrations of 0.05, 0.20 and 0.50 w/w, were determined at 20±0.5°C by means of 10 mL pyknometers (Bauer 1949). The measurements were made in triplicate using a 3-decimal balance and an average value found. Water was used as the reference (Lide 1995).

$$\rho_{\text{keratin}} = \frac{m_{\text{keratin}}}{V_{\text{keratin}}} = \frac{m_{\text{keratin}}}{V_{\text{solution}} - V_{\text{water}}} = \frac{m_{\text{keratin}}}{\dfrac{1}{\rho_{\text{solution}}} - \dfrac{1 - m_{\text{keratin}}}{\rho_{\text{water}}}}$$

where

m	= mass
V	= volume
ρ	= density

(1)

2.4 Determination of density of solid keratin

The density of solid keratin substance was determined at a temperature of 20°C using the densities of the aqueous solutions in Equation 1 and extrapolating to a solution concentration of 0 w/w keratin where the influence of the high density of the sorbed water is eliminated. The densities for the aqueous solutions were our own data, water was used as reference (Lide 1995) and all measurements were made on a 3 decimal balance.

2.5 Determination of pH in aqueous solutions

The pH of aqueous solutions, with concentrations 0.01, 0.02, 0.05, 0.10, 0.20, 0.30, 0.40 and 0.50 w/w and a temperature of 20±1°C, were measured with a pH-meter and pH-strips. All measurements were made in triplicates. The pH-meter was an IQ Scientific Instrument (model IQ 150)

equipped with an Ion Sensitive Effect Transistor (ISFET) sensor (PH37-SS). It was calibrated with two buffers, pH 4.01 and 10.00 and the pH-sensor cleaned in de-ionized water and dried between each measurement. The pH-strips were from Merck (Spezialindikator pH 4.0 – 7.0)

2.6 Determination of surface tension of aqueous solutions

The surface tensions of aqueous keratin solutions, with concentrations: 0.02, 0.10 and 0.50 w/w at 20° C, were determined by the Capillary Height Method (Harkins 1949). Equation 2 shows the calculations of the surface tension, γ_{sol}, with de-ionized water used as reference, γ_{ref}.

(2)

$$\gamma_{sol} = \frac{h_{sol} \cdot \rho_{sol} \cdot \gamma_{ref}}{h_{ref} \cdot \rho_{ref}}$$

where

h = capillary height of the solution

ρ = density of solution

γ = surface tension of solution

The solution to be measured was sucked into a capillary tube (Pyrex, Bie & Berntsen, 1.6 x 70 mm) by holding the capillary tube vertically in the solution. The tube was then lowered further into the solution and afterwards raised slowly until the capillary tube was drawn free of the water. The height of the water column in the capillary tube was measured with a digital slide gauge (0.01 mm resolution). Due to the variation in the inner diameter of the capillary tubes, the relative short column length of solution in the tubes compared to the resolution of the slide gauge and the low accuracy of the measurement caused by parallax errors, 20 measurements were made for each concentration.

2.7 Determination of viscosity of aqueous solutions

The viscosities for aqueous solutions, with the concentrations 0.0, 0.10, 0.20, 0.30, 0.40 and 0.50 w/w, were measured with a rotation viscosimeter, Brookfield Digital Viscosimeter Model LVDV-II with Spindle no. 1. Viscosities near that of water are difficult to measure with this apparatus. Further, variation in viscosity is often seen in aqueous polymer solutions, due to viscoelastic effects from the polymer chains.

2.8 Determination of binary phase diagram for aqueous solutions

As an aqueous solution with the concentration of 0.50 w/w was fully soluble at 20°C, and since solutions with higher concentrations were not to be used for conservation, precipitation/dissolutions temperatures for keratin (giving the right leg of a binary phase diagram) were not determined.

Freezing point depression temperatures for aqueous solutions, with concentrations 0.05, 0.10, 0.20, 0.30 and 0.40 w/w, were determined by the Whisking Method and by logging freezing curves in thermos flasks (Jensen & Schnell 2005). 10 g of each solution was poured into test tubes (Pyrex, Ø 15 mm, length 160 mm). The test tube was slowly cooled until ice crystals formed, and then slowly heated until all of the ice melted. During the process the solution was vigorously stirred (whisking) with a Pt-100 platinum resistance thermometer. The speed of cooling and heating were controlled by placing the test tube successively in cold water (6°C), cold 2-propanol bath (-30°C), air and heat transfer by warming the test tubes by the hand. The temperature for precipitation and melting of ice was registered by a Gantner IDL 101 data logger connected to the Pt-100 censor. Based on the freezing point depression of the aqueous solutions, the apparent molecular mass was calculated (Skau, 1949).

The freezing curves for the aqueous solutions were determined by taking 20 mL of each concentration in 20 mL Perspex vials fitted with lids with holes for Type-K thermocouples. The thermocouples were placed in the centre of the solution. The vials were hung inside 400 mL metal thermos flasks. The thermocouples were mounted through 2 mm holes in the middle of the caps of the thermos flasks. The thermocouples were connected to a data logger (Pico Technology) and the temperature was registered with an accuracy of ±0.2°C. The thermos flasks were placed in a polystyrene box inside a freezer at a temperature of -25°C for 18 hours. Subsequently the box with the thermos flasks was transferred to a freezer with a temperature of -42°C for further 27 hours. Finally the box was transferred to a freezer with a temperature of -85°C for further 25 hours. The cooling was performed in three steps in order to obtain a slow cooling rate and thereby a high resolution of the cooling curves.

2.9 Determination of moisture sorption isotherm

The moisture sorption isotherm was determined by measuring the relative humidities (water activity) over aqueous solutions of keratin with concentrations 0.20, 0.30, 0.40 and 0.50 w/w with an electronic moisture meter (Vaisala MH70) mounted with a humidity and temperature probe (HMP76). The solutions were poured into aluminum humidity calibrators (HMK 15) to a height of 4 mm. The temperature was 20±0.5°C. The water activity was determined with an accuracy of ±0.01. Based on the sorption isotherm, the apparent molecular mass of the keratin was calculated (Salisbury and Ross, 1969).

2.10 Determination of form stability of aqueous keratin solutions when air- and freeze-dried

The form stability of keratin was examined by pouring aqueous solutions of keratin with concentrations 0.01, 0.02, 0.05, 0.10, 0.20, 0.030 and 0.40 w/w, into transparent Perspex boxes (55 x 40 x12 mm) to a height of 6 mm and then air- and freeze-drying (Heto Sic with heatable shelves) at the respective climates of 20°C, 50% RH and -25°C, 5% RH. A freeze-drying temperature of -25°C was selected, as freeze-drying at lower temperatures is not economically feasible, due to very long process time. The dried keratin was examined visually and photographed.

2.11 Determination of swelling capacity of recent beech wood veneer

Beech spatulas made from rotary cut beech (Fágus sylvática) veneer (120x 18 x 2 mm) were each cut in 4 pieces of 30 mm. The test pieces were marked, dried at 105°C to constant weight and then cooled down to room temperature in desiccators with dry silica gel. The width of the test pieces, corresponding to the tangential direction of the wood, was measured with a slide gauge (0.01 mm resolution) and the mass found on a three decimal scale.

Aqueous solutions of keratin were prepared with concentrations of 0, 0.02, 0.05, 0.10, 0.20 and 0.40 w/w. Four randomly selected test pieces were placed in 100 mL bottles with 50 mL of each solution. The bottles were closed with vapor tight lids and the veneers impregnated at 60°C for 30 days. After impregnation the samples were taken up, dried, cooled, measured with slide gauge and weighed. The test pieces were then equilibrated in a climate chamber at 50% RH and 25°C to constant weight. Subsequently the samples were measured with a slide gauge and weighed. The theoretical uptake of keratin was calculated after Jensen & Gregory (2006) from the maximum theoretical water content and the solution concentration

2.12 Conservation experiments of degraded waterlogged archaeological wood

Due to their homogeneity, heavily degraded waterlogged archaeological ash (Fráxinus excélsior) spear handles from Nydam Mose (200 to 500 AD) were selected as the test materials. Three test pieces with a length of 25 cm and an average diameter of 20 mm were selected. Each piece was broken into 4 sub-samples: one sample to be kept as a wet reference, two samples to be impregnated with aqueous keratin solutions and one sample to follow the impregnation

procedure but in de-ionized water. All samples were weighed on an electronic balance (resolution 0.001 g), the diameters were measured with a dial gauge (resolution 0.01 mm), documented by digital photos and had the density determined after Jensen and Gregory (2006).

Aqueous solutions were prepared with concentrations of 0.10, 0.20 and 0.40 w/w. For each concentration two of the samples were placed in 500 mL bottles with 300 mL of solution. One sample was placed in a 250 mL bottle with 200 mL of de-ionized water. All bottles were closed with vapor tight caps and kept at 60°C for 3 months.

After impregnation the samples were removed from the solution, dried, measured and weighed. Subsequently the impregnated samples and the sample from the de-ionized water were equilibrated in a climate chamber (50% RH, 25°C) to constant weight. Finally all samples, including the wet reference, were measured, weighed and documented by digital photography.

3. Results and Discussion

3.1 Decomposition temperature

Dry hydrolyzed duck feather keratin is a light yellow powder, which does not have a melting temperature. It starts to decompose at 160°C and the keratin powder is completely black at 220°C.

3.2 Bulk density of keratin powder

The average bulk density of dry, hydrolyzed duck feather keratin powder (3% w/w water), based on three measurements, was 170 kg·m^{-3}.

3.3 Density of aqueous solutions of keratin

Figure 1 shows the density, ρ_{sol}, of aqueous keratin solutions as a function of concentration. Although only three concentrations were measured, the density can be calculated from Equation 3 for concentrations between 0 and 0.5 w/w, due to a high correlation ($R^2 = 0.999$).

$$\rho_{sol} = 49.793 \cdot c^2 + 338.43 \cdot c + 996.00 \, kg \cdot m^{-3} \tag{3}$$

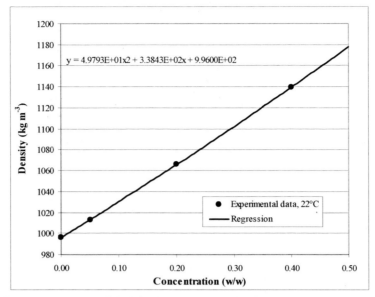

Figure 1. *Density of aqueous solutions of duck feather keratin as a function of concentration.*

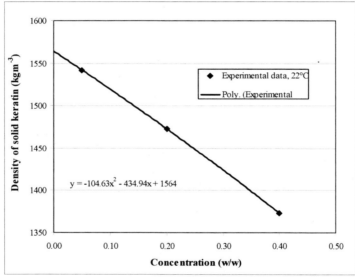

Figure 2. *Density of solid duck feather keratin as a function of concentration of the aqueous duck feather solution.*

3.4 Density of solid keratin

Figure 2 shows corresponding values for the concentration of aqueous solutions of keratin and the density of solid keratin. Extrapolation of the graph to a concentration of 0 w/w gives a value of 1564 kg·m^{-3} for solid dry keratin. The method can result in slightly erroneous values if the water bound to the keratin has abrupt changes in quality at moisture contents close to 0 w/w.

3.5 pH in aqueous solutions

Figure 3 shows the pH in aqueous solutions of keratin measured by electronic pH-meter and pH-strips at 20°C. The results from the two methods are in close agreement. The values at high keratin solutions and low water activities are uncorrected and have to be interpreted as pH is normally defined at water activities close to 1.

3.6 Surface tension of aqueous solutions

Figure 4 shows the surface tension for aqueous solutions of duck feather keratin determined by the Capillary Height Method with water as the reference. For each concentration 20 measurements were made at 20°C. The average values have standard deviations between 0.5 and 1.5 mN·m^{-1} and the accuracy is between ±3 mN·m^{-1}. The decrease in surface tension is quite high and will undoubtedly ease the penetration of keratin into not fully waterlogged wood. Further, the low surface tension will reduce the capillary forces and thereby the tendency of collapse in decayed wood when air-dried.

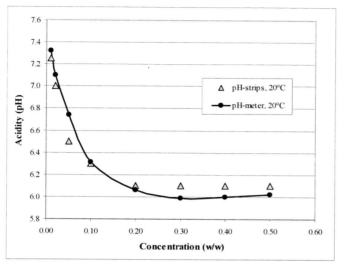

Figure 3. pH in aqueous solutions of duck feather keratin as a function of concentration.

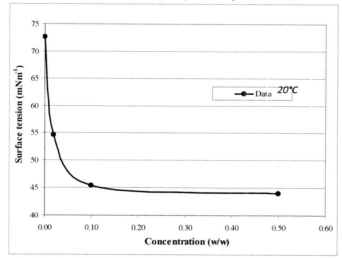

Figure 4. Surface tension of aqueous solutions of duck feather keratin as a function of concentration. at 20°C

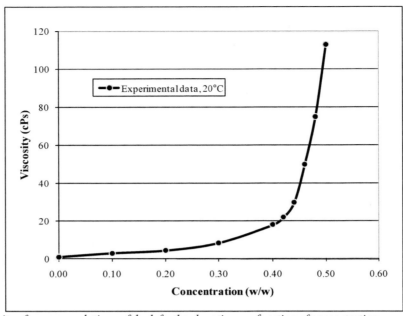

Figure 5. Viscosity of aqueous solutions of duck feather keratin as a function of concentration.

3.7 Viscosity of aqueous solutions

Figure 5 shows the viscosity for aqueous solutions of duck feather keratin measured by rotation viscosity meter. The value for 0.10 w/w keratin fluctuated between 2.8 and 3.9 cPs with an average value of 3.01 cPs. The viscosity increases steeply after 0.40 w/w, due to sorbed water, which also reflects a sudden decrease in water activity at concentrations higher than 0.40 w/w (see Figure 9).

3.8 Binary phase diagram for aqueous solutions

Dissolution/precipitation temperatures for duck feather hydrolysate (values on the right leg in the phase diagram) were not determined, as the high amounts of impurities make it difficult to produce aqueous solutions with a higher concentration than 0.50 w/w. Likewise, it is very difficult to see and measure phase changes in the turbid solutions. Keratin is difficult to dissolve in cold water (15°C),

but at temperatures over 60°C, solutions with a concentration of 0.50 w/w can be made and these solutions do not show any precipitation when cooled to 20°C.

The freezing point depression temperatures, determined by the Whisking Method (Jensen and Schnell 2005), are presented in Figure 6 together with results from the cooling curves from 20 to -25°C, see Figure 7. The values from the cooling curves, obtained in the metal thermos flasks, are lower due to sub cooling as can be seen in Figure 7. The data from the thawing curve are higher (except 0.20 w/w) than data from the freezing curve and the whisking method, due to an offset caused by the finite rate of the temperature increase.

Based on the freezing point depression of the aqueous solutions, the apparent molecular mass was calculated to be 189 $g \cdot mol^{-1}$ (Skau, 1949).

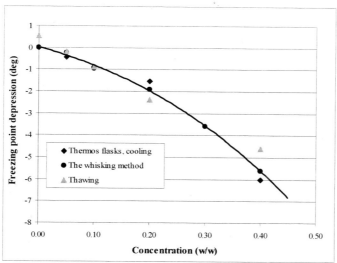

Figure 6. *Freezing point depression for aqueous solutions of duck feather keratin as a function of concentration. The standard deviation for freezing points determined by the whisking method is approximately 0.1°C.*

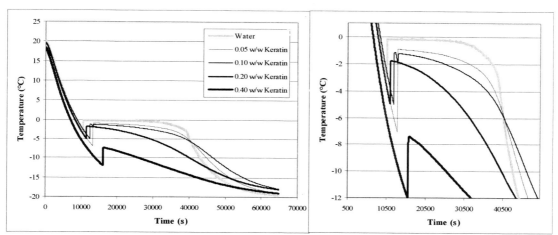

Figure 7. *Cooling curves for aqueous solutions of duck feather keratin as a function of concentration. The curves are obtained in metal thermos flasks, cooled from room temperature to -25°C. The curves are not corrected for offset of the temperature sensors. The figure to the right shows detail temperatures.*

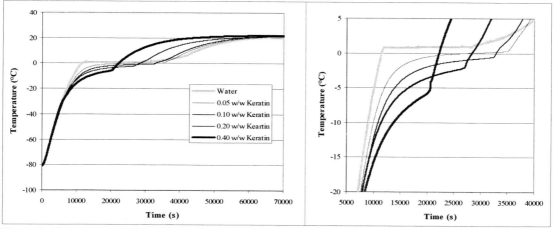

Figure 8. *Thawing curves for aqueous solutions of duck feather keratin as a function of concentration. The curves are obtained in metal thermos flasks, placed at room temperature, approximately 20°C. The figure to the right shows detail temperatures.*

The cooling curves from -25 to -42°C and further from -42 to -85 (not presented) did not show any abrupt temperature changes, indicating absence of eutectic temperatures. The same is to be seen in the thawing curves from -85 to 20°C, which are all smooth until the temperature of the freezing point depression, (see Figure 8).

3.9 Moisture sorption isotherm

Figure 9 shows the moisture sorption isotherm for concentrations between 0 and 0.5 w/w. With the present apparatus for measuring relative humidity it was not possible to measure water activities higher than 0.98, as the accuracy was lower than ±0.01 in that range. Based on the sorption isotherm, the apparent molecular mass of the keratin was calculated to 181 g·mol⁻¹ (Salisbury and Ross, 1969), being in close agreement with the value, 189 g·mol⁻¹, found from the freezing point depression curve.

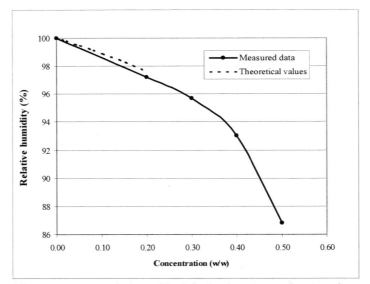

Figure 9. Relative humidity over aqueous solutions of duck feather keratin as a function of concentration.

An apparent value for the molecular mass of duck feather keratin between 181 and 189 g·mol⁻¹ is much lower than that from the data sheet (Anon. 1), which have values between 1500 and 2000 g·mol⁻¹ and is probably caused by the high amount of sodium chloride. The presence of this salt lowers the freezing point and makes it difficult to use hydrolyzed duck feather keratin as an impregnation agent in connection with freeze-drying.

Theoretical values for water activity for aqueous solutions with concentrations between 0 and 0.20 w/w are calculated from an apparent molecular mass of 181 g·mol⁻¹. These values are slightly higher than the actual measured data, as no compensation for sorbed water was made in the calculations.

3.10 Form stability of aqueous keratin solutions when air and freeze-dried

Perspex boxes with samples of aqueous solutions, with concentrations 0.01 to 0.40 w/w of duck feather keratin, left a dry, dusty residue of keratin powder at the bottom of the boxes when air-dried. The aqueous solutions did not show any ability to form a porous structure with the original volume of the solutions.

Perspex boxes with aqueous solutions, with concentrations 0.01 to 0.40 w/w, were freeze-dried at -25°C. These samples also did not show any formation of dry porous structures. Irrespective of concentration, the freeze-dried keratin just formed a dusty powder at the bottom of the boxes. Figure 10 shows a photograph of the freeze dried samples.

236

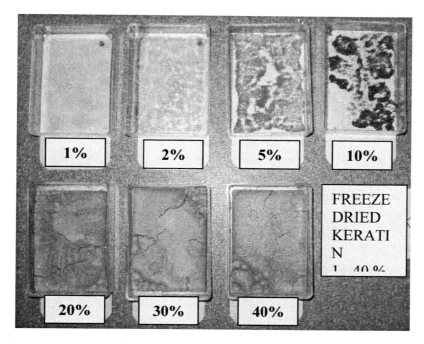

Figure 10. Aqueous solutions of hydrolyzed duck feather keratin freeze-dried at -25°C.

3.11 Swelling capacity of recent beech wood veneer

The test samples were impregnated in keratin solutions from concentrations ranging from 0.02 to 0.40 w/w for 1 month at 60°C, and then air-dried in climate chamber to equilibrium at 50% RH at 20°C. The treatment of the reference samples (beech veneer) with hot water (60°C) for 1 month resulted in an average mass loss of 13% w/w. As a massive mass loss was not expected, the impregnation experiment was not designed to measure that, but from the discoloration of the impregnation solutions it was clear that material from the wood had also been dissolved during impregnation with keratin.

Figure 11 shows the dimensional changes during the treatment process. The width of the randomly selected beech spatula varies very little, with a standard deviation of 0.25 mm. The swelling of the reference samples only treated with water is -2.1% from 0% RH to 50% after hot impregnation and air-drying. This means that even if the samples have an equilibrium moisture content (EMC) of approximately 10% w/w of sorbed water, the dimensions are smaller than they were before treatment when they had an EMC of 0% w/w. The dimensional

shrinkage is due to the average mass loss. The treatment with keratin resulted in swellings from 3.1 to 7.9%.

Figure 12 shows the actual and the estimated theoretical uptake of keratin based on mass loss and increased concentration in the aqueous impregnation solution, due to dissolved materials from the degraded wood. The two uptakes are in good agreement, and the difference is mainly due to difficulties with estimation of the mass loss and volume after impregnation in hot aqueous keratin solution. The graph shows that aqueous solutions of keratin are able to penetrate and fully saturate recent beech wood.

3.12 Conservation of degraded waterlogged archaeological wood

Archaeological waterlogged ash wood spear handles from Nydam Mose (200 to 500 AD), with an average density of 97 kg·m³ and a standard deviation of 9 kg·m⁻³, were selected for the treatment with aqueous solutions from 0.10 to 0.40 w/w. The samples were impregnated for 3 months at 60°C and afterwards air-dried in a climate chamber for approximately 5 months at 20°C and 50% RH. Figure 13 shows the dimensional changes (radial direction) from the water-soluble to the impregnated stage and from the impregnated stage to EMC at 50% RH. Each point is an average of 2 samples.

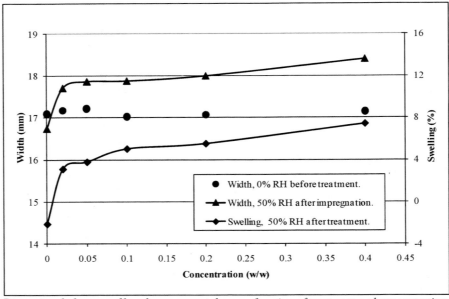

Figure 11. *Dimensional changes of beech veneer spatula, as a function of treatment and concentration. Each point is an average of 5 samples.*

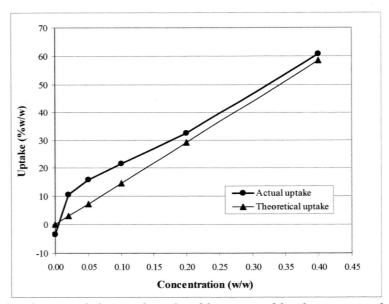

Figure 12. *Actual and estimated theoretical uptake of keratin in of beech veneer spatula, as a function of concentration. Each point is an average of 5 samples.*

The non-impregnated samples have an average radial shrinkage of 43% from the impregnated stage to EMC at 50% RH, 20°C. The impregnated samples have shrinkages from the impregnated stage to the dry stage (50% RH, 20°C) of 15 to 25%, showing that keratin does reduce the shrinkage and collapse of air-dried waterlogged archaeological wood. However, as can be seen in Figure 14a-c, the volumes of the air dried samples deviate from the waterlogged volume to such a degree that the samples have no scientific value and cannot be used for exhibition. Only the samples impregnated with keratin in a concentration of 0.4 w/w are shown, as samples treated with the other three concentrations (0.10, 0.20 and 0.40 w/w) show the same degree of collapse and shrinkage (see Figure 13).

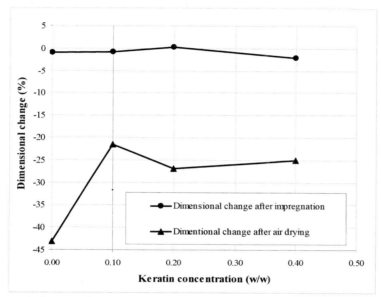

Figure 13. *Dimensional changes of waterlogged samples made of ash spear handles from Nydam Mose (200 to 500AD) after during impregnation at 60°C and air-drying at 20°C, 50% RH.*

Figure 14a. *(left) shows the wet reference sample from the side and in cross section;* *Figure 14b.* *(right) shows the un-impregnated sample from the side and in cross section.*

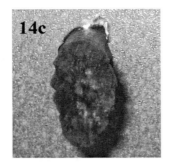

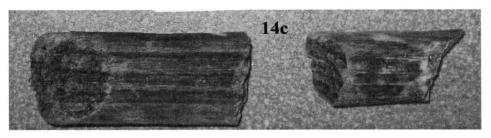

Figure 14c *Two samples impregnated with (0.40 w/w) keratin and dried at 50% RH and 20°C, in cross sections and from the side.*

4. Conclusion

The investigation of the physical properties of hydrolyzed duck feather keratin, especially its lack of form stability for aqueous solutions, when air-dried., indicate that it cannot be used for conservation of heavily degraded waterlogged wood, as it only prevents collapse and shrinkage to a limited extent if such objects are subjected to ordinary air-drying.

The surface tension of aqueous solutions with a concentration of 0.40 w/w is 45 mPa·m^{-1}. Although this is nearly half of that of water (73 mPa·m^{-1}), it is not enough to reduce the contractile forces which cause collapse during ordinary air-drying. In heavily degraded wood (100 kg·m^{-3}) a transverse shrinkage of up to 15 to 20% can be expected.

The reported molecular mass of keratin (1500 to 2000 g·mol^{-1}) combined with a relatively high solubility (more than 0.5 w/w) make it possible to enter the cell wall and replace the bound water, even in recent wood. Aqueous solutions can swell wood to the same extent as pure water, and impregnated beech veneer can maintain a swelling of 8% after air-drying to 50% RH. As high concentrations of keratin require temperatures above 50°C to go into solution, one must expect a certain degradation of the wood during impregnation. The largest degradation is expected to take place in the least degraded wood, as this still contains hemi cellulose, and this is most easily degraded by hot aqueous solutions. Well preserved wood can lose between 10 and 15% of its dry mass.

Although the reported molecular weight of the keratin is between 1500 and 2000 g·mol^{-1}, it has a high freezing point depression, due to the presence of a high amount of salts and other impurities. Moreover, it does not have well defined collapse or eutectic temperature and is therefore unsuitable as an impregnation agent for objects which are to be freeze-dried.

The general conclusion must therefore be that the present type of keratin made from hydrolyzed duck feather cannot be used for impregnation of low density waterlogged archaeological wooden artifacts prior to air drying if collapse and shrinkage are to be minimized, nor can it be used as impregnation agent for wooden objects prior to freeze-drying.

Owing to its ability to enter the cell wall, keratin may be suitable as bulking/stabilizing agents for surface treatment of non-collapsible archaeological wood, but further research has to be done, including an examination of health and safety aspects associated with its use.

References

Anon. 1: Datablad for andekeratin. Toyo Feather Industries Co. Ltd. Japan (anon): Properties of Water-soluble Duck Keratin Powder.

Bauer, Norman (1949): Determination of densities. In *Physical Methods of Organic Chemistry. Part One*. Ed. A. Weissberger. Interscience Publishers, Inc., New York, pp 253-296.

Christensen, Knud Villy; Bialas, David; Hjøllund Jensen, Dorte; Jensen, Poul (2009): Concentration of Duck Feather Keratin Hydrolysate Using Direct Contact Membrane Distillation. Poster at the conference: *Euromembrane 2009, no. 7, Montpellier, France, September 6th, 2009 – 10th September 2009*.

Endo, Rie & Kawahara, Y. (2005): Research Activities using Duck Feather Hydrolysate for Archaeological Waterlogged Wood. Red: Hoffmann et al.: in *Proceedings of the 9th ICOM Group on Wet Organic Archaeological Materials Conference, Copenhagen, 2004*. Eds. P. Hoffmann, K. Strætkvern, J.A. Spriggs and D. Gregory, MüllerDitzen Druckerei AG, Bremerhaven, pp 637-639.

Endo, Rie; Kamei, Kaeko; Ikuho, Lida and Kawahara, Yutaka (2008): Dimensional stability of waterlogged wood treated with hydrolyzed feather keratin. Journal of Archaeological Science, 35, 2008, pp 1240-1246.

Hansen, Charlotte V. (2005): Konservering af vanddrukkent træ ved brug af hydrolyserede fjer. Projektopgave 1. Konservatorskolen, Naturhistorisk Linie, Det Kongelige Danske Kunstakademi.

Harkins, William D. (1949): Determination of Surface and Interfacial Tension. In *Physical Methods of Organic Chemistry. Part One*. Ed. A. Weissberger. Interscience Publishers, Inc., New York, pp 355-426.

Jensen, Poul & Gregory, David (2006): Selected physical parameters to characterize the state of preservation of waterlogged archaeological wood: a practical guide for their determination. *Journal of Archaeological Science*, 33, 2006, pp 551-559.

Jensen, Poul & Schnell, Ulrich, (2005): The implications of using low molecular weight PEG for impregnation of waterlogged archaeological wood prior to freeze drying, in *Proceedings of the 9th ICOM Group on Wet Organic Archaeological Materials Conference, Copenhagen, 2004*. Eds. P. Hoffmann, K. Strætkvern, J.A. Spriggs and D. Gregory, MüllerDitzen Druckerei AG, Bremerhaven, pp 279-307.

Kawahara Y.; Endo, R. and Kimura, K. (2002): Conservation of Archaeological Waterlogged Woods using Keratin from Waste Down. Journal of Textile Engineering, 48, 2002, pp 107-110.

Lide, David R. (1995): Handbook of Chemistry and Physics, 76th edition, CRC Press, New York. Printed in USA.

Pedersen, Nanna (2009): Examination of azelaic acid as impregnation agent for waterlogged wood. Master thesis. School of Conservation. The Royal Danish Academy of Fine Art, Copenhagen, 2009.

Salisbury, Frank B. & Ross, Cleon (1969): Plant Physiology. Wadsworth Publishing Company, Inc., Belmont California. Printed in USA.

Skau, Evald L. (1949): Determination of Melting and Freezing Temperatures. In *Physical Methods of Organic Chemistry. Part One*. Ed. A. Weissberger. Interscience Publishers, Inc., New York, pp 49-105.

Appendix 1
Properties of Water-soluble Duck Keratin Powder
Produced by Toyo Feather Industry Co. Ltd., Japan.

- *Preparation method:*
  Duck feather waste → Dissolved in NaOH aqueous solution → Neutralised → Filtered →
  pH controlled → Removing salts → Condensed →Decolorized and removing smell →
  Precisely filtered → Powdered
- *Aspect:*
  Powder is a little coloured yellow
- *Water-solubility:* up to 50% at room temperature
- *Average molecular weight:* 1500 to 2000
- *Amino acid composition* (mol%):
  Asp 8, Glu 9.5, SER 10.2, Thr 1.7, Tyr 2.3, Lys 0.6, Arg 2.9, His 0.2, Gly 18.2, Cys 0.6, Met 0.3, Ala 7.7, Val 7.3, Pro 15.5, Ile 3.8, Leu 7.8 and Phe 3.3. Total 100.
- *Heavy metal content:* No more than 20 ppm
- *As content*: No more than 2 ppm
- *Ash content:* (NaCl, Na_2SO_4) 6.4%
- *Weight loss by drying:* 2.6%
- *Storage:* keep dry

Questions and answers

Sarah Watkins-Kenney: What wood species were your archaeological samples?

Kristiane Straetkvern: Ash wood.

Jim Spriggs: If I can make a silly comment, it does look as though the use of duck feather keratin might possibly have wings. It just needs more work to modify it and to build on the good aspects the material offers and to overcome the poor aspects. And that goes for the azelaic acid treatment as well. Finding these materials, identifying them, really working with the wood and then trying to find ways of modifying them takes time. It seems to me we are actually developing a rather good protocol for, not exactly swiftly but certainly very effectively, testing new materials. Is this something that perhaps WOAM should actually decide on-- what the protocol really should be so that we could compare the test that people are doing in different places?

Kristiane Straetkvern: Do you have a comment to that Nanna? I could comment on it. At the National Museum, we tried this protocol and it worked out fairly well and we are continuing testing other materials following this same protocol and plan to publish more on this. I think it's a very good way of finding out what are the parameters, what are the things we need to know about the material we are introducing to our archaeological wood. Does anyone have any comments to the steps that we've made in the protocol?

Ian Godfrey: I would have thought that the best thing to do was just to test the material. If you have a lot of it, and you think it's got some potential as a conservation material based on its chemical formula and so on. And then if it does actually work then go through and have a look at all the other characteristics with regard to effects, with regard to moisture uptake etc... etc.. because it seems an awful lot of work to do and then find the material isn't effective as a conservation agent.

Jim Spriggs: One does wonder sometimes whether some of the ideas for new material and so on might be dreamt up to make suitable student projects. I don't know if that was the work you did Nanna – that it was just something interesting to do as far as your learning process. There's no harm in that at all obviously--that might be the reason so many of the newer material get put through the more rigorous testing. And it's always good isn't it? If you can test them against the known materials like polyethylene glycol and that seems to be a very sensible part of the protocol as well.

Giles Chaumat: It is a very interesting very different aspect. I prefer to search for a protocol for the treatment and after the characterization will be done but my first goal is to identify the solution to a problem for conservation. I think my work is limited by the fact that I have not the time or the apparatus to perform all the characterizations I need but I do my best.

Jim Spriggs: Is anyone aware of other types of new materials people have been working on in recent years that we haven't heard about at WOAM? I can't think of any off hand I must say.

Sarah Watkins-Kenney: I have a question. I was just wondering, as keratin is a protein and we are trying to use it to treat cellulosic materials, has anyone already looked at it for trying to treat protein based waterlogged materials, such as horn or leather?

Jim Spriggs: Well it is an interesting thought isn't it? Because a material like horn, which occurs very rarely in a waterlogged state because it's so readily hydrolysable in waterlogged conditions, does turn up occasionally. I'm familiar with it from excavations in York and I don't know why it just occasionally gets preserved. It's always very fragile and it could be that a natural keratin based treatment might be quite suitable for it. It's an interesting thought to bear in mind. We'd need an awful lot of waterlogged horn to test it or to see if it's any good.

Lars Andersen: I think that with regard to making this protocol for testing treatment methods, the final step should be the big scale – how is it working in the big scale? Because it's often rather easier to get things working on the very small samples but when you scale it up and apply it to larger scale items strange things happen.

Kristiane Straetkvern: If these things already happen in the small scale there is no reason to scale it up.

Jim Spriggs: Though obviously when you scale your treatments up there are all kinds of other practical issues with health and safety and cost and all sorts of other things to do with handling large quantities of these materials, which we just don't know about until we set about trying to use it on a big scale.

Gordon Turner-Walker: You mentioned the possibility of using keratin derivatives on protenacious material. I'd be very, very wary about putting new keratin into old keratin. It's a huge resource for biomolecular research and looking at sulfur isotopes. If you stick in a whole lot of modern keratin, you won't get thanked if someone wants to do this analysis afterwards. I think everyone was thinking "in wood, you're safe because no one's going to be confused about where it came from" but if you start messing about with the integrity of the object... It's not a question of reversible, it's how do you distinguish it from the original? So, I wouldn't go anywhere near that.

Jim Spriggs: I agree entirely Gordon. It's not a terribly good idea. A thought just passed through my mind. That is people researching wood in the future wondering what its consolidated with and working out the protein inside there is derived from duck feather's might think "hang on, what on Earth is going on here!" Just a happy thought...

3.6

Preliminary Assessment of a New PEG

Clifford Cook*, Jessica Lafrance and Carmen Li
Canadian Conservation Institute, 1030 Innes Road, Ottawa, Ontario K1A 0M5

Email* cliff.cook@pch.gc.ca

Abstract

The Canadian Conservation Institute has initiated a project to assess the preservation potential of a new type of PEG produced by Hybrid Plastics Inc. These PEG POSS® cage mixtures consist of a Polyhedral Oligomeric Silsesquioxane (POSS®) cage with eight attached PEG chains. PEG POSS® PG1190 and PG1191 (with molecular weights of 5577 and 3711 respectively) were tested against other treatments for waterlogged wood such as PEG 400 and 3350. Several wood species with differing moisture contents were used as sample material in this assessment. The wood included American elm (*Ulmus americana* L.), white spruce (*Picea glauca* (Moench) Voss), eastern white pine (*Pinus strobus* L.), balsam fir (*Abies balsamea* (L.) Mill.), and white oak (*Quercus alba* L.). Various solution mixtures and concentrations were tested with each of the wood samples. The preliminary results suggested that the performance of the PEG POSS® products did not surpass that of traditional PEG and at present these products are significantly more expensive.

Keywords: polyhedral oligomeric silsesquioxane, POSS, polyethylene glycol, PEG, polydimethylsiloxane, silicone oil, hostacor IT, sucrose, lactitol/trehalose, acetone rosin, anti-shrink efficiency

1. Introduction

Over the past decades many treatments have been developed for the preservation of waterlogged organic materials in general and in particular for waterlogged wood. The Canadian Conservation Institute has been part of this multinational effort with the development of tools such as Hostacor and PEGcon and as part of continuing research efforts has started to investigate a new product called PEG POSS® (polyhedral oligomeric silsequioxane). The early development and almost universal adoption of the use of polyethylene glycol with freeze drying or air drying has likely reduced the need for different treatments for wood. However, there are many alternatives such as sucrose, acetone/rosin, alcohol/ether/resin, Arigal-C/Lyofix DML, and more recently silicone oil, Lactitol/Trehalose, and keratin. This work is an early report of another possible alternative.

PEG POSS® is one of a large group of polymers that have been produced by Hybrid Plastics Inc. in Hattiesburg, Mississippi. The development of these products began several decades ago by the General Electric Company and later by the United States Air Force Research Laboratory. Hybrid Plastics was formed in the mid 1990s by Air Force researchers to carry on and commercialize the earlier work. A few of the many examples of POSS® products are listed in Table 1. In 2008 after reading about the use of polyethylene glycol to treat waterlogged organic material, one of the researchers at Hybrid Plastics approached CCI with the idea of testing two PEG POSS® products (DeArmitt 2008). The evaluation discussed in this paper compared the results for two types of PEG POSS® against other treatment processes for waterlogged wood.

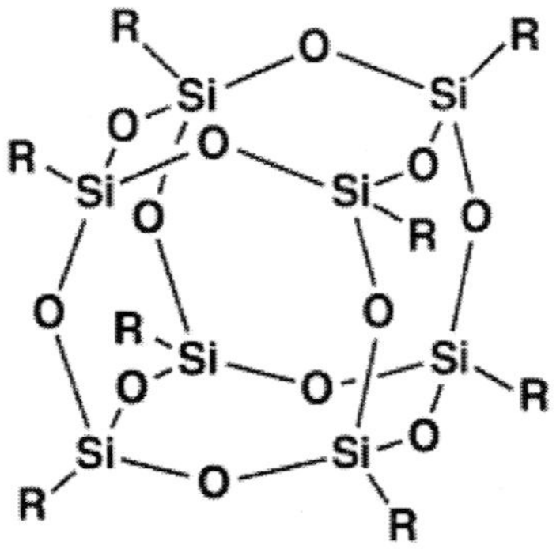

Figure 1. POSS® *structure (image © Hybrid Plastics).*

Table 1. Examples of POSS® Products

POSS® Type	Functional Group
MS0830 (solid)	octamethyl
SH1310 (solid)	octasilane
OL1160 (solid)	octavinyl
AM0270 (liquid)	aminopropyl i-octyl
SO1455 (liquid)	trisilanol i-octyl

Table 2. PEG POSS® Physical Data.

	PG1190	PG1191
Solubility	water and alcohols	water and alcohols
Insolubility	hexane	hexane
Solubility (Resins)	polyether and polyester	polyether and polyester
Appearance	pale-yellow liquid	pale-yellow liquid
Specific Gravity	~1.2	~1.13
Formula Weight	5576.6	3709.4

2. The Resins and Wood Tested

The two new products tested were PEG POSS® PG1190 and PG1191. All of the POSS® line is based on a cage-like and often cubic polyhedral oligomeric silsequioxane with the formula $(RSiO_{1.5})$ shown in Figure 1. With PG1190 R = $CH_2CH_2(OCH_2CH_2)_mOCH_3$, where m = ~13.3 and for PG1191 R = $CH_2CH_2(OCH_2CH_2)_mOCH_3$, where m = ~8. Key physical data for the two POSS® products is listed in Table 2 (Anon 2010a). Several other resins, listed in Table 3, were tested to provide comparable results for the POSS® products.

Comparing the treatment results obtained for PEG POSS® with many other treatment processes will yield the best assessment of performance. Without a thorough assessment provided by a comparison of treatments it is not possible to determine how effective a newly developed treatment really is. The earlier in the development process this comparison occurs the easier it is to determine if the research should proceed. Initial poor or mediocre results should force a questioning of the wisdom of diverting scarce resources to fine tune a process that does not appear to be a significant improvement over existing well proven alternatives.

As well as making comparisons between treatment processes it is also a wise decision to test the effectiveness of a new process on several wood samples. In this case, three of the wood samples included in this study were chosen from pieces that were left over from previous experimental work completed at CCI and elsewhere. Including this wood allows for comparisons between the calculated antishrink efficiencies (ASE) as well as other physical results for the above treatments and those from previous research. The wood samples tested are listed in Table 4.

Table 3. Wood Treatments Tested.

Resin	Concentration and Solvent
PG 1190	10, 20 and 30% v/v in tap water
PG 1191	10, 20 and 30% v/v in tap water
PEG 400	10% v/v in tap water
PEG 400 and PEG 3350	20% v/v and 5% w/v in tap water
PEG 400 and PEG 3350	20% v/v and 20% w/v in tap water
PEG 400 and PEG 3350	Suggested concentrations from PEGcon in tap water fir – 20% v/v PEG 400 and 5% w/v PEG 3350 pine – 12% v/v PEG 400 and 10% w/v PEG 3350 oak – 16% v/v PEG 400 and 27% w/v PEG 3350
PEG 400 and PEG 3350	Per Hoffmann's 2-Step Method in tap water (40% v/v PEG 400 then 50% w/v PEG 3350)
PEG 3350	Heated PEG treatment in tap water (90% w/v)
Sucrose	70% w/v in tap water
Lactitol/Trehalose	60% w/v of 9:1 mixture in tap water
Acetone Rosin	40% w/v in acetone
Polydimethylsiloxane or Silicone Oil	N/A

Table 4. Wood Samples Used in the Treatments.

Common Name	Species	Sample	Moisture Content (μ_{max})	Pin Test (mm)
American elm*	*Ulmus americana* L.	41	256% (140% in 1979) (200% in 1984)	N/A
white spruce **	*Picea glauca* (Moench) Voss	117/1	214% (172 – 203% in 1984)	N/A
white spruce **	*Picea glauca* (Moench) Voss	173/8	209% (202% in 1984)	N/A
eastern white pine***	*Pinus strobus* L.	72/1	412% (216% in 1979)	2-8
balsam fir	*Abies balsamea* (L.) Mill.	223	96%	1-4
white oak	*Quercus alba* L.	201	192%	1-3 and 4-8

* Used for the exterior freeze-drying research, Part II at CCI (misidentified as white oak in original work).
** Used in the 1986 International Comparative Wood Treatment Study.
*** Used for the exterior freeze-drying research, Part II at CCI.

The maximum moisture contents in Table 4 indicate that the wood samples were in a variety of conditions such as; slightly degraded fir and elm, moderately degraded spruce and white oak, and heavily degraded white pine (it is likely that the pine degraded during 31 years in storage at room temperature. Probing the wood surface with a pin also indicated that there was some variation between the wood samples.

3. Treatment Methods - Wood
There was some variety in the size of the wood samples used in this work. Generally the pieces were cut on a band saw in quarter rounds (if little sample was left), half rounds or complete cross sections. In all cases the longitudinal dimension was 2 to 3 cm. The stainless steel pins that were hammered into the wood were positioned to provide several radial and tangential measurements for each piece. Since longitudinal shrinkage in wood is generally very small (Anon 1942) no measurements in this orientation were made. After the wood was treated the samples were left in the laboratory at ~50% relative humidity for several months before the final pin measurements were made.

In all cases, except the silicone oil treatment, the wood was impregnated in 4 litre glass reaction kettles. The apparatus was set up on a magnetic stirrer with a timer to limit the stirring time to 10 minutes twice a day. Past experience had shown that continuous stirring warms the solution increasing the biological deterioration of the solution.

3.1. 10 % v/v PG1190, PG1191 and PEG 400

The solutions were made up with tap water and the wood samples were soaked for 35 days. The weight of one piece of wood suspended in each of the solutions was monitored for the first two weeks until there was no further gain (Figure 2). The extra 21 days in solution was designed to ensure complete penetration of the treatment solutions. After soaking in solution, the wood was quickly rinsed under running water, placed in polyethylene bags and frozen in a walk-in freezer at -30°C for several weeks until the vacuum freeze dryer was available. Freeze drying was completed at -30°C and 1.5 – 2.0 Pa.

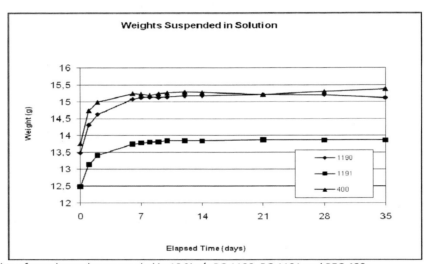

Figure2. Weights of wood samples suspended in 10 % v/v PG 1190, PG 1191 and PEG 400.

3.2. Higher concentrations of PG1190, PG1191 and PEG

The solutions tested within this group included 20% v/v and 30% v/v PG1190, 20% v/v and 30% v/v PG1191, 20% v/v PEG 400 with 5% w/v PEG 3350, and 20% v/v PEG 400 with 20% w/v PEG 3350 in tap water. As with the 10% v/v solutions the impregnant uptake was monitored by weighing the oak sample suspended in each solution. After 13 weeks the wood was removed, rinsed and frozen in preparation for vacuum freeze-drying at -30°C and 1.5 – 2.0 Pa before being stored in the laboratory.

3.3. PEG 400 and PEG 3350 (concentrations calculated with PEGcon)

The various solutions tested based on the PEGcon calculation are listed in Table 3. The wood impregnation was started at an initial low concentration of 10% v/v PEG 400 in tap water. The concentration of PEG was increased by three 7 week intervals for the fir, four 7 week intervals for the pine and five 10 week intervals for the oak. The final concentration of PEG 400 was maintained in the solution as the PEG 3350 was added. As with the other samples, when the impregnation was complete the wood was removed, rinsed, frozen and vacuum freeze-dried at -20°C and 1.5 – 2.0 Pa before being stored in the laboratory.

248

3.4. The Hoffmann 2-step method

This treatment started with an initial concentration of 10% v/v PEG 400. The quantity of PEG 400 was increased at a rate of 10% every 3 weeks until the final concentration of 40% was reached. After 5 weeks of immersion at 40 %, the samples were removed and placed in a 10% w/v solution of PEG 3350. As with the PEG 400 the concentration of 3350 was increased 10% increases every 3 weeks to a final concentration of 50% w/v. After 5 weeks of immersion at 50%, the samples were rinsed in water to remove excess PEG from the surface, and placed inside a controlled relative humidity chamber for air drying. From a start of 90% the relative humidity was decreased by 5% every 3 or 4 days, until an RH of 50% was reached (Hoffmann 1986). At this point the wood was removed and placed on the bench in the lab to complete any further drying.

3.5. Heated PEG 3350 Treatment

The test of this traditional treatment started with an initial solution concentration of 2.5% w/v PEG 3350 in tap water that was heated to 40°C. The starting temperature of 30°C recommended in the literature was not used since the lowest setting on the hotplate gave a steady temperature of 40°C (Morén and Centerwall 1960). The solution was stirred and heated continuously on a hot plate. At 3 to 4 day intervals, the PEG 3350 concentration was increased in 2.5% steps until a final concentration of 90% w/v was reached. The temperature was gradually increased with the concentration and the values are listed in Table 5.

Table 5. Temperatures with PEG 3350

PEG 3350 (% w/v)	Temperature
2.5 – 40	40 °C
42.5 – 60	50 °C
62.5 – 70	60 °C
82.5 – 87.5	70 °C
90	80 °C

Once the impregnation was completed, the samples were removed from the solution, excess PEG on the surface was rinsed and wiped off and they were allowed to come to room temperature. The wood was placed into a relative humidity chamber for controlled air drying. As with the Hoffmann method, the relative humidity was decreased by 5% every 3 or 4 days until an RH of 50% was reached then the wood was placed on the bench in the laboratory until final pin measurements could be completed.

3.6. Sucrose

Prior to impregnation, the wood samples were rinsed under running water and immersed in a 0.1% Kathon CG izathiozolone biocide solution to reduce the risk of microbiological growth during treatment. The initial concentration in the reaction kettle was 5% w/v sucrose with 0.1% v/v Kathon CG. The sucrose concentration was increased by 5% every two weeks and 0.1% of Kathon CG biocide was added every four weeks, until a sucrose concentration of 40% w/v was reached. At this point, the sucrose concentration was increased by 10% every two weeks until a final concentration of 70% w/v was reached (Morgós, Strigazzi and Preuss, 1994).

Once the treatment was complete, the wood was rinsed in water to remove excess sucrose, and placed inside a relative humidity chamber for controlled air drying. The relative humidity was decreased by 5% every 3 days, until an RH of 50% was reached, then the wood was stored on the lab bench for several months awaiting final shrinkage measurements.

3.7. Lactitol/Trehalose

The starting concentration was 30% w/v 9:1 Lactitol:Trehalose with 0.02 % Kathon CG izothiazolone biocide. The samples remained in this solution for 8 weeks, after which 10% w/v of 9:1 Lactitol:Trehalose increments were added every 4 weeks until a final concentration of 60% was reached. After 6 weeks of immersion in the final solution, the wood was rinsed in water to remove excess sugars from the surface, and placed inside a relative humidity chamber for controlled air drying and the relative humidity was decreased by 5% every 3 days until an RH of 50% was reached (Imazu and Morgós, 2002). The samples were stored on a bench in the laboratory for several months until the shrinkage could be measured.

3.8. Room temperature acetone rosin

The wood samples were dehydrated by immersion in 5 successive baths of acetone, each of four days duration. This was continued until the specific gravity of the acetone used for dewatering equaled that of fresh acetone when measured with a hygrometer. The wood samples were then immersed in a saturated, 40% (w/w) solution of acetone rosin for a period of six months. Upon removal from the rosin solution, samples were rinsed in acetone to remove excess rosin from the surface. The treated wood was placed in a fume hood for approximately one week to allow for the evaporation of the acetone (Fox, 1989). At this point the samples were stored in the laboratory until the final pin measurements were taken.

3.9. Polydimethylsiloxane (PDMS) or Silicone oil treatment

The silicone oil treatment completed as part of this work did not use the same silicone oil as the traditional patented treatment. The wood samples were dehydrated in a series of 4 baths, starting with 2 ethanol/acetone and ending with 2 baths of fresh acetone. Each bath lasted for one day except for the final bath of acetone that lasted three days.

The silicone oil chosen was Dow Corning 200 Fluid (polydimethylsiloxane) with Dow Corning CR20 cross-linker and Dow Corning CT-32 catalyst. This is a similar silicone oil to the one published by Smith (2003). The acetone-laden wood was immersed in the silicone oil in a vacuum desiccator. A manual vacuum pump was used to gradually reduce the pressure in the desiccator to 40 mmHg over a period of 4 days. The reduced pressure was held for 5 days and no bubbles came out of the wood during the last day. The wood samples were removed from the solution and allowed to drain on a screen for a day. After draining the wood surfaces were wiped off to remove any excess polymer.

The catalyst was applied topically by brushing a thin even layer on the surface, wiping off any excess after 2 or 3 minutes, and sealing the wood samples in a Ziplock® bag. After 24 hours the pine and oak still had wet areas on the surface so these samples were resealed in the bag for a further 24 hours with several drops of catalyst on a Kimwipe®. After this treatment the samples were removed from the bag and placed on the laboratory bench until the final pin measurements were taken.

4. Treatment Methods – Metal Corrosion

As part of this preliminary investigation, three metals – copper, steel and iron, were chosen to be tested with 10% v/v solutions of PG1190, PG1191 and PEG 400. The solution/metal combinations are listed in Table 6. The copper and steel coupons measuring 1.0 by 2.5 cm and the historic iron nail of unknown provenance, measuring 8 cm long were cut approximately in half to provide more samples. The 0.41 mm (0.016 inch) thick copper sheet, Unified Numbering System (UNS) 12200, was composed of 99.9% copper. The 0.91 mm (20 gauge) thick cold rolled steel sheet met the ASTM A 366/A 366M Standard Specification for Commercial Steel (CS) Sheet, Carbon, (0.15 maximum Percent) Cold-Rolled.

4.1. Sample preparation

The copper and steel coupons were cut from larger sheets using a foot operated metal shop shear. They were degreased in acetone, surface cleaned with a calcium carbonate (powdered chalk) as a slurry in ethanol and rinsed in ethanol and dried overnight. The square iron nails had the middle portion of one side filed to expose bare metal with a mill file and were not cleaned.

4.2. Test procedure

One piece of each metal was placed in the bottom of a wide mouth clear glass jar and 200 ml of the test solution was added. The jars were closed with the lids leaving an internal air space of several cubic centimeters and placed on a laboratory shaker. The shaker was set to a speed of one back and forth oscillation per second. These corrosion tests took place at the normal laboratory room temperature of about 21°C for 31 days. Photographs of the solutions were taken every few days. At the conclusion of the test the metal test pieces were removed, rinsed in deionized water and air dried

Table 6. *10% v/v Solution/Metal Combinations Tested.*

Solution	Copper Coupon	Steel Coupon	Iron Nail
PG1190 in tap water	x	x	x
PG1190 in deionized water		x	x
PG1191 in tap water			x
PG1191 in deionized water	x	x	x
PEG 400 in tap water	x	x	x
PG1190 + 1% v/v Hostacor IT in tap water			x
PG1191 + 1% v/v Hostacor IT in tap water			x
PEG 400 + 1% v/v Hostacor IT in tap water		x	**x**
Deionized water	x	x	x
Tap water			x

5. Results and Discussion

5.1. Wood samples

The wood shrinkage was determined by measuring the change in dimension between stainless steel pins hammered into the wood. The pin placement aligned with the radial and tangential directions on the wood cross section. The anti-shrink efficiencies (ASE) based on an air dried wood sample were calculated for each wood sample and for each treatment method (Table 7). An ASE of 100% indicates there was no shrinkage and a negative value is caused by more shrinkage than air drying. Each ASE was calculated as an average of the individual radial and tangential anti-shrink efficiencies. This table also includes older data for the same wood samples to provide a comparison to a wider variety of treatments.

The limited data from this work indicate that many of the traditional treatments such as the Hoffmann PEG process or sucrose give very satisfactory anti-shrink efficiencies. However, many of the newer ones such as the PEG POSS® products and silicone oil have results that appear to be less successful. It should be noted that this work is based on a very limited sample size and included only one piece of each type of wood in each of the treatment solutions.

The results of all of the PEG POSS® types and solution concentrations were disappointing. In many cases the results were worse than air drying (a negative anti-shrink efficiency). The only wood sample treated with PEG POSS® that generated potentially acceptable results was the white oak. The spruce pieces were very poor samples contaminated with fats and oils from a Canadian arctic site. The samples had many splits which made it difficult to obtain accurate shrinkage measurements.

The least successful treatment appears to be the silicone oil. This was somewhat unexpected but might be an indication that this is a treatment that requires significant experience or further optimization to obtain good results. Recent work by Kavvouras et al (2009) also had initial poor results. They reported deformation, collapse and excessive shrinkage for the first two pieces of wood treated.

There was some variation in the final appearance of the wood samples. A summary of the appearance of each sample is listed in Table 8. Generally the samples treated with 10 % PEG and 10% PEG POSS and then vacuum freeze-dried are light colored, weigh the same as wood and feel like wood.

Table 7. ASE Values.

Treatment	Elm 41	Spruce 173	Spruce 117	Pine 72	Fir 223	Oak 201	Average
10% PEG POSS® PG1190	-5.5	-8.4	21.0	15.3	34.2	66.0	20 .4
20% PEG POSS® PG1190	42.3 -6.0	-13.4	1.8	11.6	66.2	65.7	24.0
30% PEG POSS® PG1190		-11.0		32.1	49.4	54.7	31.3
10% PEG POSS® PG1191	57.4	78.3	-48.7	-11.5	54.1	62.6	32.0
20% PEG POSS® PG1191	34.9	-24.2	14.5	17.9	21.9	68.6	22.3
30% PEG POSS® PG1191	9.0		85.1	40.4	16.8	61.1	42.5
10% PEG 400	23.6	-9.05	43.2	60.3	43.4	62.0	37.2
20% PEG 400 and 5% PEG 3350	74.6			89.5	75.2	77.2	79.1
20% PEG 400 and 20% PEG 3350	65.3			108.4	30.1	70.8	68.7
PEG 400 and PEG 3350 from PEGcon				94.2	76.9	70.7	80.6
40% PEG 400 and 50% PEG 3350				106.8	99.7	86.1	97.5
90% PEG 3350				125.3	48.2	70.1	81.2
70% Sucrose				104.5	95.3	75.5	91.8
60% w/v Lactitol/Trehalose				97.0	76.5	67.5	80.3
40% w/v Acetone Rosin (room temp.)				21.7	-10.5	61.7	24.3
Polydimethylsiloxane (PDMS)				-12.3	-111.2	22.5	-36.7
Trond FD*		123.5					
ARCS FD*		100					
Trond PEG*			62				
Nara PEG*			> 50				
Hoff PEG*			100				
CTBGE RP*			-48				
CCI FD1*		76.5					
CCI FD2*			38				
CTBGE FD*		70					
WAMM PEG*		39					
RIM PEG 1-3*		34					
15% PEG 400, exterior freeze-dried**	64.8				76.0		

* Used in the 1986 International Comparative Wood Treatment Study.

** Used for the exterior freeze-drying research, Part II at CCI.

Table 8. *Appearance of each sample*

Treatment	Colour	Feel	Weight
10% PEG POSS® PG1190	brown	natural	normal
20% PEG POSS® PG1190	brown	natural	normal
30% PEG POSS® PG1190	dark brown	natural	normal
10% PEG POSS® PG1191	brown	natural	normal
20% PEG POSS® PG1191	dark brown	natural	normal
30% PEG POSS® PG1191	dark brown	natural	normal
10% PEG 400	brown	natural	normal
20% PEG 400 and 5% PEG 3350	brown	waxy	normal
20% PEG 400 and 20% PEG 3350	dark brown	waxy	heavy -
PEG 400 and PEG 3350 from PEGcon	brown	natural	normal
40% PEG 400 and 50% PEG 3350	dark brown	waxy	heavy
90% PEG 3350	dark brown	waxy	heavy +
70% Sucrose	brown	natural	heavy
60% w/v Lactitol/Trehalose	light brown	natural	heavy
40% w/v Acetone Rosin (room temp.)	greyish brown	natural	heavy
Polydimethylsiloxane (PDMS)	dark brown	waxy	heavy

5.2. Metal Samples

The metal samples reacted to exposure to the various solutions as would be expected. The iron and steel samples corroded in all solutions that did not include Hostacor IT and the copper coupons had results that were more variable.

With the iron nail samples there was no apparent difference between the results in deionized water and tap water. There was a deposit of orange and brown colored corrosion on the cleaned

metal surface in all solutions except those containing the Hostacor IT. Based on a visual interpretation the order of most to least corrosion was water → PG1191 → PG1190 → PEG 400.

The corrosion on the steel coupons was also orange and brown colored. There was also a small amount of orange corrosion on the steel in the PEG 400 / Hostacor IT solution. As with the iron nails the order of corrosion from most to least was water → PG1191 → PG1190 → PEG 400.

The copper coupons were not tested with a corrosion inhibitor. The results were slight corrosion with water, light tarnish with PEG 400, heavy tarnish with PG1190, and heavy corrosion with PG1191. The order of results for copper was slightly different than the ferrous samples with the water between the two PEG POSS® solutions.

6. Conclusions

This short preliminary examination of the suitability of PG1190 and PG1191 as impregnants for waterlogged wood produced results that were somewhat variable and generally inferior to more traditional and universally accepted treatments. This might be explained by the molecular weight of the PEG POSS® which is much higher than PEG 400 and this could restrict penetration into the cell wall. On average for all of the wood samples there appeared to be a slight improvement in performance for each PEG POSS® as the concentration increased from 10% to 30%. The wood samples chosen for this work were part of larger pieces that had been previously used which allowed a comparison to be made between the anti-shrink efficiency of the PEG POSS® solutions and other treatments done at CCI and in other laboratories in the past. These results show that room temperature acetone/rosin and silicone oil were the only two treatments in this work that had anti-shrink efficiencies equivalent or inferior to all of the PEG POSS® concentration tested.

The corrosion effect of the PEG POSS® solutions was also briefly examined in this work. The limited number of metals tested, the short duration of the test, and the restricted number of solutions included constrain to some extent the conclusions that can be drawn. It does appear that the POSS® solutions are more corrosive than PEG 400 at the same solution strength. The addition of Hostacor IT will protect ferrous metal in PEG POSS® solutions just as it does in PEG 400 solutions.

The factor that is most likely to inhibit the use of PEG POSS® as a treatment for waterlogged wood has nothing to do with its performance. At the present time (Spring 2010) the price for PG1190 and PG1191 is US$140/500g and is based on the costs of the precursor materials used in production. The last PEG 400 purchased at CCI in the fall of 2009 had a price of Cdn$5.35/kg. The higher price would likely preclude the use of PEG POSS® on anything but the smallest of objects.

Future work with PEG POSS® will include an assessment of expansion and contraction of treated wood samples when exposed to changing relative humidity levels. It is also anticipated that additional wood samples will be treated and the location of PEG POSS® in the treated wood lumen or cell wall will be determined microscopically.

References

Anon, (2010a), Hybrid Plastics 2010 POSS® Catalog, http://www.hybridplastics.com/docs/catalog2010.pdf>, PG1190 Material Safety Data Sheet, http://www.hybridplastics.com/docs/msds/chem/pg/PG1190.pdf>, and PG1191 Material Safety Data Sheet, <http://www.hybridplastics.com/docs/msds/chem/pg/PG1191.pdf>. Accessed May 2010.

Anon, (2010b), 1190 pricing <http://www.hybridplastics.com/products/pg1190.htm> and 1191 pricing <http://www.hybridplastics.com/products/pg1191.htm>. Accessed May 2010.

Anon, (1942), Technical Note Number 234, Forest Products Laboratory, United States Forest Service, Madison, Wisconsin, <http://www.fpl.fs.fed.us/documnts/fpltn/fpltn-234-1942.pdf>. Accessed May 2010.

DeArmitt, Chris, (2008), email to David Grattan.

Fox, Louise A., (1989), The Acetone/Rosin Method for Treating Waterlogged Hardwoods at the Historic Resource Conservation Branch, Ottawa, Conservation of Wet Wood and Metal. Proceedings of the ICOM Conservation Working Groups on Wet Organic Archaeological Materials and Metals. Fremantle 1987, Edited by Ian MacLoed, International Council of Museums, Paris, 1989, pp. 73-94.

Hoffmann, Per, (1986), On the Stabilization of Waterlogged Oakwood with PEG. II. Designing a Two-Step Treatment for Multiquality Timbers, Studies in Conservation, Vol. 31, No. 3, 1986, pp. 103-113.

Imazu, Setsuo and Morgos, Andras, (2002), An Improvement on the Lactitol Conservation Method Used for the Conservation of Archaeological Waterlogged Wood: The Conservation Method Using a Lactitol and Trehalose Mixture, Proceedings of the 8th ICOM Group on wet organic archaeological materials conference, Stockholm, 11-15 June 2001, Edited by Per Hoffmann, Deutsches Schiffahrtsmuseum, Bremerhaven, Germany, 2002, pp. 413-428.

Kavvouras, Panayiotis K., et al., (2009), Use of Silanol-Terminated Polydimethylsiloxane in the Conservation of Waterlogged Archaeological Wood, Studies in Conservation, Vol. 54, No. 2, 2009, pp. 65-76.

Morén, Rolf and Centerwall, Bertil, (1960), The Use of Polyglycols in the Stabilizing and Preservation of Wood, Technical Information No. 64, Mo Och Domsjö Aktiebolag, Örnsköldsvik, Sweden, 1960.

Morgós, Andras, Strigazzi, Giancarlo, and Preuss, Helmut, (1994), Microbiocides in Sugar Conservation of Waterlogged Archaeological Wooden Finds: The Use of Isothiazolones, Proceedings of the Fifth ICOM Group on Wet Organic Archaeological Materials Conference, Portland, Maine, 16-20 August 1993, Edited by Per Hoffmann, ICOM Committee for Conservation Working Group on Wet Organic Archaeological Materials; Ditzen Druck und Verlags-GmbH, Bremerhaven, Germany, 1994, pp. 463-484.

Smith, C. Wayne, (2003), Archaeological Conservation Using Polymers: Practical Applications for Organic Artifact Stabilization, College Station, Texas, Texas A&M University press, 2003.

Questions and answers

Wayne Smith: What was your motivation for painting dibutyl tin diacetate directly on to the artifact?

Cliff Cook: So you are talking about painting the catalyst onto the artifact?

Wayne Smith: Yes, that's what I believed you said – you painted a catalyst directly onto it. You topically applied it.

Cliff Cook: Applied it and it didn't work. So we put it on a kimwipe and put the kimwipe in the bag afterwards.

Wayne Smith: More appropriately, people use a vapor deposition because if you put it on to thickly… Vapor deposition can't be applied quickly, but if you topically apply a catalyst onto a piece of wood like that, it acts like putting too viscous a solution of PEG into it. It strangles it. So you're going to get bad results and you get that whitish color on the surface. And the other thing - what crosslinker did you use? Because you were using a PA20 which is a Dow Corning very, very thin polymer so I'm just curious what crosslinker did you use? Because, if you don't use a crosslinker it won't work.

Cliff Cook: So, we used the CR20 crosslinker and we used a CT32 catalyst.

Wayne Smith: Okay, well it just looks like maybe the topically applied catalyst basically strangled the artifact.

Cliff Cook: So you think the 200 fluid might not have been viscous enough?

Wayne Smith: Usually we use something bigger – PR5 or PR1. But interesting results, thanks.

Conserving Waterlogged Archeological Corks Using Supercritical CO₂ and Monitoring Their Shrinkage Using Structured-Light 3D Scanning

Stéphanie A. Cretté *
Clemson Conservation Center - Warren Lasch Laboratory, 1250 Supply Street, North Charleston, SC 29405, USA
E-mail*: scrette@clemson.edu

Néstor G. González, Benjamin Rennison, Michael P. Scafuri, Paul Mardikian and, Michael J. Drews
Clemson Conservation Center - Warren Lasch Laboratory, 1250 Supply Street, North Charleston, SC 29405, USA

Marthe Carrier
Parks Canada, Ontario Service Center, 1800 Walkley Road, Ottawa ON K1A OM5, Canada

Abstract
Waterlogged cork is one the most unpredictable archaeological materials to conserve. Over the years, various techniques utilized for the stabilization of waterlogged wood have been applied to cork with mitigated results. In 2005, a joint research project was initiated between the Clemson Conservation Center and Parks Canada to evaluate supercritical CO₂ drying on significant archaeological corks from shipwrecks including the *Machault* (1760) and the 16th century Basque whaler *San Juan*. This paper will discuss the drying process of the various corks, with a particular focus on the corks from the *San Juan*. Monitoring of their dimensions and appearance will be presented using not only conventional measurement techniques including optical photography, but also structured-light 3D scanning combined with three-dimensional inspection.

Keywords: Supercritical carbon dioxide, waterlogged cork, structured light, 3D scanning

1. Introduction

Waterlogged archaeological organic materials have been reported to be challenging to conserve due to the critical step of drying the artifacts (Grattan 1982; Jenssen 1987; Kaye 2000). Conservation of waterlogged wood has been extensively reported, however, only few accounts have discussed successful stabilization of archaeological cork (Jenssen 1987; Smith 1998).

As hygroscopicity increases, the cellular wall structure of cork become waterlogged and starts to deteriorate making it susceptible to shrinkage and collapse from drying stresses during stabilization. As the material becomes water saturated, deterioration also arises due to microbial action rendering conservation even more challenging. As long as the waterlogged material is kept wet, it will retain its shape. If air dried, it cannot redistribute the internal moisture properly during drying due to capillary tension engendering collapse and shrinkage of the material. In addition, degraded waterlogged wood and cork exhibit strength loss due to decomposition of the main polymeric structural components. Therefore, stabilization treatments must be tailored to not only control dimensional changes due to collapse and shrinkage but also improve strength and stiffness of the material. Most of the time, conservation of waterlogged wood can be classified into two groups. One consists of dehydrating the wood prior to treating it with a consolidant. As the dehydration step involves solvent exchange, it will take longer as the size of the object increases. Therefore, such a process is commonly used with small artifacts. The second group which is employed with bigger objects requires the injection of a consolidant prior to dehydration. Most consolidants utilized in the conservation field are oligomeric water soluble compounds which are introduced into the wood by diffusion, a time consuming process. Challenges in cork conservation have been attributed to its impermeability to consolidants (Jenssen 1987; Kaye 2000). The latter, such as polyethylene glycol (PEG), do not readily penetrate the cork internal structure as they do in degraded waterlogged wood. Such difficulties in cork stabilization may be attributed to the elevated amount of highly hydrophobic suberin contained in cork cell walls.

As a part of the plant constitutive defense system, cork is a tissue made of multiple corrugated cell layers. While effective at keeping wine inside a bottle, the most important function of cork in plants is to act as a diffusion barrier for water and other small, polar compounds. Cork cells are made impervious mostly by the deposition of suberin onto their walls. Indeed, the key compound for cork impermeability is suberin, a complex polymer comprising both poly(phenolic) and poly(aliphatic) domains (Kolattukudy 1980; Lopes 2000; Bernards 2002). The chemical composition of cork has been widely analyzed by chemical fractionation and showed to be quite different from the one of wood (Silva 2005; Pereira 2007). Although the amounts of the different components can show significant variations (Pereira 1988; Lopes 2001), on average it contains 15% extractives (7.5% waxes and 7.5% tannins), 41% aliphatic suberin (referred to as suberin in cork tree literature), 22% aromatic

suberin (referred to as lignin in cork tree literature), 20% polysaccharides, and 2% ash (Pereira 1988). In addition, the cork internal structure, which has been described as an alignment of closed unit cells (Gibson 1981; Pereira 1987), could be another culprit for the unsuccessful diffusion of consolidants into cork.

Over the years, various conservation techniques designed for waterlogged wood have been applied to cork with less than satisfactory results. These techniques include air-drying with or without pretreatments at various concentrations of PEG, silicone oil, consolidation using acetone/rosin treatments, or vacuum freeze drying with or without prior polyethylene glycol (PEG) consolidation. All these techniques were investigated and resulted in unacceptable shrinkage and distortion. Alternatively, recent studies demonstrated that supercritical CO_2 drying can overcome most of the limitations of the latter techniques when applied to waterlogged materials such as wood, cork, bark or bone (Kaye 2000). In 2005, a joint research project was initiated between the Hunley Project/Clemson Conservation Center and Parks Canada to evaluate the use of supercritical CO_2 drying on significant archeological corks from several shipwrecks including the *Machault* (1760) and the 16th century Basque whaler *San Juan* (1565). This paper will discuss the drying process of the various corks, with a particular focus on the corks from the *San Juan*. In addition, monitoring of their appearance and dimensions was conducted using conventional measurement techniques and structured-light 3D scanning combined with three-dimensional inspection.

2. Experimental procedures
2.1 Experimental specimens

In 2005, Parks Canada provided eight wine bottle cork specimens from the site of the *Machault*, a French frigate that sank on July 8, 1760 at the mouth of the Restigouche River, at the far end of Baie des Chaleurs, Quebec, Canada. Marine archaeologists from Parks Canada excavated the site between 1969 and 1972. The underwater environment surrounding the wreck was brackish water with temperature ranging from 5°C to 18°C. The wreck was partially exposed and laid under about 2 to 8 meters of water depending on the tides, which engendered extensive sediment movement on the site. For about 10 years after the excavation, the corks were stored in 1% phenol aqueous solution at room temperature in order to slow down mold growth. Subsequently, the corks were stored in water only, and kept refrigerated (± 5°C). The water in the storage containers were changed every five years. The cork specimens and their identification numbers are shown in Figure 1, as received from Park Canada. Conservation of these corks has been previously presented (Drews 2005) and will be summarized herein.

Figure 1. Photograph of the eight cork specimens from the Machault

In 2007, Parks Canada provided eight cork artifacts excavated from the site of the *San Juan*, a Spanish Basque galleon that sank in the autumn of 1565 in Red Bay, Labrador, Canada. Marine archaeologists from Parks Canada excavated the site between 1979 and 1985. The whaler was discovered completely covered with sediments under about 10 meters of water, in an excellent state of preservation. The underwater environment of the wreckage was sea water with temperatures ranging from -1°C to 3°C. The *San Juan* was sunk with hundreds of barrels filled with whale oil stowed aboard (Barkham 1984; Laxalt 1985; Logan 1990; Grenier 1998). The cork artifacts provided by Parks Canada were whale oil barrel bungs. The inner part of the bung (narrower end) may have been in contact with the whale oil for a certain period of time. Since their excavation in the early 80s, the bungs were stored in tap water and refrigerated (± 5°C). The water in the storage containers was changed every five years. The cork specimens and their identification numbers are shown in Figure 2, as received from Park Canada.

Figure 2. Photographs of the eight corks from the San Juan

2.2 Description of the supercritical drying process

A supercritical phase was first observed by Baron Charles Cagniard de la Tour in 1822 as a single phase where liquid and vapor phases are indistinguishable (Cagniard de la Tour 1822). Indeed, a fluid is defined as supercritical when its temperature and pressure are higher than its critical-point value (T_c, P_c), as shown in Figure 3. The primary advantage to using supercritical fluids (SCF) lies in the capability to manipulate the solvent strength (dielectric constant) by simply varying the temperature and pressure of the system. The fluid is compressed and heated beyond its critical point yielding liquid and gas properties in a single phase (McHugh 1993; Shaffer 1995; Taylor 1996).

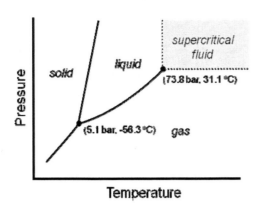

Figure 3. Phase diagram of pure Carbon Dioxide

As shown in Table 1, the compressibility of a fluid can generate liquid-like solvating power (density) while exhibiting gas-like density and diffusivity. SCF make ideal extraction solvents and chromatographic mobile phases because of their high mass transport properties. As compared to normal liquids, SCFs exhibit higher diffusivities, lower viscosities and near zero surface tension. These gas-like properties allow fast mass transfer into and out of complex matrices. The most commonly used SCF is carbon dioxide (CO_2). It is relatively inert, non-flammable, non toxic, readily available, inexpensive, and considered environmentally friendly. Also, carbon dioxide is a gas under ambient conditions. From the phase diagram of pure carbon dioxide shown in Figure 3, it can be seen that its critical point is easily accessible ($T_c = 31.1°C$, $P_c = 73.8$ bar) in comparison to other supercritical solvents such as water ($T_c = 374°C$, $P_c = 221$ bar)

Indeed, since its first technological application was developed in the seventies to extract caffeine from coffee beans (Zosel 1971; Taylor 1996), compressed CO_2 has been employed in a wide range of applications such as extractions and purifications of synthetic and natural substances, separations, precision cleaning, chemical manufacturing, polymer synthesis and processing, coating, garment cleaning, and conservation (Tewari 1985; Macquet 1994; Jessop 1995; Taylor 1996; Jessop 1999; Cooper 2000; Kaye 2000; Cretté 2001; Beckman 2004; Sousa 2007). For many applications, solubility in CO_2 could become a critical factor. Indeed, carbon dioxide is a good solvent only for many non-polar and some polar molecules with low molecular weights (O'Shea 1991). Supercritical CO_2 has a dielectric constant, as a measure of solvent strength, of 1.4 to 1.5 versus 2.5 to 4 for organic solvents and 78 for water. Furthermore, considering its structural symmetry, CO_2 does not have a permanent dipole moment, instead it has a quadrupole moment. Thus, while some polar molecules such as water are not soluble in CO_2 others such as methanol are able to dissolve in CO_2. Indeed, water with a surface tension of 73 dynes/cm is not soluble in SC-CO_2, it has to be exchanged with a lower surface tension solvent (20 to 30 dynes/cm) that is readily miscible with supercritical CO_2. It is known that at 50°C and 95 bar, methanol (23 dynes/cm) and SC-CO_2 are completely miscible. In addition, because interfacial tensions vanish at supercritical temperatures and

Table 1. Physical Properties of carbon dioxide in different phases

Phase	Density (g cm^{-3})	Diffusion Coefficient (cm^2 s^{-1})	Viscosity (g cm^{-1} s^{-1})
Gas	10^{-3}	10^{-1}	10^{-4}
SCF	0.3 - 0.8	10^{-3} -10^{-4}	10^{-4} - 10^{-3}
Liquid	1	$<10^{-5}$	10^{-2}

pressures, drying stresses are eliminated which would be created by capillary forces and surface tension during drying processes. Therefore, structural shrinkage and collapse of waterlogged archaeological materials such as wood and cork can be prevented by using supercritical CO_2. As previously reported by Kaye et al. (2000), results obtained by supercritical drying compare favorably to those obtained by air drying and freeze drying processes.

2.3 Water exchange protocol and Supercritical carbon dioxide drying

The supercritical carbon dioxide drying procedure employed was adapted from that described in the literature (Kaye 2000). Preliminary steps were taken to exchange the water out of the cork specimens utilizing anhydrous methanol. The corks were weighed, measured, photographed and scanned prior to the water-methanol exchange procedure. In a closed 500 ml polypropylene wide-mouth container, each specimen was soaked in 250 ml of anhydrous methanol and supported about 1 cm above the bottom in a strainer, sieve 0.5 mm mesh for one week. After one week, the solvent was replaced by fresh anhydrous methanol. Each specimen was subjected to at least six solvent changes. The water-methanol exchange process was considered complete when the weight of the cork specimen stabilized. During the last week of soaking, 20 g of anhydrous sodium sulfate was added to the container to eliminate any trace of water. The specimens were weighed after each solvent change.

As shown on Figure 4, the equipment used for the SC-CO_2 drying consisted of a Thar Technologies 250 ml stirred high pressure reactor capable of operating up to 300 bar at 150°C. The system pressure was maintained using a Thar Technologies ABPR-20 programmable BPR (back pressure regulator) and the

fluid flow was controlled using a Teledyne ISCO Model 260 D Syringe Pump chilled to 10°C. The liquid carbon dioxide was supplied at about 55 bar from a high pressure cylinder of SFC grade CO_2. Prior to placing the cork specimen into the reactor, 60 ml of anhydrous methanol was added to the bottom of the pressure vessel. The specimen was wrapped using a TX 1009 Alpha wipe saturated with anhydrous methanol and placed into a basket fabricated from 20-mesh stainless steel screen. Finally, the protected specimen was placed into the Thar vessel. The latter was filled with liquid CO_2 to a pressure of about 70 bar, heated to 55°C, and the final pressure was brought to 122 bar through stages. Once the system was equilibrated, the ISCO flow rate was set to 0.3 ml/min. The drying step proceeded until no additional methanol was collected into vials at the ice bath trap located at the restrictor vent. Once the drying process was complete, the system was slowly depressurized over a 6 hours period. The cork specimens were weighed, measured, photographed and scanned after their removal from the pressure vessel.

Figure 4. Supercritical Carbon Dioxide Drying Equipment

2.4 Measurements and monitoring methodologies

Inspection of the corks was conducted using conventional measurement techniques and optical photography. Ordinary straight pins were stuck on the

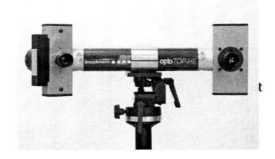

t

Figure 5. The Breuckmann OptoTOP-HE Structured-Light Scanner.

side and bottom of the specimens, as shown on Figures 8 and 10. In the case of the *San Juan* artifacts, a total of 17 different dimensions were recorded and averaged to express any dimensional change that occurred during the drying process. All before and after treatment measurements were performed with a micrometer from Mitutoyo. All photographs were taken using a FinePix S5Pro digital camera (Fujifilm Corporation).

An indication of the extent of the cork degradation is given by calculating the moisture contents using equation (1)

$$\%Moisture = \frac{Initial(wt) - Final(wt)}{Final(wt)} x100$$

2. 5 Methodologies for documentation and inspection using structured light scanning

The scanning system used for this 3D documentation was the Breuckmann GmbH Opto*TOP*-HE structured-light scanner, as shown in Figure 5. Structured-light scanning, also referred to as fringe-projection method or white–light scanning, is based on the projection of light patterns, such as lines or stripes, onto the surface of a target object. The interpretation of the distortion and displacement of these patterns when viewed by one or more cameras from different angles results in the generation of a highly accurate 3D surface representation of the object. By collecting successive scans of the object from all sides, a complete 360 degree model of the object can be constructed. The accuracy of this system (with a per scan feature accuracy of less than 0.1 mm) is such that a precise record of the objects size and physical structure can be made. This allows for the detailed measurement of surface topography, volume, and texture of scanned objects. In addition, all of this data can be

The use of structured-light scanning to monitor possible shrinkage and collapse of archaeological cork was advantageous for several reasons. Firstly, by collecting highly accurate 3D data for each cork, we could do a detailed physical comparison of each artifact before and after conservation. Using various software packages, the pre- and post-treatment corks can be compared directly and any physical changes measured. This gave us the means to get very specific quantifiable measurements of the effects of the supercritical CO_2 drying process. Secondly, structured-light scanning is an optical process. In addition to 3D data collection, the system also collects high-resolution color photographic data. This allowed us to compare surface details and color, and their changes as a result of the drying process.

Figure 6. Cork WLO451 placement on turntable for scanning.

In order to minimize possible variation in data collection, all of the corks were scanned under the same conditions using a standard procedure. All *San Juan* corks were scanned and 3D inspected. The scanner was calibrated to a 300mm diagonal field of view (FOV). This FOV was establishing by using a 382 mm sensor bar between the camera and projector and a specific lens set. The overall scanning swath was 245x180mm, with an operational stand-off of 847mm. The target objects were placed on a rubber turntable allowing the artifact to be rotated in relation to the scanner, as shown on Figure 6. All data collection took place in a closed room with no significant ambient light. For consistent texture capture, a standard light setup was used that included tripod-mounted studio strobe lights using 300W white bulbs and photographic umbrellas. The lighting settings were calibrated to a light meter reading ISO 100, F 125 with an intensity of 2.0/5. The scanner's camera settings were: Shutter 6.8, gain lowest, red gain 67, blue gain 193.

The scanner itself and studio lights were placed in a fixed position to establish consistent data collection and lighting on each object. After each scan was taken, the artifact was rotated approximately 45 degrees for the next scan. Once complete coverage was achieved on one side, each cork was flipped to expose and scan the opposite side. A similar series of scans were taken from this side, followed by select patch scans to pick up any data missed with the original passes.

Post processing of the scan data was conducted in Geomagic Studio v8. Geomagic is a type of reverse engineering and modeling software that transforms 3D scanner data and polygon meshes into 3D digital models allowing close inspection and analysis. Post processing in Geomagic allows the user to clean and repair the data. Typical cleaning procedures normally include removing extraneous data, noise reduction, decimation, filling holes, and repairing intersections. In this case, in order to ensure an accurate comparison of all relevant data, scans were assessed and post processed in exactly the same way to aid the final 3D comparison. A number of processes had to be completed in order to create a final polygonal mesh. Each data set of scans was imported into Geomagic in the Breuckmann (.bre) format and converted to Geomagic files (.wrp). Once the file is converted, all the data that are non pertinent to the study, such as the modeling wheel and stand used to orient the scans, were deleted.

As mentioned in the previous section, each scan set was organized into groups dependent upon the artifacts orientation during the scanning sequence. As the scanning process can collect a small amount of erroneous data, polygons with large edge lengths were selected and deleted in order to create a more accurate study. Also, some extraneous points created dangling triangles away from the corks surface, these were removed and cleaned (Figure 7).

Once the data was cleaned, each upper and lower group was aligned to each other to create a whole object. This phase, known as global registration, allows the software to run alignments to sort the individual scan meshes. Similar regions of each scan are made to overlap in order to create a complete composite object. Settings for the global registration phase were setting a tolerance of 0.0mm, maximum iterations 100, sample size 1000. Other controls

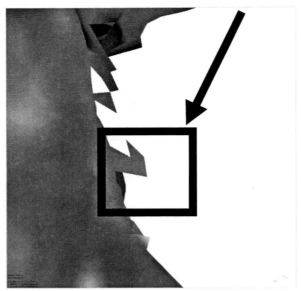

Figure 7. Dangling data clean up

included the limitation of translation between the scans and slip control to restrict the movement of scans in wrong directions. Once alignment and clean up were completed, the data was merged together to create a complete object.

The merge phase joins two or more point objects into one, automatically performs noise reduction, uniform sampling, surface wrapping, and places the resulting polygon as a single surface. Again, in order to create an accurate study the merge phase was conducted in exactly the same way for each cork. The merge phase settings were kept to a minimum; this was in order to avoid any over smoothing of the surface. Also, any floating data was removed using the delete outlier's option.

Once a full set of pre and post conservation merges were made, each of the final scan sets were surveyed. During the merge phase, settings were established to limit smoothing and preserve original data. A manual inspection however, found various errors in some of the scans. These patches of mostly intersecting scans were subsequently deleted. Cleaning the intersecting scans led to the creation of

a number of small holes in the end merges. These holes were filled or left open at the user's discretion after close inspection of the unedited scan data and the incorporated photographs generated by the OptoCAT scanning process.

3. Results and Discussion
3.1 *Machault corks stabilization using supercritical CO_2*

Figure 1 shows the eight cork specimens and their identifications from the *Machault*, as received from Parks Canada. All artifacts were SC-CO_2 dried except WL-0398 which was air-dried and utilized as a control to monitor dimensional changes and possible shrinkage among the *Machault* artifacts. Figure 8 compares WL-398 (air-dried) with WL-399 (SC-CO_2 dried). Straight pins were inserted into all the corks prior to drying treatments to allow for more accurate measurements. In addition, moisture contents for the eight corks of the *Machault* are given in Table 2.

Comparison of data and results of the SC-CO_2 drying of seven waterlogged cork specimens to the air-dried control from the *Machault* has been previously published (Drews 2005). It was concluded that the observed shrinkage in all the *Machault* corks in all directions ranged from 2 to 4%. Also, no visible evidence of movement was observed in the photographs taken prior and after SC drying. After their successful treatment in 2005, the corks were returned to Parks Canada. Currently, the artifacts are stored at 20°C and 45-50% relative humidity and no changes in any of the specimen's stability has been observed.

Figure 8. *Photograph of WL-398 and WL-399 before and after drying treatment, air-dried and SC-CO$_2$ dried, respectively.*

Table 2. *Moisture Content of the eight Machault cork specimens*

Cork identification	Treatment	Moisture Content (%)
WL-397	SC-CO$_2$	870
WL-398	Air-dried	343
WL-399	SC-CO$_2$	368
WL-400	SC-CO$_2$	685
WL-401	SC-CO$_2$	724
WL-402	SC-CO$_2$	590
WL-403	SC-CO$_2$	740
WL-404	SC-CO$_2$	540

3.2 San Juan Corks stabilization using supercritical CO$_2$

Figure 2 shows the eight cork specimens and their identifications from the *San Juan*, as received from Parks Canada. All artifacts were SC-CO$_2$ dried. As the density of methanol at room temperature is only 0.792 g/cm^3, it is possible to monitor the advancement of the water-methanol exchange process. Indeed, for each gram of water displaced by methanol, the specimen weight should decrease by 0.208g. Figure 9 illustrates the weight variation as a function of the accumulated methanol soaking time for the *San Juan* bungs. As shown in Figure 9, the weight loss for WL-452, WL-454 and WL-456 reached a constant level after 20 days while for all the other corks a constant weight was reached after 45 days. This indicates that the methanol exchange attained completion soon after the third and sixth solvent changes, respectively. In addition, the calculated moisture contents for the eight corks of the *San Juan* are compared in Table 3. The moisture contents which are indicative of their degradation are slightly lower than those from the *Machault* corks (Table 2). However, if one considers the time period of 200 more years during which the *San Juan* corks were waterlogged compared to the *Machault* specimens, it will be concluded that their degradation was much slower. The difference in the wreck environment temperatures and size of the artifacts might have played a role. Furthermore, this series of bungs differs from regular cork stoppers by the direction in which they were punched out while fabricated. Indeed, the two circular top and bottom of the *San Juan* bungs correspond to the tangential section of the original cork plank, while regular stopper have the two circular tops in the transverse section. Without a doubt, this would have affected the porosity, impermeability and degradation of the resulting corks. This deviation from

common practice is most likely due to the size requirement of the corks to fit the whale oil barrel mouths and perhaps the time period at which they were punched out.

Prior to CO_2 treatment, six straight pins were inserted into the bottom and side of each cork, as shown in Figure 10, to accurately measure any dimensional changes. Exception were made for WL-452 and WL-455 which were not stuck with straight pins, therefore they were only monitored through photography and scanning.

Table 3: *Moisture Content of the eight San Juan cork specimens, all treated by SC-CO₂*

Cork identification	Moisture Content (%)
WL-450	516
WL-451	626
WL-452	511
WL-453	572
WL-454	479
WL-455	554
WL-456	654
WL-457	653

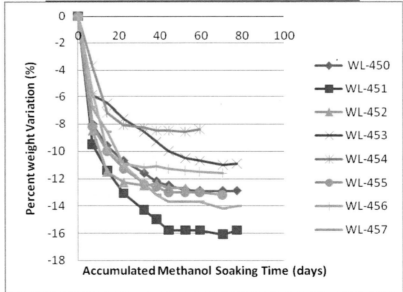

Figure 9: *San Juan corks - Variation in cork specimen weight versus accumulated soaking time in methanol.*

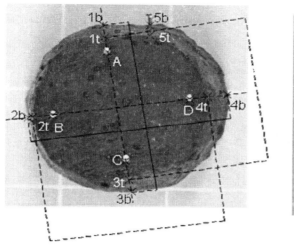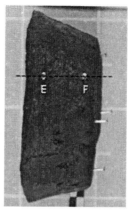

Figure 10. *Pin Measurements (Cork WL-453)*

Table 4. *Average Dimensional Changes*

Artifact identification	Average Dimensional change (%)
WL-450	-0.03
WL-451	0
WL-452	No pins
WL-453	0.1
WL-454	-3.06
WL-455	No Pins
WL-456	-1.68
WL-457	-1.37

Based on the six pins inserted in each artifact, seventeen measurements were recorded which were averaged and entered in Table 4. While WL-454, WL-456 and WL-457 show some shrinkage, WL-450, W-451 and WL-453 did not noticeably shrink. In the case of WL-454 which demonstrated the highest shrinkage, it should be noted that the highest dimensional change in one direction was only 6.85mm.

The methanol exchange combined with the supercritical drying process yielded a few stress openings perpendicular to EF in most of the corks, as shown in Figures 11 to 17. These openings seemed to have been present in the waterlogged state, but were swollen and filled with sediment and dirt. In addition, the highly porous cork interior structure fluctuated during the solvent exchange and drying process either by slight shrinkage or expansion movements, which in turn influenced the positions of the pins. Therefore, the dimensional changes recorded might contain some degree of error as a result of the altered position of the pins. Moreover, one should not ignore measurement inaccuracy due to human error. WL-454 showed the highest shrinkage of all the corks and visually presented some deep cracks on its periphery parallel to EF. This would imply that WL-454 was the worst degraded bung of all; however, it presented the lowest moisture content which implied that it is the least degraded. Therefore, it was concluded that the bung WL-454 was punched out from a defective plank and carried on the defects which created openings after

267

treatment. Overall, no obvious distortion of the San Juan bungs is apparent when comparing before and after treatment specimens (Figure 11 to 17).

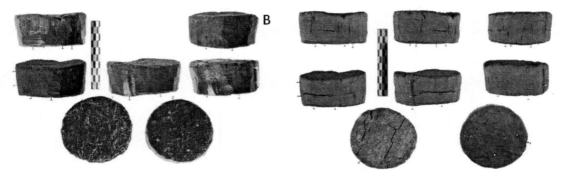

Figure 11 A and B. San Juan cork WL-450. A) before supercritical CO_2 drying, and B) dried with SC-CO_2

Figure 12 A and B. San Juan cork WL-451 A) before and B) after supercritical CO_2 drying

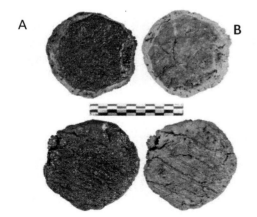

Figure 13. San Juan cork WL-452 A) before and B) after supercritical CO_2 drying

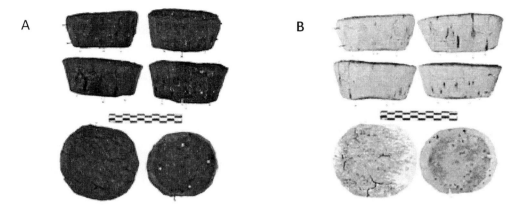

Figure 14 A and B. Cork WL-453 in A) water and B) after supercritical CO_2 drying

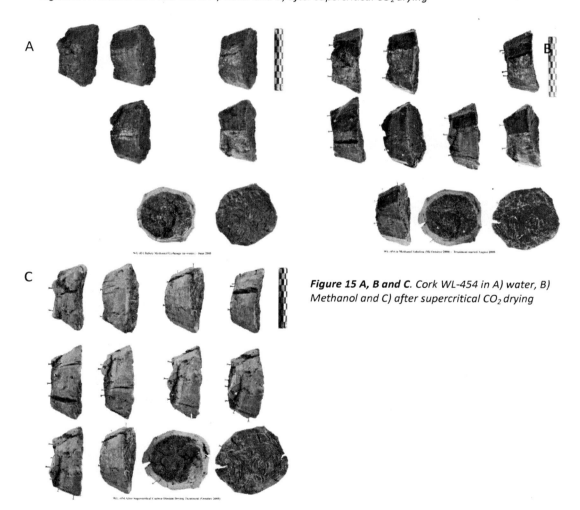

Figure 15 A, B and C. Cork WL-454 in A) water, B) Methanol and C) after supercritical CO_2 drying

3.3 Results and three-dimensional inspection

In order to survey the dimensional changes to the corks that occurred during the conservation phase a spatial analysis was conducted. Using the 3D compare tool in the inspection module of Geomagic Studio v8, the final pre and post conservation scans were aligned and their physical differences compared. Using the pre-conservation cork as reference object, the tool generates a three dimensional, color coded map of the differences between two objects.

269

Table 5 shows a comparative analysis of the corks in their pre and post conservation states. Maximum and minimum differences in the cork surfaces are shown above. The average distance of the corks is calculated by considering the variations measured upon the entire surface of each cork. The standard deviation dimensional change ranges from 0.18mm (WL-457) to 1.08mm (WL-454), as shown in table 5.

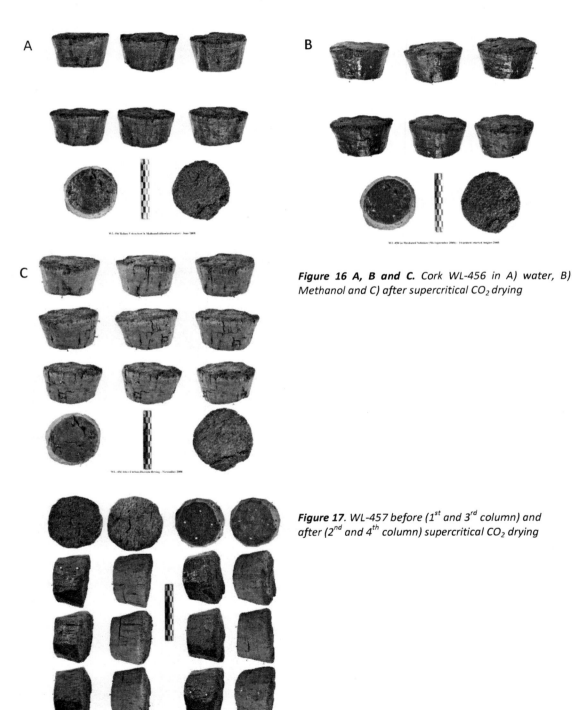

Figure 16 A, B and C. *Cork WL-456 in A) water, B) Methanol and C) after supercritical CO_2 drying*

Figure 17. *WL-457 before (1st and 3rd column) and after (2nd and 4th column) supercritical CO_2 drying*

270

Table 5. 3D Comparison Analysis of corks pre and post conservation

WL Number	Max Distance + (mm)	Max Distance - (mm)	Ave Distance (mm)	Standard Deviation (mm)
WL-450	0.96	-0.96	0.24	0.25
WL-451	1.81	-2.22	0.25	0.27
WL-452	1.41	-2.05	-0.01	0.23
WL-454	7.74	-8.10	0.50	1.08
WL-455	1.46	-1.98	0.27	0.22
WL-456	2.19	-1.92	0.23	0.30
WL-457	2.17	-1.13	0.14	0.18

In addition the median standard deviation measured from the dataset is 0.25mm. As shown in figure 18, cork WL-454 suffered from excessive cracking due to cracks present before the conservation process began. If the mean standard deviation is considered excluding this cork it becomes 0.21mm. Overall, the data sets were limited in some respects due to the recording of data within cracks. Cracks were considerably harder to collect data in as the scanning system has an occlusion of 30 degrees.

Considering the full dataset, the most significant spatial changes were concentrated at the edges of the corks. For example, figure 19 shows a 3D comparison of cork WL-450.The areas of dark grey and black on the surface of the cork show where the most dimensional change occurred. Similarly, the 3D comparison of WL-451 (figure 20) shows most difference in pre and post conservation corks around the edges. Overall, areas about the center of the corks underwent slight to no movement. It can be seen from the images below and indeed from the entire dataset that shape change was limited predominantly to the diminishment of edge surfaces.

Figure 18. WL454_A_B 3D Comparison

Figure 19. WL450_A_B 3D Comparison

271

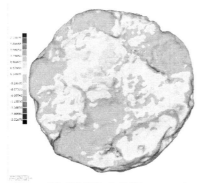

Figure 20. *WL451_A_B 3D comparison*   **Figure 21.** *WL452_A_B 3D comparison*

4. Summary and Conclusion

Sixteen waterlogged corks were successfully conserved using SC-CO$_2$ drying process. While the measured shrinkage of the *Machault* corks in all directions ranged from 2 to 4%, the dimensional changes of the *San Juan* bungs were from an average expansion of 0.1% (WL-453) to an average shrinkage of 3.06%(WL-454). The highest shrinkage was attributed to not only the direction in which the cork was initially punched out but also the quality of the cork plank from which it was made from. Interestingly, the 200 years older *San Juan* cork specimens showed a lower overall moisture content and therefore advance of degradation, when compared to the *Machault* corks. These results could be attributed to the shipwreck environment temperature and the bigger size of the corks.

In the pre and post treatment photographs, no visible changes in the artifacts was observed except for stress cracks which were initially present but swollen and filled with sediments. All the cork diagnostic features were well preserved and enhanced by the SC-CO$_2$ treatment. Finally, all dried specimens are structurally sound with a stable post-treatment weight. The color of the artifacts went from dark brown in their waterlogged state to beige after SC-CO$_2$ drying.

Enhanced accuracy in the dimensional changes between corks was observed using structured-light scanning and 3D inspection compared to traditional measurement means. By considering the full dataset, the most changes occurred at the edges of the corks rather than at the center. In the future, to improve the pixel density and generate a richer surface, a smaller FOV would be preferred. Correspondingly, further spatial analysis would be possible using more current software such as PolyWorks v.11.

Overall, this study was successful in its conservation and monitoring stage and represents a model for further waterlogged archaeological cork drying processes.

Acknowledgements

The authors would like to thank Clemson University's School of Material Science and Engineering for supporting this research. We would like to thank Mr Brian Seymour, Ms Amy Marquardt and Mr Jonathan Doan for their assistance and contribution to this study.

References

Barkham, S. H. (1984). "The Basques Whaling Establishments in Labrador 1536-1632 - A Summary." Arctic **37**(4): 515-519.

Beckman, E. J. (2004). "Supercritical and Near-Critical CO$_2$ in Green Chemical Synthesis and Processing." J. Supercrit. Fluids **28**(2-3): 121-191.

Bernards, M. A. (2002). "Demystifying Suberin." Can. J. Bot. **80**: 227-240.

Cagniard de la Tour, B. C. (1822). "Exposé de Quelques Resultats Obtenus par l'Action Combinée de la Chaleur et de la Compression sur Certains Liquides, tels que l'Eau, l'Alcool, l'Ether Sulfurique et l'Essence de Petrole Rectifiée." Ann. Chim. Phys **21**: 127-132, 178-182.

Cooper, A. J. (2000). "Polymer Synthesis and Processing Using Supercritical Carbon Dioxide." J. Mater. Chem. **10**: 207-234.

Cretté, S. A. and J. M. Desimone (2001). "Neueste Anwendungen von Komprimiertem Kohlendioxid." Nachrichten aus der Chemie **49**: 462-466.

Drews, M. J., J. Green, et al. (2005). Conservation of waterlogged cork using supercritical CO2 drying. The Conservation of Archaeological Materials: Current Trends and Future Directions, Colonial Williamsburg.

Gibson, L. J., K. E. Easterling, et al. (1981). "The Structure and Mechanisms of Cork." Proc. R. Soc. Lond. A **377**: 99-117.

Grattam, D. W. (1982). "A Practical comparative study of several treatments for waterlogged wood." Studies in Conservation **27**: 124-136.

Grenier, R. (1998). The Basque Whaling Ship from Red Bay, Labrador: a treasure trove of Data on Iberian Atlantic Shipbuilding Design and Techniques in the Mid 16th Century. International Symposium on Archaeology of Medieval and Modern Ships of Iberian-Atlantic Tradition, Lisbon, Portugal.

Jenssen, K. (1987). Conservation of wet organic artifacts excluding wood. London, Butterworths.

Jessop, P. G., T. Ikariya, et al. (1995). "Homogeneous Catalysis in Supercritical Fluids." Science **269**: 1065.

Jessop, P. G. and W. Leitner (1999). Chemical Synthesis using Supercritical Fluids. Weinheim, Germany, Wiley-VCH.

Kaye, B., J. Cole-Hamilton, et al. (2000). "Supercritical Drying: A New Method for Conserving Waterlogged Archaeological Materials." Studies in Conservation **45**: 233-252.

Kolattukudy, P. E. (1980). "Biopolyester Membranes of Plants: Cutin and Suberin." Science **208**: 990-1000.

Laxalt, R., J. A. Tuck, et al. (1985). 16th-Century Basque Whalers in America. National Geographic. **168**: 40-71.

Logan, J. A. and J. A. Tuck (1990). "A 16th Century Basque Whaling Port in Southern Labrador." APT Bulletin (Association for Preservation Technology International) **22**(3): 65-72.

Lopes, M. H., A. S. Barros, et al. (2001). "Variability of cork from portuguese Quercus Suber studied by Solid -State ^{13}C-NMR and FTIR Spectroscopies." Biopolymers (Biospectroscopy) **62**: 268-277.

Lopes, M. H., C. P. Neto, et al. (2000). "Quantitation of Aliphatic Suberin in Quercus Suber L. cork by FTIR Spectroscopy and Solid-state ^{13}C-NMR Spectroscopy." Biopolymers (Biospectroscopy) **57**: 344-351.

Macquet, C., J.-H. Thomassin, et al. (1994). "Super Critical Drying Applied on Severely Corroded Buried Glasses." Journal of Sol-Gel Science and terchnology **2**: 885-889.

McHugh, M. A. and V. J. Krukonis (1993). Supercritical Fluid Extraction, Principles and Practice. Stoneham, MA, Butterworth-Heinemann.

O'Shea, K. E., K. M. Kirmse, et al. (1991). "Polar and Hydrogen-Bonding Interactions in Supercritical Fluids. Effects on the Tautomeric Equilibrium of 4-(Phenylazo)-1-Naphthol." J. Phys. Chem. **95**(20): 7863-7867.

Pereira, H. (1988). "Chemical composition and variability of cork from Quercus Suber L." Wood Sci. Technol. **22**: 211-218.

Pereira, H. (2007). Cork: Biology, Production and Uses. Amsterdam, The Netherlands, Elsevier.

Pereira, H., M. E. Rosa, et al. (1987). "The Cellular Structure of Cork from Quercus Suber L." IAWA Bulletin N.S. **8**(3): 213-218.

Shaffer, K. F. and J. M. DeSimone (1995). "Chain Polymerization in Inert Near- and Supercritical Fluids." Trends Polym. Sci. **3**: 146-153.

Silva, S. P., M. A. Sabino, et al. (2005). "Cork: Properties, Capabalities & Applications." International Materials Reviews **50**(6): 345-365.

Smith, C. W. and D. L. Hamilton (1998). Silicone Bulking of Waterlogged Cork Using PS340, PS341 and PS 343 Silicone Oils, Archaeological Preservation Research Laboratory.

Sousa, M., M. J. Melo, et al. (2007). "The art of CO2 for art conservation: a green approach to antique textile cleaning." Green Chem. **9**: 943-947.

Taylor, L. T. (1996). Supercritical Fluid Extraction. New York, Wiley.

Tewari, P. H., A. J. Hunt, et al. (1985). "Ambient-Temperature Supercritical Drying of Transparent Silica Aerogels." Materials Letters **3**(9-10): 363-367.

Zosel, K. (1971). Procédé pour decafeiner le café. France.

Questions and answers

André Bergeron: I have a question about the price tag of your instrumentation.

Stephanie Cretté: Yeah well that's always the question...

André Bergeron: Well do you have any idea what is the range?

Stephanie Cretté: I know that the company that used to make this doesn't make it anymore or they changed – there have been some changes. The price for a small set up like this where you can do only cork is a few thousand dollars. This sort of technique has been around for a long time but the price has not gone down. I saw a gentleman this morning presenting from Grenoble and I know that supercritical companies are around in Grenoble so maybe you can collaborate with them. But it's not also a technique you're going to use often. You don't always have the cork or a small piece of wood. If you want to treat a big piece of wood it would be problematic just because of the size of the apparatus.

Ian Godfrey: Just a very practical question. With such a rare and very valuable item like this I was just wondered how do you sample them for your Umax determinations?

Stephanie Cretté: Umax?

Ian Godfrey: Maximum water content.

Stephanie Cretté: Oh well we actually found the water content by weighing the samples each time right before. We didn't sample, I guess maybe I don't do it the same way as you guys do but we weighed the sample before and during the treatment and we took the last weight.

Jim Spriggs: A retrospective approach.

Ian Godfrey: Yes.

3.8 (Sc PR)

Evaluating Treatments for Waterlogged Lignum Vitae Objects from the USS *Monitor*

Elsa Sangouard*

The Mariners' Museum, 100 Museum Drive, Newport News, VA, 23606
E-mail: esangouard@marinersmuseum.org

Susanne Grieve

East Carolina University, Program in Maritime Studies, Greenville, NC 27858

Abstract

Excavations of the USS *Monitor* have resulted in the recovery of numerous pulley blocks. The sheaves of most of the blocks are made out of a very dense wood, lignum vitae. A study was conducted to assess the most appropriate conservation treatment for these particular objects. The following treatments were applied to six wooden sheaves recovered from the warship: controlled air-drying without a bulking agent, impregnation with polyethylene glycol 400 followed by controlled air-drying and by vacuum freeze-drying, acetone-rosin, sucrose and lactitol-trehalose. The best results were achieved through controlled air-drying as evaluated by the preservation of the shape and color of the artifact, reversibility, minimal intervention, and low cost.

Keywords: waterlogged wood, lignum vitae, sheave, polyethylene glycol, sucrose, lactitol, acetone-rosin, controlled air-drying, vacuum freeze-drying

1. Introduction

The USS *Monitor*, the US Navy's first ironclad warship, sank in 240 feet of seawater off the coast of North Carolina in December 1862, less than a year after being launched. In 2002, through joint efforts between the National Oceanic and Atmospheric Administration, the United States Navy, and The Mariners' Museum, the stern of the ship was excavated and the iconic rotating gun turret was recovered from the seabed. The turret and other artifacts are currently being conserved at The Mariners' Museum in Newport News, Virginia. During excavation of the wreck, several iron and wood rigging blocks with lignum vitae sheaves were recovered. Disassembly of the blocks has produced more than 20 sheaves.

Lignum vitae, literally translated as the "wood of life," is obtained from a tropical tree, genus *Guaiacum*, and is one of the hardest commercially used woods (McEwen and Lewis 1992). The great strength of this wood, combined with self-lubricating properties that result from a high resin content, make it especially suitable for maritime use (USN 1957, Kerchove 1961, McEwen and Lewis 1992, Swindells 1997, USDA 2007). Lignum vitae is used extensively for the manufacture of block-sheaves, dead-eyes, bull's-eyes, clump blocks, and propeller shaft bearings (USN 1957, McEwen and Lewis 1992). Lignum vitae is also resistant to decay and abrasion (USN 1957). As a result, *Monitor*'s sheaves remain in good overall physical condition after 140 years underwater.

Six of the *Monitor* sheaves were treated with different methods to compare the results and provide a treatment protocol for the remaining sheaves. The treatments methods used were:

- controlled air-drying (CAD),
- 20%v/v (aq) polyethylene glycol (PEG) 400 followed by controlled air-drying (CAD),
- 20%v/v (aq) PEG 400 followed by vacuum freeze-drying (FD),
- 70%w/v colophony rosin in acetone,
- 50%w/w (aq) sucrose,
- 60%w/v (aq) lactitol-trehalose.

2. Objects Description, Prior Treatment and Documentation

2.1 Description

Five of the six sheaves were recovered from around the *Monitor*'s tiller area and the sixth was excavated from the interior of the gun turret (Johnston 2009). All were from a marine burial environment with abundant metal components nearby. The sheaves are between 10 and 13cm in diameter and 2–3cm thick. Table 1 identifies the sheaves treated, the presence of any metallic bearing inserts, the current density of the wood compared to the normal density, and the treatment method employed. The artifacts

were arbitrarily lettered for ease of citation in the following text.

Conservators performed pin tests by probing the object with a sharp pin to look for signs of softness and to give a quick indication of degradation. The tests showed that the wood was well preserved and difficult to penetrate throughout the six artifacts. Comparing the current density of the sheaves to the normal density of lignum vitae (from the PEGCON density list) confirmed that the objects were all in close state of preservation and in good condition (Table 1). Sheave B, with a lower density, appears slightly more damaged than the others. This might be the result of physical degradation from shipworms, likely *Teredo* or *Bankia* species (USDA 2007, Cronyn 1990), which left noticeable channels through the wood about 3mm in diameter. While all the sheaves were impacted by worm boring, sheaves B and D had the most channels. In addition, the lack of metal insert in sheave B may also have played a role in its degradation.

*Table 4. **Lignum vitae sheave features, densities, and treatment methods.***

Accession Number	Label	Metallic Components	Density measured/normal	Treatment methods
MNMS.2002.001.246	"A"	Cu alloy inserts	0.96/1.14	Controlled Air-drying (CAD)
MNMS.2002.001.003	"B"	none	0.73/1.14	PEG + CAD
MNMS.2002.001.150	"C"	Cu alloy inserts	0.94/1.14	PEG + FD
MNMS.2002.001.002	"D"	Fe alloy insert	0.89/1.14	Acetone-rosin
MNMS.2002.001.004	"E"	Fe alloy insert	0.87/1.14	Sucrose
MNMS.2002.001.008	"F"	Fe alloy insert	0.94/1.14	Lactitol-trehalose

2.2 Prior treatment and documentation

All metal bearing inserts were removed for separate treatment. Surface concretions were mechanically removed using ultrasonic dental tools. Baths of 2% w/v (aq) diammonium citrate were used to

remove metallic staining. Thorough rinsing with deionized (DI) water followed the chelating diammonium citrate baths. The sheaves were then weighed, drawn, scanned, and photographed to document physical changes during treatment. Individual treatment with one of the six experimental methods was followed by thorough documentation and reassembly with the treated metal bearings.

3. Experimental Method

Background for each of the treatments as well as a description of the method used is given in the following sections. Published conservation literature suggests the use of polyethylene glycol (PEG) as a bulking agent followed by vacuum freeze-drying for the treatment of waterlogged lignum vitae (Bergeron and Dunning 2002). Personal communications with other conservators recommended treatments such as controlled air-drying without any impregnation (Hamilton et al. 2007) or a sucrose impregnation treatment (Seifert 2007). PEG + FD, CAD, and sucrose were chosen for this evaluation considering the aforementioned sources. The additional techniques were selected because of the small molecular sizes of the chemicals, suitable to minimally degraded wood. A successful treatment was defined as one that preserved the artifact's shape and appearance, remained stable over time, and proved reversible and minimally intrusive.

3.1 Controlled Air-Drying (Sheave A)

3.1.1 Method and Principle

Controlled air-drying involves slowly decreasing the relative humidity (RH) around an artifact in 5% to 10% increments (De La Baume 1990). Evaporation of water within the wood cell walls in a dry, uncontrolled environment can occur quickly causing the cell wall to collapse or distort from osmotic pressure (Grattan 1987). The drying temperature can be adjusted to regulate humidity levels as lower temperatures decrease evaporation. A humidity buffer such as silica gel can be used to adjust RH within a closed environment. Alternatively, certain salts can be used to reduce the relative humidity (ASTM 1991).

3.1.2 Application to Sheave A

A dehydration chamber was set up using nested polyethylene trays covered by a Plexiglas board. An initial RH of 95% was achieved by adding one inch of water in the outer tray, while the inner tray containing the sheave was kept dry. The RH was slowly decreased first by removing the water and then with addition of silica gel in 10g packets. The RH was monitored daily with thermohygrometers placed in the chamber (see Figure 1) and was decreased as follows:

- week 1: 95% RH,
- week 2: 85% RH,
- week 3: 75% RH,
- week 4: 55% RH.

Figure 1. Sheaves A and B in the dehydration chamber with thermohygrometers.

Mold began to grow on the surface of the sheave after one week at 95% RH. The mold was removed with swabs of ethanol and DI water (50% v/v). A small dish of concentrated Lysol® was placed in the dehydration chamber as an aerosol sterilizing agent. The Lysol® was effective as no further mold formed on the wood.

3.2 20% V/V (Aq) Peg 400 Followed By Air-Drying (Sheave B)

3.2.1 Method and Principle

Polyethylene glycol (PEG) has been used for wood treatment since the late 1940s. It is a linear macromolecule of ethylene groups linked by oxygen with a hydroxyl group at the end of each chain (Grattan and Clarke 1987). Its molecular weight (MW) varies from 200 g/mol (low molecular weight or LMW) up to 100,000 g/mol (high molecular weight or HMW). The PEG used in conservation ranges between 200 and 4000 and is selected based on wood degradation: the more deteriorated the wood, the higher the MW required (Hoffman 1984, Grattan and Clarke 1987). The numerous hydroxyl groups of the molecule create hydrogen bonds with cellulose and hemicellulose molecules in wood (De La Baume 1990). Like other wood impregnation agents, PEG replaces the water present in cellular voids within waterlogged wood, allowing water to evaporate without causing cellular and structural collapse.

Advantages of PEG include its apparent stability, theoretic reversibility, ease of use, excellent penetration into wood structure (Dean et al. 1997), and relatively low cost. Drawbacks include: difficult reversibility; hygroscopicity; degradation by heat and oxygen; the need for MW>600 to be heated during treatment to remain soluble in water (Grattan and Clarke . 1987), which can involve expensive apparatus; pH is dependent on concentration; commonly used solutions, between 10 to 30% v/v, are corrosive to metal (Glastrup 1997).

3.2.2 Application to Sheave B
Sheave B was treated with PEG because it was recovered with no metal bearings. As PEG remains hygroscopic after treatment, contact with metal components could produce metallic salts and, potentially, acids (Sandstrom et al. 2003, Degrigny and Guilminot 2000). The PEGCON program was used to assist choosing the appropriate PEG concentration even though this object was not subjected to freeze-drying (Cook and Grattan 1991). The result was high PEG concentrations (36.4% PEG 400 followed by 91% PEG 3350) confirming that the program is not always suitable for well-preserved, high density wood (Cook 2009). Considering the over all good condition of the sheave, only 20% v/v PEG 400 was used and PEG 3350 was not employed. After six weeks of impregnation, the weight of the object was stable suggesting the end of the treatment. The sheave was removed from solution, lightly rinsed in DI water, blotted dry with acid-free tissues, weighed and documented (size and shape). Controlled air-drying was performed using the same method as for sheave A. Sheave B also experienced mold growth after one week of drying. Lysol® was successfully used to prevent further mold growth in the same method described above.

3.3 20% V/V (Aq) Peg 400 Followed By Vacuum Freeze-Drying (Sheave C)
3.3.1 Method and Principle
A PEG impregnation treatment followed by vacuum freeze-drying has been commonly and successfully used in conservation for over 30 years (Cook and Grattan 1985). The principle of this drying technique is to freeze the impregnated object to solidify the water molecules in the wood cell walls and, by lowering the pressure, cause sublimation of the ice in the artifact. The liquid phase is thus avoided, as are surface tension effects that damage wood tissues (Grattan and Clarke 1987). The major constraint of vacuum freeze-drying is that capacity of the apparatus may limit the size of objects that can be treated.

3.3.2 Application on Sheave C

Sheave C was impregnated with 20% v/v PEG 400 in DI water for six weeks, rinsed, and blotted of excess PEG. The sheave was prefrozen in a chest freezer at -27°C for 24 hours. It was then placed into a Virtis® General Purpose Freeze Dryer with the condenser set to -50°C, the chamber at -25°C, and the pressure at 600 microns. The artifact was weighed every eight hours for the first week of treatment. The weight should then have been taken every week until the artifact's weight stabilized, marking completion of the treatment. However, several small hairline cracks were noticed on the sheave after 16 hours of vacuum freeze-drying at 600 microns. The sheave was returned to the chest freezer, where, after few days, the cracks were less visible. Vacuum freeze-drying was applied again, with a lower pressure of 1000 microns, yet the artifact showed cracks after two days. The sheave was removed from vacuum and placed in a chest freezer for one month, where ambient freeze-drying occurred.

3.4 Acetone-Rosin (Sheave D)

3.4.1 Method and Principle

The principle of the acetone-rosin treatment is to replace water with a solvent, then introduce a bulking agent. The object is immersed in successive baths of acetone and water to eliminate the water, then rosin is added to the acetone. In the early 1980s, this treatment was frequently applied in the United States, Scotland, and England (Hawley 1989). This method has often been used on iron/wood composite artifacts since it is not corrosive to metals (Cook et al. 1985, Hawley 1989). Conservators have noticed poor impregnation and brittle objects resulting from such treatment (Grattan and Clarke 1987). It is sometimes suggested to heat the acetone to 52°C in an explosion-proof oven (Hawley 1989), potentially creating a fire hazard if treating large artifacts (Cook et al. 1985).

3.4.2 Application to Sheave D

Sheave D was immersed in a 50% DI water/50% acetone (v/v) solution and was monitored for changes. After seven days, the solution was changed to 100% acetone. The 100% acetone bath was changed every seven days for three weeks. The acetone dissolved some of the natural oils and resins in the lignum vitae and darkened the solution. The sheave was continuously weighed during the solvent dehydration and lost a total of 12% of its weight during this phase.

The sheave was then immersed in a solution of 70% rosin/30% acetone (w/v) (Hawley 1989). The mixture was heated to 50°C on a hotplate under fume extraction in an explosion proof room and continuously stirred to dissolve the rosin. The sheave was placed into the homogenous solution maintained at 50°C and sealed. It was turned over every other day to prevent build up of the rosin on one surface. The sheave was weighed during rosin impregnation and gained 5% total weight during that time.

After four weeks in the acetone-rosin solution, the sheave was removed and blotted dry with acetone-soaked, lint-free cloths to remove excess rosin and allowed to air dry at ambient conditions of 40% RH and 19°C.

3.5 Sucrose (Sheave E)

3.5.1 Method and Principle

Of the several sugars used in conservation, the best results have been obtained with sucrose ($C_{12}H_{22}O_{11}$), also known as saccharose and sorbitol (Grattan and Clarke 1987). The principle of the method is to steadily increase the sugar concentration until the wood reaches weight equilibrium (Parrent 1985). Reported successes with sugar treatments have been irregular (Grattan and Clarke 1987, Hoffmann 1996). Its principal advantages are that the materials are easy to obtain, affordable, non-toxic, and non-corrosive. The main drawback is the high risk of attack by fungi and microorganisms (Grattan and Clarke 1987).

3.5.2 Application to Sheave E

The method starts with immersion in 10% w/v white table sucrose in DI water. The concentration of sucrose was increased by 10% each week up to 50% w/v. The solution was heated in an oven at 43-50°C (Parrent 1985). Dowicide® 1E was added to prevent biological growth during treatment (Parrent 1985). After five weeks of immersion, the artifact's weight was stable allowing the air-drying process to start.

3.6 Lactitol-Trehalose (Sheave F)

3.6.1 Method and Principle

Lactitol is a disaccharide synthesized from the sugar lactose. It has antioxidant characteristics that present it as a potential treatment for composite wood/metal objects. Lactitol has limited solubility in water which may result in poor impregnation (Imazu and Morgos 1999); however, good results have been achieved when combining it with trehalose (Imazu and Morgos 2002).

3.6.2 Application to Sheave F

The treatment for sheave F follows the one described by Imazu and Morgos 2002. The sheave was first immersed in 30% concentration of 9:1 lactitol:trehalose with 0.02% Kathon CG izothiazolone biocide (Imazu and Morgos 2002). The artifact was stored in a sealed container while the impregnation was performed at room temperature.

The sheave was impregnated for eight weeks, after which the mixed sugar concentration was increased every four weeks by 10% w/v of 9:1 lactitol:trehalose until a final concentration of 60% was achieved. The total impregnation lasted 20 weeks.

Before drying, excess sugar at the surface of the sheave was rinsed with hot tap water. A thin layer of lactitol powder was then applied on the surface of the artefact (Imazu and Morgos 2002). The sheave was then dried in an oven at 50°C.

4. Results

4.1 Controlled Air-Drying (Sheave A)

The treatment was highly satisfactory because the artifact did not exhibit stress cracking or discoloration. The sheave lost about 14% of its waterlogged weight during drying. The artifact's shape, size, and appearance were preserved, even after several months in storage conditions (see Figure 2).

Figure 2. *Sheave A before (top) and after (bottom) controlled air-drying.*

4.2 20% V/V (Aq) Peg 400 Followed By Air-Drying (Sheave B)

Upon drying, sheave B lost 29% of its weight, it was dull grey in color and had several cracks on the obverse and reverse surfaces (see Figure 3). This suggests that

PEG impregnation and air-drying was not an appropriate treatment. This result can also be related to the fact that this is the most damaged of the sheaves (most worm holes and lowest density).

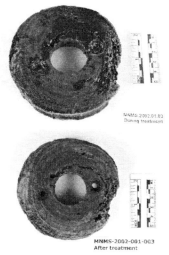

Figure 3. *Sheave B before (left) and after (right) PEG impregnation followed by controlled air-drying.*

4.3 20% V/V (Aq) Peg 400 Followed By Vacuum Freeze-Drying (Sheave C)

The observed weight loss was 5% after being removed from the chest freezer and 12% after two days at ambient temperature. The artifact size and shape did not change after treatment and the cracks mostly disappeared (see Figure 4).

Figure 4. *Sheave C before (left) and after (right) PEG impregnation followed by vacuum freeze-drying. The copper alloy insert was treated apart from the wood.*

4.4 Acetone-Rosin (Sheave D)

After one week of ambient air-drying, a weight loss of 17% was observed and no cracks were visible on the surface. The sheave was darker in color and had a plastic appearance (see Figure 5).

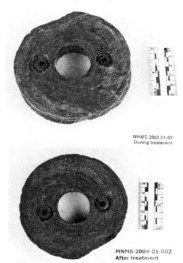

Figure 5. *Sheave D before (left) and after (right) acetone-rosin treatment.*

4.5 Sucrose (Sheave E)

After one month of drying at ambient temperature and humidity, sheave E lost 10% of the waterlogged weight. The appearance of the artifact was satisfactory because cracks and discoloration were not visible (see Figure 6).

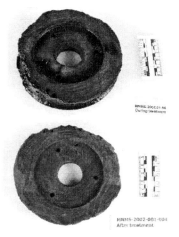

Figure 6. *Sheave E before (left) and after (right) sucrose treatment.*

283

4.6 Lactitol-Trehalose (Sheave F)

Sheave F was frequently monitored during the first eight hours of oven drying because several cracks appeared quickly. It was decided to remove the object from the oven to air-dry at ambient temperature. The departure from the treatment plan was deemed successful because the sheave did not suffer further cracking. The color of the sheave appeared slightly clearer once dried. Its shape was maintained and the cracks disappeared once the wood came into equilibrium with the ambient environment (see Figure 7). The final weight loss was 5%.

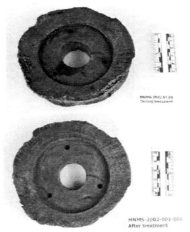

Figure 7. *Sheave F before (left) and after (right) lactitol-trehalose treatment.*

5. Conclusion

Table 2 summarizes and compares the treatment outcomes. As a result of this study, it appears that the controlled air-drying was best suited for these lignum vitae sheaves and met all qualifications for a successful treatment. The shape and appearance of the artifact were well preserved, the treatment was minimally interventive, no irreversible materials were introduced, and the object is still stable six months after its treatment.

PEG impregnation followed by controlled air-drying did not provide a satisfactory appearance. Vacuum freeze-drying following PEG impregnation was too aggressive because the object showed significant cracks after a short time in the freeze-dryer. The acetone-rosin treatment was satisfactory for structural support, but the final appearance of the sheave was not as natural looking as the sheave treated with simple controlled air-drying. The sucrose method provided a highly satisfactory appearance but the addition of sugar in an artifact enhances the risks of future degradation by pests. The major drawback of the lactitol-trehalose procedure is lengthy treatment time (more than 20 weeks) considering the small size and good preservation of the object. The final appearance of the sheave was not satisfactory either.

The outcome of these tests should be considered with care since the sheaves were all in a similar state of preservation before treatment but not in the exact same state of preservation. Sheave B is an example of this difference. PEG impregnation followed by controlled air-drying did not provide a satisfactory appearance (cracks and discoloration) but this can be due to the failure of the treatment or to the highest state of degradation of the sheave before treatment. The authors do not currently know if simple controlled air-drying, without impregnation, would have provided better results for sheave B.

On the other hand, the fact that controlled air-drying worked best among the best preserved sheaves emphasizes the generally good state of preservation of these objects before treatment. This low degradation level most likely resulted from the combined effects of the material characteristics (high density, resistance to decay) and burial conditions (protection of the sheaves between wooden shells and likely beneath heavy layers of sediment).

284

Further cross-sectional examination of the impregnated sheaves would add to this study but was not possible with the sample material. Long-term monitoring will be necessary to determine the aging characteristics of these treatments.

Table 2. Treatment summary.

Treatments	Weight Before Treatment (g)	Weight After Treatment (g)	Weight loss %	Shape and Appearance Preserved	Minimally Intrusive
Controlled Air-drying (CAD)	193.36	165.70	14.30	yes	yes
PEG + CAD	192.87	136.84	29.05	no	no
PEG + FD	188.10	165.74	11.89	no	no
Acetone-rosin	220.36	181.77	17.52	no	no
Sucrose	296.99	267.56	9.91	yes	no
Lactitol-trehalose	285.82	271.3	5.09	no	no

Acknowledgments

The authors would like to thank Andre Bergeron, Donny Hamilton, Ian Macleod, Paul Mardikian, and Betty Seifert for their suggestions.

References

ASTM. 1991. Standard Practice for Maintaining Constant Relative Humidity by Means of Aqueous Solutions, E 104-85. Philadelphia: American Society for Testing and Materials.

Bergeron, A., and P. Dunning. 2002. *Wine, punch, and a cup to drink them from!* Ministère de la culture, de la communication et de la condition féminine du Québec. http://www.mcccf.gouv.qc.ca/phips/wreck2 1.htm (accessed 07/27/2009).

Cook, C., and D. W. Grattan. 1985. A practical comparative study of treatments for waterlogged wood. Part III pretreatment solutions for freeze-drying. *Waterlogged Wood: Study and Conservation: Proceedings of the 2nd ICOM Waterlogged Wood Working Group Conference, Grenoble, 28–31 août 1984.* Grenoble. 219–240.

Cook, C., and D.W. Grattan. 1991. A method of calculating the concentration of PEG for freeze-drying waterlogged wood. *Proceedings of the 4th ICOM Group on Wet Organic Archaeological Materials Conference, Bremerhaven, 1990.* Bremerhaven. 239–252.

Cook, C., et al.1985. Experiments with aqueous treatments for waterlogged wood-metal objects. *Waterlogged Wood: Study and Conservation: Proceedings of the 2nd ICOM Waterlogged Wood Working Group Conference, Grenoble, 28–31 août 1984.* Grenoble. 147–159.

Cook, C. 2009. Personal communication. Historic Resource Conservation Brach, Parks Service, Environment Canada, Ottawa, Ontario.

Cronyn, J. M. 1990. The Elements of Archaeological Conservation. London: Routledge.

Dean, L. R., et al. 1997. Diffusion rates of PEG into wet archaeological oak. *Proceedings of the 6th ICOM Group on Wet Organic Archaeological Materials Conference, York, 1996.* York. 435–450.

Degrigny, C., and E. Guilminot. 2000. Définition d'un traitement de conservation-restauration de composites fer/bois gorgés d'eau. *Cahiers techniques de l'ARAAFU n°5 : XIVèmes journées des Restaurateurs en Archéologie – 25 et 26 juin 1998, UTICA.* ARAAFU ed., Paris. 5–10.

De La Baume, Sylvia. 1990. Les matériaux organiques. In *La conservation en archéologie*, ed. Marie-Claude Berducou Masson, 222–245. Paris: Masson.

Glastrup, J. 1997. Degradation of PEG: a review. *Proceedings of the 6th ICOM Group on Wet Organic Archaeological Materials Conference, York, 1996.* York. 377–383.

Grattan, D. W. 1987. Waterlogged wood. In *Conservation of Marine Archaeological Objects*, ed. C. Pearson. London: Butterworths. 55–67.

Grattan, D. W., and R.W. Clarke. 1987. Conservation of waterlogged wood. In *Conservation of Marine Archaeological Objects*, ed. C. Pearson. London: Butterworths. 164–206.

Hamilton D., I. MacLeod, and P. Mardikian. 2007. Personal communication. Museum Advisory Committee, The Mariners' Museum, Newport News, Virginia.

Hawley, J. K. 1989. A synopsis of current treatments for waterlogged wood and metal composite objects. *Conservation of Wet Wood and Metal, Proceedings of the ICOM Conservation Working Groups on Wet Organic Archaeological Materials and Metals, Fremantle, 1987.* Perth. 223–243.

Hoffmann, P. 1985. On the stabilization of waterlogged oakwood with PEG- molecular size versus degree degredation. *Waterlogged Wood: Study and Conservation: Proceedings of the 2nd ICOM Waterlogged Wood Working Group Conference, Grenoble, 28–31 août 1984.* Grenoble. 95–116.

Hoffmann, P. 1996. Sucrose for waterlogged wood: not so simple at all. *ICOM Committee for Conservation, 11th triennial meeting in Edinburgh, Scotland, 1–6 September 1996: Preprints.* James & James. 657–662.

Imazu S., and A. Morgos. 1999. Lactitol conservation in an open-air environment of large wood elements of the 5th century A.D. dugout pipeline. *ICOM Committee for conservation. Triennial meeting (12th), Lyon, 29 August–3 September 1999: preprints. Vol. 2.* James & James, London. 614–618.

Imazu S., and A. Morgos. 2002. An improvement of the lactitol conservation method used for the conservation of archaeological waterlogged wood (the conservation method using a lactitol and trehalose mixture). *Proceedings of the 8th ICOM Group on Wet Organic Archaeological Materials Conference, Stockholm, 2001.* Stockholm. 413–428.

Johnston, J. 2009. Personal communication. National Oceanic and Atmospheric Administration, Newport News, VA.

Kerchove, de R. 1961. *International Maritime Dictionary.* New York: Van Nostrand Reinhold Company.

McEwen, W.A., and A.H. Lewis. 1992. *Encyclopedia of Nautical Knowledge.* Centreville, Maryland: Cornell Maritime Press ed.

Parrent, J. M. 1985. The conservation of waterlogged wood using sucrose. *Studies in Conservation* 30: 63–72.

Sandström, M., et al. 2003. *The Vasa's New Battle. Sulphur, Acid and Iron.* Vasa studies 19. Swedish National Maritime Museums, Stockholm.

Seifert, B. 2007. Personal communication. Museum Advisory Committee, The Mariners' Museum, Newport News, Virginia.

Swindells, N. S. 1997. *Glossary of Maritime Technology.* The Institute of Marine Engineers.

USDA (United States Department of Agriculture). 2007. *The Encyclopedia of Wood.* Canada: Skyhorse Publishing.

USN (United States Navy). 1957. *NAVSHIPS 250-336. Wood: A manual for its use as a shipbuilding material.* Washington: Department of The Navy Bureau of Ships.

MATERIAL SOURCES

Acetone
Industrial Chemicals
2540 Bellwood Road
Richmond, VA 23237
(804) 275-9292
www.industrialchemicals.com

Dowicide® 1E
Dow Chemical Company
2030 Dow Center
Midland, MI 48674
(800) 447-4369
www.dow.com

Freeze Dryer: Virtis
Virtis/ SP Industries
815 Route 208
Gardiner, NY 12525
(877) 548-4666
www.virtis.com

Kathon CG
Sigma-Aldrich
3050 Spruce Street
St. Louis, MO 63103
(800) 521-8956
www.sigmaaldrich.com

Lactitol
Danisco
Four New Century Parkway
New Century, KS 66031
(913) 764-8100
www.danisco.com

Lysol
Reckitt Benckiser
399 Interpace Parkway
P.O. Box 225
Parsippany, NJ 07054
(800) 333-3899
www.reckittbenckiser.com

Silica Gel
Conservator's Emporium
385 Bridgepoint Drive
St. Paul, MN 55075
(651) 450-8954
www.museumservicescorporation.com

Polyethylene Glycol 400
Spectrum Chemicals
14422 S San Pedro Street
Gardena, CA 90248
(800) 813-1514
www.spectrumchemicals.com

Rosin
Fisher Scientific Inc.
2000 Park Lane
Pittsburgh, PA 15275
(800) 766-7000
www.fishersci.com

Sucrose (White Table Sugar)
Harris Teeter
P.O. Box 10100
Matthews, NC 28106
(800) 432-6111
www.harristeeter.com

Thermohygrometer
Talas
20 West 20th Street
New York, NY 10011
(212) 219-0770
www.talasonline.com

Trehalose
Cole-Parmer
625 East Bunker Court
Vernon Hills, IL 60061
(888) 358-4717
www.coleparmer.com

Questions and answers

Jim Spriggs: This is a remarkable series of tests to me because it showed up the difference as measured against each other rather than just as applicable to a certain kind of object. It's interesting from that point of view.

André Bergeron: I was just curious about the duration of your air-drying period?

Elsa Sangaourd: It was every four weeks. We started at 90% and ended at 50% decreasing it by 10% every four weeks.

Lars Andersen: I saw that one of the pieces you said you freeze-dried began cracking and then you took it out of the freeze-dryer and put it into the freezer. Why was that?

Elsa Sangaourd: Because we assumed that the vacuum was stressing the object too much so we removed it from the vacuum stress and to finish the drying we used natural ambience pressure freeze-drying.

Lars Andersen: But with such a vacuum, you could only stress the object if it was not frozen.

Elsa Sangaourd: It was frozen when we put it in the freeze-dryer.

Lars Andersen: What was the temperature of the drying chamber?

Elsa Sangaourd: Negative 25°C.

Lars Andersen: Negative 25°C?

Elsa Sangaourd: Yes, and the condenser was at minus…

Lars Andersen: You couldn't have developed the stress from the pressure I think.

Elsa Sangaourd: OK.

Cliff Cook: Did you say how much PEG you put in?

Elsa Sangaourd: 20%.

Cliff Cook: That would be frozen at -25°C.

Lars Andersen: We can find out what's wrong with this because you used PEG 400.

Elsa Sangaourd: Yes.

Lars Andersen: Yes and PEG 400 is not frozen at that temperature so you are not freeze-drying—you are accelerating the evaporation. So you have the wrong PEG or the wrong freezer.

Jim Spriggs: May I ask a question? That is, were you in anyway able to monitor the impregnation rates of the various lots with the various solvents you were using?

Elsa Sangaourd: Yes, we weighed them.

Jim Spriggs: So you could see that there was impregnation because another possible reason would be that there was far too little of the consolidant going in as this is a very hard wood.

Elsa Sangaourd: Yes.

Jim Spriggs: And the condition of this wood is that you cannot actually penetrate it with a pin.

Elsa Sangaourd: It's very hard.

Jim Spriggs: Very resistant. Can we open the discussion up to supercritical drying as well? Anything else on supercritical drying? This was a technique that received quite a lot of criticism over the years not only because of the expense of the equipment but also because of the safety grounds. Remember the facility that they had at the University of St. Andrews had to be built on the roof of the Physics block just in case it imploded during the course of the application of the treatment! I guess equipment nowadays is a little safer. But it does have benefits obviously for composite objects and certainly the objects I've seen that have gone through supercritical drying always look very fine though they sometimes do need extra consolidation afterwards as the wood is very, very light in weight.

3.9

Conservation of the Newport Ship: Challenges of Scale

Sophie Adamson
Newport Medieval Ship, Unit 22, Maesglas Industrial Estate, Greenwich Road, Newport, Wales
e-mail:
sophie.adamson@newport.gov.uk

Abstract
This is a status report on the conservation of the Newport medieval ship in South Wales. A 15th century oak clinker-built trading vessel, 26 meters in length, she was excavated from the banks of the river Usk during 2002. This paper outlines issues arising from the conservation treatment of large structural timbers. Working from a treatment proposal supplied by York Archaeological Trust, it discusses attempts at iron removal using an aqueous solution of ammonium citrate and the start of several different regimes of two-phase PEG treatment. It also covers some of the issues arising from the project's financing. The Newport Ship's situation and rescue is perhaps uniquely framed by local community politics and fundraising, which also need to be negotiated, alongside a heavy public access timetable and longer-term economic sustainability.

Keywords: Waterlogged wood, large structural timbers, iron removal, ammonium citrate, PEG, FaroArm®, community

Introduction

As the ship's first conservator, Kate Hunter, described it:

> '...the Newport ship was discovered in 2002 on the site of a new theatre and arts centre [it] is a 15th century clinker built trading vessel, 26 meters in length and with a current maximum width of 8m [...] bought into Newport South Wales for refitting or dismantling, circa 1468, she had keeled over onto her starboard side, much of which remains...'

At the time of writing in 2004, Kate had led the project through a very critical stage in the story of the ship's survival. Following an exceptional public campaign the Welsh Assembly Government pledged a substantial sum of money to lift, record, and conserve the ship for display. The site was excavated in two phases and the 25 tons of waterlogged timber, comprising 2,000 timbers and associated objects were lifted and housed at a local Corus warehouse, later to be moved again to their current home at Maesglas Industrial Estate, conversely situated on Greenwich Road, Newport Docks.

Over six years later, the ship is now undergoing remedial conservation prior to freeze drying. The project has been characterized by isolated periods of intense activity following injections of funding. In late 2004 a small team of archaeologists and conservators were employed to implement a recording trial that had been designed by Mary Rose Archaeological Services. FaroArm® digital recording, laser scanning and hand drawing were examined and it was this first comparative study that led to the use of FaroArm® recording on the project. In spring 2005, a Heritage Lottery Fund bid was prepared, using the information gathered during the first six months of the trial. An award was made in December and the following spring an enlarged team were employed, as the cleaning and recording of the ship began. (Figure 1)

The FaroArm three-dimensional digitizer captures data as a series of points or lines to create a three-dimensional wire frame image recorded using Rhinoceros

4.0 modeling software, (Jones 2009B) (Figure 2). By 2009 the entire hull had been digitally recorded, creating an archive of over 2000 "Rhino" files. Dendrochronology of all the timber had been completed, although a match to a master dendro sequence remains elusive. Repair timbers date to the 1460s and a small silver coin, a *petit blanc*, found concealed within the keel, is known to be minted in Crémieu, south-eastern France, between May and June 1446.

Figure 1. *Cleaning prior to recording. Copyright Newport Ship*

All timbers were manually cleaned of iron concretion, caulking, luting and excess tar, with over 3,000 samples collected during this period. As well as the ship, over 1,000 small finds were recovered from the site, mainly wet organic materials and a small conservation lab has now been established at the warehouse for this purpose. A Post Ex-Research Design was recently created by Oxford Archaeology and finds conservation is underway while we source further funding for possible programs of analysis and the completion of specialist reports.

Figure 2. *FaroArm digital recording. Newport Ship*

In 2008, as cleaning and recording drew to an end, the team was reduced by two thirds, being superseded by a core of five employed by the local city council. They consist of a curator; project officer; project assistant; an education and access officer and a conservator, the author. All of us manage large areas of the project although since the departure of Kate, there has been no overall project management. My role includes people, project and collections management in an unusually public facing environment.

Figure 3. *School children enjoying plank cleaning as part of the "Ship Shape" workshop. Newport Ship*

The cleaning of the ship timbers proved a highly successful way to engage local and minority community groups; school children and volunteers and for people to take ownership of "their" ship. (Figures 3 and 4) During 2009, over 25,000 people came into contact with the project. The mechanical removal of iron concretion and of the clay from the ship timbers was frequently undertaken by supervised members of the public, many of whom are still with us, cleaning another local salvage, the 19th century Chepstow Trow, in the hope that this may also be conserved. Importantly, we also work alongside many of the original people who fought for the ship to be saved. An embodiment of civic pride, some 300 people regrouped as "Friends of the Newport Ship". They remain an active force, continuing to raise funds for equipment and publicity material, rally political support and give tours of the warehouse on our monthly open days.

They are currently saving towards the cost of our freeze drier and their zeal can be demonstrated by Jean, a pensioner who is preparing for a sponsored sky-dive in aid of the cause.

The Ship Condition Survey

A conservation assessment had been built into the Heritage Lottery grant bid and in 2007, York Archaeological Trust, (YAT) won the tender to undertake a condition survey of the ship and design a treatment proposal. Samples of frames, strakes, riders, ceiling planks, stringers amongst other timbers were used to survey the condition of the surviving structures and formulate an appropriate preservation strategy. A combination of techniques was used for this purpose.

Figure 4. Some of our regular volunteers and Friends of the Ship. Newport Ship

Physical condition and pin test

The majority of the ship components are oak, although the keel is beech wood, elm and coniferous woods are also represented. The report found the timbers to be in extremely good visual condition with little evidence for outward biological growth or decay during the time the survey was undertaken. Sturgeon and goldfish were used during the cleaning and recording period to control algae formation and insect colonization in the holding tanks, (Figure 5). However, a number of fresh water crustaceans were later identified, the fresh water shrimp *Gammarus* and *Physa* "Bladdersnail", (Spriggs, 2009). Typically these feed on decaying organic matter, fungi, algae and bacteria. The timber was considered to be in a superior condition

to that of other Severn Estuary wooden finds: the medieval, Magor Pill boat and Roman, Barlands Farm boat. It is thought that this may be a consequence of the type of wood derived tar used on the strakes and a research project into the technology of ancient European maritime pitch and tar samples is scheduled to start this year.

Figure 5. Fresh water tanks prior to chemical treatment.

The ship has suffered some mechanical damage from its position inside the sheet pile coffer dam, which was inserted into the river bank during the arts centre construction, (Figure 6). The bow and stern are missing and the remaining timbers in these areas have been severed by the metal sheet pile. For example, the stem was broken into nine pieces and displaced (Jones, 2009 A). Fragmentation has also occurred where fifteen concrete piles were driven into the structure unknowingly at the start of building work. Aside from contemporary sources of damage there are the more complex earlier histories of damage, acquired during use, such as the large crack in the mast-step. Some deformation has been caused during deposition for example, the distortion of the keel and a significant area of the port side that was cut down in antiquity (Hunter, 2004). Other, lower elements of the vessel such as floor timbers, struts, and scarf joints have either warped or been forced apart during burial. The weight of the upper timbers and the alluvial clay having caused these timbers to flatten: evidence of the remarkable condition of the wood that they have not splintered.

Figure 6. The ship encapsulated by the coffer dam, looking to stern. Newport Ship

X-radiography of a sample of the iron clench nail fastenings used in the clinker construction and a sample of concretions revealed the iron to be completely mineralized. Many of the timbers had been contaminated with iron corrosion products from this source, in particular the more porous areas of sapwood and pockets of decay. 42 timbers (2.5%)

including frames, stringers, knees and the stem post were sampled for the (de Jong 1977) pin test. The results suggest these timbers are very sound, with the majority being classified as Class 3 wood with a maximum water content of less than 185%.

Sibert Drill Decay Profiles

This technique has been used successfully on archaeological wood in the UK for a number of years, as a way of detecting deep areas of decay. The drill is widely used in forestry and building conservation industries but has also been used to assess large assemblages of archaeological wood such as Seahenge and Magor Pill boat, (Panter 2007). A fine probe is used to penetrate the wood under constant pressure and the resistance met by the wood is measured, (Figure 7). This gives an indication of the soundness of the wood, with the data displayed as spectra, which can then be compared to that of standard wood species (Figure 8). 293 decay profiles were generated from approximately 3.5% of the ships timbers (approx.60 timbers). For each timber a minimum of three drillings were produced – each end and midpoint – avoiding treenail or clench nail holes and other technological details. For some timbers, such as the larger frames, a minimum of five drillings were necessary.

Figure 7.
Decay profile of beech keel from the ship. When compared to Figure 8, a standard beech profile, the spectra shows a very decayed outer surface with some wood substance preserved within the inner zone. Overall the wood has lost around 60-70% of its structure. Copyright York Archaeological Trust

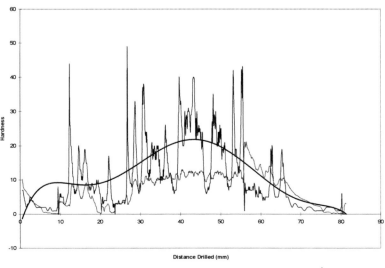

294

Figure 8.

Decay profile of "standard" beech, drilled in the tangential plane. Copyright York Archaeological Trust

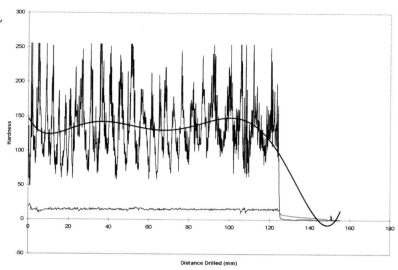

The chart displays three sets of data. The spectra with the highest peaks shows a measure of the hardness or soundness of the wood, the lowermost line records the pressure that was required to insert the probe into the wood and the thick line is the overall trend: the "decay profile" for the timber. Drilling into the wood is from the left to right on the graph. The data is then compared to a profile for "standards". These are samples of modern un-decayed wood of the same species.

Water Content and density assays

Approximately 110 wood samples (6.4%) were gathered to assess water content and wood density using this standard method of condition surveying. These were collected from a combination of dendro slices, detached fragments of wood and a limited number of core samples. Cores were taken from frames, stringers and riders. Small fragments or dendro samples were used from keel elements, braces, starboard and port planks, tingles, ceiling planks, struts and deck elements.

Scanning Electron Microscopy (SEM)

A number of samples were subject to Scanning Electron Microscopy up to

x3000 magnification. These revealed loss or pitting of secondary cell walls from bacterial activity, mineral deposits and an abundance of fungal hyphae (Figure 9). The images support findings from other assessment methods and highlight the elements of the structure, especially the non-oak timbers that have undergone high levels of decay.

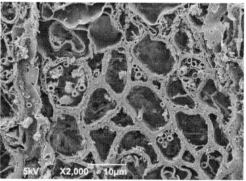

Figure 9. *This image of the sapwood from F10.1, at x2000 magnification, shows variable preservation with cellular collapse as well as relatively intact cells with cavities in the cell walls caused by bacterial activity. Fungal hyphae visible as tube shaped structures deposited within cell lumen.*

Analysis of wood to determine contamination with iron and sulfur

Samples of detached sapwood fragments and increment core samples from the ship were subject to ashing using the Tappi Standard T15m-58. Some samples were also analyzed for iron content. The results indicate that iron is present in appreciable concentrations not only where sapwood is present but also within the surface heartwood zones and that the iron has been able to penetrate to a depth of at least 40mm into the body of the timber, albeit in lower concentrations.

Core samples were oven dried at 40ºC to constant weight and were submitted for total sulfur analysis using combustion and infra red gas analysis (RWE npower plc Central Laboratories, Selby North Yorkshire).

The timbers have appreciable levels of sulfur present, although considerably lower than the Mary Rose and Vasa timbers (Panter, 2007), and the trend is towards higher concentrations within the more decayed sapwood zones. These results complement a preliminary study conducted in 2005, using the Xanes (X-ray Absorption Near-Edge Structure) process at the Daresbury facility, Salford by personnel from the Mary Rose Trust. The XANES method revealed that the timber contains both reduced sulfur forms and oxidized sulfates at depths between 6mm and 50mm at a ratio of 9:1 at 50mm, (Crawshaw 2007)

In 2005 a preliminary study of bacteria present in the Newport Ship and its burial sediment was undertaken by the Mary Rose Trust in collaboration with the School of Biological Sciences, University of Portsmouth, using RNA ribosomal analysis. Further samples will be taken during treatment and compared.

Results
The combined assessment of the wood assemblage concluded that the vessel probably remained uncovered for some period prior to being filled with riverine sediments creating anoxia. This is because the lower areas of the vessel such as the keel and frames display a different level of preservation to that of the strakes. Both port and starboard strakes are in an excellent state of preservation. Most of the samples tested exhibited a higher density value (when compared with the standard density for modern oak) due to an increase in mass brought about by an increase in moisture content. This increase could also be due to the deposition of minerals within the wood structure and the growth pattern of the wood itself. The frames have undergone variable decay, exhibiting the typical oak decay pattern of heterogeneous decay. Sapwood is present on many of the frames and is more decayed than the heartwood component of the timber, having lost on average around 70% of its cell wood structure. The beech keel has undergone the severest level of decay having lost upwards of 60% of its cell wood structure. However, the oak components, including the keelson and "brace" structures are better preserved, similar to the planking. Decay to the keelson is chiefly confined to the sapwood regions. The ceiling planks and stringers exhibit similar decay patterns to the frames, whilst the riders and large knees are as well preserved as the planks. The non-oak, deck elements and the shores located underneath the vessel appear to have suffered a similar level of decay to the keel.

The Treatment Proposal
The outcome of the survey was as follows. An intense program of iron removal using several baths of an aqueous 2% solution of the chelating agent ammonium citrate. Followed by a two phase polyethylene glycol (PEG) treatment and (accelerated) vacuum freeze-drying. Minutes from a 2008 panel meeting reveal that EDMA was also considered but that ammonium citrate proved the most cost effective with the least serious disposal issues. Welsh water has given us permission to discharge all the chemicals used including the

exhausted biocide at no cost. However, in 2008 they unfortunately connected us to a water meter.

The timbers were grouped into three different regimes based on their surveyed condition:

Regime A: 10% PEG 200 + 30% PEG 3350
The most degraded timbers: Keel; non-oak deck elements; stanchions, struts.

Regime B: 15% PEG 200 + 20% PEG 3350
The medium degraded timbers: Frames, Filler Boards, Stringers, Ceiling Planks and Bilge Boards

Regime C: 15% PEG 200 + 5% PEG 3350
The best preserved timbers: Planks, tingles, riders, knees, keelson, braces, stem, beams, Mast Partner, Mast Step

PEG 200 was selected over 400 as evidence suggests it penetrates the second order spaces more effectively, (Panter 2007), which would be necessary due to the well preserved condition of most of the timber. PEG 3350 will be required to consolidate the more decayed sapwood zones as well as washing out a limited amount of PEG 200 from the surface that could give rise to a hygroscopic surface following vacuum freeze drying. The use of a biocide was recommended to control bacterial activity and either borax or sodium bicarbonate to buffer the anticipated drop in pH in the PEG tanks.

(Accelerated) Vacuum freeze drying was deemed the fastest and therefore most economical strategy for the timber. With the use of a 6m long drier the total drying time was estimated at 24months. Surface finishing using steam and hot air were suggested and reshaping for display using high humidity and localized application of steam, post vacuum freeze-drying.

Methodology
Timber from the 16 existing, freshwater, scaffold tanks (10m x 5m x 0.5m) was condensed into 8 tanks for the chemical treatment. All timbers were arranged in their specific PEG treatment tank. 1 tank for regime A, 4 tanks for regime B and 3 tanks for regime C. One spare tank was used as a mix tank and another as a decant tank for mixing new PEG into existing tank solutions. Larger timbers (as seen in Figure 10) were stacked resting on tannilized pine battens or wedges of plastazoate foam to aid circulation and penetration of the solutions.

Figure 10. Tank 5 stacking arrangement. Newport Ship

Planking timbers were stacked horizontally supported by themselves and the buoyancy of the solutions. Wide and heavy ceiling planks were supported horizontally within the tanks using a number of foam wrapped breeze blocks covered in heat sealed polyethylene to prevent any leaching into the solutions.

It was agreed that insulating the tanks was not necessary as most heat loss would occur through the concrete floor (the surface area of each tank is 50m³). However, the warehouse has overhead suspended radiators which could be utilized in the winter to aid circulation following the addition of PEG 3350. All the tanks have black, damp proof membrane lids with chemical hazard signs for the following reasons. They help to reduce evaporation and therefore reduce gas or vapor pollution. They inhibit fungal or algae growth and help to keep the solutions clean from dust and insects. They are a good health and safety precaution, particularly when using biocides and if working with an open access policy.

Small submersible pumps (Figure 11) have been used to circulate both the chelating and the PEG solutions during treatment. Circulating the chelating agent is thought to speed extraction rates (Sandström et al, 2003), and is necessary during PEG baths to keep the solution from stratifying.

Figure 11. Mixing ammonium citrate using a submersible pump.

Iron Removal

The extent of iron removal was measured in the test tank by sampling the tank solutions from approximately the same position every few days. The samples were sent to Severn Trent Laboratories for Inductively-Coupled Plasma (ICP) analysis for total Fe in solution. The results from this tank saw the concentrations of iron in solution surge in the first two weeks and then drop or plateau off (Figure 12). It was decided that this was the exhaustion or saturation point of the bath and a regime of approximately 6 weeks per bath was implemented for all the tanks. All the tanks underwent four changes of bath. The pH was monitored for all tanks, which remained between 6.5-7 throughout the treatment: triammonium citrate was the chemical used. It was unclear why the levels of iron in solution consistently dropped. Was the chelate falling to the bottom of the tank? It was noticed that some of our control samples from the ammonium citrate mix tank often turned opaque white within a couple of days. Was the citrate breaking down or being affected by bacteria?

Some adhoc tests were carried out on tank sediments and tank solutions using FTIR and although differences in spectra were noted the decomposition of the chelating agent has not been proven.

TANK 1, Baths 1-4

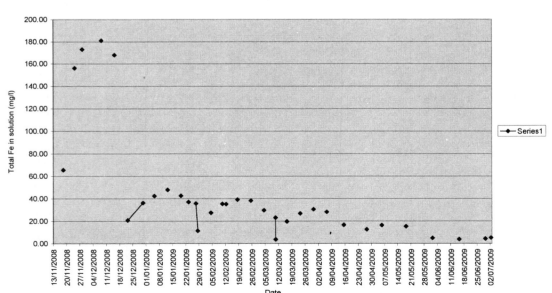

Figure 12. Iron removal from Tank 1, total Fe in solution (mg/l). The end of each series is marked with a line.

At the start of the citrate baths the warehouse was at its coldest and we had little problem with fungal growths; the solutions turned from clear or cloudy white to orange quite satisfactorily. However, as the temperature increased an assortment of mould and algae froth was noticed on the surface of the tank solutions and the samples moved from brown or grey to ink black. No biocide was used during this time and this undoubtedly contributed to the increasing problems that developed with reducing environments within the tanks. Over the summer months, hydrogen sulfide was detected. Aside from the release of the rotten gas when removing tank lids, people involved with tank cleaning prior to a new chemical bath, complained of sore throats, headaches and eye irritation, evidence of 10-50ppm. Organic vapor masks were already in use but hydrogen sulfide gas filters were procured for cleaning and hydrogen sulfide alarm monitors. Experiments into creating a fountain effect for aeration using hoses from the submersible pumps were tried but this resulted in increased off gas in the warehouse and I was advised that a source of air would need to be directly pumped into the solutions.

Initial calculations for purchasing the chemicals had been based on an estimated working volume of 12,000 liters per tank. However, all the tanks vary depending on the volume of timber and our largest working volume is actually 17, 250 liters. During the course of the iron extraction additional ammonium citrate had to be procured and during this time some of the tanks were rinsed and returned to fresh water. A series of environmental problems occurred. A thick white or brown skin of biofilm developed over entire tank surface areas within a couple of days. Blood worm established itself on the uncovered water surface. The tank water was changed and the timbers hosed down once a week. Goldfish were reintroduced into a tank that had been thoroughly rinsed as a means of

saving water but within a week one had died. It was thought that excessive nutrients relinquished from the citrate residue which would include nitrates, were causing tank eutrophication.

A further problem arose. Fresh migration of iron oxides and hydroxides appeared in great orange swathes over the timbers. Core samples were taken to try to ascertain how much iron had really been removed during the sequestering baths. These tanks were then subject to a fifth bath with remaining ammonium citrate intended for small finds, while other tanks had an extended bath in their current solution to make sure as much iron as possible was removed.

Core samples were taken directly next to known core sample holes from YATs condition assessment and the results compared. The comparable results were for ash content only but the new results also indicated iron content at decreasing 20mm depths. The results suggest over half the mineral content has been removed from the period 2007-2010 with more being removed from the outer surfaces.

A white concretion was still evident on some of the planking, although sometimes this was difficult to distinguish from the clay that the wood continues to secrete. However, all the planking had been mechanically cleaned twice by our volunteers and it was not expected that the chelating agent would be able to remove heavier deposits. All tank solutions had dropped to a very low level of iron in solution, some with a final sample < 5mg/l. It was thought that we had gone as far as we could with this particular chelating agent. The degradation of the timbers whilst in wet treatment, the timescale and budget for the project were considered and the decision was made to move to the next stage.

PEG

The tanks were cleaned thoroughly using sponges, brushes and squeegees and as much tank sediment removed as possible using a wet and dry vacuum (Figure 13). It was not possible to remove the timbers while cleaning the tanks due to the volume of material.

Figure 13. *Cleaning Tank 8 using a wet and dry vacuum.*

Movement also needed to be minimized as some timber surfaces appear softer, after the removal of the consolidating effect of the mineralized iron concretions. The timbers were rinsed by flushing through the tanks using a water hose and large submersible pumps. Water vapor masks were included in our personal protective equipment as a precaution against aerosols because organic sludges containing rust, algae and bacteria are a good medium for Legionella bacteria, even below 20ºC (HSE, 2009). The council water specialist advised that Kathon CG® at the concentrations used would be effective against Legionella and also sulfate reducing bacteria (SRBs). However, SRBs have been known to survive at pH 0, (Crawshaw, 2007). The bacteria quickly build resistance to biocides so another possibility might be the use of UV filters, although the effect on PEG solutions would also have to be investigated, (Anthony Crawshaw, pers.com).

Control of Substances Hazardous to Health risk assessments were carried out for all chemicals, biocides and biological agents. The PEG solutions are to be increased incrementally by 5% every three months with treatment times varying from 18-24months. The PEG 200 is added first (Figure 14) and is given a longer share of the treatment time for maximum absorption, with the PEG 3350 added later. The PEGCON program, (Cook & Grattan, 1990) and a refractometer will be used to help calculate our increases and maintain the correct percentages.

Figure 14. *The first batch of PEG 200 is mixed. Newport Ship.*

The tank environments are monitored for temperature, pH, redox, and brix (sugar content). Dipslides are being used for bacteria, yeast and mould count and we are currently having some of the dominant strains identified. Following an earlier tank burst, an emergency response plan is also being formulated.

More serious attempts at aeration during the PEG phase will be tried as the anoxic environment encourages the production of reduced sulfur species, (Sandström et al 2005). There are no plans to use sulfur scavengers to remove reduced sulfur or oxidized sulfates but the sulfate levels are being monitored to establish whether a recent drop in tank pH is attributable to these. Sodium bicarbonate is likely to be used as a buffer to remedy this.

The general public continues to be interested in the process. Our access policy has led to an increased effort to risk assess the hazards and also to better interpret the process using multi-media, educational tools and our *Conservation in Action* stand during open days. Having explored a number of funding options, the council recently announced that it would be willing to purchase of a 6 meter freeze drier. It is hoped that the general public will be involved during the drying phase, however, the possibility of the drying going out to tender is also being investigated as a more financially viable option.

Modeling and Display

Following the digital recording of the hull timbers the Rhinoceros files are being used to produce three dimensional physical and digital models of the ship. FaroArm® was originally chosen as the archival datasets are smaller than other techniques and the layered information sets provided are more useful for post recording processing and interrogation (Lewis, pers.com). The physical model pieces are made using a process called selective laser sintering on a 1:10 scale. They are manufactured from Polyamide 12 nylon thermoplastic dust, which is melted by lasers to form the shapes (Figure 14).

Gradually a model of the hull is being created, by manipulation of the slightly flexible nylon and with the aid of tiny screws attaching the frames to the planks. The modeling process helps to reveal how the ship was built and understand areas of damage and repair. The digital models also have the potential to model sailing and handling characteristics, cargo capacities, to accurately measure wood shrinkage after freeze drying, as well as aid future display options for the ship.

Discussion around the ethics or physical possibilities of displaying the vessel "as sailed" or "as found" continue but the consensus at the last panel meeting was to not reshape before drying, particularly if there is to be a period of storage prior to display, as any further movement in storage could undermine previous efforts

at reshaping. The size, sound condition of the wood and the conservation treatment now in process suggests this could be quite a task, particularly for the dense framing timbers.

Figure 14. Modeling in progress.

Two other conserved boats from the Severn Estuary: the Romano-Celtic Barlands Farm boat and the 13th century medieval Magor Pill boat are stored locally at Newport Museum and the National Museum of Wales. One idea is to use the Barlands Farm boat as a pilot reconstruction, perhaps encompassing an education and access program. Some work has already been undertaken at the National Museum of Wales into reconstruction techniques for the Magor Pill and another possibility might be collaboration.

Theoretically, the whole ship will be dry and ready for assembly in the next 4-5 years. The plan has always been to reconstruct the ship in a purpose built gallery with a viewing platform for public interaction. Current thinking is not to have a maritime themed museum but for the various local boats to be integrated within their specific historical contexts. For now, we await further investment from the Welsh Assembly for the design and implementation of a new building for Newport Museum, with a ship gallery at its heart.

Acknowledgements

I am grateful to CyMAL for the funding that made it possible for me to participate in the 2010 WOAM. I am indebted to all the conservators and scientists of York Archaeological Trust and the Mary Rose Trust, for their continual support. I would also like to give special thanks to Jim Spriggs, who continues to mentor and encourage; to all our panel members, the Friends of the Ship and to Kate Hunter, whom we all remember with great affection.

References

Cook C, and Grattan D.W, (1990) "A method for calculating the concentration of PEG for freeze-drying waterlogged wood" in Hoffmann P, Proceedings of the 4th ICOM Group on Wet Organic Archaeological Materials Conference, Bremerhaven. 239-250

Crawshaw A, (2007). Sulphur Analysis in Wood, Unpublished report.

de Jong J, (1977) Conservation Techniques for Old Waterlogged Wood from Shipwrecks found in the Netherlands' in A.H. Walters (Ed) Biodeterioration Investigation Techniques. London.

Health and Saftey Executive, (2009). Legionnaires' disease, A guide for employers. Web-friendly version of leaflet IACL27(rev2); p1.

Hunter K, (2004). The Newport Ship: The first two years, Hoffmann et al, Proceedings of the 9th ICOM Group on Wet Organic Archaeological Materials Conference, Bremerhaven, 2005

Jones T, (2008). Newport Medieval Ship Project Update; Archaeology in Wales V.48. 2008

Jones T, (2009 A). The Newport Medieval Ship, Her Three-Dimensional Digital Recording and Analysis; Skyllis, January 2009.

Jones T, (2009 B). Three-Dimensional Recording and Digital Modeling of the Newport Medieval Ship; ACUA Underwater Archaeology Proceedings, 2009.

Panter I, (2007). A condition Assessment and Conservation Strategy for the Newport Ship, unpublished report.
Sandström M, et al, (2003). Sulphur, Acid and Iron, Stockholm, National Maritime Museums

Sandström M, et al, (2005). Sulfur in the Timbers of Henry VIII's Warship *Mary Rose*: Synchrotrons Illuminate Conservation Concerns. Science Highlight, Structural Molecular Biology Program, October 2005

Spriggs A, (2009). Waterfouling insects on the Newport Ship, unpublished report.

Questions and answers

Khoi Tran: For the biocide how do you deal with the waste?

Sophie Adamson: We have permission from the water company to discharge all our tanks at no cost. There's the same thing with the biocide as long as it breaks down after six months. Unfortunately, they did put us on a water meter though.

The Yenikapı Shipwrecks: Dismantling Methods and First Step to Conservation

Ufuk Kocabaş*, Işıl Özsait-Kocabaş and Namık Kılıç
Istanbul University, Department of Conservation of Marine Archaeological Objects, Ordu Cad. Laleli, Fatih-İstanbul TURKEY.
*E-mail: ufukk@istanbul.edu.tr

Abstract

Thirty five shipwrecks dated to 5th-11th centuries AD, has been discovered in The Theodosian (Byzantine) harbor of Istanbul, in the district of Yenikapı. They were found by Istanbul Archaeological Museums during a rescue excavation that started in 2004. Under the "Istanbul University Yenikapi Shipwrecks Project", carried out by the Istanbul University's Department of Conservation of Marine Archaeological Objects, our team has undertaken the recording and dismantling of twenty-four shipwrecks as well as the conservation-restoration and reconstruction projects of twenty-eight shipwrecks in total. Shipwrecks of various types and sizes have been exposed since 2005; the majority is still under study.

Keywords Theodosian Harbor, Yenikapı Shipwrecks, Documentation, Lifting the ships

Introduction

The Archaeological excavations at Yenikapı station site within the Marmaray Railway and Metro Underground projects, conducted by the Istanbul Archaeological Museums since 2004, revealed 35 shipwrecks dated to the 5th to 11th century AD. It is foreseen that the total number of shipwrecks will increase with the ongoing excavations in the north of the site (Figure 1). Considered the largest medieval shipwreck collection in the world, these wrecks have survived probably due to the sedimentation of the Theodosian Harbor caused by the Lykos Stream.

The wrecks provide us with invaluable information on the Byzantine period ship typology, shipbuilding technologies and their evolution and they are regarded the most important project of recent times by the scholars in the field (Kocabaş 2008a; Kocabaş, Özsait-Kocabaş 2009; Kocabaş, Türkmenoğlu 2009; and www.yenikapibatikları.com).

Academia explains the reasons of the co-existence of ships from different periods in the harbor through various hypotheses. Among the most frequently proposed reasons are sinking due to natural disasters such as tsunami or severe storms as well as being abandoned due to finishing their service lives. Stratigraphic evidence has shown that south-westerly storms erupting in the Sea of Marmara especially in summer months paved the way for the sinking of the ships of the 10th-11th centuries uncovered in the east, where the entrance of the harbor is thought to be located. This storm caused at least 22 ships to sink and they were buried with a thick layer of sea sand. Although the silting made the harbor unusable it also preserved the shipwrecks in good condition

Figure 1. *Panoramic view of excavations at Yenikapı, former Theodosian Harbour: The Yenikapı site to the west (left) of Mustafa Kemal Street and the Sea of Marmara in the south (top left). (Photo Serhat Keskin)*

The anoxic environment created through rapid silting and burying preserved not only the ships but also rigging elements such as pulleys, toggles and ropes as well as daily use items like combs, leather sandals, reed baskets, wooden plates and inorganic items like anchors and amphorae. In addition to the ships, numerous wooden pieces belonging to ships were uncovered dispersed in the harbor area. Such finds suggest that also many others ships may have sunk and dispersed, thus not survived, or that these pieces belong to the extant wrecks. Detailed study of these pieces will allow us to identify if they belong to the extant wrecks or not.

1. Fieldwork

A total of thirty five shipwrecks uncovered in the Yenikapı excavation site of Marmaray-Metro are very important for not only constituting the biggest ship assembly from the Early and Middle Byzantine periods but also for having survived in very good state of preservation.

The Yenikapı shipwrecks can be entirely identified with their forms and *in situ* locations; and their timber elements can be followed with their original hull forms, floor timber and futtock curves. Most of them have survived with their planking preserved above the vessel bottom and some have survived up to the bulwark level; thus, supplementing our knowledge about their construction as well as revealing many new pieces of information about shipbuilding techniques.

The first step of the fieldwork is the *preservation* of the remains in the field during excavation. Before the onset of work, each wreck is covered with a protective tent containing a water spraying system.

Figure 2. *Protective tent and water spraying system (Yenikapi 12).*

Thus, the environmental effects on the wrecks are minimized and the experts can work in a more comfortable site without the negative effect of seasonal weather conditions. When the wreck is totally uncovered, a spring system up through the

304

wreck site is installed to prevent drying out of the waterlogged timbers (Figure 2).

2. Documenting Methods

The detailed *in situ* documentation of the wreck site is the prime focus of the fieldwork. This study involves mapping including 3D recordings, *in situ* photographing, cataloguing, and full scale drawings.

The labelling system, which varies according to the preservation levels and dismantling ways, has been designed in order to answer the ensuing needs during conservation, restoration and reconstruction applications. The coding system involves abbreviations for ship timbers and their place in order.

The mapping of the wreck site is attained by total station which is a combination of an electronic transit and an electronic distance measuring device (Figure 3). The angles and distances from the instrument to the points to be surveyed are determined by a total station (Eiteljorg 1994). Thereby, the actual positions of the 3D coordinate points of the outlines of each timber at short intervals are gained (about 10-15 cm, even less in some locations such as joints of timbers). In addition, the centre points of nails and treenails are also measured.

Figure 3. Total station measurements (Yenikapi 12).

Then those coordinate points are linked through AutoCAD and a preliminary 3D model of the wreck is provided. Thus the

original curvatures of the perfectly preserved Yenikapı shipwrecks are recorded, being of vital importance when future reconstruction or reassembly is considered. However, the two dimensional printout of this work shows the outlines of a wreck with relatively sharp lines and without details on it. Therefore, it is edited manually at the site and details such as the details of joints, dimensions and exact shape of nail holes and, if present, surrounding concretions, pitch traces and damages etc. are added (Özsait-Kocabaş 2008a).

Before lifting the wrecks, in addition to their scale drawings, planking that emerged after the removal of the ceiling and floor timbers and futtocks were copied 1:1 on clear acetate. For this purpose, acetates were laid over the planking strakes and permanent markers were used to mark the planking, nails, scarves, caulking etc. in different colors and hatching.

Drawings on site were made to the scale of 1:5 which allows rendering of even the smallest pieces in detail. However, even this scale does not allow marking every detail. In addition, these *in situ* drawings could not include the faces of the elements overlapping or resting on earth. Full scale drawings is a must for the detailed examination and evaluation of these surfaces that bear important evidence for their technology, periods of use, construction techniques and so on (Crisman 1993, 312; Steffy 1994, 200, 202; Matthews 2004, 78.) The need for space for the full scale drawings and for the conservation of timber elements was supplied with an area of 2,000 m^2 close to the excavation site by the Metropolitan Municipality. This area became Istanbul University Yenikapı Shipwrecks Research Centre and construction of conservation tanks as well as a building for drawings and evaluation was done, again with the support of the Metropolitan Municipality.

With the *FaroArm* device mounted in this central laboratory in November 2008, full scale drawings were started. This high technology device allows direct digital drawing through a point apparatus of all faces, edges and marks on them. With sharp accuracy, this method allows 2D and 3D drawings directly on the computer saving a lot of time (Hocker 2003, 84-92) (Figure 4).

Figure 4. *Full scale drawing of ship timbers by FaroArm.*

Photographing and video filming were done according to a regular plan for recording of the work in general, laboratory evaluations, transportation stages, uncovering of each shipwreck, its dismantling and lifting starting with the sand or cargo covering them. Besides, timber pieces placed in the pools are checked regularly and photographed for recording their condition.

In addition to general photography, photo-mosaic work obtained by bringing together numerous small images was made at various stages. The method provides ideal information and fast recording for 2D archiving and is a good supplement for drawing records. An iron construction was manufactured in order to be able to shoot the images from a certain level and angle and images taken in JPG and NEF formats were transferred to the computer and joined using *Adobe Photoshop CS3* program. Thus, photo-mosaic images of about 3.5 GB size with high resolution and

accuracy have been obtained and full scale prints can be taken from them.

On site evaluation forms filled in on the excavation site aim at recording through sketch, measurements and descriptions the overall condition of the ship timbers, voluminous wholeness and interrelation of the timbers before dismantling. These descriptions will always be referred to during the writing of inventory and catalogue descriptions.

3. Dismantling Methods
By March 15th, 2010, examination and documentation works of twenty two wrecks have been completed and the timbers moved to the laboratory. Their detailed studies and full scale drawings are still in progress. Of all the twenty two vessels we have lifted from the site, the original hull forms and slopes have been preserved as per original or with slight deformations.

One of the goals here was to identify the construction method by separating the pieces whose joining details could not be seen. This was actually very important for the identification of the shipbuilding technique. For instance, the joint details of two planks may not be visible from above or below; however, when they are dismantled from each other, it becomes possible to see the joint technique applied such as dowels, nails, mortises -and-tenons, etc. Besides, especially when the joining of planking and frames are examined on the surface they seem to have been fastened with treenails; however, when the frame of some of the vessels was removed in the course of dismantling, it was seen that the frame was also fixed with iron nails hammered from the planking side. Another point worth noting is that it is much more practical to conserve the pieces individually. The presence of many other archaeological items on the site made it impossible to use heavy machinery for the lifting of the wreck's mass; therefore, apart from a small example, the "single mass lifting method" was not implemented.

The overall idea was; that the items were to be lifted with their forms protected and that the same team would be in charge from the beginning to the end, that is, on site examination, documentation, conservation and reconstruction works were to be implemented by the same team. This strategy provided great advantages for the handling of these boats and ships as a whole. In order to avoid any potential problems in the course of restoration and reconstruction, it was necessary to lift all the wooden ship timbers using supports that would protect their forms. Thus, supporting methods were designed and developed during lifting. Fastening elements such as dowels, treenails and iron nails continued keeping the elements together thanks to their mechanical strength despite the deformation they had suffered. Therefore, in the beginning of the dismantling, these fastening elements were cut. Iron nails still retained some of their mechanical strength thanks to the deposit layer that was formed around them, although they had lost their metallic features. Especially for the removal of iron nails, a variety of methods had to be employed depending on the preservation state of the timber. Some dismantling techniques are:

1) Negative mould method for lifting the planks,
2) lifting the planking with L-shaped carriers,
3) epoxy support for lifting
4) lifting as a single mass and
5) hamburger method for lifting (Kocabaş 2008b).

3.1. Negative mould method for lifting the planking
In this method, the length and width of the plank to be lifted were determined and transferred to a drawing. Then, wooden

legs with heights varying according to the buttock of the frame to be lifted were installed at 30 cm intervals on a wooden carrier skeleton of 5x10 cm in cross-section. Fine facing timbers of 8 mm thickness and 12 cm width, which would contact the timber items being lifted, were placed on top of this construction. The carrier thus formed was checked for any mismatch on the timber. These constructions were placed inside the vessel, on top of the timber elements and fixed with Styrofoam "clips". The U-shaped Styrofoam pieces, placed under the planking so that they would sit on the carrier construction, would hold the planking when the sand underneath was removed. Even complicated pieces, such as the planking manufactured with slopes, twisting and joining the stem post could be lifted only using the carrier mould shaped into individual forms (Figure 5).

Figure 5. "Negative moulds" built for lifting planking.

Figure 6. Lifting with L-shaped carriers.

3.2. Lifting the planking with L-shaped carriers

307

Another method we devised for dismantling the planking, involved lifting them from the bottom of the vessel, in other words from the exterior of the vessel, using L-shaped carriers.

Timbers of 5x10 cm were cut at the required lengths and fitted to each other at right angles using zinc-plated treenails. Then the almost 25 cm wide surface touching the plank was formed with fine facing timber (8x120 mm). A number of L-shaped carriers, depending on the length of the planking, were prepared. All the L-shaped carriers were fixed on the timber of 5x10 cm extended above. Thus, the experts holding the construction at suitable points managed to lift the item and successfully place it inside the specially manufactured box (Figure 6).

3.3. Epoxy support for lifting

A different method, which we named as 'epoxy sheath', was used for lifting the ceiling of Yenikapi 12, which surprisingly was uncovered with its cargo and has revealed important features regarding shipbuilding technology of its time. This excitement could indeed lead to problems during lifting as some of the timbers had thinned down to 1-2 mm in thickness. In the method developed, aluminum foil was first spread on the timbers in order to protect them from epoxy and then epoxy was applied on them to obtain their moulds. Araldite® FC 52 (ABC), which solidifies very fast, was prepared at appropriate proportions and applied on the aluminum foil and supported with fiber textile (Figure 7).

Before placing these carrier moulds on the ceiling, very fine synthetic fabrics were spread under the ceiling. Then the carrier was placed on top of the ceiling strakes and the textiles spread underneath were tied around the carrier and thus the ceiling timbers were lifted retaining their forms hundred percent.

Figure 7. *Preparation of epoxy support for lifting very thin ceiling timbers.*

3.4. Lifting as a single mass

In addition to lifting timbers individually, the keel and six planking strakes joining to the keel of Yenikapi 6 vessel were lifted as a whole. First, a ditch of one-meter depth and one-meter width was excavated all around the wreck. Then the wreck was furnished with a scaffolding of 10x10 cm timbers and starting from the stem of the vessel, the sand underneath was removed in slices of 25 cm. The upper and bottom profiles of the exposed parts of the vessel were copied in full scale using a large manufactured profiler and copied unto a dense Styrofoam, 5 cm in thickness. The profile of the vessel was decoupled and cut off; the Styrofoam profile was placed in the 25 cm thick gap under the vessel and fitted onto the main 10x10 cm construction built around the vessel. The interior profile of the vessel was also supported with Styrofoam prepared using the same method. Thus, the vessel resting on a layer of sediment, was placed on Styrofoam, and hence the wooden construction that would carry it, by placing a Styrofoam profile every 25 cm. In order to reinforce the construction and increase its carrying capacity, perpendicular and diagonal supports were placed along its sides and top. Then, the vessel was lifted as a single mass and placed in the pool built at the excavation site (Figure 8).

Figure 8. Lifting as a single mass.

Figure 9. Lifting with waterproof plywood shaped into frame forms and placed on top and bottom.

3.5. Hamburger method for lifting

The much softened and sometimes brittle frames of Yenikapi 3 were lifted supporting one or two sides. In order to ascertain that the supporting material would have the same profile as the frames, an aluminum profiler was manufactured specially for this purpose. This huge profiler facilitated the determining of the timbers profile. These profiles were transferred onto waterproof plywood and cut out. Frames in better state were supported only from one side with plywood and lifted slowly. The plywood taking the shape of the floor timbers were placed safely in the chests. Deformed frames were supported with plywood both on the front and rear side, like a hamburger, and then lifted (Figure 9).

After the disassembly process, the timbers are put in tagged wooden boxes and kept in water tanks for desalination.

4. First Step to Conservation Procedure

Istanbul University has established two laboratories for the conservation and restoration of the waterlogged timber pieces from the ships. Besides, the new Department of Conservation of Marine Archaeological Objects has been founded and thus, the first academically organized training on this topic has been launched.

Figure 10. Fresh water tanks for the conservation of the wrecks. (Photo S. Keskin)

At Yenikapı, documentation and lifting of the shipwrecks on site progressed in parallel to the passive conservation of the vessel timbers. The dismantled shipwrecks were placed into stainless steel pools of 4x10x1.20 m with two compartments (Figure 10). The pools were also roofed to prevent unwanted effects of the direct sunlight.

4.1. Desalination and cleaning

In order to desalinate, the water in the pools is circulated and refreshed with new fresh water. The incoming water line is at the bottom level of the pool while the outlet is at the top; thus, contamination with bacteria, fungi and algae due to still water is prevented while the desalination continues. The present saltiness rate of the vessel timbers washed by the fresh water of Lykos Stream, which has flowed into the Ancient Harbor, has been found to be lower than first expected (Table 1). After the desalinization, to prevent the biologic activation, bacterium and fungus EXOCIDE 1012 solution has been poured into the pools in the ratio of 1/1000. The iron traces formed by the corrosion of the iron nails on the timbers, have been cleaned by using EDTA solution of 5 %. The EDTA, applied on the timbers using tampons, was left approximately 4 hours on the timbers. Finally the timber surfaces were washed under the flowing water for a long time. This process was repeated until the iron traces were totally removed (Figure 11).

Table 1. *Salt levels of some pools.*

Pool & Wreck Nr	Pool Capacity (ton)	Date & Salt Level (ppm)				
YK 17	18	13.05.09 1220	23.07.09 960	02.09.09 640	12.11.2009 460	14.01.2010 310
YK 27	38	06.08.2009 1540	06.10.2009 900	07.12.2009 680	20.01.2010 440	19.02.2010 340
YK 20	47	03.07.2009 990	11.08.2009 680	15.09.2009 580	20.10.2009 370	16.12.2009 300

Figure 11. *Final cleaning of YK 1 and preparations for PEG conservation at the Shipwreck Conservation and Reconstruction Laboratory established at IU's Faculty of Letters.*

4.2. Conservation

After the completion of the documentation and cleaning of the Yenikapı 1 and Yenikapı 12 wrecks, the conservation process has started. The analyses conducted to determine the deterioration level of some wreck timbers are shown in Table 2 (Figure 12).

We decided to implement the vacuum freeze drying method after PEG 2000 impregnation. As per 1 August 2009, PEG impregnation of Yenikapi 1 wreck was started using a solution of %10. While the Yenikapi 12 wreck, which its documentation process is about to be completed, the same procedure will be started in the days to come.

Table 2 *Deterioration level of the wreck timbers.*

Wreck	Sample no	Wet weight (g)	Buoyancy (g)	Wet volume (cm³)	Density (g/cm³)	Dry weight (g)	Weight of water (g)	Density (kg/m³)	Max water content	Actual water content	Porosity (cm³/cm³)
YK 1	F23/1 (Futtock)	4,69	4,465	4,47	0,15	0,60	4,09	134	678	682	0,90
YK12	K1	6,70	6,635	6,65	0,03	1,29	5,42	193	450	421	0,98
YK12	E2	4,20	3,890	3,90	0,23	0,71	3,49	182	481	491	0,84
YK13	Plank	6,65	5,240	5,25	0,80	1,20	5,45	229	370	454	0,47
YK27	Plank	4,48	4,000	4,01	0,36	1,40	3,09	348	220	221	0,76

Figure 12. Kristiane Strætkvern and Dr. Poul Jensen in waterlogged wood conservation workshop in Istanbul.

Because a freeze dryer device will be used in conservation applications, a vacuum freeze-dryer 10 m in length and 2 m in diameter is foreseen to be built at the new centre. Work on the technical features and manufacturing details of the above mentioned vacuum freeze-dryer is in progress at the time of writing (Jensen, Strætkvern, Schnell and Jensen 2009)

Acknowledgments

We would like to thank to Kristiane Strætkvern and Dr. Poul Jensen who participated to the workshop we organized in Istanbul between the dates 20-24 July about "Conservation of the Waterlogged Timber", and who shared their valuable knowledge and experiences with us. Yenikapı Shipwrecks Project is supported by Istanbul University's Scientific Research Projects (Project No: 2294 & 3907 & 7381).

References

Crisman, K.J., 1993, "An Archaeological Approach, Recording Boats From Their Remains and Learning From Their Parts", Eds. P. Lipke, P. Spectre, B.A.G. Fuller, *Boats*, 304-320, Nashville, Tennessee.

Eiteljorg, H., 1994, Using a Total Station. *CSA –Newsletter*, VII, 2.

Hocker, F.M., 2003, Documentation of the form and structure of the hull. In: O. Crumlin–Pedersen, A. Trakadas (eds.), Hjortspring, A Pre–Roman Iron–Age Warship in Context, 84–92. Roskilde.

Jensen, P., K. Strætkvern, U. Schnell and J. B. Jensen, 2009, Technical specifications for equipment for vacuum freeze–drying of PEG impregnated waterlogged organic materials. In: K. Strætkvern, D.J.Huisman (eds.), *Proceedings of the 10th ICOM Group on Wet Organic Archaeological Materials Conference, Amsterdam 2007*, 417-438. Amersfoort.

Kocabaş, U. (ed.), 2008a, *Yenikapi Shipwrecks, Volume I: The "Old Ships" of the "New Gate"* – 1. Istanbul.

Kocabaş, U., 2008b, IV. Dismantling of the vessel members. In: U. Kocabaş (ed.) *Yenikapi Shipwrecks, Volume I: The "Old Ships" of the "New Gate"* – 1. Istanbul.

Kocabaş, U., 1998, Arkeolojik Sualtı Kalıntılarının Konservasyonu. İstanbul.

Kocabaş, U., I. Özsait Kocabaş, 2009, İstanbul, Sultan of Lands and Seas "A Gate onto the Ancient World: The Harbour of Theodosius and the Yenikapı Wrecks, 27-45. YKY.

Kocabaş, U., E. Türkmenoğlu, 2009, *Yenikapı Shipwrecks: Fieldwork, Conservation-Restoration Procedures And Construction Features*, In: X. Nieto (ed), *Argueologia Nautica Mediterrania*, 235-243. Girona.

Matthews, S.D., 2004, "Recording the Hull", Eds. G.F. Bass, S.D. Matthews, J.R. Steffy, F.H. van Doorninck Jr, *Serçe Limanı, An Eleventh-Century Shipwreck: The Ship and Its Anchorage, Crew and Passengers*, Vol. 1, 75-80, College Station.

Müller-Wiener, W., 1998, *Bizans'tan Osmanlı'ya İstanbul Limanı*. İstanbul.

Özsait–Kocabaş, I., 2008a, Documentation: Reading the Timber. In U. Kocabaş (ed.), The 'Old Ships' of the 'New Gate'– 1, 37–72. İstanbul.

Özsait–Kocabaş, I., Kocabaş, U., 2008b, Technological and constructional features of Yenikapı Shipwrecks: A preliminary evaluation. In: U. Kocabaş (ed.), *Yenikapi Shipwrecks, Volume I: The "Old Ships" of the "New Gate" – 1*, 97–185. Istanbul.

Steffy, J.R., 1994, *Wooden Ship Building and the Interpretation of Shipwrecks*. College Station.

3.11
Conservation of a Waterlogged Mayan Paddle

Wayne Smith* and Helen Dewolf
Texas A & M University, Archaeological Preservation Research Laboratory, Center for Maritime Archaeology and Conservation, College Station, TX 77843-4352, United States
E-mail* : silicone@neo.tamu.edu

Heather McKillop,
Department of Geography and Anthropology, Louisiana State University, Louisiana State University, Baton Rouge, LA 70803, United States

Abstract
A nearly intact Mayan wooden canoe paddle, dating to the Late Classic Maya period, was excavated from the K'ak' Naab' site, in Paynes Creek National Park, Brazil. The site was situated within a submerged red mangrove peat bog in close association with a Mayan salt works. The wood species is tentatively identified as *Manilkara sapote* in the family *Sapotaceae*. This species of wood typically contains high percentages of gummy latex 'chicle' (containing 15% rubber and 38% resin) and is a strong durable timber used by the Maya for support timbers in temple, lintels, and tool handles. The paddle received conservation treatment with solvent / polymer exchange processes (silicone oils). Upon the completion of treatment, tests were conducted to assess both the effectiveness of the treatment strategy and the long-term stability of the paddle. This paper reports the initial test results.

Keywords: Mayan, functional polymers, EDS, SEM, TEM, silicone oils

1. Introduction
During archaeological excavations at the submerged K'ak' Naab' site in Paynes Creek National Park, Belize a nearly-intact Mayan paddle was recovered (see Figure 1). The paddle was brought to the Conservation Research Lab (CRL) at Texas A&M University by Dr. Heather McKillop of Louisiana State University, who requested that the artifact be conserved using silicone oil technologies developed at the Texas A&M University. The paddle was constructed of *Manilkara sapote*, a tree in the family *Sapotaceae*. Commonly known as the 'chicle' tree, this wood is extremely durable and used for construction materials and for the production of natural rubber.

Although the wood of the chicle tree is thought to be highly resistant to microbial decay, the surfaces of the artifact are deeply worn with evidence of rot and extensive waterlogged deterioration. Extensive wood samples to determine the extent of wood deterioration were not taken. Surface probing and general observations were used to design a treatment strategy using polymers as requested by the principal investigator.

2. Condition Assessment
Large cracks and surface checking on the surface of the artifact indicate that due to its deposition at the edge of a mangrove swamp the artifact experienced cycles of waterlogging followed by periods of air-drying. Superficial striations were noted along the entire length of the paddle with one deep crack extending across the width of the blade. Transmission electron microscopy (TEM) and scanning electron microscopy (SEM) cross-section images of the cellular structure of the artifact indicate that little-to-no cellular collapse damage had occurred as the result of seasonal climatic activity associated with the bog. Conservator Helen Dewolf also noted deep pitted areas on the surface of the blade of the paddle resulting from

wood-boring mollusk (*Toredo* spp) activity (see Figure 2).

Figure 1: *Side view of the paddle. The figures drawn above the artifact illustrate the paddle in use. Illustration from a carving on bone from Temple 1 at Tikal.*
Figure 2: *Side view of the paddle blade showing deeply pitted areas. In this photo, the edge of the blade is jagged but complete.*

Although a small section of the thinnest part of the lower blade was broken in transit from Belize, the paddle and blade fragment were treated with the same bulking agents and post-treatment catalyzation. In general, the core wood of the artifact was solid and the paddle was deemed to be a good candidate for treatment using the CRL polymer process. Due to the perceived fragility and rarity of the artifact, the decision was made to implement desalination and treatment immediately. This was accomplished in two stages. First, the paddle was stored and shipped in fresh water. At, the lab, the paddle was further desalinated in fresh-running water for an additional 4 weeks.

3. Objectives and Rationale For Treatment

Several factors were considered for selecting the polymer process. Controlling the long-term costs of curation and maintenance were important goals for the treatment of the paddle. Initial costs for preserving the paddle with silicone oils were substantially higher than most traditional conservation methods. Post-treatment curation and display requirements for polymer-treated artifacts are much less stringent since their long-term stability under less than ideal situations is well documented (Smith, Report 4, 1997). The ability to store such objects without the need for rigorous climatic controls lowers the long-term curation and storage costs for the artifacts and justifies the greater initial cost of treatment. The primary consideration was the need for artifact stability in the face of long-term storage in a minimally controlled environment. After treatment using polymers, organic materials do not require controlled-environment curation to ensure artifact stability. The artifact was to be returned to Belize where it would probably not be displayed in an environmentally-controlled museum; polymer treatment offered the best chance for the paddle's continuing survival.

The decision was made to use a mixture of low and medium centistokes silicone oils for treatment. The blend of polymers was designed to ensure the structural integrity of the wood by using a slow displacement process in order to minimize shrinkage and cellular distortion, and to ensure maximum distribution of the bulking agent throughout the matrix of the wood. In conjunction with the polymer mixture, methyltrimethoxysilane (MTMS), a hydroxyl-ended silane, was selected as a cross-linking agent. The resulting polymer mixture was designed to ensure that the wood matrix contained sufficient bonding agents to impart a degree of structural integrity to the paddle.

As the paddle was returning to Belize for curation and display, Dr. McKillop's decision to have the paddle conserved using functional polymers was a logical choice. Combining high and low centistokes polymers into a blended polymer ensures penetration into the core wood of the artifact and allows the conservator to create a bulking agent which imparts strength to the artifact and minimizes shrinkage. The addition of MTMS ensures thorough polymerization. After treatment polymer treated wooden artifacts are less likely to undergo chemical reactions within the microstructure of the wood.

Because the paddle was waterlogged and appeared to be fragile, the obvious option was to use passivation polymers at ambient pressure and room temperature. Unlike many waterlogged organic artifacts, wood in almost any stage of waterlogging still maintains a cellular structure. Vacuum assisted processing is never advisable when using materials as viscous as SFD-5 with any percentage of MTMS added (Smith, 2003, p.24: p.26). At ambient pressure, acetone evaporates at a slow rate ensuring that the acetone / polymer exchange is effective while minimizing cell wall stress.

4. Procedure

Silicone oil / MTMS polymer solutions are hydrophobic necessitating the removal of unbound water from the core structure of the wood. At the Conservation Research Lab (CRL), a system of baths was designed to slowly displace water with organic solvents to prevent cellular collapse in deteriorated waterlogged wood. The routinely used schedule for water / solvent displacement is listed in Table 1.

A volume of SFD-5 (70-120 centistokes) polymer, sufficient to immerse the paddle during treatment, was poured into a vat. To this polymer MTMS was added (20% v/v). After thorough mixing, the functional (hydroxyl-ended) polymer solution was ready. After water / solvent displacement, the solvent-saturated paddle was immersed in the SFD-5/MTMS polymer solution for a period of 6 weeks. At ambient pressure and room temperature, the solvents evaporate at a slow rate and are replaced by the polymer solution in the cell structure of the wood.

After removal from the polymer solution, the paddle was allowed to drain for several days in the air to remove any free-flowing polymers. Soft cloths dampened with MTMS were used to remove any pooled

Table 1: Schedule for water / solvent displacement prior to silicone oil treatment.

Stage of dehydration	% DI Water / solvent	Time in Each Bath
1	75% DI water / 25% ETOH	6 weeks
2	50% DI water / 50% ETOH	6 weeks
3	25% DI water / 75% ETOH	6 weeks
4	100% ETOH (1st bath)	6 weeks
5	100% ETOH (2nd bath)	6 weeks
6	75% ETOH / 25%acetone	6 weeks
7	50% ETOH / 50%acetone	6 weeks
8	25% ETOH / 75%acetone	6 weeks
9	100% acetone (1st bath)	6 weeks
10	100% acetone (2nd bath)	6 weeks
11	Optional 100% acetone (3rd bath)	6 weeks

315

polymer from the surfaces of the artifact. To initiate the polymerization process the paddle was placed into a large polyethylene zip-top bag with an aluminum sample dish containing thirty grams of dibutyltin diacetate catalyst in close proximity to the artifact. The old catalyst was replaced with fresh catalyst daily for 7days. Over several days, Dr. Dewolf cleaned the surface features of the paddle to ensure that all remnants of polymers were removed.

Generally, stainless steel vats with tight fitting lids are used for Passivation Polymer treatments. Polyethylene containers are used for smaller artifacts. Careful testing should be carried out to ensure that these containers do not deteriorate from exposure to acetone. Weather stainless steel or polyethylene vats are used, tight-fitting lids are important to keep contaminants from coming in to contact with the polymer solution because after treatment, the used SFD-5/MTMS solution can be re-used for other artifacts. Because of its high alcohol content, MTMS evaporates over time. Accordingly, before re-use, fresh MTMS should be added and thoroughly mixed. Use of passivation polymers should be carried out in a well-ventilated work space.

5. Observations
Before treatment, the wood was dark and surface details were difficult to assess. Notably, the wood is substantially lighter in color after treatment. After treatment the paddle was a light gray-brown to very pale brown in color (Munsell Soil Color Charts, 2000) (Munsell Chart 10YR 7/2 gray to 10YR 8/2 white). Note that the texture of the wood is natural in appearance Surface checking and cracks noted in the wood prior to treatment remained unchanged as the result of treatment. The artifact was transported to the Women's Hospital in Baton Rouge, Louisiana, where it was scanned using computer tomographic imaging (CT). Images clearly showed that the largest crack, running across the lower face of the blade, is more extensive than could be assessed in its pre-treatment state (see Figure 3).

Before treatment, the thin section of wood forming the blade of the paddle was very soft and spongy in nature. Post treatment assessment of the same area-of the paddle shows that the polymer process has imparted greater stability and durability to the artifact. Timbers from the *Sapotaceae* family are resinous in nature and, despite the paddle's close association with a bog environment, this attribute of the wood has helped to prevent intercellular deterioration of the wood.

Figure 3: *Side view CT image of the paddle showing large cracks and extensive surface checking*

Post treatment scans CT scans, TEM and SEM images and energy dispersive x-ray spectroscopy (EDS) were used to determine the degree of cellular deterioration and distribution of silicone oil bulking agent in the wood. In Figure 4 cell wall splitting is evident but is not as extensive as expected.

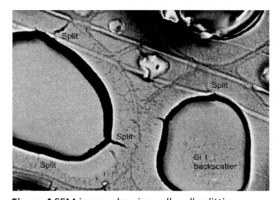

Figure 4 *SEM image showing cell wall splitting.*

The wood specimens were prepared so that an image and an analysis of the elemental composition could be made. The specimens were fixed in 2.5% Glutaraldehyde and HEPES buffer, 1% Acrolein and HEPES buffer, 1% Osmium and HEPES buffer (pH 7.3). Dehydration was conducted using methanol (5% steps), followed by 3 changes of Hexamethyldisilazane (HMDS). The dry specimens were mounted on stubs with double stick carbon tape and coated with 5nm gold/palladium using a Technics Hummer II sputter coater for optimal Scanning Electron Microscopy (SEM) imaging and Energy Dispersive Spectroscopy (EDS) analysis. Gold/palladium coating was used to obtain a high quality image and this coating did not impede the resolution of elements which were significant for this project. Images and EDS analysis were completed on a JEOL JSM-6400 SEM operating at 10 KeV (electron volts accelerating voltage) using 15 mm working distance and EDS analysis was performed using a PGT (Bruker) detector operating at 15 keV (electron volts accelerating voltage) and 15mm working distance. The images and EDS results were obtained on the SEM through the use of the PGT Spirit (Bruker) software interface (Mike Pendleton).

EDS spectra indicate that silicone is present in the compound middle lamella, comprised of middle lamella and adjacent primary cell walls (MLC and ML) (see Figures 5 and 6).

 _S001.txt

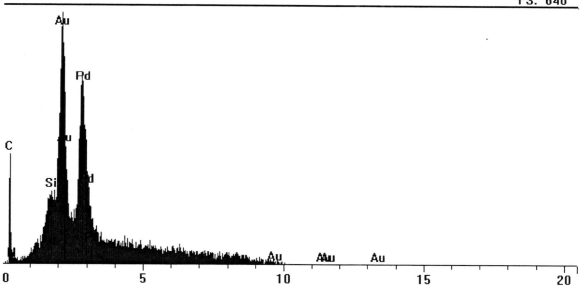

Figure 5: *EDS spectra indicating the presence of Si at a test site identified as the middle lamella and adjacent cell walls. Gold (Au) and palladium (Pd) were used to apply a light sputter coating on the sample to help eliminate scatter and data errors.*

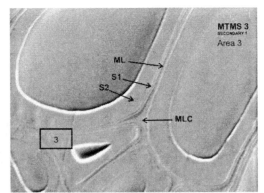

Figure 6: *Sample site for EDS analysis. Passivation Polymers are concentrated in the middle lamella (ML).*

6. Conclusions

Given the time constraints for preservation and the desire to preserve the integrity of the artifact,—only a cursory evaluation of the artifact was conducted. Conservators at CRL and numerous other conservation facilities have successfully used polymer processes to conserve waterlogged wooden artifacts. Fifteen years after developing the process, protocols for using functional polymers are well defined. In light of these successes, conservation of the paddle using polymer processes was done. The results were a paddle with a light, natural-colored wood which will withstand the environmental changes it will undergo in storage in Belize. Analysis indicates that the silicone has penetrated to the compound middle lamella, the secondary cell walls appear to not be deteriorated and treatment has prevented cell wall collapse.

Clearly additional research is needed to define the role of functional (hydroxyl-ended) polymers in preserving the micro structure of waterlogged wood. Better protocols are needed for pre and post treatment assessment to better understand the attributes of mechanical strength and cell wall chemistry that appear to successfully preserve the diagnostic attributes of wooden artifacts.

Materials

SFD-5 is a colorless medium viscosity functional (OH end-blocked polydimethylsiloxane) polymer. This material is available thru XIAMETER® as PMX-0156 silanol fluid. It is chemically equivalent to DOW CORNING® 2-1273 FLUID.

MTMS is a crosslinking agent. Methyltrimethoxysilane is used in many aspects of the polymer chemistry. The product is distributed by XIAMETER® Corporation as well as numerous other distributors.

Dibutyltin diacetate (DBDTA) is a tin-based catalyst ($C_{12}H_{24}O_4Sn$). DBTDA is a clear, yellow compound. DBDTA is also known as Fascat 4000 Series organotin catalysts, manufactured by Arkema Incorporated. It is used for silicone cross-linking reactions as well as many other applications. It's chemical formula is $C_{12}H_24O_4Sn$.

References

Barbour, James, R. (1990), Treatments for Waterlogged and Dry Archaeological Wood, Archaeological Wood, Properties, Chemistry and Preservation, Roger M. Rowell and R. James Barbour, Editors, Advances in Chemistry Series, ISSN 0065-2393; 225.

Munsell Soil Color Charts, Munsell Color, Editors, Grand Rapids, MI, 2000.

Pendleton, Mike, Texas A&M University Microscopy and Imaging Center, 2010 - technique submitted by e-mail.

Smith, C. Wayne (1997), Conservation of Waterlogged Leather Using Polymers , Report 4, Conservation Research Laboratory/Archaeological Preservation Research Laboratory, College Station, TX, 1997.

Smith, C. Wayne (2003), *Archaeological Conservation Using Polymers, Practical*

Applications for Organic Artifact Stabilization, Texas A&M University Press, College Station, Texas, 2003 – Page 24.

Smith, C. Wayne (2003), *Case Study: Waterlogged Wooden Buttons with and without Associated Thread*, Archaeological Conservation Using Polymers, Practical Applications for Organic Artifact Stabilization, Texas A&M University Press, College Station, Texas, 2003, Page 26.

Acknowledgements

The author would like to thank Dr. Michael Pendleton and Anne Ellis of the Microscopy and Imaging Center, Department of Biology, Texas A&M University. The author would like to acknowledge Brian Ostrowski and the entire team at Dow Corning Corporation, Midland, Michigan. Their technical expertise and advice is greatly appreciated.

Questions and answers

Anthony Kennedy: I have a question about the Mayan paddle. Has anyone studied the heat of the reaction between the methoxy silane and the molecule that you are reacting it with?

Wayne Smith: I actually didn't hear you, I'm sorry.

Anthony Kennedy: Has anybody studied the heat of reaction between the methoxy silane and the molecule you are crosslinking it to? And is that a concern for damaging the artifact?

Wayne Smith: I still don't think I'm getting it but you are talking about reactions that are occurring?

Anthony Kennedy: Yes, I'm wondering if the heat of reaction is going to cause damage to the artifact?

Wayne Smith: No. I can confidently say that because in the earliest stages of research that we did, we did exhaustive accelerated weathering tests and we put things through months and months and months of accelerated chemical testing etc...and once these things are put in place, most of you would argue that's a bad thing, they are really very stable. In fact what we've been able to figure out, that from the first time that I reported this at a WOAM conference, we've got about 250 years before you even get to a half life of the usefulness of this polymer. Basically you can reset its time clock by a small retreatment. So it's pretty stable stuff but it was designed that way. It's a good question.

Mikkel Christensen: I have a question for Wayne Smith. I completely agree with you that total reversibility is desirable but not actually feasible. So given that, we need to be extremely careful about the durability of things we put into the wood because we don't want them to degrade. You said that you carried out accelerated aging tests but it's notoriously difficult to move from the results of accelerated aging tests to actual real time aging in a museum environment so I'm very curious how you estimate that life time.

Wayne Smith: Good question. How we did it is fairly simple. We used 70 years of data from Dow Corning working with the sulfactant polymers that we use and so we've got a head start of about 60 years of looking at things that have been done. To that we can add models of accelerated weathering which then compound what we've seen from that 60 or 70 years and we can extrapolate fairly reasonably from that what kind of actual life we have for a polymer in something. So it's not something that you can do by three months of working with accelerated weathering – it's impossible. But if you take the data that's in the industry and in the case of Dow Corning they spent billions to know these models and they have so many years of things to fall back and look at, so if we're smart, we're going to use the data that exists and then try to build on it.

In this case, for the accelerated weathering, we couldn't project it ourselves, as a matter of fact it would almost be irresponsible too, so that was done by Dow Corning and a few other industries and people who just do that and so from that perspective, I feel reasonably confident that we've got good figures. It's a good question. It's the same way with... a lot of people have asked why we in fact patented everything that we did and it falls into the same thing. I'll explain really briefly. Seventeen, eighteen, twenty years ago when we started this stuff there was nobody in the ICOM that could talk organosilicone chemistry, it didn't exist in that form, so when we started to work on this stuff and get results, the only responsible thing to do was to take it to people that knew the stuff – the organic chemists – and we applied for patents. In doing so they had to take it seriously and look at it from a money making perspective. So when they came back and said "yes, this is viable chemistry, here's your patent" we immediately signed away all rights to money so that we weren't using it as a money making proposition. In fact, one thing that nobody seems to have gotten from discussions in the past is simply the fact that if you want polymers, you can have them. We gave the rights to these things away so that you don't necessarily have to go out and buy them. When I was working with Ian in Australia, we had some stuff there, there was no charge. Same in Greece, same in Turkey, same in Israel, same in France –these things are there because we need the dialog. So that's kind of how we've done what we've done. We've gone out to the industry who have already paid for this stuff and we've used their data to build on. Good enough?

Mikkel Christensen: Yes, indeed. Thank you!

3.12

Twenty-five Years Later: the Treatment and Display of a Group of XVIIIth century Boats

André Bergeron*and France Rémillard,
Centre de conservation du Québec
E-mail: andre.bergeron@mcccf.gouv.qc.ca

Abstract

In 1984-85, several boats constructed in the first half of the XVIIth century were found on the construction site of the Musée de la civilisation, in Quebec City. Some of these were treated using Polyethylene Glycol (PEG) 400 at low concentrations, followed by outdoor freeze-drying; while another group was treated by saturation with PEG 540 blend at high relative humidity, followed with slow drying at room temperature. Among these, one boat was block-lifted, progressively reshaped using the reconstruction data provided by the archaeological team, and transported back to the museum where it is still on display today. This paper presents the main results of these treatments and some lessons learned from this adventure.

Keywords: outdoor freeze-drying, PEG pre-treatment, Québec batoes

A first discovery

Since the beginning of the XVIIth century, New France as a colony developed in part because of the seaway centered around the Saint-Lawrence River and its tributaries. Early on, shipbuilding played a key role in economic life; in the absence of roads, ships were ubiquitous, used for the transportation of goods and people as well as for the defense of the colony.

Quebec City, founded in 1608, developed by encroaching on the river. In 1974, a first batteau (note 1) was discovered, on what was at the time the river's shore. It was then reburied because of the lack of knowledge of what to do with it.

Ten years later, when the construction of the Musée de la civilisation was beginning at that site, it was decided to document and preserve this specimen thinking it was a unique occurrence. (Figure 1). Then, in January 1985, another group of four batoes was discovered, followed by three other boats of a different type of construction. (Laroche, 2008) Owing to their size, and in order to allow for their treatment, two of these were block-lifted (figure 2) and transported in March of that year to a temporary open-air location to allow for their documentation by the archaeologists. In June 1985, a working space vast enough for the treatment of the boats was found.

Figure 1: The first batteau (numbered 12A-9) discovered in 1974, during its archaeological documentation in 1984. Photo: Centre de conservation du Québec, André Bergeron

321

Figure 2. The block-lifting of the boat 10C-3, discovered on the construction site of the Musée de la civilisation. Photo: Daniel LaRoche

The conservation work

Selecting the best approach for all this waterlogged wood was not an easy task. As the discoveries were being made, 1985 also found the Centre de conservation du Québec (CCQ) planning the conservation treatment and evaluating various scenarios. After much reading and consultation with colleagues from Canada and abroad, (Rémillard, 1985) two options were considered, both of them using PEG impregnation. The batoes, smaller in size and more fragmented would be placed in tanks with solutions of PEG 400, starting with a 10% solution and increasing up to 30% for 12 months. Outdoor freeze-drying would then be used to complete the treatment. Determination of the water content and penetration tests revealed that the wood was quite degraded. For example, the water content of the biggest boat (10C-3) ranged from 543% to 703%.

The boats, whole or dismantled, were placed in polyethylene tents (figure 3) at high relative humidity, as high as our small humidifiers would allow. Then, they were sprayed with 10% solutions of PEG 400 and after several weeks, switched to the use of PEG 540 blend for 3 months. Relative humidity in the tents was slowly reduced over the course of one year. Evaluating the penetration of the PEG was undertaken using the colored impression technique developed by Per Hoffmann (Hoffmann, 1983). This technique requires a small sample of wood, which can be removed with the same wood borer that is used in dendrochronology. A blotter is sprayed with a tracing liquid. The wood sample is simply placed on the blotter and the area impregnated with PEG then takes on an orange color. Our results showed that the wood treated by immersion in PEG 400 solutions for one year was thoroughly impregnated with the PEG, while the surface of the bigger boats, composed of oak planking that had been treated by spraying and daubing of PEG solutions and

322

the 540 blend had absorbed much less PEG.

Parallel to the conservation work, the archaeological team was documenting the boats and remains from the batoes in order to propose plausible lines for their interpretation. In February 1986, the decision was taken to reshape the biggest of the boats, numbered 10C-3, which had been found in two parts. The drawings of the archaeological team proved very useful when this work began. Samples of the wood were also taken for wood species identification. Dendrochronology was conducted on the stem post of this boat, indicating a possible construction date in 1735. Determination of the ballast showed that the boats were constructed locally, the ballast stones originating from the Quebec City area.

Figure 3. The biggest boat, numbered 10C-3 in its treatment tent. In the back, one can see the moving platform that was used to consolidate and study the inner planking of the boat. Photo: Centre de conservation du Québec, André Bergeron

Figure 4. The boat 10C-3 is progressively reshaped using temporary frames and supports. Photo: Centre de conservation du Québec, André Bergeron

Taking advantage of the 'plasticity' of the wet wood, the sides of the boat were progressively raised by inserting various sizes and types of wedge (Figure 4). When a proper level was reached, temporary plywood frames were constructed; those frames were then joined together with H beams to allow for transport when the boat was moved to the museum for display.

Outdoor Freeze-drying

While the bigger boats were treated with a PEG controlled drying approach, the batoes, smaller in size and dismantled when lifted from the site were slowly impregnated with PEG 400. Over the course of one year, the concentration was progressively increased from 10% to 39%. These pieces would be treated with outdoor freeze-drying, a process greatly influenced by the architecture of the treatment shelter. In January 1986, pieces from the batoes were installed in a disaffected greenhouse. Evolution of the treatment was monitored by weighing specific pieces with a load transducer; temperature probes were placed into the wood, with one probe left to monitor the temperature of the shelter. By the end of March, when the outdoor temperature was beginning to warm up, the pieces were brought back inside and placed at room temperature on shelves, enclosed with polyethylene sheets.

The results from this first attempt did not conform to expectation. The loss in weight was minimal and most of the water loss occurred later during the controlled drying phase. The design of our treatment room was not conducive to freeze-drying because snow accumulation on the roof was blocking penetration of light from the sun. Also, because of a lack of ventilation, any water vapor lost during the process stayed in the shelter, creating a high relative humidity not conducive to wood drying.

The next year, after some consultation and a better understanding of the process, the design of the shelter was radically changed. A new installation was found, with a better overall exposure to the sun. A polyethylene car shelter, very common in our country in winter time, was used for the treatment.

Apertures at both ends were opened each day to maximize humidity loss; these were closed at night, over the week-ends and during snow storms, but they were equipped with screening to allow for some ventilation when the doors were closed (Figure 5). This configuration was a significant improvement over our first experience. Even so, our winter was not long enough to achieve thorough drying. Once more, the pieces of wood were brought back inside and placed in a shelter to continue the drying.

Figure 5: *A view of the shelter used for our second attempt at outdoor freeze-drying, with the doors opened. The wood was placed on shelves along the sides of the shelter, while the center was used for the treatment of a dugout. Orientation of the shelter running from west/east was based on the direction of the prevalent winds during winter. The southern part was equipped with as many windows as we could afford. The upper right image shows the same shelter, with its doors closed. Photo: Centre de conservation du Québec, Guy Couture*

The display in the Museum

After the boat was given a shape consistent with its period of use, it was transported back to its site of discovery within the Musée de la civilisation. There, the temporary transportation system was progressively replaced with a series of metallic frames that would allow for a safe and adequate support. The frames were cushioned with Ethafoam ™ along the points of contact, and the outlines of the boat were filled in along the upper section and the missing extremity.

The display room was equipped with a controlled environment and appropriate lighting. Several panels were used to explain to visitors the context of the discovery, the tradition of shipbuilding in Quebec City and the conservation treatment of the boats found on the museum site (figure 6). In 2002, the boat was relocated in a new environment, very close to where it was originally found (Figure 7). Unfortunately, the outlines of the missing part of the boat, originally suggested with a metallic frame, have been removed. A simple panel now explains to visitors the nature of this artifact, the oldest example of Québec maritime heritage on display, dating before the 1759 conquest. Since 1988, more than 10 million visitors have seen the boat in the museum.

Figure 6. *A view of the boat 10C-3 as displayed between 1988 and 2002. Photo: Musée de la civilisation, Pierre Soulard*

Figure 7. *A view of the boat 10C-3 as displayed from 2002. Photo: Centre de conservation du Québec, André Bergeron*

Conclusion

Overall, this project which lasted over the course of five years contributed to a better knowledge of the tradition of shipbuilding in New France and the recognition of the key role it played in the development of French settlement in North America. The discovery of the boats found on the construction site of the Musée de la civilisation is mentioned in the British Museum Encyclopedia of Underwater and Maritime Archaeology.

As the boats were constructed without using plans, finding several boats was a unique opportunity to study and document the construction techniques of the time. Also, this project allowed us to develop an expertise in the treatment of waterlogged finds. Now, work should continue to give those specimens the place they deserve in Québec maritime history and heritage.

Acknowledgements

The authors would like to express their thanks to Lorne Murdock, from Parks Canada, to David Grattan, from the Canadian Conservation Institute, to J. Sommers from the Rijksdienst voor de IJsselmeerpolders, to Anton Wevers from the Museum voor Scheeparcheologi, to Kirsten Jespersen from the Viking Ship Museum, to Maj Stief, from the Nationalmuseets Konserveringsaf deling for Jordfund, to Sven Bengtsson from the Statens Sjohistoriska Museum, to Lars Barkman from the Swedish Central Office of National Antiquities and to Per Hoffmann, from the Deutsches Schiffahrts Museum. Their advices and expertise helped us in deciding on many conservation scenarios. We also express our gratitude to the following people, for their expertise in this project: Marc-André Bernier, Charles Dagneau and Daniel LaRoche, from Parks Canada, and to Jean Bélisle, and Alain Franck, also specialists in maritime heritage. From the Centre de conservation du Québec: Susanne-Marie Holm and Monique Benoit for their help in the translation of this paper, Michel Élie for the preparation of the photos; Daniel Bastille, Francine Lalonde, Ariane Lalande and Blandine Daux for their comments on this text.

Note 1: In this text, the term "batteau" refers to a flat double-ended craft, as described by Dagneau (2004). The term translates in English as batoe.

References

Bergeron, A. and F. Rémillard, (2008), "Une flotte sous un musée", Continuité, number 116, spring, pp 48-50.

Bergeron, A. and F. Rémillard (1989) "Le traitement de conservation des embarcations gorgées d'eau du Musée de la civilization", Proceedings of the 14th Annual International Institute for Conservation, Canadian Group Conference, Toronto, pp137-152.

Bergeron, A. (1987), "Le séchage à froid en milieu extérieur: évaluation de l'efficacité de l'hiver québécois ", Preprints Volume 1, ICOM Committee for Conservation, 8th triennial meeting, Sydney, Australia, pp 297-300.

Dagneau, C. (2004), "The Batteaux Plats of New France", The International Journal of Nautical Archaeology, 33.2: pp 281-296.

Grattan, D.W, McCawley, J.C., (1978), "The potential of the Canadian Winter climate for the Freeze-Drying of Degraded Water-Logged Wood, Studies in Conservation, vol. 23, n.4, November, pp 157-167.

Grattan, D.W, McCawley, J.C., and C. Cook, (1983), "The potential of the Canadian Winter climate for the Freeze-Drying of Degraded Water-Logged Wood, Part II, Studies in Conservation, vol. 25, n.3, August, pp 118-136.

Hoffmann, P, (1983), "A rapid method for the detection of polyethylene glycols (PEG) in wood", Studies in Conservation, 28 (4), pp 189-193.

La Roche, D., (2008), "Au gré des vents et marées à Québec! Embarcations naviguant sur le fleuve Saint-Laurent au XVIIIème siècle : tradition ou adaptation", Archéologiques, collection Hors-série 2, Rêves d'Amériques : regard sur l'archéologie de la Nouvelle-France, pp 221-242.

Rémillard, F., (1985), "Objets de grandes dimensions en bois gorgé d'eau, techniques européennes de traitement et de mise en valeur", unpublished manuscript, Centre de conservation du Québec, 43 p.

3.13

From Excavation to Presentation: 17 Years Work on a Roman Barge from Xanten-Wardt

Axel Peiß

LVR - Regional Museum Bonn
E-mail: axel.peiss@lvr.de

Abstract

The barge (a pram) was found in the summer of 1991 near a former Roman city on the Lower Rhine. Some 7 meters of the original 15 meters long barge survived. 17 years had passed since its discovery in a gravel-pit and its laborious salvage operation up until its spectacular presentation in a newly built museum. The planning and implementation of the chosen presentation of the pram - suspended from the ceiling – proved to be a particular challenge. This required the combination of two intrinsic opposites, namely that of a fragile, heavy, ancient object and its presentation as a floating exhibit in a modern building. The barge has now been on display in the new Roman Museum in Xanten since August 2008.

Keywords

Roman pram, block-recovery, PEG conservation, steel-foundation, suspended exhibit.

1991

On 7th July 1991 dredging work was underway on a canal section between two lakes not far from the Dutch border near Xanten, a region in which the Roman riverbed of the Rhine is to be found. An observant resident discovered part of a Roman barge one meter below the water-surface. In order to recover the barge, a dam had to be raised along the bank, which was secured with sandbags. The water-level was lowered by 2 meters using 3 pumps, which were sunk some 12 meters into the ground.

Figure 1: Excavation of the Roman barge

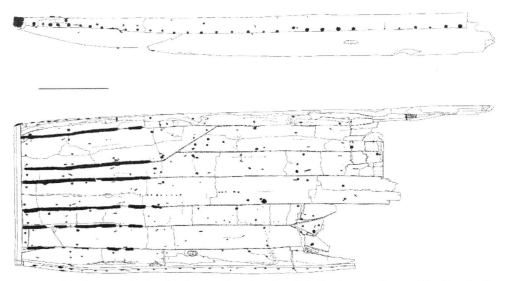

Figure 2. Drawing of the bottom planks with 2 meter long iron bands in the bow-section and the 7 meter long port side

The oak barge was originally almost 15 meters long, of which a 7 meter section survived (Figures. 1 and 2). As a section aft of the prow was completely preserved, it seems likely that the dredger had destroyed some or all of the other parts. The Zwammerdam type pram was dated to A.D. 95 ± 5. Unusually the barge lay bottom up. Once the barge was uncovered, it was clear that prolonged deposition in fluctuating groundwater-levels had caused severe structural changes. This had led to a loss of flexion and compression strength. As a result, the upturned bottom planking was strongly abraded and undulated. Plans of recovering the barge in one piece, and concurrently turning it over were therefore abandoned. Owing to the steadily rising water-table, there was not sufficient time to dismantle the barge into transportable pieces on site. It was decided to recover the barge in a large single block (Figure. 3). This was carried out by the firm Hoch-Tief, which had also salvaged the ships in Mainz.

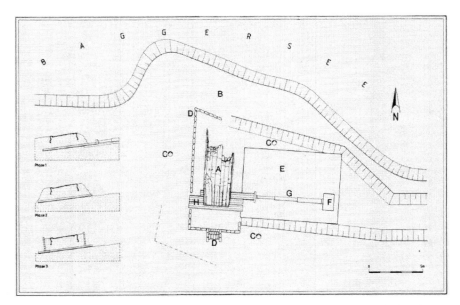

Figure 3. Salvage technique: A barge; B dam; C pumps; D sandbags; E working-area; F hydraulic unit; G telescopic hydraulic press; H pilings

In preparation, a protruding part of the side-planking was sawn off, in order to shorten the block by 2 meters. For the block-recovery, 5 m long and 60 cm wide sheet-piling was pressed through the subsoil underlying the pram using hydraulic presses. Then a steel-frame was welded over the piling and filled with sand. This block, which now weighed 40 tons, was lifted by mobile cranes onto a low-loader and transported to a workshop of the Archaeological Park in Xanten (Figure 4). There a steel container was welded and filled with water for temporary storage of the block. This first phase of work took 5 months and cost some 200,000 €.

Figure 4. Lifting of the block with two mobile cranes

1992

In the meantime, it had been decided to conserve the wood by impregnation with PEG. At that time, the LVR- Regional Museum in Bonn did not have sufficient capacity for the conservation of such a large object. Therefore, the workshop of the Schleswig Regional Museum, Schloss Gottdorf was commissioned with the conservation.

The next phase of work began in autumn 1992. The block was opened in the workshop. The deformed and fractured bottom planking was recovered first. Beforehand, the well-preserved nails had to be removed. In order to avoid damaging the wood, the hammered down nail-ends were severed using an electrical cutter. A wooden dowel was found in one of the nail holes.

After the bottom planking had been removed a unique feature was revealed, which was hitherto unknown on this type of pram. In contrast to a conventional construction of alternating knee-frames, in this barge the gaps are filled with crossbars. The crossbars were probably installed at a later time. This resulted in an even walking surface. Here three conifer planks were used. The large number of unused nail holes indicates that these crossbars were made of recycled material. The knee-frames and crossbars are provided with differently arranged grooves on the underside, which served to channel any infiltrating water to the deepest point of the vessel.

The identification of the recovered part as the prow was confirmed, when a 40 cm wide mast-step was found between the frames, which is commonly found in the anterior third of this type of barge. Here the frames are not of one piece, but a floor timber is placed respectively on both sides of the mast-step. Along the gunwale is a recess in the area of the mast-step specifically for a mast-thwart. The bottom is carvel-built and consists of 6 planks varying in width between 25 and 55 cm. Towards the prow, the joints between the planks were reinforced with iron bands ca. 2 meters in length and 4 cm wide, so that the pram could land on the river flat. The caulking, consisting of three braided strands of bulrush, was in good condition. The chine plank was made from an L-shaped piece of wood. The ship's side terminated in a rubbing strake, a 25 cm wide plank executed in clinker technique. The preserved maximum width of the barge measured 2.60 meters. It tapered towards the bow by only 30 cm. Along the full width of the forward prow block was a strong iron hem with an iron ring set in the middle. The maximum height of the barge's side measured 65 cm.

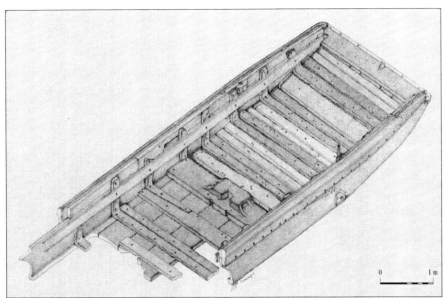

Figure 5. *Drawing of the interior*

On the interior an inwale was fixed to the knee-frames. Between the rubbing strake and the knee-frames is a gunwale, in which a completely preserved pinrail was set. On the opposite side only a broken piece survives between the frames. Owing to the degree of abrasion of the wood, pieces were often broken. Altogether some 1,000 individual wooden pieces were recovered (Figure 5). After 3 months, the pram had been completely dismantled, secured on support-frames with foamed plastic and textile tape, and placed in water tanks for temporary storage. In mid-December the packed wooden parts were taken by 2 lorries to Schleswig.

1993-1994
The conservation was carried out using a sequence of two solutions, PEG 200 followed by PEG 4000. Because of the large volume of finds, it was necessary to divide them into two batches. The first batch consisted of knee-frames, crossbars and inwales. The conservation process took 2 years.

1995
With the aid of 3 conservators from the LVR- Regional Museum Bonn, the first batch of wood was removed from the conservation tanks at the beginning of the year. Following the full impregnation treatment, the parts were cleaned and glued together in Schleswig using BISON® PU gel wood-adhesive. The work took three weeks. This was followed by their transportation to Cologne, where every five years the latest archaeological finds from the Rhineland are presented in a state-wide exhibition. The intention was to present the pram in this exhibition. The knee-frames, crossbars and the mast-step with the inwales were exhibited in a wooden mock-up of the barge's exterior.

1995-1998
The conservation of the second batch, with the larger parts, took place over a period of 3 years. Afterwards, the wood was left to rest in storage for 8 years. The second phase of work cost 80,000 €.

2000-2005
The planning for the building of a new museum in the Archaeological Park Xanten began in May 2000. The winner of the architectural competition was the Büro Gatermann + Schossig from Cologne. Upon the foundations of the basilica of the

Roman baths a structure was set which measured 70 meters by 22 meters with a height of nearly 25 meters.

The planning of the final presentation of the barge within the LVR-Archaeological Park Xanten only commenced in 2005. The architects wanted to display the barge as one of the exhibition's highlights by suspending it in the air. This hanging construction placed particular demands upon the restoration, as the fragility of the timbers, safety within the exhibition and a preferably freely floating presentation had to be taken into consideration. In order to deal with these contrasting needs, it was necessary to employ both a stress analyst and a boat-builder.

As far as safety was concerned the fire-risk of a wooden object impregnated in wax had to be looked at. A report of a materials' testing institute in Stuttgart graded the barge as normally inflammable with the classification of B2 building material. In order to achieve the desired suspended display, the stress analyst designed a metal supporting frame (Figure 6). This was meant to be seen as little as possible between the ribs and the outer planking. If the mode of presentation had

been known before the conservation, one would have chosen a partial PEG impregnation with subsequent freeze-drying, thereby reducing the weight of the object considerably and making the type and thickness of the supporting frame thinner and less obtrusive.

2006-2007
Only after the decision for the exact type of display had been made did the assembly of the timbers of the second batch and the reworking of the first begin in the new conservation workshop of the LVR-Regional Museum Bonn (Figure 7).

The pieces were assembled with the aid of wooden dowels and the Polyurethane Liquid Glue from Titebond®. Thus, the original roughly 1,000 fragments yielded some 50 constructive elements with a maximum length of 2·5 meters. For this part two conservators needed eight months work. After the fixing the breaks and the smaller missing parts were supplemented with special filler solely developed in the LVR- Regional Museum Bonn for this purpose. This filler is completely reversible, as on warming it softens and thus can be separated from the wood. The recipe is as follows:

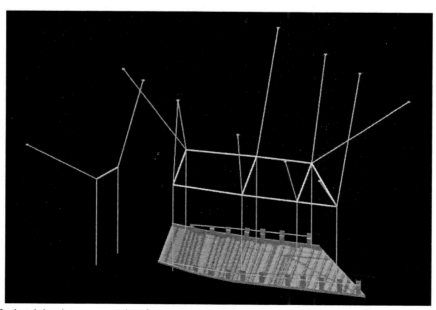

Figure 6. Draft sketch by the stress analyst for suspending and making the steel construction

Figure 7. Fixing the washboard

40% PEG 3000
12% Primal® WS24
40% quartz / silica powder
8% Sikron® SF 300 finest silica powder;
coloring with color pigments.

First the PEG is melted at 60° C, and then the Primal is added while stirring continually. Finally, the other ingredients are added slowly under continual stirring. This results in a substance of syrup-like consistency, which, if necessary, one can thicken with Aerosil. The warm compound can be worked for about 15 minutes. (see Figure 11)

October 2007

The next phase in the autumn of 2007 was to take the barge into the workshop of a boat-builder specializing in the production of wooden boats. As a platform for the individual construction pieces of the find a metal-worker made the steel structure designed by the stress analyst (Figure 8). At first a frame of rectangular steel tubing was constructed corresponding to the shape of the boat. For stability there was attached to it an 8 mm thick metal plate, onto which U-shaped brackets were welded fitting the shape of the rising knee frames. Simultaneously, individual partitions for the crutch-frames and the cross-beams were attached to the metal plate for extra reinforcement.

The only partly surviving frames and cross-beams of the barge's stern section were supplemented with new timbers. As in the times of Roman ship-building, for the crutch-frames oaks were sought in the woods whose crotches displayed a right-angle. On the lateral superstructures of the construction a solid L section was fastened, to which the chines were attached to the exterior using steel bands (Figure 9 and 10).

Figure 8. Completed steel construction at the boat-builder's

Figure 9 and 10. Fitted steel band to support the vessel's side

For protection all timbers were shimmed with a strip of PE foam. Every 60 cm a steel band was fastened for support, on the one hand as the result of the heavy weight which had to be evenly distributed, on the other hand because of the degree of decay of the timbers.

As a result of the intensive deformation of one of the chines of over 20 cm, the front one with a length of some 1.9 meters was replaced by a replica. In the case of the bottom planks it was also decided to replace them with reproduced timbers. These bottom planks were so heavily decayed that warming and reshaping them was impossible. In order to fit new bottom planks into the construction, this had to be carefully turned over using a trestle crane.

Following historical tradition the curvature of the new board-planks towards the bow

333

was achieved through bending them in hot steam. The new timbers were screwed to the steel construction with 150 carriage bolts. To obtain an optically ancient look, the round heads of the carriage bolts were heated in a forge and reworked by hand. In the case of the original timbers over 100 new, hand forged nails were set into the nail-holes with filler.

Subsequently, in the joint area of the bottom planks four steel bands with nail-heads welded on replaced the iron bands in the length and width which had badly survived in the original. Owing to the integrated steel construction the size of the barge has increased. The bottom is 4 cm thicker, to the stern it is 20 cm wider. The new bottom planks have, therefore, been adapted in size to the larger barge. The vessel's side is up to 5 cm higher than in the original find. Since the slightly deformed chine does not lay absolutely plane on the steel construction, the first five crutch-ribs protrude beyond the vessel's side.

Finally, the newly reproduced timbers were given a dark brown staining and the steel construction an anthracite-colored protected coating.

2008

At the beginning of 2008 the barge was brought into the new LVR-Roman Museum Xanten as its first archaeological object (Figure 11 and 12). The conserved timbers were mounted onto the metal construction together with the reconstructed timbers and the final cracks luted. Finally, the surviving iron hem was attached. To prevent possible falling of small debris, the original timbers were secured with a thin mesh of stainless steel. The whole construction weighs 3·1 tons, of which 1·4 tons are the original timbers, 500 kg the reproduced timbers and 1·2 tons the steel construction.

For the exhibition the object was carefully raised 10 meters by hand using chain hoists and fastened to seven steel rods (Figure 13). In the new LVR-Roman Museum Xanten the visitors have been able to see the suspended barge since 16.08.2008 (Figure 14 and 15).

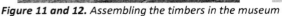

Figure 11 and 12. Assembling the timbers in the museum

Figure 13. *Raising the barge with four chain hoists*   **Figure 14**. *Exhibit since August 2008*

Figure 15. *Exhibit since August 2008*

The museum contains no separate floors. The exhibition also rises upon a series of ramps and platforms in the airy space. Thus, the barge can be seen from various perspectives.

The third phase of work cost € 400,000; thus the whole cost was some € 680,000. Retrospectively, the successful result has justified the high financial cost and the commitment of personnel. At the beginning there were some who doubted this type of presentation. Only through working with specialists from different areas of expertise could this task be fulfilled. It will be some time before the next flying barge from antiquity will appear.

References

Harald Berkel /Julia Obladen-Kauder (1992) Das römerzeitliche Schiff von Xanten-Wardt. (Ed. Harald Koschik) Archäologie im Rheinland1991. Köln Rheinland-Verlag GmbH 1992 pp74-77

Harald Berkel /Julia Obladen-Kauder (1993) Das Schiff von Xanten Wardt zwischen Bergung und Konservierung. (Ed. Harald Koschik) Archäologie im Rheinland1992. Köln Rheinland-Verlag GmbH 1993 pp56-58.

Julia Obladen-Kauder (1995) Das römerzeitliche Plattbodenschiff von Xanten-Wardt. (Ed. Heinz Günter Horn, Hansgerd Hellenkemper, Harald Koschik, Bendix Trier) Schriften zur Bodendenkmalpflege in Nordrhein-Westfalen Band 3 Mainz Philipp von Zabern 1995 pp220-222

Julia Obladen-Kauder (2008) Spuren römischer Lastschifffahrt am Unteren Niederrhein. (Ed. Martin Müller, Hans-Joachim Schalles, Norbert Zieling) Colonia Ulpia Traiana Xanten und sein Umland in römischer Zeit. Mainz Philipp von Zabern 2008 pp507-523

Julia Obladen-Kauder (2009) Der Weg des Prahms aus Xanten-Wardt ins LVR-RömerMuseum. (Ed. Jürgen Kunow) Archäologie im Rheinland 2008. Stuttgart Konrad Theiss Verlag GmbH 2009 pp185-187

Axel Peiß (2008) Ein Schiff Lernt Fliegen. (Ed. Franz Hülsbusch) Junge Leute im Museum 2/2008. Troisdorf Rautenberg Media und Print Verlag KG 2008 pp16-19

Axel Peiß (2010) Restaurierung und Präsentation des Römischen Prahms im LVR-RömerMuseum Xanten. +45 Jahre Nassholzkonservierung am LVR-LandesMuseum Bonn. (Ed. Tomas Otten, Hansgerd Hellenkemper, Jürgen Kunow, Christoph Grünewald) Schriften zur Bodendenkmalpflege in Nordrhein-Westfalen Band 10. Mainz Verlag Philipp von Zabern 2010 pp356-361

Translation:
Jennifer Gechter-Jones, Overath
Clive Bridger-Kraus, Xanten

Questions and answers

Kristiane Straetkvern: How do you plan to maintain the Xanten barge?

Axel Peiss: Yes (chuckling). I talked to the museum and the Director says this ship must hang there for 40 years maybe….

Kristiane Straetkvern:- But what about dust etc…

Axel Peiss: There was a plan to make a long arm to pick up bubblegum papers. When the architect designed the museum, I said to him: "It's not a good idea to hang the ship because it's so difficult and there are so many problems" and the Director of the museum at that time said "It's not a problem. It's a good idea. We must win a prize for this beautiful museum." And she got the prize. Another benefit is for the politicians…a lot of people come there. Last year 700,000 people came to the museum and that's the only two big things that archaeologists and politicians want—prizes and attendance!

Quo Vadis- Do We Need Swimming Pools for Wood Conservation?

Nicole Ebinger-Rist
Regierungspräsidium Stuttgart, Landesamt für Denkmalpflege, Referat 84/ Archäologische Restaurierung, Berlinerstr. 12, 73728 Esslingen am Neckar, Germany
E-mail: Nicole.ebinger-rist@rps.bwl.de

Ingrid Wiesner
Wet Organic Materials
Regierungspräsidium Stuttgart, Landesamt für Denkmalpflege, Referat 84 / Archäologische Restaurierung, Berlinerstr. 12, 73728 Esslingen am Neckar, Germany
E-mail: Ingrid.wiesner@rps.bwl.de

Although the number of findings of enormous pieces of wood in Baden-Württemberg is minimal compared with those of northern Germany and the Scandinavian countries, enough objects have been accumulated that it is indisputable that a new solution for storage and preservation is needed. Some of the objects at hand are remnants of ships and buildings found as a result of building and road construction, yearlong peat soil harvesting, agriculture, as well as lakeshore erosion.

To make matters worse, sufficient strategies for preserving these immense wooden-made objects haven't been developed over the last twenty years in Baden-Württemberg. On the one hand, from the archaeological point of view, there is the problem of the selection as to which pieces should be preserved. On the other hand, from the conservative point of view, there is the problem of the handling and caring for the objects as well as the logistical problem of where to store the objects. The findings are presently spread around Baden-Württemberg and the goal is to bring all the findings to one central storage facility. Currently the objects are conserved by impregnating them in vats using PEG 3350 solution. However, due to aesthetics and the element of time, the results of this method are unsatisfactory. The weight of the objects is colossal when using this method of impregnation. The object's weight can reach up to one ton, therefore, making it impractical for exhibition and storage purposes.

This is the reason that so many pieces have now accumulated in the laboratories; enough to nearly fill an entire swimming pool. Again, they aren't just the problems of aesthetics, logistics and methods of conversation, but the need to work on ways to more efficiently preserve these objects as well as categorizing the importance of them is long overdue.

However, when talking about objects of a smaller scale, current standards are used with regard to their preservation. The method of impregnation into the PEG solution is used in combination with the freeze-drying method. The greatest challenge for the Department of Archaeological Conservation and Restoration is finding and implementing working strategies and solutions for the aforementioned problems. The goal is to apply the solutions already implemented for smaller objects to those when working with enormous waterlogged artifacts. Therefore, a well-directed organization on conservation research is needed.

Finally, another challenge is dealing with the balance of daily work and research. It is necessary to implement new research projects in order to receive a funded program for targeted conservation research in order to optimize the conservationist's time and methods. In addition, the institution, "Landesamt für Denkmalpflege" should provide the necessary facilities as well as the equipment such as larger freeze-dryers, appropriate sized vats and laboratories.

Figure 1. Construction of gas lines running several hundred kilometers through Baden-Wurtemberg. Photo: LAD-Esslingen

Figure 2.More and more shipwrecks are being discovered at Lake Constance due to erosion. Photo: LAD Esslingen.

338

3B

Making Sucrose Work: Treating the Medieval Bridge Timbers from Hemington, Leicestershire.

Grace Deeks
Conservation Manager, Leicestershire
County Council, The Sherrier Centre
Church St., Lutterworth, Leicestershire
LE17 4AL

Jim Spriggs*,
Conservation Consultant, 20 Portland St,
York YO31 7EH
*E-mail: spriggs.conserve@hotmail.co.uk

Abstract

This poster reviews the progress to date of the conservation of a collection large waterlogged oak timbers with sucrose. The difficulties of keeping the treatment solutions sterile have resulted in a large proportion of the impregnant in the wood being the degradation products of sucrose. The implications of this are considered in relation to the future stability of the wood to environmental fluctuations.

The project

A team from Leicestershire Museums is just completing the final stage of the conservation of one of Britain's largest archaeological finds of wood, which relate to a bridge that crossed the River Trent at Hemington Fields, near Castle Donington, Leicestershire, UK. The find includes the trestle frames, pile posts and caisson timbers of subsequent bridges dating to the late 11thC/early 12th C, many timbers displaying unusual and elaborate jointing techniques (Ripper & Cooper 2001) [Figure 1]. Discovered during quarrying in 1993, the structures were excavated, recorded and lifted by Leicestershire Archaeological Unit and the 50 or so timbers, some of considerable size and weight, were taken to a Leicestershire Museums Facility for storage and conservation. Roly Reed, then conservator at Leicester Museums, made the decision to stabilise the wood in

sucrose, to be supplied by British Sugar. It was anticipated that this would be a cheap, simple and effective treatment that would take 3 to 5 years to complete. So, in 1996, the oak timbers, some measuring up to 7 metres and weighing up to 900 kg, were immersed in a 67% sucrose solution in three flexible tanks, provided by English Heritage.

Figure 1. 11thC bridge timbers in-situ, 1993

Museum reorganization in 2001 necessitated moving the timbers across the county to Leicestershire Council's Snibston Discovery Park, Coalville, Leics, causing extra effort and expense. The three tanks were relocated in an old colliery building and another 15 tons of concentrated sucrose solution added, again provided courtesy of British Sugar. Despite good care being taken of the process by Leicestershire's Conservation Manager Grace Deeks, the building was in a poor state of repair, fungal infection of the solutions had taken a firm hold, and the area had become infested with wasps.

Over the next 7 years there were many attempts to progress this project all of which came to nothing, and by early 2008 it was clear that urgent action was needed. Grace Deeks, Conservation Manager for Leicestershire, brought in Jim Spriggs as project consultant to assist her in completing the project. Jim had previously assisted with the completion of the Poole Museum Logboat project which had also been treated with sucrose (Hutchings & Spriggs 2008). A plan was agreed and funding put in place for the project to be completed in four stages:

Stage 1: Sample analyses by British Sugar using high performance liquid chromatography (HPLC) showed that the sucrose solutions were badly infected with micro-organisms and had inverted to glucose and fructose [Diagram 1.]. The solutions smelt alcoholic and vinegary and were also very acidic (down to pH 3.7). The presence of glucose and fructose, plus a low pH, were all tending to promote further microbial activity and hydrolysis of the sucrose. The timbers were tightly packed in the tanks giving too small a ratio of solution to timbers, making circulation and exchange difficult [Figure.2]. A final

change of sucrose solution was made in October 2008 and the tank solutions buffered with sodium hydroxide to pH7.

Figure2. Leics Museums and British Sugar staff by one of the sucrose treatment tanks

Figure 3. Interior of drying chamber, showing bank of heating fans, and dehumidifier at center.

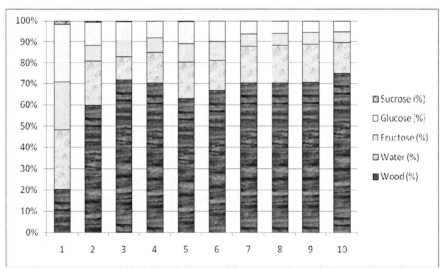

Diagram1. Core sample analysis by HPLC of timber T953 before drying, showing large proportions of sucrose inverts

Meanwhile, an insulated 40ft long sea container had been acquired second-hand and sited close by. It was provided with power, and fitted out as a drying chamber using equipment donated by Poole Museum on completion of their logboat project. The container was fitted with an internal insulated baffle between the external doors and the timbers, to allow inspection via a window, and adjusting of the humidistat and temperature controls without disturbing the environment within. [Figure.3]

Figure 4. Steam hosing timbers to remove excess sucrose

Stage 2: The last week in February 2009 was dry and fine, but the previous cold spell had caused the solutions to solidify into thick white slurry. Space heaters were brought in to blow hot air over the tanks, until some of the solution was liquid enough to pump. A waste disposal firm was engaged to pump out the solutions and a mechanical handling company to undertake the lifting and moving. But much of the slurry, by now a thick paste, remained, which made the job of removing the timbers very messy and difficult. On removal from their tanks, the timbers were taken to an outdoor holding area close by for surface-cleaned with a steam power-hose to remove excess sucrose slurry and insect debris [Figure 4.] Health and safety and personal protection was a major issue!

Once cleaned, labeling was checked by Leicestershire Museums' Curator of Archaeology, Richard Pollard, and the surface painted with a fresh solution of sucrose solution to replenish the wood surfaces. A selection of the timbers were weighed, using electronic transducer weigh-beams, and pairs of brass pins set across the main axes to allow measurements to be made to assess shrinkage during drying.

Stage 3: The timbers were stacked in the drying chamber, heaviest on the bottom, lightest at the top, with spaces between for air circulation [Figure 5]. Drying followed the theoretical regime suggested for the Poole logboat (Hutchings & Spriggs 2004) and has continued since April 2009, with a calculated end-point in summer 2010. Keeping the air temperature at 30°C, the humidity has been reduced in gradual steps from 75%RH to 50%RH. Over 380 liters of water have been extracted to date, and the sample wood pieces have lost 10% (av.) of their weight, whilst dimensional change has been minimal. The wood surfaces are a pleasant, natural color once dry, but some surface detail has been lost.

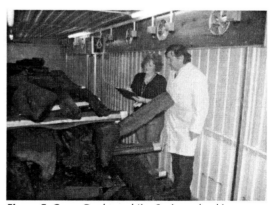

Figure 5. Grace Deeks and Jim Spriggs checking on timbers stacked in drying chamber

Stage 4: When drying is considered to be complete, the drying equipment will be modified to allow it to be used to maintain a suggested even environment within the container of 50%RH ±5%RH at 20°C ±3°C. The future of this important collection of

341

timbers has not been decided, but meantime, it will remain safe within the modified sea container until the next decisions are made.

Discussion

Wood stabilized with pure sucrose will, once dried to equilibrium moisture content (i.e. normal museum conditions), be stable across a broad range of humidities. It will absorb only 5.5% of its weight of water at 81%RH and will not deliquesce until the conditions have reached almost 90%RH. Glucose is more reactive to changes in RH and at 60%RH will have absorbed up to 9% weight of its in water but will only start to deliquesce at 98.8 %RH. Fructose is more hydrophilic still, and will absorb up to 22% of its weight in water in an environment of 63%RH at which point it will also deliquesce (Solokowski 1937). The presence of glucose and fructose in treated wood thus offers much reduced dimensional stability in a changing environment compared with pure sucrose, with the added possibility of wood surfaces becoming sticky and the sugars, especially fructose, oozing out. This could occur in conditions as low as 60%RH.

Conclusions

- Sucrose treatments must be closely monitored and frequent checks made for solution infections and lowering of pH
- Glucose and fructose (produced by sucrose degradation) provide wood with much poorer environmental protection than sucrose for wood in storage and on display.
- Sucrose treatments give the best results if coupled with a controlled air-drying stage
- Any treatment for wood must be carefully designed, adequately resourced and properly supervised. Appropriate accommodation should be provided, heated if necessary.

- This treatment went wrong and was only partially salvaged with considerable effort and expense. It might have been better to have sent the wood to a specialist laboratory for treatment.

References

Hutchings J & Spriggs JA (2004) 'The Poole Logboat: A Treatment update, and Investigation into a Suitable Drying Regime for Large-scale Sucrose Impregnated Waterlogged Wood' in (eds) Hoffmann P, Strætkvern K, Spriggs JA, Gregory D, Proceedings of the 9th[th] ICOM Group on Wet Organic Archaeological Materials Conference, Copenhagen (Bremerhaven)

Hutchings J & Spriggs JA (2008) 'Conservation of the Poole Logboat, part 3: Slow drying and display' in Straetkvern K, Spriggs JA, Gregory D, Grant T (eds) Proceedings of the 10th[th] ICOM Group on Wet Organic Archaeological Materials Conference, Amsterdam. (Amsterdam)

Ripper S and Cooper LP (2010) 'The Hemington Bridges: The excavation of three medieval bridges at Hemington Quarry, near Castle Donington', Leics. Leicester Archaeology Monograph No. 16 (Univ of Leics)

Solokovsky,A (1937) Ind.Eng.Chem., 29, 1422-3.

3C (Sc PR)

The Ability of Waterlogged Wood to Resist Freezing

Hanne Billeschou Juhl*
Bevaringscenter Nordjylland, Storemosevej 8, DK- 9310 Vodskov.
*E-mail: hbj@bcnord.dk

Knud Botfeldt
The Royal Danish Academy of Fine Arts, School of Conservation, Esplanaden 34, DK- 1263 København.

Lars Brock Andersen
Museernes Bevaringscenter i Skive, Strandvejen 15, DK- 7800 Skive.

Abstract

This paper focuses on freezing of unimpregnated waterlogged wood. A series of experiments was carried out, in which samples of highly degraded and well-preserved waterlogged wood were frozen, to examine the ability of waterlogged wood to withstand the effect of freezing in relation to state of degradation and temperature. The expansion of waterlogged wood in various states of degradation during the freezing process was also investigated. Water expands approx. 9 % when it crystallizes to ice. This expansion in itself is not considered crucial for the frost resistance of waterlogged wood. Theory tells us that mechanical damage is to be found in other thermodynamic mechanisms such as microscopic lens growth. The experiments show that the ability of waterlogged wood to withstand damage depends on various factors such as freezing temperature, state of degradation and freezing method. Finally it is discussed how the results can be used to give a better understanding of PEG impregnation.

Keywords: Freezing of waterlogged wood, microscopic ice lens growth, pore size distribution, expansion, PEG impregnation, freeze drying.

Introduction

How does freezing affect waterlogged wood? Among conservators it has been discussed what happens when unimpregnated waterlogged wood are frozen (Ambrose 1970, Caarlee 2002, Florian 1990, Grattan & Clarke 1987, Heinonen 2005, Jensen el al. 2001, Oddy 1975). If unimpregnated waterlogged wood cannot be frozen without damaging the wood structure, freeze lifting as a field recovery method for waterlogged wood could be hazardous. To investigate this a series of experiments was carried out, in which samples of highly degraded and well-preserved waterlogged wood were frozen, to examine the ability of waterlogged wood to withstand the effect of freezing in relation to state of degradation and temperature. The expansion of waterlogged wood during freezing was also investigated.

Theory

The thermodynamics of crystallization of water in porous materials is closely related to the vapor pressure of water in the structure. Two factors affect the vapor pressure: Adsorption of water to hydrophilic materials and water trapped in microscopic pores in the structure. Adsorbed water and capillary-trapped water both hamper the freezing process, as the tendency of both the adsorbed and the capillary-trapped water to move into crystals will be impeded. Very little work has been done on the freezing behavior of water in wood structures and therefore parallels must be sought for in other material groups.

Economically the freezing behavior of concrete and soil structures is important and therefore research has been carried out into these materials (Soroka 1979). As the effect of the porous structure has proved to be a primary factor for the freezing behavior in concrete and soil, this will be the focus of the present work.

Unlike in concrete and soil structures the effect of capillary trapped water probably plays a minor role in waterlogged wood compared to the effect of the adsorbed water. As the effect on the crystallization process will be quite similar for both, the overall conclusion of this work should however not be affected.

Free water without impurities freezes at 0 °C and when the water transforms to ice, it expands approx. 9 %. This process releases huge forces, that are able to break even very strong materials such as metal and stone. This expansion causes problems when the water is enclosed without room for expansion. Water present in porous materials, such as concrete and soil structures, will be able to expand, and the expansion forces are therefore of less importance for the amount of damage to the structure (Muldrew 2004). Experiments on concrete have shown that there is no connection between the degree of expansion and the damage to materials. The reason for the mechanical damage is to be found, in other thermodynamic mechanisms such as microscopic ice lens growth (Hansen 1996).

Pore distribution
The pore diameter of porous materials determines at what temperature the water in the pore will crystallize. As in other porous materials, the pores in waterlogged wood are of different size, which mean that the water in the structure will freeze at different temperatures. The reason for this is that the mobility of the molecules is limited because of the size of the pore space. The limited mobility inhibits the crystallization process (Soroka 1979). As an example the water in a pore of 30 nm in diameter, will freeze at -2 °C, and a pore with a diameter of 1 nm will freeze at -80 °C (Grattan & Clarke, 1987).

As the pore distribution in a porous material is crucial for the amount of freezeable water in the material at a given temperature, it is important to study the pore size distribution in waterlogged wood, to determine the amount of frozen water at a given temperature. Grattan & Clarke (1987) describes that water in the cell wall in

waterlogged wood is held in micro capillaries below 10 nm in diameter. The total pore distribution in waterlogged wood has not yet been studied, but if we look at the pore distribution for a standard concrete, only half of the water in the structure freezes at -10 °C (Hansen 1996) (see Figure 1).

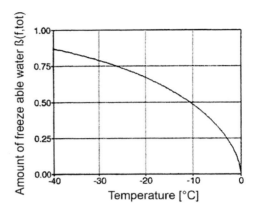

Figure 1. *Exemplified representation of the amount of freeze able water in concrete, according to the total pore size distribution as a function of the temperature (Hansen 1996).*

Microscopic ice lens growth
Microscopic ice lens growth is a freezing mechanism which is used to explain the behavior of porous materials such as concrete and soil during freezing. The theory behind microscopic ice lens growth is based on the fact that the ice crystals at a given temperature have a lower water vapor pressure than non-crystalline water in the smaller pores. Due to the difference in energy/water vapor pressure, water diffuses from the smaller pores to the bigger pores, where it freezes and causes ice lens growth. This is the reason why the structure and the pore size distribution are of importance for the amount of freeze able water (see Figure 2).

The ice lens growth is a slow diffusion process and will continue until equilibrium between ice and water has been reached. Because water diffuses from smaller to bigger pores, the small pores dehydrate and a contraction of the pores is observed. The amount of frozen water in the cell cavity will therefore increase with decreasing temperatures (Soroka 1979).

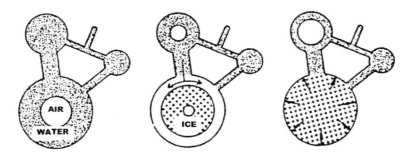

Figure 2. A principle sketch of tree stages during the freezing process in concrete, according to the microscopic ice lens growth theory. Due to the difference in energy/water vapor pressure, water defuses from smaller pores to bigger pores, where it freezes and causes ice lens growth. Because water diffuses from the smaller pores to the bigger pores, the small pores dehydrate and a contraction of the pores is seen. The arrows illustrate pressure (after Hansen 1996).

Method and equipment

In the experiments archaeological waterlogged wood dated to approx. 500 AD was used. Samples of highly degraded wood, represented by homogeneous degraded birch wood (*Betula sp.*) and samples of oak wood (*Quercus sp.*) with well-preserved heartwood and highly degraded sapwood, were used. The samples were cut from posts with a diameter between 15 and 23 cm into pieces with a thickness of 3 cm. Six samples were used for each experiment. Due to suspected variations caused by insects, secondary cracks and variations in degradation, the samples were cut from different areas of the post.

The density (g/cm³) based on the dry weight and water saturated volume of the waterlogged wood, was measured to be 0.50 g/cm³ for the well-preserved heart wood of oak, equal to a maximum water content (Umax) of 156 %. The density of the degraded birch wood was measured to be 0.12 g/cm³, equal to Umax value 729 %.

Prior to the freezing process the samples were evacuated in a vacuum chamber to remove any trapped air in the structure. The samples were frozen in thermo boxes to ensure a slow and homogenous freezing process. The samples were frozen for three days and to ensure that they were frozen, the freezing process was monitored by

thermocouple sensors, Type K (chromel/alumel), inserted in a reference sample of oak wood. Tap water was used for samples frozen immersed in water. After the freezing process the samples were thawed immersed in cold water to eliminate water evaporation during thawing. The samples have been documented by digital photo before freezing, during freezing and after thawing.

Experimental
Experiments on the ability of waterlogged wood to resist freezing.

To examine the ability of waterlogged wood to withstand the effect of freezing in relation to degree of degradation and temperature, a series of experiments was carried out, in which the sample material was frozen either at -10 °C or -40 °C, respectively immersed in water and not immersed in water. The method of freezing the samples immersed in water was employed in an attempt to determine whether the method by which the wood is frozen has an impact on the ability of the wood to withstand the effect of freezing. The samples were exposed to up to five freeze/thaw cycles to enhance the possible effect of the freezing process

A visual evaluation of the samples after freezing was based upon damage to the structure. The samples were divided into four categories in relation to the macroscopic damage which had occurred after freezing:

- Category **A**: No cracks have occurred.
- Category **B**: Single or few small cracks < 1 mm wide. The cracks are visually insignificant.
- Category **C**: One - two single big cracks > 2 mm wide and/or many tiny cracks. The cracks are visually disruptive and therefore unacceptable.
- Category **D**: More than two big cracks > 2 mm wide. The cracks are visually disruptive and therefore unacceptable.

Damage in category A and B was categorized as visually acceptable and damage in category C and D was categorized as visually unacceptable due to the size and number of cracks. Both sides of the samples were evaluated. The categories are shown in Figure 3.

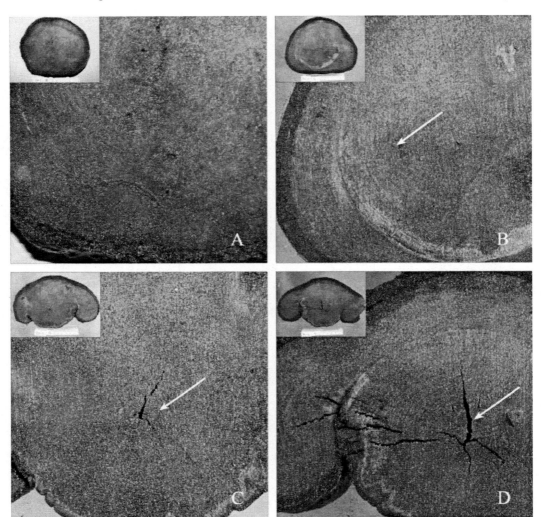

Figure 3*. Examples of the four damage categories based on visual observation of macroscopic damage. Examples shown are samples of birch wood.*

This categorization only deals with the macroscopic damage to the wood, which shows up as cracks. Apart from the macroscopic damage some of the samples became spongy after freezing, probably due to damage to cell walls in the structure by crystallization. A note on this microscopic damage is therefore included in the overall assessment of the samples

Expansion of the waterlogged wood during freezing

To determine the expansion of the wood during freezing, measurements were taken at fixed measuring points before, during and after freezing with an electronic caliper. The expansion measurements were only conducted on samples frozen at -40 °C, immersed in water. The samples were placed in shallow water in aluminum trays. Measuring points were marked with pins inserted into the wood. Measurements were taken in a centre area of the wood as shown in Figure 4. In samples of oak wood the well-preserved heartwood was measured.

The measurements express the linear expansion of the wood. Based on the suggestion that the expansion will be equal in all directions, the linear expansions are cubed to calculate the volumetric expansion. These calculations are therefore estimates, in which the volumetric expansion of ice serves as a base for comparing the expansion of the tested wood sample. Volumetric expansion is marked %′. The value is calculated as follows:

$$\left(\frac{Dimensions \ after \ freezing}{Dimensions \ before \ freezing} \right)^3 \times 100 - 100 = \% \ Volumetric \ expansion$$

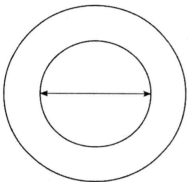

Figure 4. Position of measuring point. Measurements were taken in the centre area of the wood. In samples of oak wood the well-preserved heartwood was measured.

Results
Experiments on the ability of waterlogged wood to resist freezing
Samples frozen at -40 °C, not immersed in water
As seen from Table 1, samples of birch wood and oak wood are affected differently by freezing at -40 °C, as samples of oak wood are less affected. Microscopic damage in sapwood occurs.

Samples frozen at -10 °C, not immersed in water
To examine whether the temperature has any influence on the ability of waterlogged wood to resist the effects of freezing, samples of birch wood were frozen at -10 °C. In only one sample minor acceptable damage occurred. Microscopic damage in sapwood occurs (see Table 2).

Samples frozen at -40 °C, immersed in water
A different result was found when freezing samples immersed in water (see Table 3). Samples frozen at -40 °C immersed in water were almost unaffected by freezing, as there were only minor almost invisible cracks in the structure. These cracks were present in the wood before freezing and only expanded slightly during the freezing process. Microscopic damage in sapwood occurs.

Samples frozen at -10 °C, immersed in water
To determine whether the microscopic damage can be avoided, if the wood is frozen at higher temperature and in water, samples of birch wood were frozen at -10 °C, immersed in water. All samples were unaffected by freezing. Neither

macroscopic nor microscopic damage occurred (see Table 4).

Expansion of waterlogged wood
In Table 5 below, the results for the average volumetric expansion in %′ of birch wood and oak wood samples are shown. Figure 5 shows the expansion for each test sample of oak wood and birch wood.

Table 1. *Macroscopic and microscopic assessment of samples frozen at -40 °C, not immersed in water. In all samples of birch wood cracks appear and four out of six samples have unacceptable damage. In two out of six samples of oak wood, cracks were seen; all were categorized as acceptable damage. All samples of birch wood and oak wood appeared spongier after freezing due to microscopic damage of the cell structure.*

Macroscopic assessment					Microscopic assessment
	Acceptable damage		Unacceptable damage		
Category	A	B	C	D	
Birch wood	0	2	2	2	Microscopic damage
Oak wood	4	2	0	0	Microscopic damage in sapwood

Table 2. *Macroscopic and microscopic assessment of samples frozen at -10 °C, not immersed in water. In only one out of six samples cracks appeared after freezing, in which all were categorized as acceptable damage. All samples appeared spongier after freezing due to microscopic damage of the cell structure.*

Macroscopic assessment					Microscopic assessment
	Acceptable damage		Unacceptable damage		
Category	A	B	C	D	
Birch wood	5	1	0	0	Microscopic damage

Table 3. *Macroscopic and microscopic assessment of samples frozen immersed in water at -40 °C. In three out of six samples of both oak wood and birch wood cracks appeared after freezing, all of which were categorized as acceptable macroscopic damage. All samples of birch wood and the degraded sapwood of oak appeared spongier after freezing due to microscopic damage in the cell structure.*

Macroscopic assessment					Microscopic assessment
	Acceptable damage		Unacceptable damage		
Category	A	B	C	D	
Birch wood	3	3	0	0	Microscopic damage
Oak wood	3	3	0	0	Microscopic damage in sapwood

Table 4. *Macroscopic and microscopic assessment of samples frozen immersed in water at -10 °C. All samples were unaffected by freezing. Neither macroscopic nor microscopic damage occurred.*

Macroscopic assessment					Microscopic assessment
	Acceptable damage		Unacceptable damage		
Category	A	B	C	D	
Birch wood	6	0	0	0	No microscopic damage

Table 5. *Average volumetric expansion in %′, of birch wood and oak wood samples. The centre part of birch wood expands considerably more than the heartwood of oak. The expansion is not permanent. The samples almost regained their original size after thawing.*

	Volumetric expansion %′	
Phase	Frozen samples	Thawed samples
Oak wood	2.4	0.6
Birch wood	8.2	1.6

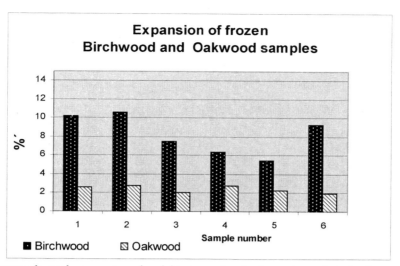

Figure 5. The diagram shows the expansion of each birch wood and oak wood sample in the frozen state.

Discussion

The experiments described in this article originate from a project on freeze-lifting (Juhl 2009). The freezing temperatures were -10 °C and - 40 °C because this would be a realistic span in temperatures for freeze-lifting.

Oak wood is a natural choice for test materials since it is so common in Danish archaeological finds, often with the heartwood very well-preserved, and with the sapwood poorly preserved. The birch wood was chosen because it has no heartwood and there was enough heavily degraded material available. The well-preserved oak wood with degraded sapwood together with the heavily degraded birch wood were considered suitable for showing the consequences of freezing waterlogged wood.

Samples frozen at - 40 °C, not immersed in water

As can be seen from Table 1, samples of birch wood and oak wood are affected differently by freezing at -40 °C, where samples of oak wood are less affected. There is major macroscopic damage on samples of birch wood, in which more than half of the samples have large unacceptable cracks. It is characteristic of the damage that cracks mainly occur in the centre area of the samples and that they occur in areas were the surface seems to be dry and ice free (see Figure 7). After thawing the cracks minimized a bit. Samples of birch wood were slightly deformed in the frozen state, but this disappeared after thawing.

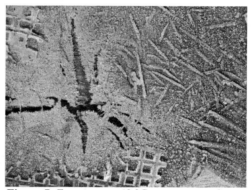

Figure 7. Freezing at -40 °C, not immersed in water, Birch wood sample in frozen state. Notice the cracks in the dry and ice free area in the center.

Figure 8. Freezing at -40 °C, not immersed in water. Oak wood sample after freezing. A single crack has occurred in the sapwood area.

349

Samples of oak wood seem to be almost unaffected by freezing. The samples had only minor cracks in the sapwood (see Figure 8). The cracks also appeared between sapwood and heartwood, which might be a result of tension between two degradation zones.

After freezing, the texture of birch wood and the sapwood of the oak wood appeared spongier due to microscopic damage in the structure. The heartwood of oak wood seems to be unaffected by the freezing.

Samples frozen at -10 °C, not immersed in water

To examine whether the temperature has any influence on the ability of waterlogged wood to resist the effects of freezing, samples were frozen at -10 °C. In the experiment where samples were frozen at -40 °C major cracks occurred mainly in birch wood samples. For this reason experiments at -10 °C were only conducted on birch wood and not on oak wood. The experiments show that the temperatures, at which the wood is frozen, influence the extent of damage. Contrary to samples frozen at -40 °C only a single sample had a minor crack in the centre after the first freezing process and this did not develop further during the subsequent freezing (see Table 2). After the first freezing process the wood got a spongy texture due to the resulting microscopic damage in the structure.

Samples frozen at -40 °C, immersed in water

A different result was observed when freezing samples immersed in water (see Table 3). All samples were almost unaffected by freezing, as there were only minor almost invisible cracks in the structure. These minor cracks were present in the wood before freezing and the freezing process only expanded them slightly. However, these cracks have a very minor impact on the visual impression of the wood; because of their minimal size (see Figure 9). In a single sample of oak wood, a small crack developed in the

sapwood. The heartwood was unaffected by freezing. Again the highly degraded parts developed a spongy texture after freezing, due to microscopic damage of the cells in the structure.

Samples frozen at -10 °C, immersed in water

To determine whether the microscopic damage can be avoided if the wood is frozen at higher temperatures, samples of birch wood were frozen at -10 °C. Even after five freeze / thaw cycles the samples were unaffected by freezing and there were no visual effects to be seen on the samples. Furthermore, there were no changes in the texture after freezing, suggesting that no major damage to the cell in the microscopic structure had occurred (see Figure 10).

Unlike the experiment in which samples were frozen in water at -40 °C, the natural cracks did not expand. The results are shown in Table 4.

Expansion of waterlogged wood

According to the experiments conducted, the highly degraded birch wood expands considerably more than well-preserved oak wood. 8.2%´ versus 2.4%´. The expansions are not permanent for either birch wood or oak wood samples. After thawing the samples have almost regained their original size, however a trend towards a minimal permanent expansion is seen (see Table 5). Figure 5 shows the expansion for each test sample of oak wood and birch wood. The calculations of the volumetric expansion in %´ are estimated because it was assumed that the expansion is the same in all directions. The measured values do not necessarily reflect the actual physical values, but serve as basis for comparing the tested wood samples. The spongy appearance due to microscopic damage in the structure for all the degraded samples, except those frozen at -10 °C in water, is without doubt caused by damage to the cell wall. However, it is not the aim of this article to explain this phenomenon.

Figure 9. Freezing at -40 °C, immersed in water. Birch wood sample before freezing (Left). The sample had a nearly invisible crack in the centre before freezing. Same birch wood sample after freezing (Right). After five freeze / thaw cycles, the crack, which was present in the centre before freezing, developed slightly.

Figure. 10. Freezing at -10 °C in water. The picture shows a detail of thawed birch wood; before freezing (top) and after five freeze/thaw cycles (bottom).

Conclusion

The experiments preformed have shown that the ability of waterlogged wood to resist freezing depends on various factors such as decomposition degree, temperature, the number of freeze/thaw cycles and finally on which freezing method is used:, i.e. immersed or not immersed in water.

Even at very low temperatures (-40 °C), damage does not occur in well-preserved waterlogged wood, while highly degraded waterlogged wood is highly affected at this temperature. The extent of damage to the degraded wood increases with decreasing temperature. It has been shown that macroscopic damage occurs if highly degraded wood is frozen at -40 °C but only microscopic damage occurs if the same wood is frozen at -10 °C. The experiments also show that the extent of damage which occurs increases with the number of freeze/thaw cycles. In the experiments cracks was seen in subsequent freezing.

The method by which the wood is frozen is significant for the extent of damage. The experiments have shown that waterlogged wood can withstand the effect of freezing without macroscopic or microscopic damage occurring, if the wood is frozen immersed in water at -10 °C. In contrast microscopic damage occurs if the waterlogged wood is frozen at -40 °C, immersed in water. Table 6 summarizes the results.

Table 6. The ability of waterlogged wood to withstand the effects of freezing, at different temperatures, immersed or not immersed in water, in relation to degradation degree. As shown, no damage occurs when the wood is frozen immersed in water at -10°C. Samples frozen at -10°C, not immersed in water and samples frozen at -40 °C, immersed in water had only minor almost invisible cracks, which were present in the wood before freezing.

Method/temperature	Microscopic damage		Macroscopic damage	
	Highly degraded	Well-preserved	Highly degraded	Well-preserved
Frozen at -40 °C Not immersed in water	Yes	No	Yes	No
Frozen at -10 °C Not immersed in water	Yes		No	
Frozen at -40 C ° immersed in water	Yes	No	No	No
Frozen at -10 C ° immersed in water	No		No	

Perspective

The results of the freezing experiments may have an impact on conservation of waterlogged wood in a broader sense.

The expansive forces released by the crystallization of water by far exceed the strength of a degraded wood structure, and the structure will not be able to prevent the expansion. Therefore the expansion of the wood structure during freezing must reflect the amount of crystallized water at a given temperature. The water content and the theoretically maximal expansion can be calculated on the basis of the wood densities.

At -40 °C the measured expansion rates indicate that the amount of crystallized water is very different for the well-preserved wood samples compared to the highly degraded samples. For the highly degraded samples of birch wood, with a density of 0.12 g/cm^3 (Umax 729 %), the expansion values are close to the theoretical maximum, and nearly all water must be crystallized. For the well-preserved oak wood, with a density of 0.50 g/cm^3 (Umax 156 %), the expansion values are distinctly less than the theoretical maximum, which indicates that far from all water in the samples has crystallized (see Table 7).

The distinct difference of the ability of water to crystallize in the highly degraded wood compared to the well-preserved wood can be explained by the water being trapped in the microscopic porosities of the primary and secondary cell walls in the well-preserved wood, thereby preventing it from crystallizing. In the highly degraded wood most of the primary and secondary cell walls have been degraded, leaving the middle lamella with only a small amount of microscopic porosity in which water can be trapped.

Bearing these results in mind, it is obvious that when evaluating the freezing of PEG impregnated wood, the effect of the wood structure on the ability of water to crystallize has to be taken into account when the freezing parameters are determined. There is hardly any doubt that the wood structure will affect the freezing process of PEG impregnated material in much the same way as we see in the experiments on freezing of unimpregnated waterlogged wood. Therefore, when working with impregnated wood structures, standard phase diagrams for mixtures of PEG and water can only be used to determine a "best case scenario". How

much the actual freezing process will differ from the phase diagram depends on the degradation of the wood structure.

Table 7. If water in % of the volume is calculated, it is possible to estimate the maximum theoretical expansion of the wood in %. The maximum theoretical expansion in % is calculated as followed:

	Density g/cm^3	Umax %	Average volumetric expansion %´	Water in % of the volume	Maximal theoretically expansion in %
Oak wood, heartwood	0.50	156	2.4	77.5	7,0
Birch wood	0.12	729	8.2	90.7	8.2

$$\frac{\left(\dfrac{Wet\ mass\ of\ wood\ -\ Dry\ mass\ of\ wood}{Density\ of\ water} \right)}{Wet\ volume\ of\ sample} \cdot 100 = \frac{Volume\ of\ water}{Wet\ volume\ of\ sample} \cdot 100 = water\ in\ \%\ of\ the\ volume \Rightarrow$$

$$\frac{Water\ in\ \%\ of\ the\ volume}{100} \cdot Expansion\ of\ water = Maximum\ theoretical\ expansion\ in\ \%´$$

In PEG impregnated wood we cannot expect, even at very low temperatures, to gain overall stable crystalline systems, but rather "semi dynamic" systems where a fraction of the water and PEG on the microscopic level will still be able to move.

In literature the function of PEG impregnation in connection with freeze drying is normally described as a combination of three factors:
1) To reduce the effect of the expansion of water when it crystallizes.
2) To strengthen the structure by filling the cell cavity with a porous matrix of PEG.
3) To stabilize the cell walls of the structure through replacement of adsorbed water with PEG, and thus preventing shrinkage of the cell walls and subsequent transverse cracking of the structure (Jensen 1995).

To explain and document the two first effects is simple, but explaining the third effect, which is considered to be the most important, has proved to be more difficult. In theory it is the hydroxyl groups in the

cell wall material and in PEG that are responsible for the interaction between PEG and wood. But as long as water is present, the affinity between both water and wood substance and between water and PEG will be considerably bigger than the affinity between wood substance and PEG. Thus the presence of water will prevent a stable bond between wood substance and PEG. To facilitate stable bonds between PEG and wood substance the materials must be dehydrated, and PEG and wood substance must be brought into contact with each other to enable the bond (Jensen 1995).

The freezing experiments put forward in this paper suggest that it might be by microscopic ice lens growth during the freezing process that the necessary combination of dehydration, mobility and contact between the materials evolve. And thus it might well be the freezing process that turns out to be the crux of the conservation process. It is during the freezing process that most of the water leaves the wood substance to make up the

353

ice crystals. The extent of this dehydration by crystallization depends on the temperature of the freezing process, and to a certain extent also on how long the freezing process proceeds. It is to be expected that the number of bonds that will be established between PEG and wood substance during the freezing process will depend on the same factors. If this is to be trusted, it is important that PEG impregnated waterlogged wood, prior to freeze drying, will be frozen as deeply as possible in a slow freezing process, in order to facilitate the bonding between PEG and wood substance. The subsequent sublimation process can be conducted at "normal" process temperatures.

The freezing experiments with unimpregnated waterlogged wood have highlighted the importance of establishing an overall view of the interaction of all materials in the conservation of waterlogged wood, to reveal the full picture of the conservation process. It is our hope that this preliminary work will help to increase the interest in conducting further research into the interaction between wood PEG and water.

Acknowledgment
The authors wish to thank Christina Lund from The Royal Danish Academy of Fine Arts, School of Conservation warmly for proofreading the text.

References
Ambrose, W., 1970. Freeze-drying of swamp degraded Wood. In: Conservation of stone and wood: IIC New York conference 1970. London, pp. 53-57

Caarlee, E., 2002. Summary of potential artifact damage from low temperature pest management. In: AIC Textile Specialty Group Post print. 30th annual meeting, Miami, Florida, pp. 76-83

Florian, M., 1990. The effects of freezing and freeze-drying on natural history specimens. In: Collection Forum, Vol. 6. Nr.2. Society for the Preservation of Natural History Collections, pp. 24-52

Grattan, D.W & Clarke, R.W. 1987. Conservation of waterlogged wood. In: Person, C. (ed). Conservation of Marine Archaeological Objects. Butterworth & Co. London pp.164-206

Hansen, E.J. De Place., 1996. Byggematerialers frostbestandighed. Modellering af kritiske vandmætningsgrader. PhD. Thesis from Statens Byggeforskningsinstitut. SBI-rapport 268

Heinonen, J., 2005. Mass conservation of waterlogged wood in the field and laboratory. In: Meddelelser om konservering no. 2. IIC Nordic Group. Nordisk konservatorforbund, pp. 17-21

Jensen, P., 1995. Sorption of water and watersoluble agents in waterlogged wooden cell walls. Unpublished PhD. Thesis from The Royal Veterinary and Agricultural University, Denmark.

Jensen, P; Jørgensen, G. & Schnell, U., 2001. Dynamic LV-SEM analyses of freeze drying processes for waterlogged wood. In: Hoffmann, P. Spriggs, J.A., Grant,T., Cook C. and Recht, A. Proceedings of the 8th ICOM Group on Wet Organic Archaeological Materials Conference. Stockholm, pp. 319-331

Juhl, H.B., 2009. Frysning af vanddrukkent træ – med udgangspunkt i fryseløftning. Konservatorskolen, Det Kongelige Danske Kunstakademi, København. Unpublished thesis from the School of Conservation in Denmark.

Muldrew, K., 2004, The water to ice transition: Implications for living cells. In: Fuller, B.J., Lane. N. and Benson. E.E, (ed), Life in the Frozen State, CRC Press, pp. 67-108

Oddy, W. (ed), 1975, Problems of the Conservation of Waterlogged wood. Proceedings of a Symposium at the National Maritime Museum, 1973. London, National Maritime Museum.

Soroka, I., 1979, Portland Cement and Concrete. The Macmillan Press.

3D

Quantitative Evidence of Sucrose Hydrolysis in Wood Artifact Conservation

Fletcher B. O'Cain
Department of Biology, East Carolina University

Sarah C. Watkins-Kenney
QAR Conservation Lab, Underwater Archaeology Branch, NC Department of Cultural Resources

Dr. Anthony Kennedy
Department of Chemistry, East Carolina University

Dr. John M. Kenney
Department of Physics, East Carolina University

Introduction:

In the 1980s, approximately 30 pre-Columbian dugout canoes were discovered in Lake Phelps, NC. Four canoes were recovered and conserved by sucrose impregnation in 1986 (Figure 1).

Later on, the treated canoes exhibited surface deposits (figures 2, 3 4 and 5). In 2007 samples were taken for analysis. It is hypothesized that these deposits are sucrose disaccharide hydrolyzed to monosaccharide constituents, glucose and fructose (figure 6).

Figure 1. Canoe at Lake Phelps

As reducing sugars, the presence of glucose and fructose can be indicated via a reduction reaction with Copper (II) ions in Benedict's Reagent.

To test our hypothesis, we used this reaction to determine ratio of reducing sugars to non-reducing sugars, thus the extent of sucrose hydrolyzation.

Figure 2. Canoe 4, May 2007.

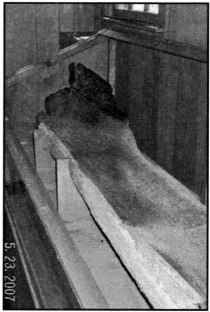

Figure 3. Canoe 4, May 2007.

355

Figure 4. Example of Canoe 4 degradation, Nov 2009

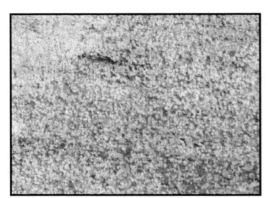

Figure 5. Close-up of Canoe 4 surface crystallization, Nov 2009

Method:

Benedict's quantitative reagent (w/v = 1.8% cupric sulfate, 12.5% potassium thiocyanate, 10% anhydrous sodium carbonate, 20% sodium citrate, and water) and a sucrose-plus-glucose/fructose mix at 0%, 25%, 50%, 75%, and 100% were incubated at 95°C for 20 min. A UV spectrum for each sample was obtained and absorbance at first-derivative peak 269nm was recorded. Observed percent reducing sugar was calculated as a ratio based on absorbance assuming the 100% and 0% reducing sugar values were defined. Filtered sugar solution was then extracted from canoe wood sample and incubated with Benedict's reagent. Absorbance at 269nm was compared to glucose/fructose absorbance standards allowing percent reducing sugar value to be estimated. Final percent reducing sugar value was the average of the result of the glucose and fructose trials. Uncertainty was estimated as the average difference in observed versus actual percent reducing sugar values.

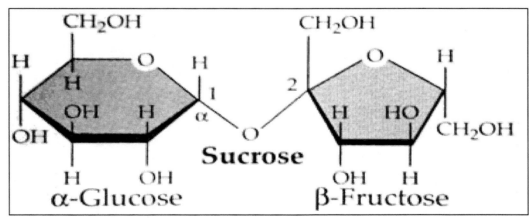

Figure 6. Sugar structures.

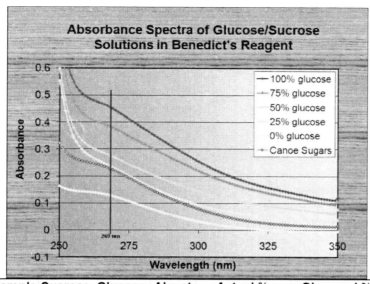

Sample #	Sucrose (mL)	Glucose (mL)	Abs at 269nm	Actual % reducing sugar	Observed % reducing sugar
1	0	2	0.45	100%	100%
2	0.5	1.5	0.38	75%	78%
3	1	1	0.27	50%	45%
4	1.5	0.5	0.23	25%	33%
5	2	0	0.13	0%	0%
canoe	-	-	0.22	-	30%

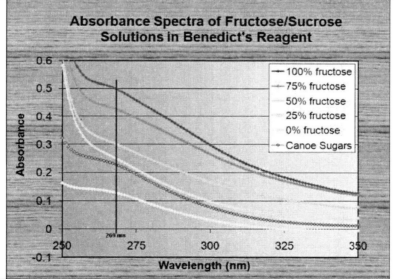

Sample #	Sucrose (mL)	Fructose (mL)	Abs at 269nm	Actual % reducing sugar	Observed % reducing sugar
1	0	2	0.49	100%	100%
2	0.5	1.5	0.42	75%	80%
3	1	1	0.30	50%	47%
4	1.5	0.5	0.25	25%	33%
5	2	0	0.13	0%	0%
canoe	-	-	0.22	-	27%

Conclusion:

We showed that UV spectrophotometry can be used to quantify the amount of reducing sugars in solution. For the Lake Phelps canoes, we found that a surface sample was 20-30% reducing sugars.

We have established a quantitative method for analyzing sugar constituents and confirmed the hypothesis that sucrose hydrolysis has occurred and an alternative means of wood conservation is required.

Acknowledgements:

ECU Physics Department; ECU Department of Chemistry; ECU Department of Biology; 2009 Undergraduate Research/Creative Activity Grant ECU Department of Anthropology; NC Department of Cultural Resources, Underwater Archaeology Branch; Dr. Mary Farwell, NC Division of Parks and Recreation; The Staff at Pettigrew State Park; Dr. Paul Hager; 11th International Conference on Wet Organic Archaeological Materials; Colleen Ryan
Photos 1, 2, & 3 courtesy of NC Department of Cultural Resources

End of theme 3:
General discussion on freeze-drying and the use of low molecular weight PEGs

Kristiane Straetkvern: I have a general question regarding the use of low molecular weight PEG in impregnation in particular ahead of freeze-drying. We've seen several places that it's been used during the papers today and in Denmark and Scandinavia we really don't use low molecular PEGs at all ahead of freeze-drying because we can see that it does not solidify, so we don't have sublimation. Do any of today's speakers have a comment on this?

André Bergeron: In my mind the 400 grade is naturally a consolidative process. To me it is more of a cryoprotector. I didn't put this slide in my presentation but I took one of those pieces from the museum that's in the surplus and I cut it in three and I just took one part to air dry, one part to be treated by freeze-drying in my freeze-dryer and we have PEG and a lot of hard PEG treated and freeze-dried and the results are just incredibly different. You get a lot of warping, of course, in the air dried one, the one with freeze-drying without PEG 400 has hundreds of cracks all over the place and the one treated with PEG 400 is in almost pristine condition, when compared to when we first found it. So in my mind it's not the consolidating process that we want here - it's this cryoprotection for the actual freeze-drying of the wood itself and it works very well.

Kristiane Straetkvern: Same in my opinion, but you can also achieve cryoprotection with high molecular PEG. We found that PEG 2000 works as an adequate cryoprotective and we are getting more and more worried about the low molecular weight PEGs in wood because they are so hygroscopic, they are difficult to control, more often than not. We've seen earlier this week all these salts we have in the wood, they tend to be more mobile and

tend to creep more when you have the low molecular weight PEG in the wood and that's why we are very sceptical about introducing this kind of PEG.

Cliff Cook: Yes, Kristiane, you have really raised good points. When using low molecular weight PEGs you have to be very conscious of the freezing points. You have to have a freeze-dryer with the capability to go beyond it, your concentration is critical because you can very easily put in too much low molecular weight PEG and then you do not have the freeze-drying conditions because the PEG won't freeze. The low molecular weights, there's some questions, because it's a solvent at room temperature so it's not a solid in the material. The question of the salt problem is because the low molecular weights have been shown to be more hygroscopic. The reason we continue to use the two molecular weights is that the low molecular weights can penetrate the cell wall and our research, many years ago, showed that reduced cell wall shrinkage was a different effect from cell wall collapse which was dependent on high molecular weights. So that was always the rationale for using the mixture but you do raise good points in that the hygroscopicity is an issue so correct storage afterwards can be critical. If you know your storage will not be optimal then using any significant concentrations of low molecular weight might be a bad choice. As we just heard in the talk the ultimate display of the object up in the air would have been a lot easier if it hadn't involved as much PEG as it did. There are so many parameters involved in your choice of treatment, I could argue that it's not healthy to choose one treatment and have that as your only tool in your toolbox. You have to have choices of treatments and make that choice based on your experience and your knowledge. So I don't have a problem with the concept of using this high molecular weight of PEG, but I would argue that you have to consider the whole situation from excavation to wood condition to the final display, etc.

Lars Andersen: I think some of the confusion is caused by the fact that we use PEG both as a method for / together with freeze-drying and for the controlled air drying and maybe the low molecular weight PEG has a point when you are using it with slow air drying, but I don't think it has a real good effect together with freeze-drying. I think that the hazardous point in using this defeats what we gain.

Cliff Cook: The risk is too high.

Lars Andersen: Yes! The risk is too high and if we use the low molecular weights together with freeze-drying we have an even more expensive process than this one with the high molecular weight because you have to go so very low in temperature and the processes are getting very very long. So in my opinion, low molecular weight should not be used in connection with freeze-drying.

Suzanne Grieve: I can say just based on usual observations that I treated hundreds of artifacts of various wooden materials and they've all worked out wonderfully, perfectly with PEG 400 followed by freeze-drying but I don't have any statistical or scientific data to back that up, just visual observation. Is the suggestion that the PEG is preventing the water from freezing completely? Is that what the problem is?

Cliff Cook: The PEG, like salts, depresses the freezing point of the solution. There is a point of concentration of PEG around 50 or 60% where you get no freezing at all. You cannot get it cold enough to freeze. That is the eutectic point. We caution against having the concentration anywhere near that in the PEGCON program for example. If you're going to have high concentration PEG in very degraded wood in the freeze-dryer, then you should hop over the eutectic point and put in 70 or

80% and go beyond that. If you're going to freeze-dry, you have to …the freezing curves of PEG are very important… you have to look at your overall concentration and look at the parameters of your freeze-dryer and if you don't have…For example, non-vacuum freeze-drying is a big problem. With non-vacuum freeze-drying you're not running at the cold temperatures available to mechanical freeze-dryers so you have to use a lot less PEG. If you use a lot less PEG, then you can only treat wood of reasonable quality. If it's very degraded and you have a non-vacuum freeze-dryer, you are better using Per Hoffman's treatment for example and air drying. So you have to know the mechanical parameters of your freeze-dryer and you have to carefully choose how much and what PEG to use based on the requirements of your object. So again, as I said, not all objects can be treated with the same treatment and you have to make that kind of choice. And if you keep your PEG concentrations away from the eutectic point, you have a mechanical device and your cold temperatures are appropriate, our chamber is -30°. It will take you longer to freeze-dry at those lower temperatures, that's very true also. So it's a complete package that has to be looked at. I can't say that just using high molecular weight PEG… I haven't had that much experience there, Lars, you probably have significantly more experience there than I have so I can't comment on that. Our experience is that we like the results that we get using the combined molecular weights and keeping our PEG concentrations at the minimum possible for the object. It results in a lighter weight, lighter color object and, to me, a more acceptable product but you have to look at your ASE's, determine what shrinkage you are getting and monitor the process continually through your run.

Lars Andersen: Of course, you have some experience that is getting nice results and things like that. But what I'd say is maybe that you'd also get nice results if you kept out the low molecular weight PEG and then maybe you'd have a more uniform, safer product and a better idea of how it would react in the future. So I think you should give it a go – try high molecular weight.

Anthony Kennedy: I thought I'd give my perspective from a chemistry point of view, unlike Suzanne, I have no experience with treating waterlogged wood with PEG but I have quite a bit of experience working with blood products and trying to conserve blood products by freeze-drying and the issue is that if you use high molecular weight molecules, they are not going to go inside cells. It's not going to penetrate deep into the wood. So when you go to do the freeze-drying process you are going to get micro ice crystal formation and you are going to cause severe damage to the cell walls which is ultimately going to lead to deterioration of your wood over time and is going to give it less structural strength. Whereas low molecular weight PEG is more likely to actually penetrate deep within the wood and actually prevent the ice crystal formation during your freeze-drying process.

Ellen Carrlee: I'm wondering about the eutectic and using low molecular weight; if you're actually getting freezing and if you're not getting freeze-drying then are you just slowly air drying in the freezer? What's happening in the freezer?

Lars Andersen: Of course it depends very much on the concentration of the low molecular weight PEG, but when you lower the temperature you get some other combinations of water and PEG because it's clean water that is freezing out and the remaining fraction will be concentrated PEG. So you get a fraction that will not freeze. For example, with 200 the freezing point is around -80°C. Of course it doesn't matter that much if it's a small amount because you have a lot of the other things that have solidified but the result is always a balance. When we heard about the

Newport ship where they tend to use very high concentration of PEG 200, I think that it will be very hard to make a true freeze-drying there, and you have this big proportion of liquid that you just evaporate instead of sublimate.

Cliff Cook: Yes, Lars, and if you have evaporation, that's the problem we have with air drying. Evaporation leads to huge capillary pressures in the wood and you get major collapse of the structures that are in the wood because of that capillary pressure due to the surface tension on evaporation. That's the whole point of freeze-drying to solidify the whole process and have sublimation, which is the movement to a vapor which doesn't induce any of those pressures in the objects. So if you're trying to vacuum freeze-dry an object that's not completely frozen, you are causing more damage than you would by air drying because you are pulling the water off at even more increased rate due to the vacuum, so you're drying faster that you would by air drying and resulting in more physical damage internally through that surface tension of the water.

Khoi Tran: I would like to make one comment. In Grenoble we don't use low molecular weight PEG anymore for the treatment of our artifacts. Why? Because we think that PEG 200 or 400 is too hygroscopic and it could cause long-term problems. For instance, the salt migrations within the artifact could be enhanced or influenced by low molecular weight PEG. And the second point is that we have problems freeze-drying artifacts when we use low molecular weight and I think that the key point is the penetration amount of PEG 2000 or 4000 within the cell walls. In our opinion, and we have done research studies about the diffusion of PEG 4000 in the cell walls to prove it, we can say that PEG 4000 can diffuse within the cell walls so that's the reason why we only use PEG 4000 in our treatment whether air drying or freeze-drying.

Kristiane Straetkvern: I have a couple of comments. I agree totally with you Cliff that we don't want to say that one method is <u>the</u> method because we need this factor of numbers. There are many factors to be taken into consideration when choosing methods. End use, for example, is a very important piece. Axel's, if they knew what would happen in the end, they would never have treated it that way. Another thing is of course the degree of degradation of the wood and I think that that is why Suzanne has achieved such good results with her wood – that the wood is in such good condition that it will not collapse and that is a very important parameter – if the wood is in good condition it can withstand the forces of normal evaporation that will happen even if it is not freeze-dried.

Khoi Tran: We have talked for many years about the different methods for the treatment of archaeological wooden artifacts. PEG is the oldest most reliable and still used method. Sucrose, is the second process. And in Europe, I have been contacted by different people – perhaps you know that in Italy they've developed their own process using starch. And we have been contacted by them to develop this process abroad, outside of Italy, and in Mainz in the Museum of Roman ships they have developed a unique process using Kauramin. So we have to assess once more the different processes to build the pros and cons of each process and to try to unify our efforts in the future to apply which process is most suitable for which kind of artifacts. Because I think that we are too dispersed so far.

Kristiane Straetkvern: Thank you Khoi. I think you are very right that we need to open this forum to all kinds of experiments and discuss them together – the pro's and con's because there is no single answer to the conservation of waterlogged wood.

Wayne Smith: I agree too, of course. I think there is room for greater involvement, …there's a project out of Germany called the KUR project, but it's starting to look at taking things out of their normal parameters. For instance, the silicone oils are being tested on bigger pieces of wood – ship timbers – and other processes are being stretched to their limits so we can see what they can do. And I encourage that we need to have a real community that's trying to stretch this stuff because the starch methods are going to be great - however we're going to find out that they have their parameters just like everything else, and so I'm really big on encouraging people to ask some really bad questions and then go after some really good answers.

Suzanne Grieve: I just have one question for you Wayne. I'd heard through the grapevine that you are installing a freeze-dryer system that is 30 feet long and I was wondering if the plans are to treat the *La Belle* with PEG and freeze-drying?

Wayne Smith: Yes! In fact it's going to be a <u>really</u> big freeze-dryer. It will allow you to drive them in with a forklift but this is a very, very major production. And yes it has to have proper vacuum and yes it needs an amazing system for cooling and getting the freezing temperatures we need, so it's not something that's been undertaken lightly. It's going to be massive but we kind of need it. It's going to be tricky. I'm not sure about the final designs but it may be that we can split it in two for smaller artifact work. Obviously that would be easier on the compressors etc…but the design of it is going to be quite impressive and large. And it's not because we want it that way, it's just because that's what we're getting for timbers. Good Question!

Shanna Daniel: I have a question about the method of just using one molecular weight of PEG—PEG 4000—what are the advantages and disadvantages of that? I know it has been talked about a little throughout the conference so I just wanted to ask that question.

Cliff Cook: I was thinking about this actually. The idea of a low molecular weight PEG stems from work done by Stamm at the US Forestry Products laboratory in the late 50s/ early 60s and Stamm published work where he suggested adding low molecular weight PEG or salts as an additive to lumber to reduce degradation during kiln drying which was basically cell wall shrinkage. This is for drying lumber from the green stage from the fiber saturation point down to room conditions. I'm assuming, I don't know this for a fact that Wally Ambrose was aware of that and he started the idea of freeze-drying with a low molecular weight PEG. Dave and I picked up on that and our early work just included low molecular weight PEG 400. The idea was to reduce cell wall shrinkage as opposed to cellular collapse. This would be with wood where the cell wall was not completely degraded. It eventually evolved into the PEGCON program which is just 400 depending on how degraded the wood is according to species. So if you've got material where it's heavily degraded, where the cell wall is pretty much gone, the requirement for 400 is minimal at best.

Lars Andersen: I totally agree

Kristiane Straetkvern: If I could add a comment to that? In Denmark, we started with the conservation of the Nydam find in the 90s and the Nydam find is a lot of spear shafts and shields and 15,000 objects in several thousand pieces. So it's really quite a lot of objects and they are heavily degraded. In the beginning they were very careful with adding anything. They hadn't investigated that much in freeze-drying so we started with 25%PEG 2000 and 5% PEG 200 and these objects looked okay at the start but they seemed to be...They were very, very vulnerable regarding the relative humidity and they didn't have successful consolidation so we had to reconsider and started to investigate what happens with the freezing and I think Lars has been working with this for several years. As with the freeze-drying from his project we learned that if we stopped using the low molecular weight PEG and concentrate on the PEG 2000, that the 2000 will go in and stabilize the wood and the low molecular weight PEG will only create accidents because it will collapse as long as it doesn't freeze during the drying process.

Lars Andersen: I think there are two main problems with using the low molecular weight PEG. One thing is in the freeze-drying process, I'm only taking freeze-drying, and that's the point where the low molecular weight PEG, depending on how much you add, it will make a certain portion of non-frozen material... Of course if you have a high molecular weight and water you'll have stabilization by the ice crystals and things like that so you won't get collapse. Anyway this is a potential hazard and then there is the other part of it: after conservation you tend to have this low molecular weight PEG which is active in another way. It is able to move and move things about and it's also more hygroscopic so it leads to a product that tends to be more hygroscopic.

Kristiane Straekvern: And don't forget that the low molecular weight PEG is liquid after conservation and if you have surface layers there may be liquid in the core. If you use the high molecular weight PEG, that is solid at room temperature.

Lars Andersen: But my point in this is that after 25 years of experience in Scandinavia with freeze-drying using only high molecular weight PEG 2000, we feel that we get very nice results. What I am trying to say is that I think that the benefits outweigh the hazards in this case. So you have a more predictable process and you have more predictable properties afterwards.

Cliff Cook: Okay, counterpoint. The point of using the low molecular weight is that it's designed to penetrate the cell wall and to chemically bond with the cellulose in the cell wall replacing the bound water in the cell wall so you should not have liquid PEG in your object after freeze-drying. It should be contained in the cell wall, not sloshing around in the wood. But if you put in excess low molecular weight beyond the capacity of the cell wall to absorb (and as the cell wall degrades the need for PEG decreases) then you will have liquid PEG in your object and it's going to be gooey really quickly when exposed to high humidity, because that Peg will absorb water from the air and you will get a sticky object. Guaranteed! I've seen it happen, as you have, I'm sure. So the point is, my argument is that you need a little bit of 400 if you've got some cell wall left. If you don't have cell wall left than certainly do not use it. Dave's paper in *Studies* shows that at 60% or higher if you have a significant amount of 400 there you are going to have a problem, guaranteed, if the humidity goes up. Reducing the amount of 400 will to some extent, I would suggest, make your treatment a little riskier but it will reduce the risk of problems later on if your storage is not 100%. No question, it makes your collections management a lot easier. So I guess the bottom line is, like anything else we do, you have to understand what you are doing and do it with care. The eutectic point on the graph there, that's where it does not freeze. You can see the freezing curves, this is based on Union Carbide literature, for the PEGs. We've been using Union Carbide PEG for years. So that's out of the Union Carbide literature but you can see as your concentration goes up your temperature has to decrease. So if you can't freeze-dry at -20°C, -25°C or -30°C then don't put in any low molecular weight PEG because you won't get a frozen object and if you try to freeze-dry a non-frozen object you are vacuum drying your object, which is even worse than air-drying. So, you have to have the right equipment in order to get a result that is consistent and meets your needs and the object's.

Jim Spriggs: There is something rather important here which we mustn't forget and that is that there is a great difference between small portable artifacts made of wood and large oak timbers and certainly where you've got a relatively small non-oak artifact there is no point in putting low molecular weight into it, particularly because where you have a high ratio of surface to volume then any changes in humidity are going to go straight through the surface and they are going to create a patch or stain on the side of the object. Conversely the much larger oak timbers where you have a lower ratio of surface to volume then you are not going to get the low molecular weight PEG inside where it is really needed in those second order walls and cell spaces. The atmosphere is not going to affect those nearly so much because you are going to have, with any luck, a reasonable build up of high molecular weight PEG on the surface which is effectively insulating what is going on inside. But whereas you can probably get away with most small artifacts, even made of oak, if you are not using low molecular weight wax, you have substantial cores of well-preserved wood in the larger timbers. So when we're talking about this issue, we must try to differentiate between the small portable non-oak species of objects and the much larger structural timbers which are of oak. They are two rather different things.

Kristiane Straetkvern: We do have large timbers as well, ships timbers, and very often they are more degraded in the in the core and still we tend to use only PEG 2000. And then choose to deal with the cracks that are made, because then we know, or at least we think we know, more about the risks that we are creating for the objects.

Gilles Chaumat: One comment about your comment before. I agree with you about the fact that the low molecular weight PEG is always liquid. If you decide to put an archaeological wood in the freeze-dryer you must have a part of the object made up of soft wood. And the definition of soft wood is a wood with no more cell walls. So if you put a solution with 20% PEG 200 or 400 when you remove this water during freeze-drying, the remaining PEG in the lumen must go to the cell wall. But the cell wall is very thin so there are no more sites for this PEG to disappear. So a big part of this very soft wood will contain a liquid mess of low molecular weight PEG and this could be destabilizing for the future especially if it is stored in climatic conditions which are not very well controlled. So for me low molecular weight PEG gives good short-term results but for the long-term it is risky and for soft wood it is not really good to have liquid PEG because this soft wood needs consolidant and the liquid phase is not a good consolidant.

Lars Andersen: I think this is a very interesting point that when you have this liquid, the low molecular weight PEG, in the process when you freeze the thing this is disposed in the cell lumen so you have this low molecular weight lying in between the ice crystals in the lumen and maybe that's alright. But of course when it is liquid it will move to the cell walls and then create an excess of low molecular weight and kind of lubricate the cell walls. We agree that the point of putting PEG into the cell wall or into the wood at all is that the wood and the PEG should combine so that the PEG can stabilize the cell wall. But at what point in the process does this occur? Because you have water, PEG, cell wall and the affinity of the water to the cell wall is far greater than the affinity of the PEG for the cell wall. So you have a system where

the water at any time is blocking the combination of the cell wall and the PEG. So how does this work? Because, we know it is working. So it must be able to make this bond, otherwise we would see all these cracks and everything. We think from the latest work on these freeze-drying experiments that maybe the freezing itself, the dehydration of the materials is evolving during the freezing and in fact you have your stabilization when the freezing has taken place and it has taken place for some time. And the rest is more or less to remove the water from these ice crystals. In the paper, we've included a few of these thoughts but I think it is very interesting to ask "why?" What is happening to make this work? Because we know it works but we don't know how.

Cliff Cook: That's a very good point. What's actually happening at the freeze-drying front? Because when you take an object and you've got PEG and a water system and you freeze it to a temperature where you actually have it in an immobile solid state and you throw it in your freeze-drier and then you start pumping off the vacuum, the ice starts to sublime. So, as you think about a block of ice it's going to move inward as it dries and that's what you're always doing. The outer surface get's dry, the inner surface is still frozen and waterlogged. So what's actually going on at the interface where that ice is subliming off? As the ice moves off you're getting a phase changes going on at that interface that's moving through your object. So if you look at the freezing point diagram, your concentration is changing because you are making ice all the time so that drying front moving through your wood right on top of the frozen ice/PEG mixture, that's still there and what's going on at the front, I have no idea. I'm hoping the PEG is maybe rearranging itself to go where it's supposed to go. Maybe not. It depends. But I would suspect that because of the phase change occurring there that something might be going on at the cellular level as your drying front moves through the wood.

Lars Andersen: I'll say that that was my opinion until this last freezing experiment where I think we have to look at the crystallization process instead of the drying process. This freezing process is a much more dynamic thing than I'd ever thought. It showed that everything is governed by the vapor pressure of water in the bound state of water or water trapped in small cavities and things like that. And all these different water molecules have a different level of vapor pressure. And this is a very, very intriguing machine so it's getting very complicated and I think that is the place to look to find out what is happening.

Cliff Cook: Yes, it's a very dynamic system, you're right. Because the reverse is happening as your object starts to freeze, you may not freeze the solution equally through. If the water freezes first, you are going to have liquid PEG there because again you've gone into maybe a eutectic zone where you're not going to get it freezing. So actually what's going on there—the impact of the cellulose, the physical structure of the wood—I'm not even going to guess. I have no idea. It could be, you're right, a very dynamic situation and eliminating...

Lars Andersen: You concede this point.

Cliff Cook: ...eliminating one variable from an already dynamic situation might make it simpler to evaluate. I guess I'll come back to my worry about my shrinkage. I don't know what goes on either during the freezing process or the drying process in a phase system with that many components—two or three, four if you count your wood. I'm not equipped to guess maybe there is some research that needs to be done in that area.

Howard Wellman: Let me ask from a different angle, maybe a practical aspect.

When you stopped using low molecular weight PEG did you find it necessary to change your freeze-drying protocol? And this is mostly for those of us who are actually going to go home and turn the machine on. Did you find it necessary to change your protocol to make it work better?

Lars Andersen: I would very much like to answer that question. Most of our freeze-drying machines have a limit of what they can do but this limit has never really met the demands of the process. So in fact as a practical thing, most of us have been running these freeze-drying processes as far as the machine could do it. So maybe we are telling ourselves it's very scientific when in fact it's mainly dictated by the machine. So we freeze-dry at a chamber temperature of -20°C or -22°C or something like that, and that's what the machines have been able to do all the time and we still do that. So we have not changed the protocol

Kristiane Straetkvern: We designed our freeze-dryers to run at about -25°C or-30°C. But in fact when we do our freeze-drying, we can raise the temperature to about -20°C. But we are still a little chickenish so we run it a little lower, but the fact that you can run it at -20°C enables a shorter drying period.

Cliff Cook: The colder your chamber temperature, the lower your sublimation rate. The only way to counteract that is to get a higher vacuum level. Those are the two parameters you can adjust to control your rate of sublimation.

Emily Williams: I'd like to back the practical questions up just a little further. For those of us who are used to a two-step PEG method, PEGCON provides us a nice starting point which we can adjust based on our experience. What I'm wondering is, is there a sort of standard that you tend to apply using only the PEG 2000 or how do you vary the approaches? How do you begin to apply it is really what I'm asking?

Cliff Cook: How much PEG?

Emily Williams: Yes!

Lars Andersen: You see when you have only solid PEG, high molecular weight PEG, excess PEG is in fact not a problem because it will only fill out the cell lumena so it won't do any harm. So the problem is it can make the freeze-dried material a little harder and we tend to think is this an object that needs to have strength and we give it a little more. And if the strength is no problem we tend to give it a little less but it is not scientific in any way. So the standard treatment is between 35% and 45%

Kristiane Straetkvern: I'm actually a bit ashamed to say we also have some sort of standard, because that's life. But we try to start at a reasonable point, depending on the dimensions of the wood and the degree of degradation and the end use of our wood and what we are going to do with it. But we tend to go to an end concentration at 40% maximum. Above that the sublimation is difficult because it is too dense. If we have larger objects we have to take care that we don't start with too high a concentration, otherwise you get osmosis in your objects.

Cliff Cook: You get osmotic collapse.

Kristiane Straetkvern: Yes.

Cliff Cook: That's a good point, Kristiane, when you're using the high molecular weights you've got to go in a stepwise process typically in small 5% increments. Otherwise you run the risk of osmotic collapse in your objects which is irreversible.

Lars Andersen: As a rule we start with 15% and then it's not stepwise but it's by evaporation

Cliff Cook: So slowly ramps up.

Ian Godfrey: I just have a point to raise: I was wondering whether it might be worthwhile and going back and reevaluating the results of that international study that took place in 1987 because I just recall that the WA museum was probably the least sophisticated of all when it came to treating waterlogged wood and we used one grade of PEG, PEG 1500, freeze-dried and our results were probably the worst of all the timbers that were treated. So I'm just wondering whether we should go back and look at those where there was a range of different treatments applied and reevaluate them and just see how this fits in with this current debate.

Cliff Cook: They're sitting in Trondheim right?

Ian Godfrey: They are.

Cliff Cook: It's been a few years now.

Vicki Richards: Roar Saeterhaug said last WOAM that we could come over and get them so I think they are available.

Anthony Kennedy: I just had a question about the eutectic point and just looking at the graph, it is for a binary system of water and PEG. I'm wondering if the eutectic point changes when you have a ternary system that includes wood?

Cliff Cook: Yes.

Anthony Kennedy: How significant is that change?

Lars Andersen: In fact this has not been investigated but you would expect that the eutectic point would be lower. But in fact you have two liquid systems and then a solid thing so it's very complicated.

Cliff Cook: Well, for example in a capillary system you can get freezing point depression. Wood is a capillary system, so it stands to reason that you're going to get depression just because of the physical structure of the wood. This is taken from the PEG literature as I said, this is the best case. It may be a lot worse than what we've seen.

Lars Andersen: It's not only a capillary system, but it's also a capillary system that is very hygroscopic so it's really very complicated.

Cliff Cook: And any impurities, salts or other junk that is in the wood may play a role. I'd hate to try to map or model the system. It would be difficult, I think. There is still a lot of art involved with this. We are trying to bring in more science, but there's still a lot of art here.

Jim Spriggs: Just before we dump all our drums of PEG 400 and PEG 200 down the drain altogether, I want to go on about size again. Size is everything sometimes in wood. If you are treating large timbers and you want to cut the time down, you really need to use the small molecular weight PEGs because they are just going to penetrate faster. They are more mobile in a water solution. With big timbers, I've never seen any problem at all with anything up to 8-10% of PEG 400 so long as you apply PEG 3500 or 4000 on the surface. Maybe I should go back and have a look at all the stuff we've treated before but no one's come back and complained about it so that's just another parameter isn't it, if you think about the time it's going to take. And if you are slightly higher in the PEG 2000's it is not actually penetrating very, very far into the pores and you are going to get terrible splitting and shrinkage so again, it's to do with the

scale of the work that you are doing and what you are trying to treat.

Kristiane Straetkvern: We did a really big keelson a couple of years ago and it went in PEG 2000. Of course you have PEG going only into the outer surface because it never penetrated all the way in. But still it turned out rather well. But the thing is, you don't need that much in the sound wood. The PEG goes in where it's a little harder and then upon drying...the point is there weren't many shrinkage cracks in the keelson so it turned out really well.

Jim Spriggs: If you don't get any PEG into those unaffected cell walls then presumably when the water freezes you get crystals of ice expanding and that's going to rupture the cell walls. That's what we're trying to do. It's this cryoprotector idea, isn't it partly? So how are you going to get around that problem?

Kristiane Straetkvern: We haven't cut this wood so there might be cracks inside it...

Jim Spriggs: It sounds to me as though we need to reexamine the theory behind this all again because I seem to remember the size of those second order spaces is something in the order of 200 microns across or something like that and the molecule size of PEG is 200 or 400 – a little bigger. The 2000 is very much bigger so that wouldn't go into the second order spaces really. So what do we do? Go back to square one and start looking at the theory again?

Lars Andersen: I think that would be a good idea.

Cliff Cook: One possibility is people go back and look at objects treated decades ago if they can gain access or have them in the lab and see what they look like today. It's a quick visual examination, touch the object, if it's sticky you'll be able to tell really quickly and get an idea of what kind of environment it's been exposed to since it's been treated and maybe we can start to map out just how widespread this problem is at the various collections that we have access to. I must admit, I never went through. I saw a problem with the forks collection and all the stuff from Red Bay that I treated over the years. I have seen end grain of wood with bubbles of PEG coming out of it because we didn't have a frozen situation and the PEG had slipped right down the little vessels and you can see little bumps on the end of the wood. So it is really mobile if it's under vacuum and not frozen. There's all kinds of stuff going on so it can be a real problem if the PEG you choose is not adequate for the wood you've got and the equipment you've got to dry that wood.

André Bergeron: And also the pump must not be operated until the object is frozen solid. If you just put your object in the freeze dryer and you start your pump...

Cliff Cook: Bad idea! André you talked about non-vacuum freeze-drying and that's an issue there too. Because you haven't got the same temperature controls so I'd be very cautious about how much low molecular weight PEG I put in if I was doing non-vacuum freeze-drying because you tend to not have such cold temperatures necessarily and it's really much, much slower – like 10 times slower – than vacuum freeze-drying. So it will take a lot longer to dry your objects using a non-vacuum system, like in our Canadian climate, for example, while it has its uses you have to be especially cautious there. The stuff we did on the roof of CCI years ago, we had very low concentrations of PEG because we were worried about that exact issue. So PEGCON is on the web as you can see. All those Mac users who've been deprived all those years, well...

4.1
Vasa – Recent Preservation Research

Lars Ivar Elding
Swedish National Maritime Museums,
Box 27132, SE-102 52 Stockholm,
Sweden.
E-mail: Lars-Ivar.Elding@maritima.se

Abstract
The multi-disciplinary work within the research programs *Preserve the Vasa* (2003-2006) and *A Future for Vasa* (since 2008) is reviewed. Objectives are: to further develop the fundamental understanding of the processes occurring in marine archaeological wood and their influence on wood mechanical properties, to elucidate the time dependencies of chemical and mechanical degradation processes and to slow them down or, if possible, stop them. The ultimate goal is to suggest improved methods for practical preservation work based on this research. In this work, differentiation between the hull of 900 tons and the several thousand loose objects has to be considered. Current degradation processes in wood and conservation agent are catalyzed by iron compounds and depend on pH and access to atmospheric oxygen and humidity. Methods to remove iron, neutralize acids, exclude oxygen, adjust physical parameters such as support structure, temperature, relative humidity and light are discussed. A bibliography of the research papers produced in these programs so far is given.

Keywords: *Vasa*, wood, PEG, sulfur, iron, oxalic acid, sulfuric acid, formic acid, oxygen, humidity, degradation, microbial, Fenton, free radical, acid hydrolysis, oxidative degradation.

Introduction
The history, rescue operations and archaeology of *Vasa* have been extensively reviewed, most recently by C.O. Cederlund and F. Hocker [1]. The ship sank, fully equipped, on its maiden voyage out of Stockholm in August 1628, after having sailed less than one nautical mile. Salvage attempts during the following decades were fruitless. Only the bronze cannons were recovered in reckless diving operations during the 1660s. The shipwreck was relocated on the bottom of Stockholm harbor during the 1950s and was raised to the surface in 1961.

The hull was spray treated with aqueous PEG solutions between 1962 and -79, dried for another ten years, and moved to the present museum in 1988. Loose objects were PEG-conserved in tanks. The conservation has been described by Barkman [2] and Håfors [3-7, 66]. Emma Hocker has recently given an excellent review of the conditions of the ship and the early preservation research [8]. The absence of shipworm in the brackish waters of the Baltic Sea, the anaerobic conditions in the bottom sediments and the low temperature 30 m below the surface, contributed to the preservation of the ship and loose objects during the 333 years on the seabed. Several tons of iron compounds from rusting cannon balls and bolts, and sulfur compounds from the water and polluted effluents from the town impregnated the wood. Attacks by erosion and sulfur-metabolizing microorganisms softened the wood surfaces. During conservation, large amounts of polyethylene glycol and boron compounds were added [7, 66].

During the 30 years of conservation and drying, and the almost 20 years of display under controlled climate conditions in the present museum, the ship and its loose objects have been exposed to atmospheric oxygen and various degrees of humidity. Together with the large quantities of chemicals in the wood, this has created favorable conditions for chemical processes and transport of chemicals. Already during the 1990s, conservators observed acidic salt deposits on the surfaces of some timbers and loose objects [9], indicating transport of chemicals from the interior to the surface.

After the rainy summer of 2000, when the museum climate by far exceeded the recommended relative humidity of 55±5 %, the situation became alarming. A pilot study was initiated, aimed at identifying the chemical composition of the salt outbreaks. X-ray powder diffraction and synchrotron-based spectroscopy (XANES) by Sandström, Persson and coworkers identified the deposits as composed of hydrated iron sulfates, gypsum and elemental sulfur [10-12]. It was concluded that hydrogen sulfide, formed during the anaerobic conditions on the seafloor, had penetrated the submerged wood, accumulated as mainly elemental sulfur, and later, during museum conditions, oxidized to sulfuric acid in iron-catalyzed processes. Wood hydrolysis due to internal sulfuric acid formation was assumed to be a serious matter of conservation concern [10-15]. This pioneering work, summarized in *Nature* [12], formed the basis for much work on the "sulfur problem" during the years to follow. It also was the basis and rationale for the continued and extended research efforts on the processes in *Vasa* wood during the years to follow. However, it is now (2010) clear that the situation in the timbers is much more complicated than initially assumed ten years ago. Novel results indicate that the original strong focus on the oxidation of sulfur to sulfuric acid has to be modified – this is one of several possible reactions, and several other acids contribute to the acidity of the wood (*see below*).

Preserve the *Vasa*

In the beginning of 2003, the Swedish National Maritime Museums (SMM) received funding for research in the chemical and microbial processes occurring in the timbers of *Vasa*. At that time, very little was known about the ongoing processes in PEG-treated archaeological wood. It was explicitly stressed that the research should result in a fundamental understanding of these processes as a basis for practical preservation work. The transformation of sulfur compounds either by iron-catalyzed processes involving atmospheric oxygen and humidity, or by activities of sulfur-oxidizing bacteria, was assumed to result in formation of sulfuric acid [12]. The possible degradation of PEG was also a matter of concern. After announcement of this program and review of received proposals, the research program started Oct 1st, 2003 [16].

Microbial activities - Initially, it was considered important to differentiate between chemical and microbial processes. It was known early that the outer regions of *Vasa* timbers were degraded due to bacterial attacks during the time on the seabed [7]. This fact was confirmed by light microscopy [17] and scanning electron microscopy, showing that the outer ca 1-2 cm of *Vasa* oak – and more in the case of softwood - was degraded by erosion bacteria. Later, the processes involving erosion bacteria and sulfate-reducing bacteria and the mechanisms for accumulation of organic lignin-bound sulfides and inorganic iron-sulfur compounds under seabed conditions were comprehensively elucidated by Fors et al. in laboratory simulations [18].

As a result of a co-operation between the School of Biology at the University of Portsmouth and the Department of Wood Chemistry at the Swedish Agricultural University, it could relatively soon be concluded – perhaps not too surprising – that microbial activity under the present relatively dry museum conditions was of minor importance, with the exception of the wood surfaces, always exposed to contamination from the public. All samples taken from interior *Vasa* wood in its present dry state failed to provide any signs of ongoing microbial activity. But the DNA analysis afforded interesting information on the microbial history of the ship and the species present during the wet periods [19-21]. Based on these results, all research and preservation efforts could be concentrated to the chemical processes.

Sulfur and iron chemistry - Speciation and distribution of sulfur and iron compounds in *Vasa* wood was under intense study by Sandström's group at Stockholm University. It resulted in a number of seminal publications [22-27], including comparative studies of some other ships [23-26]. The novel discovery of accumulation of reduced sulfur as thiols bound to lignin and as solid particles of iron sulfides was found to be of general occurrence for water-logged marine-archaeological wood recovered from sea water under anoxic conditions. By use of synchrotron-based methods, *i.e.* XANES (X-ray Absorption Near Edge Spectroscopy) and SXM (Scanning X-ray Microscopy) at Stanford and Grenoble, together with X-ray fluorescence, ESCA (Electron Spectroscopy for Chemical Analysis), SEM (Scanning Electron Microscopy) and X-ray powder diffraction, valuable new information on the distribution and speciation of sulfur and iron was obtained. High concentrations of sulfur and iron, in some cases up to 10% by weight, were observed in the bacterially degraded surface regions of Vasa wood down to 1-2 cm. These observations match the results of the simulations of the microbial processes [18].

Iron extraction - At an early stage, removal of the iron impurities was identified as an important remedy to minimize their catalytic action. Extraction methods by use of strong EDTA-related complexing agents (EDDHMA and DTPA) were tested from the start of the project and are described in a number of publications by Persson and Almkvist [28-30]. These extractions require several months of exposure, and the interior of very massive pieces might be inaccessible. The treatment removes all water-soluble compounds including the PEG, and it neutralizes acids, since the pH of the extraction solution is ca 9 in the case of EDDHMA. This means that extracted objects have to be re-conserved. Successful extractions of pine species have been performed [29, 30], and the practical use of DTPA is reported at this conference [31]. Exposure to high pH for prolonged times might be a threat to the cellulose. In the case of *Vasa*, final decisions and tests of the implications of the method for the wood are still under evaluation and it may be that only the more robust objects will be able to withstand this treatment (*see below*).

PEG degradation - Initially, it could not be excluded that degradation of PEG to formic acid, for instance, also contributed to the acidity observed in some *Vasa* samples. Moreover, the stability of the conservation agent is of great importance *per se*, in that even a very slow decomposition of PEG to shorter fragments is expected to increase the hygroscopicity and impair the efficiency of the PEG stabilization of the impregnated wood. The distribution of PEG in *Vasa* wood and its stability and degradation mechanisms was therefore studied.

The model molecule tetraethylene glycol and its degradation reactions as a function of temperature and chemical environment, and PEG from *Vasa* and other ships were analyzed by Glastrup, et al. at the Danish National Museum [32-35]. They conclude that PEG is relatively stable under museum conditions and that formic acid is a possible product of a slow degradation. Recently, Mortensen reviewed and extended these studies in his PhD thesis [36] and in his report to this conference [37]. Based on carbon-14 experiments, it can be concluded [36, 37] that the observed formic acid is a degradation product of PEG, not a result of a solvolytic degradation of wood as hypothesized earlier [38]. According to these experiments, the half-life of PEG under museum conditions is - in practice – sufficiently long (thousands of years) for all practical purposes.

Parallel to these studies, work by Persson and Almkvist on PEG properties and reactions [39-45] resulted in a partly different picture. The two groups agree that the PEG in the surface region is stable [36, 39]. However, mass spectra of PEG from the interior wood (where PEG concentrations are low) indicate a predominance of low-molecular PEG. Combined with the hypothesis that high concentrations of iron(II) might give rise to Fenton-type free radical attacks on macromolecules in these samples, they conclude that PEG in the interior wood might be degraded due to free radical attack in a random-cleavage process [43-45]. Alternatively, these observations might be interpreted as a result of a chromatographic separation of PEG in the wooden matrix [36]. Summarizing, since the concentrations of PEG in the interior wood are low, and even if there is a degradation of PEG at these low concentrations, the present view of the Vasa Museum authorities is that PEG degradation is not of high priority in the applied preservation work. Further, solvolysis of wood in the presence of acids and PEG according to [38] can definitely be ruled out.

Wood chemistry and stability – During the second phase of the *"Preserve the Vasa"* project, starting early 2005, a comprehensive study of the chemical and mechanical properties of *Vasa* oak compared to reference wood (fresh wood and waterlogged, non-conserved contemporary oak) was launched. The aim was to answer the most important question for the long-term preservation of the ship: *Is there an ongoing deterioration of the wood under the present museum conditions, i.e. since 1990, weakening the structure, as a result of chemical processes in the timbers?*

Systematic sampling from the ship [17] and analysis of organic acids and other degradation products by NMR and of cellulose and hemicellulose by SEC (Size Exclusion Chromatography) were initiated. The SEC analytical studies by Iversen, et al. [46, 47] indicated that most of the observed degradation of cellulose has occurred after the salvage, most likely as a consequence of the iron contaminated and humid wood being in contact with air, creating possibilities for Fenton-type oxidative degradations and acid-initiated hydrolysis reactions. Similar conclusions were derived by Godfrey, et al. using solid state carbon-13 NMR [48]. pH measurements and proton-NMR data for D_2O extracts of finely divided wood samples by Persson and Almkvist also indicated the presence of organic acids and degradation in the interior wood through the same possible mechanisms. Noteworthy, in the interior wood, Almkvist observed positive correlations between the occurrence of high concentrations of iron(II) and increasing acidity and signs of degradation of PEG and cellulose [41-45].

Parallel to these chemical studies, a program on the mechanical properties of Vasa wood had been initiated. A study using high-energy multiple impact milling within the Vasa wood project [17] at the University of Hannover indicated degradation but gave no conclusive results [49]. Studies at the Royal Institute of Technology in Stockholm resulted in publications on fundamental physical properties of *Vasa* wood in comparison with fresh wood and correlations between moisture and PEG content and radial and tangential compression [50-52]. A ca 50% reduction of compressive strength of *Vasa* oak was derived. There was an obvious need to extend these studies and to correlate the physical properties of *Vasa* oak with its chemical condition.

Evaluation – The *"Preserve the Vasa"* project was accomplished in 2006-2007 and evaluated in December 2006 [53]. The reviewers recommended phasing out of parts that had accomplished the goals (microbial biology, sulfur spectroscopy, PEG decomposition) and suggested that future research should focus on, for instance, acid formation, mechanisms for oxidative degradations, neutralization methods, wood mechanical properties and practical applications [53].

A Future for Vasa

A research plan for *A Future for Vasa* was formulated based on the knowledge of 2007 and the reviewer's recommendations [53], including the following main objectives:

- Understand and if possible arrest the decay processes occurring in *Vasa* wood
- Elucidate the time dependence of these processes
- Clarify the relations between the chemical status of the wood and its physical-mechanical properties
- Elucidate the effect of PEG conservation on long-term wood mechanical properties
- Apply research results in new methods for practical preservation work, including a new support structure
- Elucidate consequences of re-conservation compared to the effects if no such actions are taken
- Investigate possibilities of future non-destructive monitoring of ship and loose artifacts

The project received funding from Swedish research foundations in 2008. It was launched in October 2008 and is scheduled

for 3 years. At present five research laboratories are involved. A short summary of current activities is as follows:

Wood chemical properties – The analytical work by Iversen, et al. [46, 47] on authentic *Vasa* wood referred to above, indicates that cellulose degradation also occurs in the interior wood. Comparison with non-conserved reference wood indicates that degradation has occurred since the material was exposed to air. The relative contribution from oxidative degradation (Fenton chemistry) and acid hydrolysis is still an open question. Based on carbon-13 NMR, Iversen recently reported quite high concentrations of oxalic acid in the interior wood, in addition to the formic and acetic acids present. Since this is a strong acid (pKa 1.3) it may contribute to the over-all acidity and to hydrolysis of cellulose.

Similarly, the work by Persson and Almkvist [41-45] indicates degradation in the inner parts of the wood. The positive correlation between high iron(II) concentrations and degradation [41] most likely speak in favor of an oxidative degradation. Noteworthy, samples containing rather high concentrations of sulfur in addition to the iron show less degradation [42]. This is an important observation; it might be interpreted as a possible inhibition of free radical processes by reduced sulfur compounds acting as scavengers. Thus, the original hypothesis [12] of a sulfuric acid mediated acid hydrolysis of the cellulose as the main degradation mechanism seems to be an over-simplification. Other processes and other acids might be equally - or most likely more - important. Reactions depending directly or indirectly on the iron(II/III) redox chemistry are definitely key processes.

Intensified studies of oligosaccharide decay products and lignin status of *Vasa* wood is in progress in co-operation with the Department of Wood Technology at the Royal Institute of Technology (KTH) in

Stockholm. The aim is to retrieve more information of importance for the determination of degradation reaction mechanisms.

Accelerated ageing – Almkvist, in co-operation with Ingela Bjurhager at the Royal Institute of Technology (KTH), has launched a series of model experiments, reported at this meeting [54]. Fresh oak is exposed to iron compounds, PEG and various oxygen pressures, relative humidities and temperatures. Interestingly, the conditions of authentic *Vasa* wood can be reproduced quite well, and the ageing experiments indicate that the degradation is rather rapid initially and then decelerates to become rather slow. The chemically treated model samples are subjected to mechanical testing as described below in order to establish relations between chemical status and mechanical properties.

Wood mechanical properties – The early work at the Fibre and Polymer Technology department at KTH referred to above [50-52] is continued. Bjurhager has devised methods for determination of mechanical properties of hardwoods and PEG-impregnated waterlogged wood [55, 56]. Axial tension of *Vasa* oak as well as fresh oak treated in the accelerated ageing experiments are determined [54]. There is a good correlation between the observed tensile strength and the degradation status of these samples. Thus, a relatively good mechanical stability is observed in the wood below the soft bacterially degraded PEG-rich surface region. But further inside the timbers, the mechanical properties again get worse, in agreement with the chemical results indicating degradation processes in this region. Current results indicate a decrease of mechanical strength of *Vasa* wood compared to fresh oak of ca 30 %. Further work in this field will include compression tests.

Reaction rates – Most chemical reactions in archaeological wood consume oxygen, directly or indirectly. Oxygen consumption rates can be used to determine reaction rates [57]. In a co-operative project with Matthiesen and Mortensen at the Danish National Museum oxygen consumption and diffusion in *Vasa* wood is being studied, as reported at this meeting [58]. Diffusion rates in wood vary depending on the properties of the particular sample, but oxygen concentrations inside wood are lower than in the atmosphere, indicating oxygen consumption inside wood. Iron(II) impregnated samples consume more oxygen, indicating an iron(II) catalyzed process.

Implementation

It was early recognized that different treatment methods are needed for the hull of 900 tons and the ca. 20 000 loose wooden artifacts. The hull can hardly be treated with wet-chemical or gas methods in the presence of the public. Closing the museum during a couple of years for extensive re-conservation operations is not realistic. *Vasa* attracts more than 1 million visitors annually and - under all circumstances - the museum authorities want the ship and the collections to be exposed in a visitor-friendly manner.

Thus, the climate will be the most important parameter. In 2004, a new climate system was installed, which has proven capable of keeping RH and temperature under very good control, independent of the number of visitors and the outdoor climate, as reviewed by E. Hocker [59]. The question is how low the temperature and – in particular – the RH can be taken without detrimental effects. As a result of the very stable climate, salt deposits resulting from transport of humidity inside the timbers have decreased in number and occurrence [60].

Another important parameter is the support structure. The ship is now resting on the original keel blocks and supporting elements installed in 1964 with some provisional improvements. A geodetic positional system indicates that the hull is moving very slightly. A plan for a better support system has to take into consideration the rates of the chemical degradation processes and the accompanying mechanical weakening of the timbers, since a new support system should be dimensioned to last for many decades.

Several methods are now available for treatment of loose objects. The iron extraction method, which is also a neutralization method, works well with the exception of very thick timbers, whose interior is inaccessible. But the long-term effects on the wood caused by the strongly basic extraction solutions are still a matter of uncertainty. Further experiments to investigate the practical parameters are now in progress in co-operation with the Swedish National Heritage Board.

Other wet-chemical neutralization methods involving nano particles of calcium or magnesium hydroxides with propanol as carrier solvent also seem to work well and have been tested on *Vasa* material [61-63], but the penetration depth remains to be studied. The original – and detrimental - method of neutralization with poultices soaked with sodium bicarbonate suggested early [9, 11, 13] was fortunately discontinued in 2005. In general, use of wet chemical methods means that all soluble substances are removed and re-conservation is necessary.

Treatments with gaseous ammonia have been tested on *Vasa* material [64, 65]. The penetration of the gas is limited to 5-10 mm from surface, *i.e.* only to the bacterially degraded regions. Since current research indicates degradation processes and acidic conditions at greater depths, the method is probably not useful in practical preservation work. Its use will be impossible for the hull. Common to all neutralization methods is that they will inhibit not only acid degradation processes, but also Fenton-type free radical processes, which require pH values below ca 4.

The research work shows that oxygen is necessary for the degradation processes. Keeping valuable objects under inert gas after extraction or neutralization treatment followed by re-conservation by PEG treatment and freeze drying would be one safe method for long-lasting preservation.

One very important parameter, still unknown, is the rate and extent of the observed degradation processes. Model experiments by accelerated ageing might give some information but are inherently difficult to interpret. Authentic *Vasa* material has now been under inspection with state-of-the-art experimental techniques for nine years. This period is probably too short to allow for estimation of the slow rates involved – one decade might only represent one point on the on a very long time axis. On several occasions researchers have been asking for samples representing the wood status say, at the time of salvage in 1961, when conservation was finished in 1979, or when the ship entered the new museum in 1988. Such samples are not available. Probing *Vasa* today and saving these samples for a couple of decades under anaerobic conditions at low temperature would enable researchers of future generations to compare these samples with the status of the timbers kept under normal museum conditions. Such strategy would admit better estimations of the changes of wood properties over time.

It is desirable to keep sampling of wood at a minimum, both with respect to number and size. Plans for shared use of samples by several research groups and non-destructive methods, such as ultrasound, are under consideration. Noteworthy, different methods of treatment will be necessary for different groups of objects depending on for instance degradation status, wood species and cultural-historical value. This is a matter of present evaluation.

Acknowledgements
The Swedish National Maritime Museums' research programs *"Preserve the Vasa"* and *"A Future for Vasa"* were financially supported by The Swedish Research Council (VR), The Swedish Foundation for Strategic Research (SSF), The Swedish Research Council for Environment, Agricultural Sciences and Spatial Planning (FORMAS), The Swedish Agency for Innovation Systems (VINNOVA), The Bank of Sweden Tercentenary Foundation and the Swedish National Heritage Board. This support is gratefully acknowledged.

Note added in proof
Since this meeting, a PhD thesis by B. Håfors on the conservation of *Vasa* and the PEG conservation programs used has appeared, to be defended in Oct 2010 (66).

References
1) C.O. Cederlund, *Vasa I. The Archaeology of a Swedish Warship of 1628.* F. Hocker (ed), The National Maritime Museums of Sweden, Stockholm 2006.

2) L. Barkman, *The Preservation of the Wasa.* Vasa Studies 5, Swedish National Maritime Museums, Stockholm 1965.

3) B. Håfors, *The role of Wasa in the development of the polyethylene glycol preservation method*, in *Adv. in Chemistry Series*, 225, 1990, 195-216, American Chemical Society, Washington DC.

4) B. Håfors, *Improvements of the Conservation Program for Tank Treatment with PEG at the Vasa Conservation Laboratory*, Proc. 5th ICOM-WOAM Conf., Portland, Maine 1993.

5) B. Håfors and U. Persson, *Monitoring Changes in Water Content of the Vasa Wood with a Resistance Meter*, in P. Hoffmann, T. Grant, J.A Spriggs and T. Daley (eds.) Proc 6th ICOM-WOAM Conf., York 1996.

6) B. Håfors, *Procedures in Selecting and Evaluating the Conservation Liquid for the Vasa Wooden Material*, in P. Hoffmann, C. Bonnot-Diconne, X. Hiron and Q. Khoi Tran (eds.) Proc. 7th ICOM-WOAM Conf., Grenoble 1998.

7) B. Håfors, *Conservation of the Swedish Warship Vasa from 1628*, Vasa Studies 18, The Vasa Museum, Stockholm 2001.

8) E. Hocker, *From the Micro- to the Macro-: Managing the Conservation of the Warship, Vasa*, in *Proc. 2nd Int. Workshop on Science, Technology and Cultural Heritage 2005,* Catania, Italy, in *Macromolecular Symposia*, 238, 2006, 16-21.

9) T.P.A. Sandström, I. Hall-Roth and A. Karlsson, *Salt Precipitation on Vasa Timbers: An Introduction to a Problem* Proc. 8th ICOM-WOAM Conf., Stockholm 2001, P. Hoffmann, J.A. Spriggs, T. Grant, C. Cook, A. Recht (eds.) Bremerhaven 2002, 55-66.

10) M. Sandström, F. Jaliehvand, I. Persson, U. Gelius and P. Frank *Acidity and Salt Precipitation on the Vasa: The Sulfur Problem* Proc. 8th ICOM-WOAM Conf., Stockholm 2001, P. Hoffmann, J.A. Spriggs, T. Grant, C. Cook and A. Recht (eds) Bremerhaven, 2002, 67-89.

11) M. Sandström, I. Persson, F. Jaliehvand, Y. Fors, E. Damian, U. Gelius, I. Hall-Roth, V. L. Richards and I. Godfrey *The sulfur threat to marine-archaeological artefacts: acid and iron removal from the Vasa,* in Conservation Science 2002, J. H.

Townsend, K. Eremin and A. Adriaens (Eds), Archetype Press, London 2003, 79-87.

12) M. Sandström, F. Jaliehvand, I. Persson, U. Gelius, P. Frank and I. Hall-Roth, *Deterioration of the seventeenth-century warship Vasa by internal formation of sulfuric acid*, in *Nature*, 415, 2002, 893-897.

13) M. Sandström, Y. Fors and I. Persson, *The Vasa's New Battle: Sulfur, Acid and Iron*, Vasa Studies 19, Swedish National Maritime Museums, Stockholm 2003.

14) I. Hall-Roth and L. Dal *The Sulfur Threat to the 17th Century Warship Vasa* in *Maritime Heritage 2003*, WIT press, Southampton 2003, 175-183.

15) I. Hall-Roth *New Threats to the 17th Century Warshp Vasa* in *Art et Chimie*, CNRS Editions, Paris 2003, 159-163.

16) I. Hall-Roth and L. Malmberg, *Save the Vasa – an Introduction*, in *Proc. 9th ICOM-WOAM Conf.*, Copenhagen 2004, P. Hoffmann, J.A. Spriggs, T. Grant, C. Cook and A. Recht (eds) Bremerhaven 2005, 171-179.

17) C. Gjelstrup Björdal and T. Nilsson, *Outline and results from the "Vasa Wood Project" with emphasis on the microscopic investigations*, in *Proc. 10th ICOM-WOAM Conf.*, Amsterdam 2007, K. Strætkvern and D.J. Huisman (eds) Amersfort 2009, 483-491.

18) Y. Fors, T. Nilsson, E. Damian Risberg, M. Sandström and P. Torssander, *Sulfur accumulation in pine wood (Pinus Sylvestris) induced by bacteria in a simulated seabed environment: Implications for marine archaeological wood and fossil fuels*, in *Int. Biodeterioration & Biodegradation*, 62, 2008, 336-347.

19) K.-L. Pang, R.A. Eaton and J. Mitchell, *Molecular detection of bacteria in the seventeenth century Swedish warship Vasa*, in *Proc. 9th ICOM-WOAM Conf.*, Copenhagen 2004, P. Hoffmann, J.A. Spriggs, T. Grant, C. Cook and A. Recht (eds) Bremerhaven 2005, 243-259.

20) J. Mitchell, I.B. Beech, S.A. Campbell, J.A. Sunner, S. Hotchkiss and A. Smith, *Bacterial sulfur and iron cycling and deterioration of historic ships*, in *Geophysical Res. Abstr.*, 2007, 9, 04551.

21) S. Hotchkiss, E. Landy, K.-L. Pang and J. Mitchell, *Bacteria in Archaeological and Waterlogged Wood: Molecular Protocols for Diversity and Community Studies*, in *Heritage, Microbiology and Science*, E. May, M. Jones, J. Mitchell (eds), Roẏ. Soc. Chem. Special publ. No. 135, Cambridge 2008, 108-127.

22) Y. Fors *Sulfur Speciation and Distribution in the Vasa's Wood* Licentiate thesis, Structural Chemistry, Stockholm university, 2005.

23) M. Sandström, Y. Fors, F. Jaliehvand, E. Damian and U. Gelius, *Analyses of sulfur and iron in marine archaeological wood*, in *Proc. 9th ICOM-WOAM Conf.*, Copenhagen 2004, P. Hoffmann, J.A. Spriggs, T. Grant, C. Cook and A. Recht (eds) Bremerhaven 2005, 181-202.

24) M. Sandström, F. Jaliehvand, E. Damian, Y. Fors, U. Gelius, M. Jones and M. Salomé, *Sulfur accumulation in the timbers of King Henry VIII's warship Mary Rose: A pathway in the sulfur cycle of conservation concern*, in *Proc. Nat. Acad. Sci. USA*, 102 (40) 2005, 14165-14170.

25) Y. Fors and M. Sandström, *Sulfur and iron in shipwrecks cause conservation concerns*, in *Chem. Soc. Rev.*, 2006, 35, 1-17.

26) Y. Fors, *Sulfur-Related Conservation Concerns for Marine Archaeological Wood*, PhD thesis, Stockholm University, 2008.

27) F. Jaliehvand, *Sulfur: not a "silent" element anymore*, in *Chem. Soc. Rev.*, 35, 2006, 1256-1268.

28) G. Almkvist, L. Dal and I. Persson, *Extraction of iron compounds from Vasa wood*, in *Proc. 9th ICOM-WOAM Conf.*, Copenhagen 2004, P. Hoffmann, J.A. Spriggs, T. Grant, C. Cook and A. Recht (eds) Bremerhaven 2005, 203-211.

29) G. Almkvist and I. Persson, *Extraction of iron compounds from wood from the Vasa*, in *Holzforschung*, 60(6), 2006, 678-684.

30) G. Almkvist and I. Persson, *Extraction of iron compounds from waterlogged pine wood from the Vasa*, in *Heritage, Microbiology and Science Conf.*, E. May, M. Jones, J. Mitchell (eds), Roy. Soc. Chem. Special publ. No. 135, Cambridge 2008, 245-256.

31) E. Phillips and I. Godfrey Nyström, *Removing iron compounds from a waterlogged wooden gun-carriage using the chelating agent DTPA*, in *Proc. 11th ICOM-WOAM Conf.*, Greenville, N.C., 2010, *in press*.

32) M.N. Mortensen, H. Egsgaard, Y. Sashoua and J. Glastrup, *PEG in the warship Vasa and the Viking ship Skuldelev 2*, in *Proc. 9th ICOM-WOAM Conf.*, Copenhagen 2004, P. Hoffmann, J.A. Spriggs, T. Grant, C. Cook and A. Recht (eds) Bremerhaven 2005, 261-268.

33) J. Glastrup, Y. Sashoua, H. Egsgaard and M.N. Mortensen, *Degradation of PEG in the warship Vasa*, in *Proc.2nd Int. Workshop on Science, Technology and Cultural Heritage, 2005*, Catania, Italy, in *Macromolecular Symposia*, 238, 2006, 22-29.

34) J. Glastrup, Y. Sashoua, H. Egsgaard and M.N. Mortensen, *Formic and acetic acids in archaeological wood. A comparison between the Vasa warship, the Bremen cog, the Oberländer boat and the Danish Viking ships*, in *Holzforschung*, 60(3), 2006, 259-264.

35) M.N. Mortensen, H. Egsgaard, S. Hvilsted, Y. Sashoua and J. Glastrup, *Characterization of the polyethylene glycol impregnation of the Swedish warship Vasa and one of the Danish Skuldelev Viking ships*, in *J. Archaeol. Sci.*, 34(8), 2007, 1211-1218.

36) M. N. Mortensen, *Stabilization of polyethylene glycol in archaeological wood*, PhD thesis, Technical university of Denmark and National Museum of Denmark, Lyngby 2009.

37) M.N. Mortensen, H. Egsgaard, S. Hvilsted and J. Glastrup, *Formic acid as a marker molecule for polyethylene glycol degradation in conserved archaeological wood – a radiocarbon study*, in *Proc. 11th ICOM-WOAM Conf.*, Greenville, N.C., 2010, *in press*.

38) U. Westermark, B. Steenberg and B. Sundqvist, *Impregnation with PEG and solvolysis of wood – reflections from analysis of the ancient warship Vasa*, in *Proc.13th Int. Symp. for Wood, Fibre and Pulping Chemstry*, Auckland, N. Zealand, 2005, 229-231.

39) G. Almkvist and I. Persson, *The movement and stability of polyethylene glycol (PEG) in the Vasa wood*, in *Proc. 9th ICOM-WOAM Conf.*, Copenhagen 2004, P. Hoffmann, J.A. Spriggs, T. Grant, C. Cook and A. Recht (eds) Bremerhaven 2005, 269-278.

40) C. Lindblad and I. Persson, *Polyethylene glycol/Polyethylene oxide: An overview of the physical-chemical properties of PEG/PEO*, in *Proc. 10th ICOM-WOAM Conf.*, Amsterdam 2007, K. Strætkvern and D.J. Huisman (eds) Amersfort 2009, 507-516.

41) G. Almkvist and I. Persson, *Degradation of polyethylene glycol and hemicellulose in the Vasa*, in *Holzforschung*, 62(2), 2008, 64-70.

42) G. Almkvist and I. Persson, *Analysis of acids and degradation products related to iron and sulfur in the Swedish warship Vasa*, in *Holzforschung*, 62(6), 2008, 694-703.

43) G. Almkvist and I. Persson, *Fenton-induced degradation of polyethylene glycol and oak holocellulose. A model experiment in comparison to changes observed in conserved waterlogged wood*, in *Holzforschung*, 62(6), 2008, 704-708.

44) G. Almkvist and I. Persson, *Iron catalyzed degradation processes in the Vasa*, in *Proc. 10th ICOM-WOAM Conf.*, Amsterdam 2007, K. Strætkvern and D.J. Huisman (eds) Amersfort 2009, 499-506.

45) G. Almkvist, *The Chemistry of the Vasa – Iron, Acids and Degradation*, PhD thesis, Swedish University of Agricultural Sciences, Uppsala 2008.

46) E.L. Lindfors, M. Lindström and T. Iversen, *Polysaccharide degradation in water-logged oak wood from the ancient warship Vasa*, in *Holzforschung*, 62(1) 2008, 57-63.

47) T. Iversen, E.L. Lindfors and M. Lindström, *Polysaccharide degradation in Vasa oak wood*, in *Proc. 10th ICOM-WOAM Conf.*, Amsterdam 2007, K. Strætkvern and D.J. Huisman (eds) Amersfort 2009, 493-498.

48) I. Godfrey, L. Byrne, E. Ghisalberti and V. Richards. *Nuclear Magnetic Resonance Spectroscopic Analyses of Acid-Affected Waterlogged Archaeological Wood*, in *Proc. 11th ICOM-WOAM Conf.*, Greenville, N.C., 2010, *in press*.

49) A.O. Rapp, C. Brischke, C.R. Welzbacher, T. Nilsson and C. Björdal, *Mechanical strength of wood from the Vasa shipwreck*, in *Proc. 39th Annual Meeting of the Int. Res. Group on Wood Protection*, Istanbul, 2008.

50) J. Ljungdahl, *Structure and properties of Vasa oak*, Licentiate thesis, Roy. Inst. of Technology, Stockholm, 2006.

51) J. Ljungdahl, L.A. Berglund and M. Burman, *Transverse anisotropy of compressive failure in European oak. A digital speckle photography study*, in *Holzforschung*, 60(2), 2006, 190-195.

52) J. Ljungdahl and L.A. Berglund, *Transverse mechanical behavior and moisture of waterlogged archaeological wood from the Vasa ship*, in *Holzforschung*, 61(3), 2007, 279-284.

53) A. McAuley, B. Holmbom, P. Hoffmann and P. Jensen, *International Evaluation of the Preserve the Vasa Project*, Statens Maritima Museer, Stockholm 2006.

54) G. Almkvist, I. Bjurhager and C. Johansson, *Accelerated ageing of recent oak – impact from iron ions and oxygen on mechanical properties in the longitudinal direction*, in *Proc. 11th ICOM-WOAM Conf.*, Greenville, N.C., 2010, *in press*.

55) I. Bjurhager, *Mechanical behavior of hardwoods – effects from cellular and cell wall structures*, Licentiate thesis, Roy. Inst. of Technology, Stockholm 2008.

56) I. Bjurhager, J. Ljungdahl, L. Wallström, E.K. Gamstedt and L.A. Berglund, *Towards*

improved understanding of PEG-impregnated waterlogged archaeological wood: A model study on recent oak, in Holzforschung, 64, 2010, 243-250.

57) H. Matthiesen, A Novel Method to Determine Oxidation Rates of Heritage Materials in Vitro and in Situ, in Studies in Conservation, 52, 2007, 271-280.

58) H. Matthiesen and M.N. Mortensen, Oxygen measurements in conserved archaeological wood, in Proc. 11th ICOM-WOAM Conf., Greenville, N.C., 2010, in press.

59) E. Hocker, Maintaining a Stable Climate: A New Climate Control System for the Vasa Ship, in Assoc. Preservation Technol. Bull., 2010, in press.

60) E. Hocker, L. Dal, F. Hocker, Understanding Vasa's Salt Problem: Documenting the Distribution of Salt Precipitations on the Swedish Warship Vasa, in Proc. 10th ICOM-WOAM Conf., Amsterdam 2007, K. Strætkvern and D.J. Huisman (eds) Amersfort 2009, 469-481.

61) R. Giorgi, D. Chelazzi and P. Baglioni, Nanoparticles of Calcium Hydroxide for Wood Conservation. The De-acidification of the Vasa Warship, in Langmuir, 21, 2005, 10743-10748.

62) R. Giorgi, D. Chelazzi and P. Baglioni, Conservation of acid in waterlogged shipwrecks: nanotechnologies for de-acidification, in Appl. Phys. A, 83, 2006, 567-571.

63) R. Giorgi, D. Chelazzi and P. Baglioni, Nanoscience contribution to preservation of acidic shipwrecks, in Proc. 10th ICOM-WOAM Conf., Amsterdam 2007, K. Strætkvern and D.J. Huisman (eds) Amersfort 2009, 525-537.

64) Y. Fors, Ammonia treatment of acidic Vasa wood, in Proc. 10th ICOM-WOAM Conf., Amsterdam 2007, K. Strætkvern and D.J. Huisman (eds) Amersfort 2009, 539-561.

65) Y. Fors and V. Richards, The Effects of the Ammonia Neutralizing Treatment on Marine Archaeological Vasa Wood, in Studies in Conservation, 55, 2010, 41-54.

66) B. Håfors, Conservation of the Wood of the Swedish Warship Vasa of A.D. 1628 – Evaluation of Polyethylene Glycol Conservation Programs. PhD thesis, University of Gothenburg, Sweden, 2010.

4.2

Iron Removal from Waterlogged Wood and the Effects on Wood Chemistry

Vicki Richards*, Kalle Kasi and Ian Godfrey
Western Australian Museum, Shipwreck Galleries, 45-47 Cliff St, Fremantle, Western Australia, 6160
*E-mail vicki.richards@museum.wa.gov.au

Abstract
One of the major problems associated with the conservation of cellulosic materials is the detrimental effect that incorporated iron corrosion products have on their post-treatment stability. A series of extraction experiments were carried out to determine the impact of different chelating agents on the iron removal efficiency from some heavily iron impregnated waterlogged wooden chocks recovered from the *Xantho* shipwreck site in Western Australia. Various combinations of polyethylene glycol and different chelating agents were investigated. The rates of iron extraction were monitored and the effect of exposure to the chelating agents on the wood chemistry was examined using Fourier transform infrared (FTIR) spectroscopy.

Keywords: iron corrosion products, waterlogged wood, iron extraction, chelating agents, polyethylene glycol, Fourier transform infrared spectroscopy

1. Introduction
The destructive effects caused by actively corroding iron in contact with wood are well known. Where iron is found in intimate contact or in close proximity to wooden artifacts their corrosion products will diffuse into and remain in the wood matrix. The presence of these iron corrosion products in the wood has several effects. There will be an effect on the mechanical strength, the chemical stability of the wood structure and the rate of biological degradation. The precipitation of iron corrosion products will also replace water in the swollen state of the timber and plug the voids in the internal wood structure providing stability to the wood cells by a bulking process. However, they can prevent penetration of consolidants into the interior cells and degrade cellulose by hydrolysis and iron catalyzed auto-oxidation (Farber 1954, Bell and Gibson 1957, Morgan 1962, Pinion 1970, Jespersen 1989, Fengel and Wegener 1989, Richards 1996, Ghisalberti et al. 2002, Sandström et al. 2003, Almkvist et al. 2005, Fors 2005, Sandström et al. 2005, Almkvist 2008, Almkvist and Persson 2009).

Major post treatment changes can occur in conserved iron impregnated waterlogged wood. These detrimental changes are predominantly associated with acid degradation of the carbohydrates in the wood structure, caused primarily by the oxidation of reduced sulfur species and iron sulfides producing acidic iron sulfates and hydrogen ions. The acidic conditions produced also promote acid hydrolysis of cellulose and hemicelluloses and other degradation reactions of lignin. In addition, iron ions are renowned for catalyzing oxidation of wood components. The expansion in the molar volumes of the oxidized sulfur species and iron corrosion products also results in physical deterioration of the wood fibers (Emery and Shroeder 1974, Watson 1976, Lowson 1982, Jespersen 1989, MacLeod and Kenna 1991, Richards 1996, Sandström et al. 2002, Sandström et al. 2003, Fors 2005, Almkvist 2008, Almkvist and Persson 2009, Huisman 2009, Iversen et al. 2009). Hence, suitable conservation treatments have to be found where the iron salts are removed from within the wood structure before and/or during treatment but the wood is still bulked and sufficiently stabilized to minimize shrinkage on drying.

Over the years many different methods have been used to extract iron corrosion products from waterlogged wood, with varying degrees of success. Treatments have included the application of a variety of acids (hydrochloric acid, citric acid and oxalic acid), chelating agents (ammonium citrate, ammonium oxalate, ethylenediamine tetraacetic acid (EDTA), dimethylglyoxime, porphyrins etc), corrosion inhibitors such as tannic acid, hot steam, boiling and running water, sodium hydroxide and hydrogen peroxide solutions, electrolysis and electrophoresis (Hackerman and Oagura 1975, Pang 1981, Hawley 1989, Jespersen 1989, La Baume 1989, MacLeod 1990, Chartier 1991, MacLeod et al. 1991, Palmer and Boden 1992, MacLeod et al. 1994, Richards 1996).

In the early 1990s preliminary experiments on the extraction of iron corrosion products from degraded, iron impregnated waterlogged wood found that the use of sodium dithionite in conjunction with diammonium citrate and PEG solutions at neutral pH was very effective in removing iron minerals from iron impregnated timber whilst successfully stabilizing the wood structure (MacLeod et al. 1991, 1994). More recently, high performance iron chelators (HPIC), diethylenetriamine pentaacetic acid (DTPA) and ethylenediimino-bis (2-hydroxy-4-methylphenyl)acetic acid (EDDHMA), have proven very successful in removing iron corrosion products from acid-affected, PEG treated waterlogged wood (Almkvist and Persson 2006).

Based on these results, a series of extraction experiments were carried out to determine the impact of different chelating agents on the iron removal efficiency from some heavily iron impregnated waterlogged wooden chocks recovered from the Xantho shipwreck site in Western Australia. Various combinations of polyethylene glycol and different chelating agents, including DTPA and EDDHMA were investigated. The rates of iron extraction were monitored and the effect of exposure to the chelating agents on the wood chemistry was examined using Fourier transform infrared (FTIR) spectroscopy.

1.1. Recovery of the iron impregnated wooden chocks

The SS Xantho was an iron steamship, wrecked in 1872 at Port Gregory 600km north of Perth, Western Australia. Although salvaged at the time, significant portions of the original structure, including the steam engine and the boiler, remained on-site when it was discovered in 1979. Based on the results of an extensive on-site pre-disturbance conservation survey conducted in 1983 (MacLeod et al. 1986), it was decided to recover and conserve the engine. In May 1985 the engine was recovered and transported to Fremantle. The engine was placed in a custom-built tank and the deconcretion phase began. After several deconcreting sessions however, it became apparent that removal of all the concretion and disassembly of the engine would have to be undertaken in stages over many years. Hence, the engine was set up for conventional electrolysis treatment in sodium hydroxide solution. The solution was periodically drained and the deconcreting sessions continued until the engine was totally dismantled in the mid 1990s.

In 1994, the base plate that supported the engine was deconcreted and removed, exposing about 100 wooden chocks that were used to stabilize the engine in the hull of the ship. The chocks were in excellent condition as they had been protected from the alkaline sodium hydroxide electrolytic solution by encapsulation in the concretion and were coated in tallow (rendered animal fat) that was used to keep the engine lubricated during its working life. However, due to the corrosion of the iron engine on the seabed, the wooden chocks were also heavily impregnated with iron corrosion products (Figure 1). The chocks were stored in deionized water until the research designs for each experimental phase were finalized.

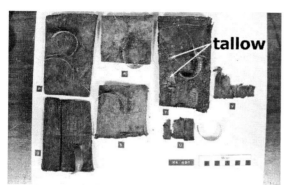

Figure 1: *Examples of iron-impregnated Xantho chocks immediately after recovery in 1994.*

2. Experimental
2.1. Experiment 1
2.1.1. Wood identification
The cross-sectional, radial and tangential longitudinal surfaces of the wood samples were polished to a 1200 grit finish using silicon carbide paper and then examined by optical transmission microscopy (low and high power).

2.1.2. Total iron content
Total iron contents of the wood samples were determined by ashing the samples at 500°C for approximately 12 hours and acid digesting with nitric acid. The resultant solutions were made up to volume and analyzed for iron on a Varian Techtron atomic absorption spectrophotometer (AAS) at a wavelength of 248.3nm, lamp current of 8mA, with an oxidizing air/acetylene flame.

The concentration of iron in the treatment solutions was determined by thoroughly stirring the solution prior to removing an accurate, known volume (10ml) of the experimental solution and placing in a conical flask. The solution samples were then evaporated to dryness on a hotplate and placed in a furnace at 500°C for about 12 hours. The ashed samples were then digested with nitric acid and analyzed for iron as described above.

2.1.3. Maximum water content (U_{max})
Small sections of the control chocks were removed, accurately weighed after drying for 15 minutes in ambient conditions on the bench, dried in an oven at 105°C for 24 hours, removed and cooled in a desiccator to constant weight. The maximum water content was then calculated according to Grattan (1987).

2.1.4. Mass
Accurate weights of the wooden chocks were measured after blotting the surfaces dry with lint-free tissue then allowing the chocks to stand on the bench in the laboratory at ambient conditions for exactly 5 minutes.

2.1.5. pH measurements
The surface pH values of the wooden chocks were measured by blotting the surfaces with lint-free tissue, placing one drop of distilled, deionized water on the lower, left hand side, thinner edge of the chocks and measuring the pH with a BDH GelPlas gel-filled combination flat surface pH electrode in direct contact with this wetted surface. The minimum surface pH was recorded.

The pH values of treatment solutions were measured with a BDH GelPlas gel-filled combination flat surface pH electrode after thorough stirring of the solution.

2.1.6. Surface area
The surface areas of the wooden chocks were measured by photocopying the faces of the samples, which normally incurs about a 2% error due to photocopying distortions of the solid face. The area of the 2-D projections were then measured with a Planix 7 planimeter and the total surface area calculated by addition.

2.1.7. Color measurements

The precise colors of the wooden chocks were measured in duplicate using a Minolta Chromameter CR-100 and the data collected by a Minolta Data Processor DP-100. The chocks were blotted dry with a lint-free tissue and the measuring head of the chromameter placed directly onto the dry surface of the upper right hand, thicker edge and the lower, left hand, thinner edge of the chock.

2.2. Experiment 2
2.2.1. Total iron content
The total iron contents of the wood chocks were determined before and during treatment by coring the chocks with a cork borer (8mm ID), then sectioning the cores into three equal lengths. The two outer sections of the core were combined and labeled 'outer' sample and the remaining inner section was labeled 'mid' sample. The wet 'outer' and 'mid' samples were weighed, dried in an oven at 105°C for eight hours and the dry weight recorded. The entire sample was digested with 10ml of a 4:1 mixture of redistilled nitric:perchloric acid solution at 170°C for 24 hours. This solution was evaporated to dryness and redissolved, with slight warming, using 0.5ml hydrochloric:nitric acid (4:1) solution and 5ml deionized water. The solubilized sample was then made up to approximately 10g using deionized water and the final dilution mass recorded to three decimal places. The samples were then analyzed for sulfur and iron content with reference to in-house calibration standards using a Thermo Scientific iCap 6000 inductively coupled atomic emission spectrophotometer (ICP-AES).

The concentration of iron in the treatment solutions was determined by thoroughly stirring the solution prior to removing an accurate, known volume (10ml) of the experimental solution. The solution sample was then acidified with nitric acid to dissolve any iron precipitates, made up to

volume and analyzed for iron by flame atomic absorption spectrometry (AAS).

2.2.2. Mass
Accurate weights of the wooden chocks were measured after blotting the chocks dry with lint-free tissue and allowing the chocks to stand on the bench in the laboratory at ambient conditions for exactly 5 minutes.

2.2.3. pH measurements
The surface pH of the wooden chocks were measured by blotting the surfaces dry with lint-free tissue, placing one drop of distilled, deionized water on the lower, left hand, thinner edge of the chocks and measuring the pH with a VWR International gel-filled combination flat surface pH electrode in direct contact with this wetted surface. The minimum surface pH was recorded.

The solution pH was measured with a VWR International gel-filled combination flat surface pH electrode after thorough stirring of the solution.

2.2.4. Surface area
The surface areas of the wooden chocks were measured by photographing the planar, edge and base surfaces of each chock, using Adobe Photoshop software to accurately measure the surface area of each photographed surface and then calculating the total surface area by addition.

2.2.5. Color measurements
The precise colour of wooden chocks was measured in duplicate using a Konica Minolta Chroma Meter CR-400 using D_{65} as the standard illuminant with the data collected by a Konica Minolta Data Processor DP-400. The chocks were blotted dry with a lint-free tissue and the measuring head of the chromameter placed directly onto the dry surface of the upper right hand, thicker edge and the lower, left hand, thinner edge of the chock.

2.2.6. Fourier Transform Infrared Spectrometry (FTIR)

FTIR analyses of the wooden chocks were collected before and during treatment. The upper surface of the chock was named 'outer' and the lower surface of the chock, facing down against the bench was named 'inner'. The entire width of the chock was cored near the thicker edge of the chock with a cork borer (8mm) and the resultant core samples were cut in half. The outermost surface of the upper 'outer' core section was labeled 'outer:outer (OO)' and the middle of the upper 'outer' core section was labeled 'mid:outer (MO)'. Pin-head size samples were taken from the outer:outer (OO) surface and the mid:outer (MO) surfaces of the same upper 'outer' core section and examined using a Perkin Elmer Spectrum 100S FTIR spectrometer. The sample spectra were collected using a UATR accessory with 1 bounce Diamond/KRS-5 crystal combination, accumulated over 4 scans. The spectral range was 4000-600 cm^{-1} with a resolution of 4 cm^{-1}. The Spectrum v6.3.5 software package from Perkin Elmer Inc was used to collect the spectra with the ATR correction applied and conversion from transmittance (%T) as its ordinate to absorbance units (A). The OPUS v6.5 IR package from Bruker Optik GmbH was used to calculate peak intensities by setting up the integration method 'L' with the baseline from about 1800 to 800 cm^{-1}, dependent on the minima observed in the spectra at these approximate wave numbers.

3. Results and discussion

3.1. Experiment 1

3.1.1. Extraction of iron corrosion products with dithionite and citrate

Iron oxy hydroxides, such as goethite and lepidocrocite, are often the major corrosion products identified on the surfaces of heavily iron impregnated waterlogged wood stored in deionized water (MacLeod et al. 1991, MacLeod and Kenna 1991, Richards 1996). This iron oxyhydroxide corrosion product matrix is voluminous and can block the internal wood structure, effectively decreasing diffusion rates of chemical species into and out of the wood.

Sodium dithionite is a strong chemical reducing agent that will reduce some of the ferric ions to ferrous ions in this iron oxyhydroxide lattice. Iron (II) hydroxides are much more soluble, at a level of 8 x 10^{-2}M at neutral pH, than ferric hydroxide which has a solubility of 4 x 10^{-19}M under these conditions (Chemical Society 1971). Once some of the ferric ions have been reduced by the dithionite, the lattice becomes unstable and more susceptible to complexation with citrate ions (MacLeod et al. 1994). If citric acid is represented as H_3L, mononuclear ferric ion complexes may form from among the series MHL, ML, MOHL and $M(OH)_2L$ as the pH becomes successively more alkaline (pH ≈ 1.0 - 7.5). At acidic pH values (pH < 3.0) the major ferric ion-citrate complex formed is the neutral tridentate mononuclear complex, [Fe(III)cit], which has a $log_{10}K_{stab}$ of about 11.4. In the pH range 4.0 to about 6.5, hydrolysis occurs and [Fe(III)OHcit]⁻ is the major tridentate complex formed ($log_{10}K_{stab}$ ≈ 8.60), then as the pH increases from 6.5 to about 7.0-7.5 the second hydrolysis step occurs and results in the formation of [Fe(III)(OH)_2cit]$^{2-}$ and the $log_{10}K_{stab}$ is dramatically reduced to between 1.9-2.6. This significant loss in stability suggests the formation of a weaker mononuclear bidentate complex at more neutral pH (Lanford and Quinan 1948, Warner and Weber 1953, Hamm et al. 1954, Field et al. 1974, Francis and Dodge 1993). It is important, however, to allow air to circulate in the solution containing citrate ions after the reducing action of the dithionite has ceased so that any ferrous ions present will be oxidized to ferric ions, which form more stable citrate complexes (Hamm et al. 1954).

So given the effectiveness of dithionite, in the presence of citrate ions, to promote the dissolution of iron corrosion products, it was decided to further investigate the nature of these chemical interactions on the extraction of iron from the heavily iron-impregnated *Xantho* chocks. Five solutions were chosen for Experiment 1 utilizing different combinations of PEG 400, citrate and dithionite plus one control solution of distilled deionized water. Due to the natural acidity of wood, diammonium hydrogen citrate was chosen as the source of the citrate ions as it has an initial pH in distilled water of about 5.0 at a concentration of 2% weight/volume and the stability constant of the associated ferric ion/citrate complex at this pH was still acceptable. The composition of the six treatment solutions is described in Table 1.

Table 1. Composition of the treatment solutions (A-F) for Experiment 1.

Solution Code	Solution Composition[1]
A	5%[2] PEG 400
B	5% PEG 400/2% diammonium hydrogen citrate
C	5% PEG 400/2% diammonium hydrogen citrate/5% sodium dithionite
D	2% diammonium hydrogen citrate
E	5% sodium dithionite
F	distilled deionized water

[1] All solutions were made up to 4L in total with distilled deionized water.
[2] All percentages were in weight/volume (w/v).

3.1.2. Initial measurements

Prior to the commencement of Experiment 1, two wooden chocks were chosen as controls and have been stored in distilled deionized water since their recovery in 1994. The chocks were sampled and analyzed for total iron content, maximum water content and wood speciation. The wood was identified as a beech and most likely of European origin (*Fagus sylvatica* L.) because of the *Xantho*'s provenance (McCarthy 2000). The average total iron content before treatment was $21.2 \pm 3.6\%$. The average U_{max} of the wood samples was $54 \pm 15\%$. This very low average figure indicated that these wooden chocks were relatively undegraded despite immersion in a marine environment for over one hundred years. Encapsulation by concretion, the more protected position beneath the engine and the fatty organic surface coating on the chocks had provided considerable protection from major physico-chemical and biological degradation.

Four chocks were used in each of the six experimental treatment solutions (A-F). Before treatment commenced the surface pH, weight, surface area and color of each chock was measured. The twenty four chocks used in Experiment 1 had an average surface area of $272 \pm 43cm^2$, an average weight of $182 \pm 61g$ and an average surface pH of 5.26 ± 0.21.

Overall the *Xantho* chocks were thought to be a good choice for use in our experiments. As there were over 100 similar chocks they minimized the inherent heterogeneity and therefore, unrepresentative comparative nature of most maritime archaeological wood; they were assumed to be mostly beech; they had been exposed to the same micro-environment for the same length of time and hence had similar extents of deterioration. They also contained similar concentrations of iron and were relatively similar in size and weight.

However, one potential problem was the presence of the tallow, which could adversely affect the diffusion of the complexing solutions into and the iron corrosion products out of the wooden chocks due to the hydrophobic nature of the fats. On visual inspection of the surfaces, it appeared that the tallow coatings were relatively thin and consistent across all chocks, but the amount within the internal structure of the wood was not measured. After some discussion, it was decided to use the chocks in these iron extraction experiments as the positives associated with the relative homogeneity of the samples far outweighed the negative impact the fatty residues may have on diffusion rates.

3.1.3. Iron extraction efficiency

In Experiment 1 the initial effectiveness of these treatments on removing iron corrosion products was determined by monitoring the quantity of iron extracted from the wooden chocks in each solution over the first four months of treatment. The total mass of iron released in each solution was plotted against a range of time functions but the most consistent results were obtained for correlations with the square root of time in hours from the

inception of the experiment. This linear dependence is characteristic of diffusion controlled processes. The total amount of iron released into each experimental solution is shown in Figure 2.

The apparent rates of iron extraction for each experimental solution were calculated from the slopes of the plot of total iron released versus time ($t^{\frac{1}{2}}$). Since the release of iron is diffusion controlled, the extraction rate will be dependent on the surface areas of the chocks in the treatment solutions. So in order to compare the 'real' release rates, the apparent extraction rates were normalized by correcting for the total geometric surface area of the four chocks in each reaction solution. This is obviously more important when attempting to compare release rates of artifacts with significantly different surfaces areas. The normalized release rates for all extraction stages are shown graphically in Figure 3.

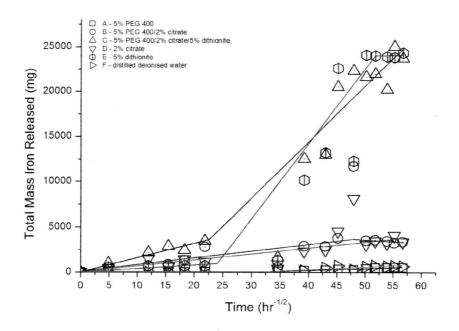

Figure 2. Total amount of iron released from the Xantho chocks into each treatment solution (Experiment 1).

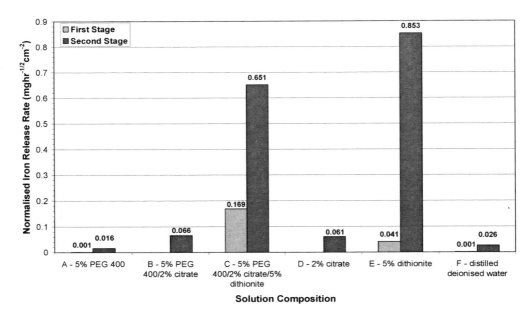

Figure 3: Normalized iron extraction rates for each treatment solution (Experiment 1).

The extraction results in these solutions were basically characterized by a two stage process (Figure 2 & 3) where there was a significant increase in release rate after about 20 days (Figure 2). These induction periods are commonly observed with iron-impregnated artifacts that have been in storage for several years (MacLeod et al. 1991, 1994, Richards 1996). The existence of these induction periods may be associated with diffusion kinetics and the time required for the dithionite to effectively reduce enough of the Fe(III) so the iron corrosion product matrix on the surface of the wooden chocks becomes unstable.

From the graph in Figure 2 it is obvious that solutions C (5% PEG 400, 2% citrate and 5% dithionite) and E (5% dithionite) extracted the most iron over the 4.5 month period. It is notable however, that after about 3.5 months the extraction of iron ceased in solution E but continued in solution C. This is not unexpected as dithionite reduces some of the Fe^{3+} to Fe^{2+}, assisting in the dissolution of the oxidized iron corrosion products in the wood, but once this solubilization process ceases there is no complexing agent present to continue the iron extraction process.

The normalized iron release rate graph (Figure 3) shows the aforementioned induction stages quite clearly. For example, in solution C (PEG/citrate/dithionite) the iron extraction rate in the first or induction stage was $0.169 mghr^{-\frac{1}{2}}cm^{-2}$ while in the second stage the rate of iron release increased to $0.651 mghr^{-\frac{1}{2}}cm^{-2}$. Similarly, the extraction rate in the first stage for solution E, containing only dithionite, was initially lower than for solution C, at $0.041 mghr^{-\frac{1}{2}}cm^{-2}$ but increased markedly in the second stage to $0.853 mghr^{-\frac{1}{2}}cm^{-2}$, the highest iron extraction rate observed. Based solely on these results, solution E, containing dithionite only would appear to be the most efficient solution at extracting iron. The release rate graphs however, do not indicate exactly when the induction periods finished and the extraction rates increased and more importantly, when iron release ceased, as signified by a plateau for the dithionite plot at about $50hr^{\frac{1}{2}}$ in Figure 2. Hence, the different information gained from Figures 2 and 3, emphasizes the importance of mathematically manipulating the same data in a number of different ways to obtain the optimum amount of information.

3.1.4. Changes in solution pH

Another important parameter to monitor is the solution pH as this will have an effect on the efficiency of the complexation reactions that occur in the solution and more importantly, on the degradation of the wood during treatment. The change in solution pH over time for Experiment 1 is shown in Figure 4

The pH of the solutions containing dithionite (C and E) decreased over time and by the end of the experiment the pH in both solutions was about 3.70. As time progresses, the dithionite loses its reducing power as it is oxidized to sulfates and hydrogen ions, rendering the aqueous solutions more acidic. Hence, solutions containing dithionite need to be monitored closely to avoid the solutions becoming too acidic and causing damage to the wood over extended periods of time.

3.1.5. Conclusions

The most effective experimental solution for extracting iron corrosion products from the iron-impregnated waterlogged wooden chocks was 5% PEG 400, 2% diammonium hydrogen citrate and 5% sodium dithionite.

This solution extracted approximately 25g of iron from the four chocks and the release of iron appeared to be continuing after this 4.5 month monitoring period.

3.2. Experiment 2

3.2.1. Extraction of iron corrosion products with DTPA and EDDHMA

More recently, due to the acid problems experienced by the *Vasa*, research into the extraction of iron from acid affected treated wood using HPIC, namely DTPA and EDDHMA has been conducted by Almkvist and Persson (2006). The results showed that these multidentate ligands formed very stable complexes with Fe(III) ions (FeEDDHMA $log_{10}K_{stab}$ = 38; FeDTPA $log_{10}K_{stab}$ = 28), the complexes were stable over a wide pH range (FeEDDHMA pH ~ 3-11; FeDTPA pH ~ 1.5-7.5), resisted hydrolysis even at relatively high pHs (FeEDDHMA pH ~ 11; FeDTPA pH ~ 8) and were effective at extracting iron from acid-affected *Vasa* timbers (Almkvist and Persson 2006, Almkvist 2008). Therefore it was decided to compare the extraction rates of iron in the most effective solution from Experiment 1 with DTPA and EDDHMA, again using the iron-impregnated *Xantho* chocks.

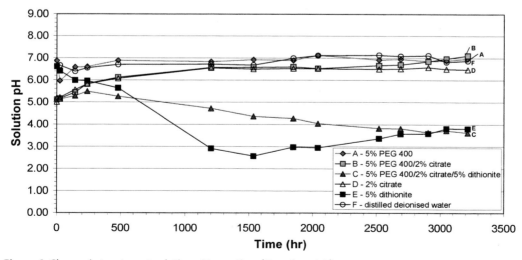

Figure 4. *Change in treatment solution pH over time (Experiment 1).*

Table 2. *Composition of the treatment solutions (A-H) for Experiment 2.*

Solution Code	Solution Composition[1]	Solution pH
A	distilled deionized water	Not controlled
B	5%[2] PEG 400	Not controlled
C	5% PEG 400/2% diammonium hydrogen citrate/5% sodium dithionite	Not controlled
D	2% DTPA	6
E	5% PEG 400/2% DTPA	6
F	2% EDDHMA	7
G	2% EDDHMA	Not controlled
H	5% PEG 400/2% EDDHMA	7

[1] All solutions were made up to 4L in total with distilled deionized water.
[2] All percentages were in weight/volume (w/v).

Seven solutions were chosen for investigation utilizing the 5% PEG 400, 2% diammonium citrate and 5% dithionite solution from Experiment 1 (C) and different combinations of 5% PEG 400, DTPA and EDDHMA plus 1 control solution of distilled deionized water (A). In addition, both DTPA solutions (D and E) were kept at pH 6, which was determined to be the optimum pH for both the complexation reaction and the wood (Akzo Nobel 2004). Two of the three EDDHMA solutions (F and H) were kept at pH 7, which was a compromise between the optimum pH for complexation and the effect on the wood. The pH of the third solution (G) was allowed to change freely over time. The composition of the six treatment solutions is described in Table 2.

3.2.2. Initial measurements

Again, four chocks were used in each of the eight experimental treatment solutions (A-H). Before treatment commenced the surface pH, weight, surface area and color of each chock was measured. In addition, core samples of the chocks were recovered for FTIR analyses and total iron content before and during treatment. After the core samples were collected corks were pushed into the holes in an attempt to minimize the possible increase in iron release from these recently exposed areas during the course of this experiment.

The thirty two chocks used in Experiment 2 had an average surface area of 232 ± 105cm^2, an average weight of 130 ± 98g and an average surface pH of 4.37 ± 0.40. The most notable differences with these chocks compared to the chocks used in Experiment 1 was the 75% decrease in the total iron content and the statistically valid decrease in the average surface pH. This decrease in the total iron content could easily be explained by the fact that the chocks had been stored in deionized water for 17 years with periodic changes in solution since the beginning of Experiment 1 and even though extraction of iron is extremely slow in deionized water it will still occur, especially over this extended storage period. The decrease in surface pH is a little more difficult to explain but it was obvious that the amount of tallow on the surface of the chocks had decreased over time and therefore, possibly the inherent natural pH of beech of about 4.5 is starting to have an effect. Hydrolysis and oxidation of the tallow may also contribute to this decrease in pH. Experiment 2 is continuing but some preliminary results after 4 months of iron extraction are presented below.

3.2.3. Iron extraction efficiency

Again the most consistent results were obtained for correlations of total mass of iron released into the solution versus the square root of time, indicative of diffusion controlled processes (Figure 5).

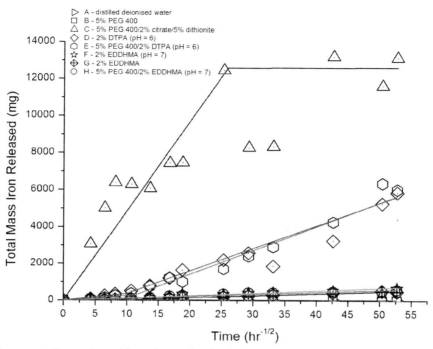

Figure 5. *Total amount of iron released from the* Xantho *chocks into each treatment solution (Experiment 2).*

As with Experiment 1 there was a two stage process for the DTPA and EDDHMA solutions in which there was a noticeable increase in the release rates after about one week, however there was no apparent induction period for the PEG 400/citrate/dithionite solution in this experiment. This apparent anomaly may be due to the significant decrease in the amount of observable iron corrosion products on the surface of the wooden chocks used in Experiment 2. As a result, the dithionite did not have to reduce as much Fe(III) as it did in the first experiment before the iron corrosion product matrix became unstable. The induction periods observed for the DTPA and EDDHMA solutions may be attributed to the larger molecular size of the chelating agents and associated slower diffusion kinetics.

From the graph in Figure 5 it is obvious that solution C, 5% PEG 400, 2% citrate and 5% dithionite, extracted the most iron over the 4 month time period. After about a month however, iron release ceased in this solution indicated by the plateau while iron release continued in the DTPA (D and E) and EDDHMA (F, G and H) solutions. In addition, the solutions containing DTPA released considerably more iron than those treatment solutions containing EDDHMA.

Again, the apparent iron extraction rates were calculated from the slopes of the total mass of iron released plots for the different stages then normalized using the surface areas of the chocks in each solution to obtain the 'real' iron extraction rates. The results are shown graphically in Figure 6.

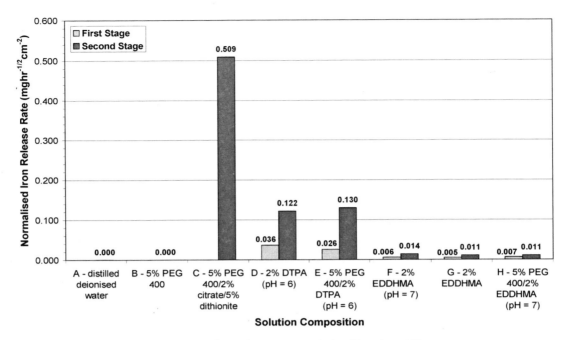

Figure 6. *Normalized iron extraction rates for each treatment solution (Experiment 2).*

Based on this data, the iron extraction rate in the combined 5% PEG/2% citrate/5% dithionite solution (C = 0.509mghr$^{-1/2}$cm^{-2}) was about 4 times higher than the average iron release rate in the DTPA solutions D and E (0.126mghr$^{-1/2}$cm^{-2}) and about 40 times higher than the average extraction rate in the EDDHMA solutions F, G and H (0.012mghr$^{-1/2}$cm^{-2}).

3.2.4. Changes in solution pH

Although the change in solution pH was monitored over the 4 month time period for the treatment solutions in Experiment 2, only the results for the solutions where the pH was allowed to change freely over time (A, B, C and G) are shown in Figure 7. The other solutions (D, E, F and H) were kept at a constant pH (Table 2).

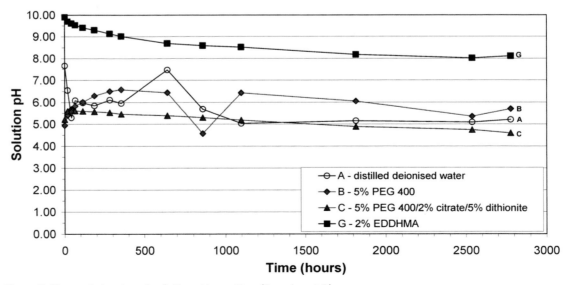

Figure 7. *Change in treatment solution pH over time (Experiment 2).*

The solutions A (water) and B (5% PEG 400) are noticeably more acidic than the same solutions measured in Experiment 1, most probably because of the more acidic nature of the chocks used in Experiment 2. As in Experiment 1, the pH of solution C containing dithionite decreased over time but the pH was less acidic at 4.80 after about 4 months than for the same solution in experiment one, which was about 3.80 after the same period of time. This smaller change in the pH of solution C in Experiment 2, would be due to the fact that less iron was extracted (12g) from the chocks when compared to the total iron released in Experiment 1 in the same solution (24g). Hydrolysis of Fe^{3+} to insoluble $Fe(OH)_3$, which can occur even at acidic pHs (pH ~ 3.0) and the formation of the major Fe(III) complex $[Fe(III)OHcit]^-$, produces hydrogen ions and therefore hydrolysis of lower amounts of iron will results in less acidic solutions over time if the oxidation rate of the dithionite is assumed equal in solution C for both experiments. The pH of the non-buffered 2% EDDHMA solution decreased steadily over the 4 months from about pH 10 to pH 8 and appears to be leveling off.

3.2.6. Fourier Transform Infra-red Spectroscopy

In order to ascertain if the different chelating solutions had any detrimental effect on the wood chemistry, two chocks from each solution were cored before treatment and 70 days into Experiment 2 with the outer and mid sections of the core samples analyzed by FTIR. The major diagnostic peaks used to determine extents of deterioration of polysaccharides and lignin in wood have been previously described in Fors and Richards (2010). Unfortunately on inspection of the 128 spectra collected, the tallow interfered with almost every peak in the spectra assigned to these specific wood components. This interference is more readily discerned in the close up of the fingerprint region $1800-800cm^{-1}$ in Figure 8 where the tallow interfered with the hemicellulose peak at $1732cm^{-1}$, the lignin peaks in the $1500-1600cm^{-1}$ region, the cellulose peaks in the $1400-1500cm^{-1}$ area and the peak at $898cm^{-1}$ assigned to the β-anomeric linkages between discrete cellulose and hemicellulose units.

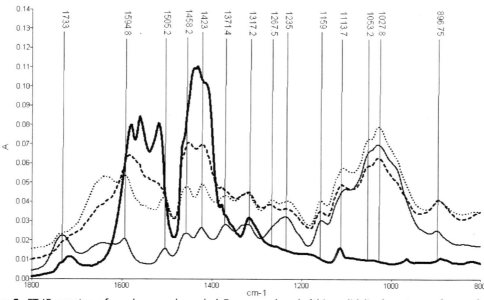

Figure 8. FT-IR spectra of modern, undegraded European beech (thin solid line), outer surfaces of waterlogged wooden chock samples, XA432K (dashed line) and XA431T (dotted line) before treatment and a sample of tallow extracted from the surface of chock XA431T (thick solid line).

Table 3. *Further treatment, monitoring and analyses planned for Experiments 1 and 2*

EXPERIMENT 1*	EXPERIMENT 2*
Continue iron release experiments	Continue iron release experiments
Stabilization by PEG impregnation	Total iron content AT
Total iron content AT	FT-IR analyses AT
FT-IR and ^{13}C-NMR analyses AT	^{13}C-NMR analyses BT, DT and AT
Freeze drying	Stabilization by PEG impregnation
Shrinkage, mass AT	Freeze drying
Color measurement AT	Shrinkage, mass AT
Surface pH AT	Color measurement AT
Post-treatment changes over time	Surface pH AT
	Post-treatment changes over time

* BT = before treatment; DT = during treatment; AT = after treatment

3.2.6. Conclusions

Based on these preliminary results from Experiment 2 it appears that a combination of 5% PEG 400, 2% diammonium citrate and 5% dithionite (C) remains the most effective chelating solution for extracting iron corrosion products from the waterlogged wooden *Xantho* chocks. This solution extracted approximately 12g of iron from the four chocks but the release of iron appeared to plateau after about a month.

Controlling the pH of the EDDHMA solution did not seem to have any impact on the chelating efficiency of these solutions as the total amount of iron released and the extractions rates in all solutions containing EDDHMA were very low, independent of the pH.

In addition, any detrimental effects of the treatment solutions on the wood chemistry of these *Xantho* chocks cannot be ascertained with FTIR as the impregnation of the chocks with the tallow interfered with the diagnostic peaks used to measure the extent of deterioration of the polysaccharides and lignin components in the wood structure.

4. Final Conclusions and Further Work

Based on these preliminary results from Experiment 1 and 2, it appears that the most effective chelating solution for iron removal is the combination of 5% PEG 400, 2% diammonium citrate and 5% sodium dithionite. However, the pH has to be closely monitored to avoid the solutions becoming too acidic and potentially causing damage to the wood components.

Due to the interference with the tallow, FTIR is not a suitable instrumental technique to assess the effects of the different chelating solutions on the wood chemistry of these *Xantho* chocks. To overcome this problem, the core samples collected before, during and after treatment will be analyzed by solid state ^{13}C nuclear magnetic resonance spectroscopy (^{13}C-NMR), which will easily separate the different carbon atoms associated with the lignin, carbohydrates and the fatty material and ascertain whether there has been any damage to the wood components by these different treatment solutions. However, characteristic peaks at between approximately 1520 and 1560 cm^{-1} in the FTIR spectra may provide information regarding the amount of tallow in the chocks and assist in determining if there is any relationship between iron release and tallow incorporation. The other alternative to overcoming this interference problem may be to extract the tallow from the very small wood samples (µg) collected for FTIR analysis and then reanalyze.

Further monitoring and analyses planned for Experiments 1 and 2 are outlined briefly

396

in Table 3. In addition, Experiment 2 will be extended by incorporating two additional treatment solutions containing 2% DTPA/5% dithionite and 2% EDDHMA/5% dithionite (Almkvist 2010). Both Experiments 1 and 2 will continue until the chocks have been properly consolidated with PEG 3350, followed by freeze drying. The effect of the iron extraction experiments and the completed treatment regimes on the long-term post conservation stability of the wooden chocks will then be ascertained by further chemical and spectroscopic analyses.

References

Akzo Nobel, (2004), Conditional Stability Constants for Metal Chelates, Technical Leaflet 217, Akzo Nobel.

Almkvist G., (2008), The Chemistry of the *Vasa* – Iron, Acids and Degradation, Doctoral Thesis, Uppsala, Swedish University of Agricultural Sciences.

Almkvist G., (2010), personal communication.

Almkvist G., Dal, L. and Persson I., (2005), Extraction of Iron Compounds from *Vasa* Wood, in P. Hoffmann, K. Strætkvern, J.A. Spriggs and D. Gregory (editors), Proceedings of the 9th ICOM Group on Wet Organic Archaeological Materials Conference, Copenhagen, 7-11 June 2004, Bremerhaven, The International Council of Museums, Committee for Conservation Working Group on Wet Organic Archaeological Materials, 2005, pp 203-211.

Almkvist G. and Persson I., (2006), Extraction of Iron Compounds from Wood from the *Vasa*, Holzforschung, Vol. 60, 2006, pp 678-684.

Almkvist G. and Persson I., (2009), Iron Catalyzed Degradation Processes in the *Vasa*, in K. Straetkvern and D.J. Huisman (editors), Proceedings of the 10th ICOM Group on Wet Organic Archaeological Materials Conference, Amsterdam, 10-15 September 2007, Amersfoort, Rijksdienst voor Archeologie, Cultuurlandschap en Monumenten (RACM), 2009, pp 499-506.

Bell W.A. and Gibson J.N., (1957), Degradation of Cellulosic Fibers in Contact with Rusting Iron, Nature, Vol. 4594, 1957, p 1065.

Chartier D.R., (1991), Cation-Selective Reagents for Conservation Treatments, Mat. Res. Soc. Symp. Proc., Vol. 185, 1991, pp 73-79.

Emery J.A. and Schroeder H.A., (1974), Iron-Catalyzed Oxidation of Wood Carbohydrates, Wood Science and Technology, Vol. 8, 1974, pp 123-137.

Farber E., (1954), Chemical Deterioration of Wood in the Presence of Iron, Ind. Eng. Chem., Vol. 46, 1954, pp 1968-1972.

Fengel D. and Wegener G., (1989), Wood. Chemistry, Ultrastructure, Reactions, Berlin, Walter de Gruyter.

Field T.B., McCourt J.L. and McBryde W.A.E., (1974), Composition and Stability of Iron and Copper Citrate Complexes in Aqueous Solution, Can. J. Chem., Vol. 52, No. 17, 1974, pp 3119-3124.

Fors Y., (2005), Sulfur Speciation and Distribution in the *Vasa*'s Wood. Protection by Water Pollution Leaves a Sour Aftertaste, Licentiate Thesis, Stockholm, Stockholm University.

Fors Y. and Richards V., (2010), The Effects of the Ammonia Neutralizing Treatment on Marine Archaeological *Vasa* Wood, Studies in Conservation, Vol. 55, No. 1, 2010, pp 41-54.

Francis A.J. and Dodge C.J., (1993), Influence of Complex Structure on the Biodegradation of Iron-Citrate Complexes,

Applied and Environmental Microbiology, Vol. 59, No. 1, 1993, pp 109-113.

Ghisalberti E., Godfrey I.M., Kilminster K., Richards V.L. and Williams E., (2002), The Analysis of Acid Affected *Batavia* Timbers in P. Hoffmann, J.A. Spriggs, T. Grant, C. Cook and A. Recht (editors), Proceedings of the 8th ICOM Group on Wet Organic Archaeological Materials Conference, Stockholm, 2001, Bremerhaven, The International Council of Museums, Committee for Conservation Working Group on Wet Organic Archaeological Materials, 2002, pp 281-307.

Grattan D.W. (1987), Waterlogged Wood, in C. Pearson (editor), Conservation of Marine Archaeological Objects, Sydney, Butterworths, 1987, pp 55-67.

Hackerman N. and Ogura K., (1975), The Effect of Chelating Agents on Iron Passivation, in Proceedings of the Sixth International Congress on Metallic Corrosion, Sydney, Australia, December 1975, Victoria, Australasian Corrosion Association, 1975, pp 129-138.

Hamm R.E., Schull C.M. and Grant D.M., (1954), Citrate Complexes with Iron(II) and Iron(III), J. Am. Chem. Soc., Vol. 76, No. 8, 1954, pp 2111-2114.

Hawley J.K., (1989), A Synopsis of Current Treatments for Waterlogged Wood and Metal Composite Objects, in I.D. MacLeod (editor), Conservation of Wet Wood and Metal: Proceedings of the ICOM Conservation Working Groups on Wet Organic Archaeological Materials and Metals, Fremantle 1987, Perth, Western Australian Museum, 1989, pp 223-243.

Huisman D.J., (2009), Where Does it All Start? The Origin of Reduced Sulfur Species in Marine Archaeological Wood, in K. Straetkvern and D.J. Huisman (editors), Proceedings of the 10th ICOM Group on Wet Organic Archaeological Materials Conference, Amsterdam, 10-15 September 2007, Amersfoort, Rijksdienst voor Archeologie, Cultuurlandschap en Monumenten (RACM), 2009, pp 577-588.

Iversen T., Lindfors E. and Lindström M., (2009), Polysaccharide Degradation in *Vasa* Oak Wood, in K. Straetkvern and D.J. Huisman (editors), Proceedings of the 10th ICOM Group on Wet Organic Archaeological Materials Conference, Amsterdam, 10-15 September 2007, Amersfoort, Rijksdienst voor Archeologie, Cultuurlandschap en Monumenten (RACM), 2009, pp 493-498.

Jespersen K., (1989), Precipitation of Iron-Corrosion Products on PEG-Treated Wood, in I.D. MacLeod (editor), Conservation of Wet Wood and Metal. Proceedings of the ICOM Conservation Working Groups on Wet Organic Archaeological Materials and Metals. Fremantle 1987, Perth, Western Australian Museum, 1989, pp 141-152.

La Baume S. de, (1989), Archaeological Wood Desalting by Electrophoresis, in I.D. MacLeod (editor), Conservation of Wet Wood and Metal. Proceedings of the ICOM Conservation Working Groups on Wet Organic Archaeological Materials and Metals. Fremantle, 1987, Perth, Western Australian Museum, 1989, pp 153-162.

Lanford O.E. and Quinan, J.R., (1948), A Spectrophotometric Study of the Reaction of Ferric Iron and Citric Acid, J. Am. Chem. Soc., Vol. 70, pp 2900-2903.

Lowson R.T., (1982), Aqueous Oxidation of Pyrite by Molecular Oxygen, Chemical Reviews, Vol. 82, 1982, pp 461-497.

MacLeod I.D. (1990), Conservation of Waterlogged Timbers from the *Batavia* 1629, Bulletin of the Australian Institute for Maritime Archaeology, Vol. 14, 1990, pp 1-8.

MacLeod I.D., Brooke P. and Richards V., (1991), Iron Corrosion Products and Their Interactions with Waterlogged Wood and PEG, in P. Hoffmann (editor), Proceedings of the 4th ICOM Working Group on Wet Organic Archaeological Materials Conference. Bremerhaven, 20-24 August 1990, Bremerhaven, The International Council of Museums, Committee for Conservation Working Group on Wet Organic Archaeological Materials, 1991, pp 119-132.

MacLeod I.D. and Kenna C., (1991), Degradation of Archaeological Timbers by Pyrite: Oxidation of Iron and Sulphur Species, in P. Hoffmann (editor), Proceedings of the 4th ICOM Working Group on Wet Organic Archaeological Materials Conference. Bremerhaven, 20-24 August 1990, Bremerhaven, The International Council of Museums, Committee for Conservation Working Group on Wet Organic Archaeological Materials, 1991, pp 133-142.

MacLeod I.D., Mardikian P. and Richards V.L., (1994), Observations on the Extraction of Iron and Chloride from Composite Materials, in P. Hoffmann, T. Daley and T. Grant (editors), Proceedings of the 5th ICOM Group on Wet Organic Archaeological Materials Conference. Portland/Maine, 16-20 August 1993, Bremerhaven, The International Council of Museums, Committee for Conservation Working Group on Wet Organic Archaeological Materials, 1994, pp 199-211.

MacLeod I.D., North N.A. and Beegle C.J., (1986), The Excavation, Analysis and Conservation of Shipwreck Sites, Preventative Measures During Excavation and Site Protection. ICCROM Conference Proceedings, Ghent, 6-8 November 1985, Rome, International Centre for the Study of the Preservation and the Restoration of Cultural Property (ICCROM), 1986, pp 113-132.

McCarthy M., (2000), Iron and Steamship Archaeology. Success and Failure on the SS Xantho, New York, Kluwer Academic/Plenum Publishers.

Morgan P.G., (1962), The Chemical Deterioration of Wood in the Presence of Iron, Wood, 1962, p 492.

Palmer J.W. and Boden P.J., (1992), Corrosion of Steel in EDTA, Br. Corros. J., Vol. 27, 1992, pp 305-309.

Pang J.T.T., (1981), The Treatment of Waterlogged Oak Timbers from a 17th Century Dutch East Indiaman, Batavia, Using Polyethylene Glycol, in ICOM Committee for Conservation. 6th Triennial Meeting. Ottawa, 21-25 September 1981, Paris, The International Council of Museums, 1981, pp 81/7/6-1-81/7/6-13.

Pinion L.C., (1970), The Degradation of Wood by Metal Fastenings and Fittings, in Timberlabs Papers, Forest Products Research Laboratory, 1970, pp 1-13.

Richards V.L., (1996), The Degradation and Conservation of Natural Organic Polymers from Historic Shipwrecks, Masters of Philosophy thesis, Perth, Western Australia, Murdoch University.

Sandström M., Fors, Y., Jalilehvand, F., Damian, E. and Gelius, U., (2005), in P. Hoffmann, K. Strætkvern, J.A. Spriggs and D. Gregory (editors), Proceedings of the 9th ICOM Group on Wet Organic Archaeological Materials Conference, Copenhagen, 7-11 June 2004, Bremerhaven, The International Council of Museums, Committee for Conservation Working Group on Wet Organic Archaeological Materials, 2005, pp 181-202.

Sandström M., Fors Y. and Persson I., (2003), The Vasa's New Battle. Sulfur, Acid and Iron. Vasa Studies 19, Stockholm, The Swedish National Maritime Museums.

Sandström M., Jalilehvand F., Persson I., Gelius U., Frank P. and Hall-Roth I., (2002), Deterioration of the Seventeenth Century Warship, *Vasa* by Internal Formation of Sulfuric Acid, Nature, Vol. 415, 2002, pp. 893-897.

Warner R.C. and Weber I., (1953), The Cupric and Ferric Citrate Complexes, J. Am. Chem. Soc., Vol. 75, pp 5086-5094.

Watson A.J., (1976), Chemical Degradation of Cellulosic Materials, in S. Walston (editor), Conservation in Australia. Proceedings of the ICCM National Conference, Canberra May 1976, Canberra, ICCM, 1976, pp 60-63.

Questions and answers

Anthony Kennedy: I would be very wary of pinning your hopes on carbon[13] NMR. I think the ability to separate the components using that technique gives you far less than with Infrared.

Vicki Richards: We've actually used it before and it's quite good.

Anthony Kennedy: And you don't get overlapping peaks? Because carbon[13] peaks are going to be quite broad.

Ian Godfrey: I'll show some in the next talk so you can have a bit of a look at it.

Vicki Richards: We use it quite regularly.

Howard Wellman: For Vicki, in terms of the acidity of your PEG- citrate-dithionite solution; would adding a buffer change the effectiveness of that solution or is it a question of stopping the treatment when it's getting too acidic?

Vicki Richards: I haven't looked at buffers. It's a good idea but I haven't so I wouldn't like to say. It may affect it, it probably would affect the complexation reactions because they are very dependent on pH.

Cliff Cook: You showed it plateauing with the dithionite – was that because the solution was exhausted or the iron was gone?

Vicki Richards: The solution was exhausted. Then you put it in again and it takes off again.

Cliff Cook: So you just didn't show the saw tooth effect you get by successive baths.

Vicki Richards: No, I didn't because I've only got a certain amount of time, sorry.

4.3

Nuclear Magnetic Resonance Spectroscopic Analyses of Acid-affected Waterlogged Archaeological Wood

Ian Godfrey*, and Vicki Richards
Department of Materials Conservation, Western Australian Museum, Shipwreck Galleries, 45-47 Cliff St, Fremantle, WA 6160, Australia
*E-mail: ian.godfrey@museum.wa.gov.au

Lindsay Byrne, Emil Ghisalberti
School of Biomedical and Chemical Sciences, University of Western Australia, 35 Stirling Highway, Crawley, WA 6009, Australia

Abstract

Wood samples from the *Vasa*, two reference wrecks and modern oak were analyzed by solid-state ^{13}C nuclear magnetic resonance spectroscopy (NMR). Application of this technique, particularly useful for the comprehensive analysis of archaeological wood without recourse to extraction or degradative procedures, allows all wood components to be analyzed simultaneously. Information is given about chemical changes that have occurred in the wood including relative cellulose retention, the extent of cleavage of cellulosic linkages, hemicellulose degradation, oxidative changes and the extent of cleavage of the β-O-4 lignin linkage. In addition to solid-state ^{13}C-NMR analyses, deuterium oxide extracts have been obtained from the same samples and analyzed using proton (^{1}H) NMR techniques in order to determine the extent and nature of water-soluble degradation products. The information obtained will assist in establishing appropriate conservation strategies to avoid or at least ameliorate post conservation problems.

Keywords: *Vasa*, archaeological wood, post-conservation degradation, solid-state ^{13}C nuclear magnetic resonance spectroscopy, proton nuclear magnetic resonance spectroscopy, water-soluble degradation products

1. Introduction

The impacts on wood of marine and burial environments are quite well known, with carbohydrates such as cellulose and hemicellulose usually preferentially degraded relative to lignin and microbiological degradation, not unexpectedly, occurring from the outer regions and proceeding inwards (Wilson et al. 1993, Blanchette 1995, Björdal et al. 2000).

Many techniques have been used to characterize waterlogged wood and thereby guide the choice of the most appropriate conservation treatment. Some of these include the determination of maximum water content, density, hardness, the application of traditional wet chemical extractive techniques, the application of Fourier Transform infrared (FTIR) spectroscopy, combined pyrolysis gas chromatography/mass spectrometry (GC/MS), nuclear magnetic resonance (NMR) spectroscopy and combinations of these.

An NMR spectroscopic study of degradation in historic Indian Ocean shipwrecks for example, found that samples of outer wood, in closer proximate contact with the marine environment lost carbohydrates whereas the inner wood was found to be relatively intact. There did not appear to be any correlation between the age of the shipwrecks and degradation. Samples recovered from one of the wrecks, located in an anaerobic site, appeared to have undergone little degradation, unlike those taken from aerobic sites (Wilson et al. 1993).

Although many studies have been devoted to the analysis of waterlogged wood prior to conservation treatment, it was not until the late 1980s that problems emerged with polyethylene glycol (PEG) treated wood, prompting investigations into the nature of post-treatment degradation of formerly waterlogged wood (Jespersen 1989). The development of high levels of acidity in timbers associated with the Viking ships in Denmark (Jespersen 1989), the *Batavia* in Western Australia (MacLeod and Kenna 1991), the iconic *Vasa* in Sweden (Sandström et al. 2002) and the *Mary Rose* in England (Wetherall et al. 2008) led to many investigations aimed at determining the nature and causes of the problem. It was hoped that the results of these studies would help guide measures to prevent on-going deterioration. The Preserve the *Vasa* project, which has continued in a variety of incarnations for nearly a decade, has been pivotal in focusing research into the post-treatment problems of formerly waterlogged wood (Hall-Roth and Malmberg 2005).

Traditional methods of wood analysis rely on extractive techniques in which lignin, cellulose and resin fractions are isolated separately (Hedges 1990). As well as being time-consuming, extractive techniques are potentially unsatisfactory because the composition of any fraction is necessarily method dependent.

High-resolution solid-state ^{13}C-NMR spectroscopy is particularly useful for the comprehensive analysis of whole wood without recourse to extraction or degradative techniques, allowing all components comprising the sample under examination to be analyzed simultaneously. While extractive or degradative techniques suffer the disadvantages that the composition of any one fraction is dependent on the

procedure used and that the isolated fractions may be subject to loss of material and possible structural alteration during these processes, they may still allow comparisons to be made between samples that have gone through the same process. Lindfors et al. (2008) for example, developed a treatment regime to isolate carbohydrates from similar *Vasa* and reference wreck samples to those used in this study. Although the techniques used may have had an effect on the isolated material, because the same technique was applied to all samples, qualitative comparisons and valid conclusions were made regarding the extent of oxidative change that had occurred following conservation treatment of the timbers.

This paper provides information regarding the nature and extent of deterioration of oak samples taken from the *Vasa* and from unexcavated, reference shipwrecks, *Gröne Jägeren* and *Riksäpplet*. The results of the NMR analyses support findings regarding oxidative changes occurring in treated archaeological wood (Lindfors et al. 2008), while providing additional information regarding other chemical changes that have occurred in the wood.

2. NMR Spectroscopic Analysis of Wood Samples

Solid state NMR spectroscopy provides structural information that can be linked to the chemical composition of wood components, thereby allowing information to be obtained about changes that have occurred following immersion or burial in archaeological contexts (Table 1, Figure 1).

The presence of syringyl lignin in hardwoods produces resonance peaks in NMR spectra that are not present in softwood spectra while spectra from archaeological samples are often characterized by significant differences between the spectra of modern counterparts including losses of peak intensity, decreases in peak resolution and peak broadening. This latter effect is particularly evident if paramagnetic impurities, such as iron corrosion products, are present in samples as for *Vasa* samples CB 2A and 2B examined in this study.

Care is needed in the analysis of iron-rich samples as induced line broadening may lead to the apparent reduction in the intensities of some peaks, to the point where particular peaks may not appear to be present. In addition, complexation of iron with wood components may produce shifts in peak positions. Both of these considerations have obvious consequences for spectral interpretation and highlight the need for all analytical data, in particular the concentrations of iron species in the wood, to be taken into account before firm interpretations and conclusions are drawn from NMR spectra.

NMR spectroscopic analysis of wood may allow the following information to be determined:

- Relative quantities and distributions of lignin and holocellulose components in core samples.
- The relative loss of hemicellulose components.

Table 1: NMR peak assignments for wood

Peak Frequency	Due to: (softwood)	Due to: (hardwood)
~ 174 ppm	Weak peak due to the lesser fraction of **hemicelluloses** in softwood compared to hardwood	Carboxyl groups of acetyl sidechains (**hemicellulose**) Weak contribution from carbonyls (**lignin**)
~ 153		*C3, C5 syringyl carbons (**lignin**)
~ 148	*C3, C4 guaiacyl carbons (**lignin**)	*C3, C4 guaiacyl carbons (**lignin**); C3, C5 syringyl carbons (lignin) with β-O-4 linkage cleaved
~ 133	C1, C4 non-protonated, substituted aromatic carbons in guaiacyl **lignin**	C1, C4 non-protonated, substituted aromatic carbons in guaiacyl and syringyl **lignin**
106	C1 carbon in **cellulose** and **hemicellulose**	C2, C6 syringyl carbons (**lignin**); Oxygen-substituted furans found in **tannins** ; C1 carbon in **cellulose** and **hemicelluloses**
89 ppm	C4 carbon in crystalline **cellulose**	C4 carbon in crystalline **cellulose**
84 ppm	C4 carbon in amorphous **cellulose**	C4 carbon in amorphous **cellulose**
74 ppm	Aliphatic C-O carbons in **lignin** (generally masked by carbohydrate peaks)	Aliphatic C-O carbons in **lignin** (generally masked by carbohydrate peaks)
71-74 ppm	C2, C3, C5 CHOH carbons in **cellulose** and **hemicellulose**	C2, C3, C5 CHOH carbons in **cellulose** and **hemicellulose**
66 ppm	C6 carbons of crystalline **cellulose**	C6 carbons of crystalline **cellulose**
63 ppm	C6 carbons of amorphous **cellulose**	C6 carbons of amorphous **cellulose**
63-64 ppm	Broad peak from C6 carbon of hexose units in **hemicelluloses**	Broad peak from C6 carbon of hexose units in **hemicelluloses**
56 ppm	Methoxy carbons of **lignin**. Small contribution from 4-methoxy groups of glucuronic acid in **hemicelluloses**.	Methoxy carbons of **lignin**. Small contribution from 4-methoxy groups of glucuronic acid in **hemicelluloses**.
~21 ppm	Weak peak due to acetate methyl carbons in **hemicelluloses**	Acetate methyl carbons in **hemicelluloses**

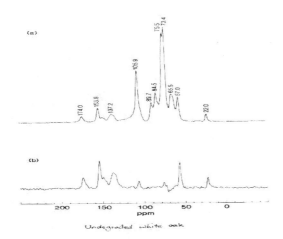

Figure 1. (a) Cross polarization magic angle spinning (CPMAS) and (b) dipolar dephased spectra of undegraded white oak

- Identify the presence of syringyl and guaiacyl lignin components, thereby allowing softwoods and hardwoods to be distinguished.
- The degree of cellulose crystallinity in wood.
- Identify degradative changes in lignin components, such as cleavage or retention of β-O-4 linkages, demethylation and increases in vanillic acid structures and α-carbonyl moieties.
- The degree of protonation of the aromatic rings in lignin components by applying dipolar dephasing (DPDP) techniques to samples with low carbohydrate contents.

In summary, NMR can provide information about the type and relative degree of deterioration of waterlogged wood samples. The type and extent of deterioration can then be related to the physical properties of the wood. For example, the strength of wood is affected by changes that occur in the degree of crystallinity of the wood, the hemicellulose composition and the length of the polymer chains.

Although it is not the aim of this document to discuss in detail the relative advantages and disadvantages of the various analytical techniques as applied to wood analysis, some mention should be made of these aspects as they relate to NMR spectroscopy, the main focus of this report.

As stated above, a considerable advantage of the NMR technique is that all of the components comprising a wood sample are analyzed simultaneously, with no recourse to differentiation of components by extraction or on the basis of solubility, volatility or the need for derivatization. A further advantage of the NMR technique is that none of the sample is consumed during the analytical process. All of a particular core sample is therefore available for further analyses, with the initial NMR analytical data available to guide the selection of subsequent procedures.

In addition, because 100 - 300 mg of sample is often used to accumulate a spectrum, NMR data is more likely to be representative of the particular sample that is under examination. This may not always be the case for other techniques, such as FTIR and GC-MS which use milligram or sub-milligram samples for analysis. Careful choice of samples for analysis and multiple analyses can be used however, to assist in obtaining representative data in these latter instances. Techniques such as FTIR and GC-MS often become very significant in the analysis of precious archaeological wooden objects for which only very small amounts of sample material are available for analysis.

As with any analytical technique, NMR spectroscopy has its negative aspects. Quantitation of individual components in a mixture can be difficult, the instrumentation is often not readily available and the interpretation of spectra requires considerable expertise. Also, since the sample for NMR analysis must be powdered prior to spectra being obtained, the physical form of the sample is destroyed. In order to maximize information from all analytical techniques for a particular wood core sample therefore, it is very important that the overall analytical pathway is clearly defined before analytical processes commence.

3. Objectives of This Investigation
- Determine the nature and extent of degradation of wood samples from the Vasa (Vasa, CB) and reference

wrecks, Gröne Jägeren (GJ) and Riksäpplet (RÄ).
- Compare the degradation of wood from the Vasa and the reference wrecks to gain information regarding the extent of post-conservation deterioration in Vasa wood.
- Use analytical results to guide conservation management decisions.

4. Experimental
4.1. Samples
Samples for which NMR spectra were obtained are shown below (Table 2) along with any other available relevant data that was available to the investigators

Table 2. Samples analyzed by solid state ^{13}C-NMR spectroscopy

Sample	Wood type	Core depth	PEG present	Special features
Vasa 4	oak	0-8 mm	No	Not recorded
		36-41 mm	No	Not recorded
CB 2A	oak	Outer	Yes	Iron present, very hard
CB 2B	oak	Inner	Yes	Iron present, very hard
CB 6A	oak	Outer	Yes	Salt-affected, softer than 2A
CB 6B	oak	Inner	Yes	Salt-affected, hard
CB 8A	oak	Outer	Yes	Unevenly degraded –soft and firm areas
CB 8B	oak	Inner	No	Hard
CB 13A	oak	Outer	Yes	Soft, 'sticky'
CB 13B	oak	Inner	No	Hard
CB 17A	oak	Outer	Yes	Very soft, 'sticky'
CB 17B	oak	Inner	Slight amount	Hard
GJ 197y	oak	Outer	No	Very brittle
GJ 197i	oak	Inner	No	Very hard
RÄ 204y	oak	Outer	No	Brittle
RÄ 204i	oak	Inner	No	Hard

Samples showed considerable variation in physical properties. Color, hardness, texture and uniformity of degradation all varied from sample to sample. The iron-containing Vasa samples (inner and outer) for instance, were very dark and extremely hard, while the condition of some other Vasa samples gave a qualitative indication of the extent of PEG incorporation. Many of the outer samples were sticky when ground with the mortar and pestle, indicating a relatively high PEG content (later confirmed by ^{1}H-NMR spectroscopy), while the corresponding inner samples powdered well with the particles remaining free and not aggregated in 'sticky' bundles (as for the outer shaved particles).

4.2. Sample Preparation and Analyses

4.2.1. Sample Preparation for Solid State ^{13}C-NMR Analyses

Vasa core samples (CB 2, 6, 8, 13, 17), which had all been treated previously with polyethylene glycol (PEG) were supplied dry. They were shaved and cut with a scalpel and then powdered in a mortar and pestle prior to NMR spectroscopic analysis. Sample Vasa 4, used in a previous spectroscopic investigation, was from a piece of untreated Vasa wood that has been stored in water since its recovery. It was supplied dry and powdered in the same way as described above. The samples from the reference wrecks (GJ, RÄ), which were supplied wet, were dried over silica gel under an argon gas atmosphere before powdering. Approximately 200 mg samples were used in the NMR analyses.

4.2.2. Extraction of samples for ^{1}H-NMR Analyses

After the solid state ^{13}C-NMR spectra were run, deuterated water (D$_2$O, 1 ml) was added to each of the wood samples. The samples were then agitated in an ultrasonic bath for two 5 minute periods each day for 3 days before being centrifuged and the supernatant liquid used in ^{1}H-NMR analysis.

4.2.3. NMR Spectroscopic Analysis

Solid state ^{13}C-NMR spectra were recorded with a Bruker ARX-300 spectrometer operating at 75.47MHz. A sample spinning speed of 5kHz was used in all cases. [13]C CPMAS experiments were measured with a 1ms contact time, 20ms acquisition time

and a 2s relaxation delay. Dipolar dephasing experiments employed a dephasing time of 50μs.

The ^{1}H-NMR spectra of the D$_2$O solutions were recorded at 25ºC using a Bruker AV-500 spectrometer. The instrument parameters for the 500.13MHz ^{1}H spectra were as follows: pulse angle, 30°; acquisition time, 4.4 s; relaxation delay, 6 s and 256 scans of 64k data points were acquired with a spectral width of 7507 Hz. After recording the spectra of the pure samples, 1 drop of methanol was added to each sample. [1]H spectra were then re-recorded to allow calibration of spectra relative to the methanol signal (3.34ppm).

5. Results and Discussion

NMR spectroscopic data and spectral interpretations are presented in Figures 3, 4, 6-8 and 11 with typical NMR spectra shown in Figures 2, 5, 9 and 10. It is important to stress that these results have been obtained from a small number of wood samples. Further work, using a more extensive suite of samples, is necessary to obtain more conclusive data before these preliminary findings can be regarded as conclusive.

In a marine environment it has been demonstrated that carbohydrates degrade in preference to lignin components in waterlogged wood (Wilson et al. 1993). An indication of the relative degree of deterioration of wood samples can be obtained therefore, by comparing ratios of NMR peaks attributed to carbohydrate signals with those of lignin components. The CPMAS spectra of the outer samples of wreck RÄ 204y and Vasa sample CB 8A (non-salt affected) clearly show differences in the relative amounts of cellulose and lignin in these samples (Figure 2).

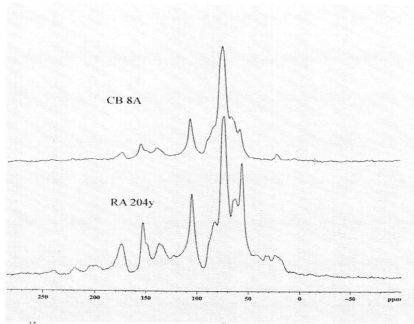

Figure 2. Solid state ^{13}C-NMR spectra of outer samples of RÄ 204y and CB 8A

5.1. Relative Cellulose Retention

Examination of the NMR data indicated that there is cleavage of the β-O-4 lignin bond (Figure 8) and of the C-1 anomeric carbohydrate linkage (Figure 4) in most samples when compared to modern oak. Despite the presence of PEG in many of the samples, which increases the intensity of the signal centered at approximately 72 ppm (C-2, 3, 5) the ratio of this signal to the lignin signal centered at 56 ppm (methoxyl CH_3) was chosen as the best indicator of the extent of carbohydrate retention relative to lignin. The lignin 56 peak was chosen because little loss of this peak was expected as condensation reactions are less significant in hardwood lignins.

This data is presented below in Figure 3. As indicated by their physical characteristics, the outer samples of the reference wrecks are significantly more degraded than the outer sample of Vasa 4 (non PEG treated). Firm conclusions cannot be drawn regarding the deterioration of most of the outer Vasa samples however, as the 72/56 ratios are increased by the presence of incorporated PEG. Despite the substantial PEG presence in CB 2A however, the 72/56 ratio is very low in comparison to other Vasa samples, indicating that significant cellulose degradation has occurred in this iron-contaminated sample.

The inner regions of all samples can be compared directly however, because of the small amount of PEG present in these regions. With the possible exception of the Vasa 4 sample all samples show a similarly high degree of cellulose retention in the inner regions. It is possible that the reduced, relative cellulose content in the inner regions of Vasa 4 is due to continued cellulose degradation while the wood was stored in aqueous solution. Such degradation has been observed anecdotally in similar situations in which waterlogged wood has been stored for prolonged periods (Cook 2010).

407

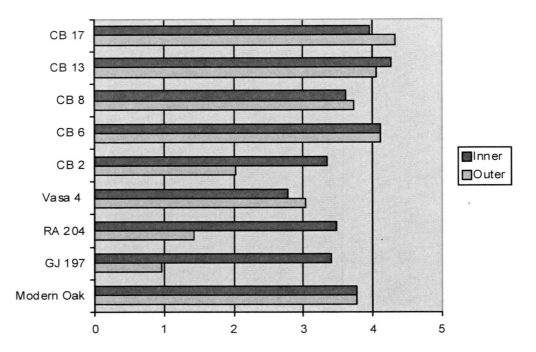

Figure 3. *Relative cellulose retention (72/56)*

5.2. Cleavage of Cellulose Linkages

Cleavage of the C-1 anomeric linkage in the cellulose chains results in a change in the chemical shift of this carbon atom. The nature of the cleavage, hydrolytic or oxidative, will determine the end products and hence the size of the changes in chemical shift. Regardless, the intensity of the C-1 signal at 106 ppm will be reduced if the cellulose chains are cut to any significant extent. Comparison therefore between the signals at 106 ppm and the carbohydrate signal intensity centered at approximately 72 ppm (C-2, 3, 5) allows a determination to be made of the relative extent of cleavage of the C-1 linkage. This data is presented in Figure 4.

With the exception of the inner core sample of Vasa 4, all samples showed evidence of C-1 cleavage relative to modern oak. There appeared to be slightly less cleavage in the outer samples from the reference wrecks (GJ, RÄ) compared to the inner samples from the same wrecks. For the Vasa samples however, there was no clear trend with some outer samples (CB 2, 6, 8) and some inner samples (CB 13, 17)

showing more cleavage. The presence of varying amounts of incorporated PEG, which would increase the signal at 72ppm, may account for some of these inconsistencies.

5.3. Hemicellulose Degradation

Signals at approximately 21 and 174 ppm correspond respectively to the methyl and carbonyl carbons present in acetyl groups typically associated with hemicellulose components. Measurements of the relative intensities of these signals can sometimes be used to compare the extent of hemicellulose retention in the wood substance. For the samples examined in this study however, the low intensity of the signals at 21 ppm, the presence of what are likely to be waxes in the reference samples in the high field region (15-35 ppm) and the possibility of oxidative changes occurring in the wood that produce signals in the down field region (165-180 ppm), precluded comparative studies for this group of samples. Despite this, some qualitative information was obtained from individual spectra.

408

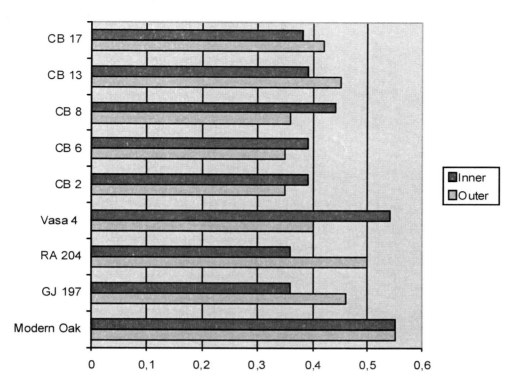

Figure 4. *Cleavage of C-1 cellulose linkage (106/72)*

For sample CB 6A depletion/hydrolysis of hemicellulose components, is clearly shown by the loss of the signal at 21 ppm when compared to the spectra of the inner core sample CB 6B (Figure 5). The presence of acid salts on the wood surface of sample CB 6A and the loss of acetyl groups indicate that acid hydrolysis has occurred in this instance.

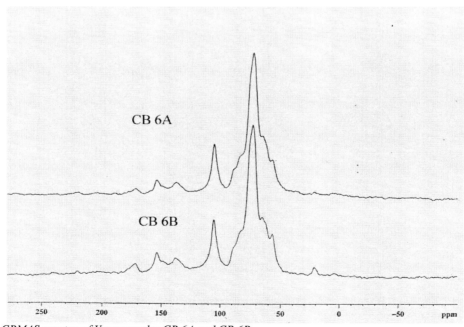

Figure 5. *CPMAS spectra of Vasa samples CB 6A and CB 6B*

5.4. Oxidative Change

In an attempt to further understand the possible degradative processes that have taken place in Vasa wood, an examination was also made of the relative integrations of the regions 180-165 and 30-15 ppm (Figure 6). Relative determinations covering these areas can provide information on the extent of oxidative change. Signals in the latter region can comprise alkyl groups associated with carbonyl/carboxyl groups (such as in hemicelluloses, waxes etc) while signals in the former region correspond to carbonyl carbons present in acids and esters. Oxidative processes that produce species without associated alkyl groups (formic, oxalic acids, etc) will therefore be reflected in increased 180-165/30-15 ratios and allow differentiation between the naturally occurring components of the wood samples. Comparisons were made between samples for which integrations of the above area were carried out (Figure 6) and also for samples for which both ratios of the integrated areas indicated above and intensity ratios could be determined for the signals at 174 and 21 (Figure 7).

Increased values for the integration ratios 180-165/30-15 for the PEG treated Vasa samples indicate the likely presence of more carbonyl-containing components, other than hemicelluloses in these samples, an indication that they have undergone some form of oxidative change. Although similar values were obtained for the inner and outer cores from the reference wrecks, some of the Vasa samples showed greater oxidative change in the outer regions (CB 13, 17) while others showed greater oxidative change in the inner regions (CB 2, 6, 8).

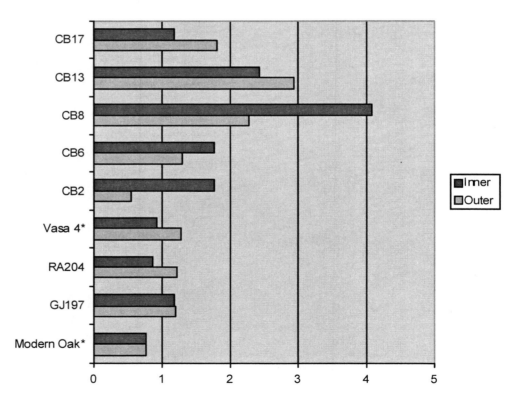

Figure 6 Ratios of integrated areas 180-165/30-15

* Values used for modern oak and Vasa 4 in Figure 6 are peak intensity ratios 174/21 (integration data not available) and are included as indicators of baseline hemicellulose content only.

For sample CB 2, the iron-containing sample, greater oxidation in the inner core sample as compared to the outer surface is indicative of the anticipated presence of more reduced iron species [Fe (II)] in the inner parts of the wood.

For sample CB 17, the Vasa sample that appeared to be the least degraded spectroscopically, oxidation of the inner core sample was similar to that of the corresponding reference wreck samples.

An analysis of these data confirm that oxidative changes have occurred in the inner core parts of the Vasa samples, with the 'normal' sample CB 8 showing the greatest degree of oxidative change and only a very slight degree of change demonstrated for sample CB 17.

5.5. Cleavage of β-O-4 Lignin Linkage

When β-O-4 linkages are broken in syringyl lignin units, the signals for the C-3 and C-5 aromatic carbons shift upfield, from 153 ppm to 148 ppm. As β-O-4 linkages are present in 40 – 60% of lignin sub-structures and syringyl lignin units are known to depolymerize more readily than guaiacyl units, changes in the ratios of these peaks therefore provides direct information about depolymerization of lignin via cleavage of these bonds. While neither condensation nor demethylation reactions have been observed in heat treated hardwoods, significant cleavage of the β-O-4 linkages has been observed. Use of DPDP spectra allows for clear and ready determination of this and other changes in lignin sub-structures.

Data pertaining to all samples is shown in Figure 8.

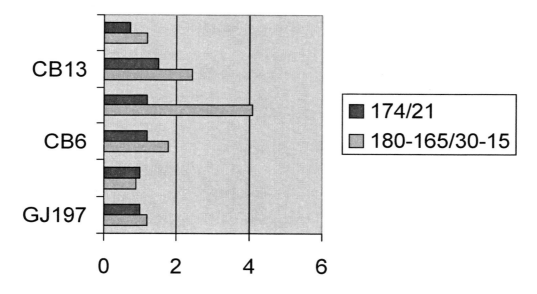

Figure 7. *Comparison of hemicellulose carbonyl/alkyl ratios with integrated carbonyl-carboxyl/alkyl ratios for **inner** cores of reference wrecks and Vasa samples*

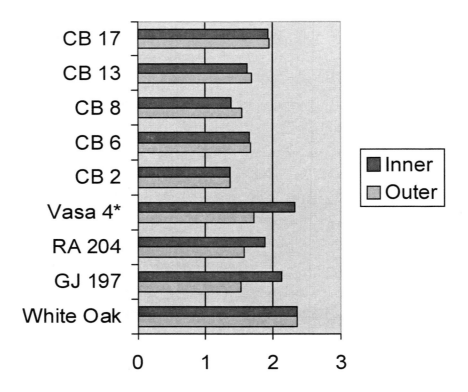

Figure 8. *Cleavage of β-O-4 linkages in lignin substructures (153/148)*
* CPMAS data only for Vasa 4 as DPDP data was not available

All samples, except the inner part of Vasa 4, showed some degree of depolymerization via cleavage of the β-O-4 linkages in syringyl lignin, with more depolymerization evident in the outer layers than in the inner layers of the reference wreck samples. The PEG-treated Vasa samples showed more uniform depolymerization changes with little difference in the extent of degradation between the outer and inner samples. As with cellulose deterioration, Vasa sample CB 17 was the least degraded and the iron-containing sample CB 2, the most degraded of the PEG-treated Vasa samples. As it is known that lignin is more susceptible to oxidation than hydrolysis, these results are not unexpected.

5.6. ¹H-NMR Spectral Analysis of Wood Extractives

Soluble short-chain sugars, degraded PEG, low molecular weight organic acids (formic, acetic, glycolic and oxalic acids) and PEG-formate have all been identified in PEG-treated waterlogged wood in varying amounts. Formic acid concentrations are enhanced in the presence of degraded PEG and in iron-rich areas and increased acetic acid concentrations may be attributed to the hydrolysis of acetyl groups in xylan (Almkvist and Persson 2008).

¹H spectra of extractives from samples CB 2A and CB 2B are shown below (Figure 9) with spectra of extractives of the inner regions of 'normal' Vasa wood (CB 8B) and one of the reference wreck samples (RÄ 204i) shown in Figure 10. Information regarding relative quantities of acetic acid, PEG-acetate, formic acid and PEG-formate from all samples is presented in Figure 11.

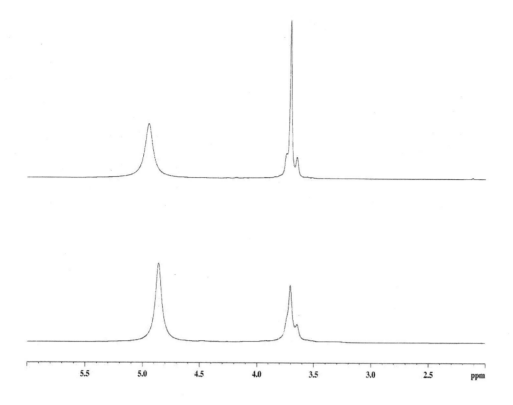

Figure 9. *^{1}H spectra of CB 2A (top) and CB 2B (lower) showing signals due to the chain methylene protons (δ 3.70) and terminal methylene protons (δ 3.65) in PEG extracted from the outer and inner regions respectively*

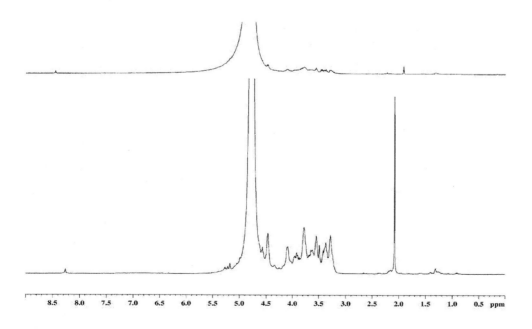

Figure 10. *^{1}H spectra of RÄ 204i (top) and CB 8B (lower) showing signals for acetic acid (2.1ppm), formic acid (8.3ppm) and degraded sugars (3.2-4.2ppm)*

413

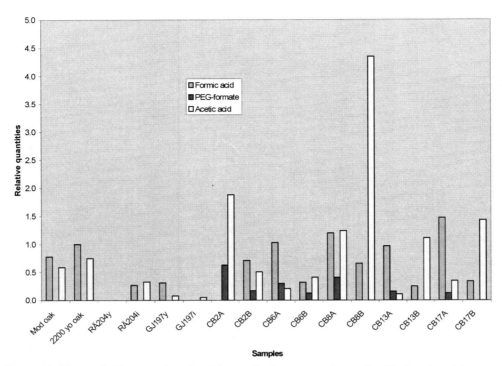

Figure 11. *Water-soluble extractives from* Vasa *and reference wreck samples. The 'acetic acid' contents of samples CB 6A, CB 8A, CB 13A and CB 17A comprise acetic acid and what is likely to be PEG-acetate (to be confirmed)*

While more analysis and additional experimental work is required, preliminary data from the ^{1}H-NMR study showed very clear trends and provided information consistent with earlier work described by Almkvist and Persson (2008). Specifically:

- Except for CB 2B, more formic acid is present in the outer PEG-rich areas, indicating preferential oxidative breakdown of PEG, rather than cellulose, in these areas.

- More PEG-formate, the oxidative precursor to formic acid, is present in the outer areas of the conserved Vasa samples than in the inner areas.

- Except for CB 2B, more acetic acid is present in the inner regions, indicative of hydrolytic cleavage of hemicelluloses (generally more abundant in the inner regions).

- Ratios of the signals due to terminal and chain methylene groups in extracted PEG indicate that PEG chains are shorter in the inner regions, with the greatest degree of change evident in the iron-rich CB 2 samples. Although this trend may be due to either PEG degradation, selective diffusion of smaller PEG molecules into the denser inner regions, or a combination of both factors, the former explanation appears most likely (Almkvist and Persson 2008). While this likely increased PEG degradation is not reflected in the presence of more formic acid in the inner areas of the samples, this apparent anomaly may simply be due to the presence of lesser quantities of (more highly degraded) PEG in these regions.

- Similar levels of formic acid are found in 2 of the reference wreck samples as in the relatively undegraded, non-PEG containing inner samples CB 13B and CB 17B, indicating similar levels of cellulose oxidation in these samples.

The presence of reduced iron species in the inner regions of the Vasa samples, particularly sample CB 2, is likely to have influenced chemical changes in this region (such as oxidative PEG depolymerization).

414

6. Summary and Conclusions

- The outer samples of the reference wrecks are significantly more degraded than that of the untreated Vasa sample.

- Of the PEG-treated Vasa samples, cellulose degradation is most severe in the iron-containing sample CB 2 samples.

- With the exception of the inner core sample of Vasa 4, all samples showed evidence of C-1 cleavage relative to modern oak.

- While hemicellulose ratios could not be compared for all samples, significant hemicellulose degradation was noted in the acid-salt affected sample CB 6A, indicating that acid hydrolysis is likely to be an important deterioration mechanism in such areas.

- Oxidative changes are indicated in most of the PEG-treated Vasa samples. These changes are not uniform across the Vasa samples however, with little oxidative change evident, for example, in the relatively undegraded inner core of sample CB 17B.

- All samples, except the inner part of the untreated Vasa 4 sample, showed some degree of lignin depolymerization via cleavage of the β-O-4 linkage, with relatively uniform degradation observed in the inner and outer cores from the PEG-treated Vasa samples but more degradation in the outer parts of the reference wreck samples.

- Water-soluble extractives provided clear evidence to support conclusions drawn from the solid state ^{13}C-NMR spectra and to give valuable information regarding PEG degradation and the relative concentrations of formic and acetic acids.

Overall, it is clear that the Vasa samples and the reference wreck samples have degraded in different ways. It is important to relate the extent of cellulose retention to the nature of the retained cellulose and also to the resultant physical characteristics of the wood. This is critical if the physical integrity of the hull structure is to be appropriately maintained.

There is clear spectroscopic evidence that cellulose retention in the Vasa samples is high. However there is also evidence of cleavage of the cellulose chains and oxidation of cellulose, lignin, PEG and/or combinations of all of these (Almkvist and Persson 2008, Lindförs et al. 2008). Relating these to the strength and integrity of the wood will allow appropriate decisions to be made for the long-term conservation of the Vasa hull.

7. Conservation Implications for Peg-Treated Waterlogged Wood

- Where possible iron corrosion products should be removed from individual wooden artifacts.

- The moisture content in the ship's timbers should be reduced to decrease the rate of chemical reactions in the wood.

- The moisture content in ship's timbers should be monitored to determine the impact of gallery environmental changes on moisture retention in the wood.

- Outbreaks of acid treated timbers should be documented over time for use as an indicator of the effectiveness of gallery climate changes on chemical reactions occurring in the wood.

- Subject to consideration of all analytical data, deacidification of the artifacts and hull timbers may be necessary to reduce acid-catalyzed deterioration reactions.

References

Almkvist G. and Persson I., (2008), Analysis of Acids and Degradation Products Related to Iron and Sulfur in the Swedish Warship Vasa, Holzforschung, Vol 62, No. 6, pp 694-703.

Björdal C.G., Daniel G. and Nilsson T., (2000), Depth of Burial, An Important Factor in Controlling Bacterial Decay in Waterlogged Archaeological Poles, International Biodeterioration & Biodegradation, Vol. 45, No. 1-2, pp 15-26.

Blanchette R.A., (1995), Biodeterioration of Archaeological Wood, Biodeterioration Abstracts, Vol. 9, pp 113-127.

Cook C., (2010), personal communication.

Hall Roth I. and Malmberg L. (2005), Save the Vasa – An Introduction, in P. Hoffmann, K. Straetkvern, J.A. Spriggs and D. Gregory (editors), Proceedings of the 9th ICOM Group on Wet Organic Archaeological Materials Conference, Copenhagen, 2004, Bremerhaven, The International Council of Museums, Committee for Conservation Working Group on Wet Organic Archaeological Materials, 2005, pp 171-180.

Hedges J.I., (1990), The Chemistry of Archaeological Wood, in R.M. Rowell and R.J. Barbour (editors), Archaeological Wood: Properties, Chemistry and Preservation, Washington DC, American Chemical Society, 1990, pp 111-140.

Jespersen J., (1989), Precipitation of Iron Corrosion Products on PEG-Treated Wood, in I. MacLeod (editor), Conservation of Wet Wood and Metal, Proceedings of the ICOM Conservation Working Groups on Wet Organic Archaeological Materials and Metals, Fremantle, 1987, Perth, Western Australian Museum, 1989, pp 141-152.

Lindfors E.-L., Iversen T. and Lindström M., (2008), Polysaccharide Degradation in Waterlogged Oak Wood from the Ancient Warship Vasa, Holzforschung, Vol. 62, No. 1, pp 57-63.

MacLeod I. and Kenna C., (1991), Degradation of Archaeological Timbers by Pyrite: Oxidation of Iron and Sulfur Species, in P. Hoffmann (editor), Proceedings of the 4th ICOM Group on Wet Organic Archaeological Materials Conference, Bremerhaven, 1990, Bremerhaven, The International Council of Museums, Committee for Conservation Working Group on Wet Organic Archaeological Materials, 1991, pp 133-142.

Sandström M., Jalilehvand F., Fors Y., Frank P. and Hall-Roth I., (2002), Deterioration of the Seventeenth-Century Warship Vasa by Internal Formation of Sulphuric Acid, Nature, Vol. 415, No. 6874, pp 893-897.

Wetherall K.M., Moss R.M., Jones A.M., Smith A.D., Skinner T., Pickup D.M., Goatham S.W., Chadwick A.V. and Newport R.J., (2008), Sulfur and Iron Speciation in Recently Recovered Timbers of the Mary Rose Revealed via X-ray Absorption Spectroscopy, Journal of Archaeological Science, Vol. 35, pp 1317-1328.

Wilson M.A. Godfrey I.M., Hanna J.V., Quezada R.A. and Finnie K.S., (1993), The Degradation of Wood in Old Indian Ocean Shipwrecks, Organic Geochemistry, Vol. 20, pp 599-610.

Questions and answers

Mikkel Christensen: Very nice spectra I have to say! I'm a little bit envious because we tried to do some liquid state NMR and we couldn't get proper carbon spectra due to iron content – metal ions. So how come that's not a problem for you with these *Vasa* timbers?

Ian Godfrey: Well, it is still a problem. The spectra for the sample two for instance because you've got the paramagnetic material in there and they're quite broad. You can remove the iron if you want to as long as you just do it quickly. If you've got powdered samples you will be able to get it out pretty quickly and then rerun the spectra. What we want to do with this by the way, is rerun the spectra now that we've extracted the PEG and then redo the solid state spectra. But we're also fortunate that we've got a spectroscopist who is a colleague of mine. He's extremely thorough in the work that he does but he does work very, very hard. He's meticulous in trying to get the best spectra that he can.

4.4

Conservation of *Mary Rose* Timbers

Eleanor J. Schofield* and Alan V. Chadwick
School of Physical Sciences, University of Kent, Canterbury, CT2 7NS
*E- mail: e.j.schofield@kent.ac.uk

Mark J. Jones
Mary Rose Trust, College Road, HM Naval Base, Portsmouth, PO1 3LX

Abstract

Henry VIII's flagship, the *Mary Rose* is currently being preserved for public viewing. Unfortunately, the *Mary Rose* suffers from the 'sulfur problem' whereby the presence of various sulfur compounds within the timbers can lead to the production of acid and ultimately the breakdown of the structure. Here we show, via Scanning Electron Microscopy that strontium carbonate nanoparticles can be incorporated into the wood and have the potential to reduce the threat to the wood of acid attack.

Keywords: waterlogged, archaeological wood, deacidification, sulfur, nanoparticles

1. Introduction

Henry VIII's flagship, the *Mary Rose,* sank off the coast of Portsmouth in 1545. The lower structure, which was preserved under a layer of anaerobic silt, was raised from the seafloor in 1982 (McKee 1982) and is currently the focus of one of the world's largest conservation projects. Unfortunately, the *Mary Rose* suffers from the 'sulfur problem' whereby the presence of sulfur within the timbers can lead to the production of acid and ultimately the breakdown of the structure (Sandström et al. 2005, Wetherall et al. 2008). The need for a remediation strategy is critical as the ship is due to be housed in a museum for

viewing in 2011, giving the public a unique historical insight into Tudor times.

Figure 1. *The section of the* Mary Rose *raised from the seabed currently undergoing conservation*

The 'sulfur problem' was first observed during the preservation of the Swedish Warship *Vasa* (Sandström et al. 2002) and now has been observed for a number of important historical shipwrecks. The *Vasa* was salvaged in 1961 after spending 333 years on the seabed of Stockholm harbor. Shortly after being housed in a museum in 1990, a large amount of acidic salt precipitates, mostly sulfates, were discovered on the surface of the timbers. This caused major concern for the stability of the structure of ship and initiated the 'Preserve the *Vasa*' project in 2003. Since this time a number of studies have been carried out on assessing the source of sulfur and subsequent treatments for its presence.

The source of the sulfur can be traced back to the seabed. Reduced sulfur compounds, such as hydrogen sulfide, accumulated in the wood, in the seawater, by the interaction of sulfate-ions with sulfate-reducing bacteria. These reduced compounds pose no threat to the structure of the wood whilst maintained under anoxic conditions on the seabed. However, when exposed to an oxygen environment these reduced sulfur compounds can oxidize and eventually produce sulfuric acid. This leads to the breakdown of the wood by acid hydrolysis of the cellulose fibers within the structure. As the oxidation proceeds, the precipitated salts form in constricted areas and cause the cellulose fibers to divide and split. The potential for the sulfur to oxidize to an acidic state is exacerbated by the presence of iron ions. These originate from the many corroded iron bolts, which were present in the hull and act as a catalyst for the oxidation reaction. Since the raising of the *Mary Rose*, analysis has confirmed that approximately 2 tons of sulfur, in varying oxidation states, reside within the timbers (Jones 2003). This is comparable to the amount of sulfur within the timbers of the *Vasa* and confirms the need for treatment.

To date, the *Mary Rose* has been undergoing a spray treatment with polyethylene glycol (PEG), following a technique developed during the preservation of the *Vasa* (Hafors 2001). polymer, applied in varying grades over time to ensure full penetration within the wood, acts to mechanically and physically stabilize the wood when drying and prevent any shrinkage from occurring. Now, the acidification process must be addressed. Previous studies have explored the use of chelating studies to remove the iron from the wood and therefore reducing the rate of the process (Berko et al. 2009). Whilst some success has been had, this does not fully terminate the oxidation and gives no guarantee of the ship's stability indefinitely. This is critical when dealing with an item of such historical importance.

An alternative treatment proposed for the timbers is de-acidification, *via* the incorporation of suitable nanoparticles into the wood. This method was pioneered for the restoration of cultural heritage art work (Giorgi et al. 2002). Calcium hydroxide [$Ca(OH)_2$] nanoparticles dispersed in a suitable medium (2-proponal) were found to adhere to cellulose fibers, after the medium had volatized. Results indicated that the nanoparticles acted to neutralize the fibers and those resultant products would react with CO_2 to form a calcium carbonate reservoir. It was anticipated that this alkaline reservoir could act as a long-term protector of the wood. The clear advantages of this method are the ability to leave all present elements within the wood and merely add a reagent which will act as a long term neutralizer. In addition, the size of the reagent compared with the structure of the wood ensures that no mechanical damage would occur.

This method has been successfully applied to the *Vasa* timbers (Giorgi et al. 2005, Giorgi et al. 2006) using both $Ca(OH)_2$ and magnesium hydroxide [$Mg(OH)_2$] nanoparticles but some criticism has surmounted regarding the long term stability. It has been postulated that further moisture incorporated into the wood would increase the alkalinity near the hydroxide nanoparticles, which could hydrolyze any exposed lignin. It was also questioned as to whether sufficient CO_2 could penetrate the wood to form the alkaline reservoir. There is great potential for this method to be a suitable method for treating waterlogged archaeological wood suffering from the 'sulfur' problem. However, the reaction pathways, and subsequent compounds formed have not been clearly examined.

In this study Sr-based nanoparticles will be used to de-acidify *Mary Rose* timbers. Nanoparticles of $Sr(OH)_2$ (Ciliberto et al. 2008) have been previously applied to paper but to date have not been used with waterlogged timbers. Sr-based nanoparticles are more favourable as this element it is not expected within the timbers, whereas it is known that Ca and Mg are already present.

2. Methodology

420

2.1. Preparation of SrCO₃ (Strontium Carbonate)

$SrCO_3$, obtained from Aldrich, was ball milled using an alumina ceramic vial and balls for 8 hours using a SPEX 8000 M Mixer/Mill. X-ray powder diffraction patterns of the samples, shown in Figure 2, were collected on a conventional laboratory diffractometer, a Philips PW1720, using a Cu Kα tube operating at 35 kV and 20 mA.

2.2. Impregnation of wooden samples

Mary Rose oak was used in this study. $SrCO_3$ nanoparticles were dispersed into 2-proponal and sonicated for 1 hour. Two concentrations were used: 0.01 and 0.05 M. The concentration was based on the amount of $SrCO_3$ dissolved in a certain volume of 2-propanol. Samples were placed in the nanoparticles medium and left for 3 days whilst being sonicated throughout. Samples were removed from the solution and rinsed with distilled water.

2.3. Scanning Electron Microscopy – Energy Dispersive Microscopy

Scanning Electron Microscopy (SEM) analysis was performed using a JEOL JSM-6610LV. An Oxford Instruments energy dispersive spectroscopy (EDS) microanalysis spectrometer with INCA software was used to perform compositional analysis. Nanoparticles were analyzed for composition and morphology. Wooden samples were analyzed for structure and compositional distribution using the EDS mapping mode.

3. Results and Discussion

X-ray diffraction was completed on the $SrCO_3$ powder before and after ball milling. The patterns can be seen in Figure 2. From the full-width half maximum of the peaks in the diffraction pattern the particle sizes were determined from the Scherrer equation (Klug et al. 1974). Prior to ball milling the particle size was determined to be approximately 50 nm. After ball milling for 6 hours, the mean particle size had reduced to approximately 20 nm.

The nanoparticles easily agglomerated as seen in the micrograph in Figure 3. This made it essential to sonicate the nanoparticles and 2-propanol medium prior to adding the wooden sample. It ensured that the nanoparticles were disassociated and therefore would be able to penetrate the wood.

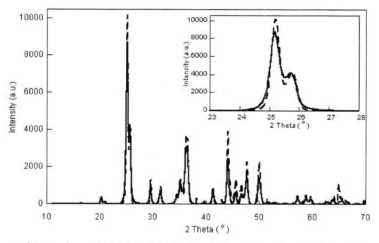

Figure 2. *XRD pattern of SrCO3 from Aldrich (straight line) and after ball milling (dashed line)*

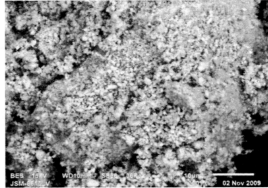

Figure 3. *SEM image of SrCO₃ nanoparticles after ball milling*

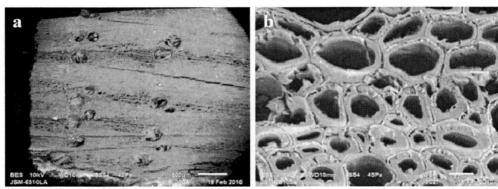

Figure 4a & b. *SEM images of* Mary Rose *oak*

Electron micrographs of *Mary Rose* oak prior to treatment, at different length scales, can be seen in Figures 4a and 4b. The size of samples typically used in this study was 5 x 5 x 1 mm. Whilst there is some damage to the wood, there is still structural integrity.

An initial concentration of 0.05 M SrCO₃ was applied to the *Mary Rose* oak. The micrographs of wood treated with this concentration can be seen in Figures 5a and 5b. When comparing these micrographs to those shown in Figures 4a

and 4b for the untreated *Mary Rose* oak, there is a clear difference. The SrCO₃ deposits into and on the wood and can be seen as white particles, which due to the size we can conclude are often agglomerations of smaller particles.

Attributing the white area to a strontium based particle can be confirmed by the EDS mapping shown in Figure 5c, the area of which correlates exactly to the image in Figure 5b. Strontium is convincingly distributed throughout the oak.

Figure 5a, b & c. *SEM images and EDS map of* Mary Rose *oak treated with 0.05 M SrCO₃ nanoparticle medium*

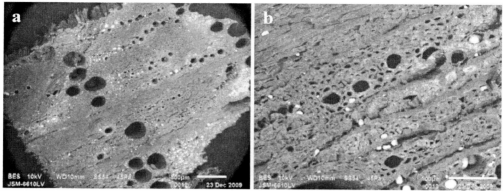

Figure 6a & b. SEM image of Mary Rose *oak treated with 0.01 M SrCO₃ nanoparticle medium*

However, it is clear to see that there is an excess of $SrCO_3$ in this case. The excess was also visible to the naked eye as a white coating was present on the surface of the wood. An alteration of the surface of the wood is not desirable and therefore if a lower concentration can be applied and the same affect achieved, this is favorable.

Electron micrographs of *Mary Rose* oak treated with a 0.01 M $SrCO_3$ solution can be seen in figures 6a and 6b. In this case, the addition of the strontium did not alter the visibility of the wood to the human eye. In contrast to Figure 5, there are much fewer white agglomerates and coatings of smaller particles can be seen particularly in figure 6b. Therefore in terms of the aesthetic properties of the wood, the lower concentration is more suitable.

4. Conclusions and Future Work

The work here has shown that $SrCO_3$ nanoparticles can be successfully impregnated into *Mary Rose* timbers. Nanoparticles, with a diameter as small as 20 nm were produced by ball milling. Alternative routes may be explored in order to fabricate smaller particle size, but for ease of production this route is favorable. SEM work confirmed the migration of the particles within the wood predominantly via open vessels or cracks in the wood. By imaging the wood before and after treatment it is easy to see the presence of a new substance in the treated sample. By employing EDS mapping we are able to confirm that this new substance is Sr-based.

Further work will be completed to confirm the speciation of this strontium compound throughout the wood. The expectation is that the $SrCO_3$ added will react with sulfate ions or compounds to form $SrSO_4$. This product is relatively insoluble in water, when compared to $CaSO_4$ and $FeSO_4$ which are known to reside in the wood. In addition, the stability of the wood after treatment needs to be assessed. pH tests will give an indication of whether the alkaline reservoir has been formed as predicted.

After ascertaining the viability of this technique, the question will be addressed of how to treat larger sectors of the ship and other wooden artifacts found. Initially a spraying technique will be developed. This will start will small artifacts and will gradually scale up.

References

Berko A., Smith A.D., Jones A.M., Schofield E.J., Mosselmans J.F.W. and Chadwick A.V., (2009), XAS Studies of the Effectiveness of Iron Chelating Treatments of *Mary Rose* Timbers, Journal of Physics: Conference Series, Vol. 190, 2009, pp 012417-012422.

Ciliberto E., Condorelli G. G., La Delfa S. and Viscuso E., (2008), Nanoparticles of $Sr(OH)_2$: Synthesis in Homogeneous Phase at Low Temperature and Application for

Cultural Heritage Artefacts, Applied Physics A, Vol. 92, 2008, pp 137-141.

Giorgi R., Chelazzi D. and Baglioni P., (2005), Nanoparticles of Calcium Hydroxide for Wood Conservation. The Deacidification of the *Vasa* Warship, Langmuir, Vol. 21, No. 23, 2005, pp 10743-10748.

Giorgi R., Chelazzi D. and Baglioni P., (2006), Conservation of Acid Waterlogged Shipwrecks: Nanotechnologies for De-acidification, Applied Physics A, Vol. 83, 2006, pp 567-571.

Giorgi R., Dei L., Ceccato M., Schettino C. and Baglioni P., (2002), Nanotechnologies for Conservation of Cultural Heritage: Paper and Canvas Deacidification, Langmuir, Vol. 18, No. 21, 2002, pp 8198-8203.

Hafors B., (2001), Conservation of the Swedish Warship *Vasa* from 1628, Vasa Studies 18, Stockholm, Vasa Museum.

Jones A.M., (2003), For Future Generations: Conservation of a Tudor Maritime Collection, Portsmouth, The Mary Rose Trust.

Klug H.P. and Alexander L.E., (1974), X-ray Diffraction Procedures, New York, Wiley-VCH.

McKee A., (1982), How We Found the *Mary Rose*, Souvenir Press Ltd.

Sandström M., Jalilehvand F., Damien E., Fors Y., Gelius U., Jones M. and Salome M., (2005), Sulfur Accumulation in the Timbers of King Henry VIII's Warship *Mary Rose*: A Pathway in the Sulfur Cycle of Conservation Concern, PNAS, Vol. 102, No. 40, 2005, pp 14165-14170.

Sandström M., Jalilehvand F., Persson I., Gelius U., Frank P. and Hall-Roth I., (2002), Deterioration of the Seventeenth-Century Warship *Vasa* by Internal Formation of Sulfuric Acid, Nature, Vol. 415, 2002, pp 893-897.

Wetherall K.M., Moss R.M., Jones A.M., Smith A.D., Skinner T., Pickup D.M., Goatham S.W., Chadwick A.V. and Newport R.J., (2008), Sulfur and Iron Speciation in Recently Recovered Timbers of the *Mary Rose* Revealed via X-ray Absorption Spectroscopy, Journal of Archaeological Science, Vol. 35, 2008, pp 1317-1328.

Questions and answers

Susan Braovac: I'm sorry is the pH of the treated samples what you'd expect?

Eleanor Schofield: I don't know yet. I haven't measured the pH. That's the next stages measuring the pH and mass spec. We know it changes but what is it. So that's the more in depth work.

Hartmut Kutzke: Do you have any idea or experience of this strontium carbonate interacting in any way with any impregnation materials?

Eleanor Schofield: I don't. No, I started doing some experiments trying to get it into the PEG but I haven't done any characterization yet about what's formed. Hopefully I'm going to be doing that this summer on the PEG treated samples to see if there is any interaction with that.

4.5

Extraction of Sulfur Compounds from Archaeological Wood by Chemical Oxidation with Sodium Persulfate

Khôi Tran*, Fanny Bauchau and Clément Werner

ARC-Nucléart, CEA-Grenoble, 17, rue des Martyrs, Grenoble 38 054, France
*E-mail: quoc-khoi.tran@cea.fr

Abstract

Unstable sulfur efflorescences and acid attack of the wood appeared on the surface of some artifacts from the shipwreck *La Lomellina* (16th century, Villefranche sur Mer, Mediterranean Sea) following PEG treatment and during storage in air-conditioned rooms. The present research focused on this question by studying the process of chemical oxidation of these reduced sulfur (mono and disulfide iron) compounds into stable products such as sulfates. The chemical oxidant selected was sodium persulfate, and the neutralizing chemical added to the medium to prevent a decrease in pH was sodium hydrogen carbonate. Kinetic studies were performed first in solutions in order to optimize the formulations. With a view to preventive conservation, this study also considered the case of waterlogged artifacts containing sulfur compounds, prior to conservation treatment. Chemical oxidation was carried out in solutions containing the oxidant-neutralizing agent pair and the wooden artifact. This paper will present the concrete results obtained with two different artifacts, one already treated by PEG and then air-dried, and the other still waterlogged. In the case of the former, applications of poultices swelled with the oxidant solution to the efflorescence areas of the object are described.

Keywords: salt efflorescence, archaeological wood, iron sulfide,

oxidation, iron sulfates, buffer sodium hydrogenocarbonate

1. Introduction

In recent years, the question of sulfur has been studied on some archaeological artifacts from marine excavations at ARC-Nucléart. Indeed, important collections treated by the polyethylene glycol (PEG) method present crystalline efflorescences on some parts of their surface and suffer acid attack during storage in air-conditioned rooms, due to the oxidation of sulfur compounds. Mention should be made of the shipwreck *La Lomellina* (16th century, Villefranche sur Mer, Mediterranean Sea) (see Figure 1).

Figure 1: *Salt efflorescence on a PEG treated timber from the* La Lomellina *shipwreck.*

To deal with this problem, several ways of extracting the reduced sulfur compounds from the wood were investigated (Tran et al. 2004, Guinard 2006, Pagel-Prevoteau 2006, Morlay 2007, Bauchau 2008, Werner 2009). ARC-Nucléart focused mainly on the development of a chemical process in an aqueous medium, involving oxidizing sulfur compounds into stable products such as sulfates and removing it from the archaeological wood. This research was carried out with a view to providing both preventive and curative treatment. The effect of several oxidants was tested, mainly on two unstable sulfides that were identified in contaminated wood by X-ray powder diffraction analysis: mackinawite (FeS) and pyrite (FeS$_2$) (Schuster, Pécaut and Tran 2004, Sandström et al. 2005). The most suitable oxidant (providing a good compromise between efficiency and respect for the condition of the wood) seemed to be sodium persulfate (Na$_2$S$_2$O$_8$) (Pagel-Prevoteau 2006, Morlay 2007, Bauchau 2008, Werner 2009). To prevent any decrease in pH due to the formation of sulfuric acid as a product of oxidation, and hence damage to the wood structure, a neutralizing chemical agent was also added to the medium. The agent selected was sodium hydrogen carbonate (NaHCO$_3$).

The final aim of this research was to treat two archaeological artifacts with this oxidant-neutralizing agent pair: one already treated by PEG and then air-dried, and the other still waterlogged. In the first case, the object had unstable sulfur efflorescences that needed to be removed and stabilized for it to be displayed in a museum (curative treatment). In the second case, the wet artifact had mineral concretions on its surface and sulfur compounds at depth. These minerals had to be removed from the wood firstly to allow PEG impregnation and secondly to avoid the occurrence of future efflorescences (preventive treatment).

For this purpose, kinetic studies were performed firstly in solutions with commercial iron mono- and disulfide in order to optimize the formulations. Simultaneously, experiments were carried out to examine wood alteration by these reagents, in order to ensure that the treatment was not too aggressive. The treatments were then applied. Chemical oxidation was carried out by applying poultices swelled by the oxidant solution to the efflorescence areas in the case of the dried object and by soaking the wooden artifact in the oxidant solution in the case of the waterlogged object.

2. Experiments on Commercial Sulfur Compounds

2.1. Materials and methods

2.1.1. Reactions Involved and Monitoring

Persulfates are strong oxidants that have been widely used in many industries for initiating emulsion polymerization reactions, clarifying swimming pools, bleaching hair, micro-etching copper printed circuit boards and destroying groundwater contaminants (Block, Brown and Robinson 2004). The persulfate anion is the most powerful oxidant of the peroxygen family compounds. The standard oxidation-reduction potential for reaction (1) is 2.1 V$_{|ESH}$.

$$S_2O_8^{2-} + 2H^+ + 2e^- = 2 HSO_4^- \quad (1)$$

This potential is higher than the redox potential of other oxidants tested in past studies (Tran et al. 2004), such as 1.8 V$_{|ESH}$ for hydrogen peroxide (H$_2$O$_2$) or 1.7 V$_{|ESH}$ for the permanganate anion (MnO$_4^-$).

Sodium persulfate also has the advantage of being highly soluble (550g/L), which makes chemical oxidation easier in an aqueous medium. And while the formation of additional sulfate salts may appear to be a drawback, it is not in fact a practical problem, since sulfates, with their high solubility, can be removed after treatment with a water rinse bath.

The proposed overall oxidation reactions with FeS$_2$ and FeS are as follows:

$$FeS_2 + 7 S_2O_8^{2-} + 8 H_2O \rightarrow Fe^{2+} + 16 SO_4^{2-} + 16 H^+ \quad (2)$$

$$FeS + 4 S_2O_8^{2-} + 4 H_2O \rightarrow Fe^{2+} + 9 SO_4^{2-} + 8 H^+ \quad (3)$$

To monitor the extent and calculate the efficiency of the oxidation reactions, the quantity of iron in solution was measured by atomic absorption spectroscopy (Perkin-Elmer PE 3110 spectrometer), during and at the end of the experiments. In the case of the experiments performed without a buffering agent, the pH was also measured (Metrohm 692 pH/ion Meter) in order to monitor the reaction.

2.1.2. Experimental Protocol

A first series of experiments was performed on commercial powders of FeS_2 (95% purity, STREM) and FeS (Sigma-Aldrich) in a free pH solution, in order to judge the efficiency of $Na_2S_2O_8$. The same experiments were performed on FeS_2 and FeS since both of them are present in the wood and have to be extracted by the same treatment. A fixed quantity of FeS_2 (resp. FeS) (2g) was placed in a beaker with oxidant solutions of different concentrations. The oxidant solutions were prepared with quantities of $Na_2S_2O_8$ (99+% purity, Chem-Lab) varying from 0 to 30 g in 0.25 L of deionized water (which corresponds to concentrations varying from 0 to 0.5 mol/L). These values were chosen in order to test reaction (2) (resp. (3)) stoichiometry and off-stoichiometry (below and over) $Na_2S_2O_8/FeS_2$ (resp. FeS) ratios. The experiments were conducted at room temperature, under continuous stirring, for 48 hours. This first part of the study allowed us to choose an efficacy mass ratio $Na_2S_2O_8/FeS_2$ (resp. FeS) so that the quantity of oxidant to be used to treat an artifact can be determined by estimating the quantity of sulfur compounds present in the object.

Simultaneously, a study of wood degradation was performed by introducing samples of wood, without archaeological interest and free of sulfur compounds, into oxidant solutions of different concentrations. Unfortunately, it was impossible to perform analyses to determine the alteration caused by the oxidant. We focused mainly on macroscopic characteristics: preservation of the physical integrity and stain of the wood.

Finally a series of experiments were carried out in a buffer medium in order to determine the quantity of neutralizing agent necessary to maintain the pH between 5 and 10 throughout the experiment. $NaHCO_3$, which was used curatively on the *Vasa* (by applying poultices on the surface of the shipwreck to neutralize the acid formed) (Sandström, Fors and Persson 2003, Fors 2005), appeared to be efficient in buffering the medium in past studies on chemical oxidation processes carried out at ARC-Nucléart. It stabilizes the pH value between 6 and 10. In contact with the acidic solution, the harmless product carbon dioxide ($CO_2(g)$) is formed by neutralization:

$$HCO_3^- + H_3O^+ \rightarrow 2\ H_2O + CO_2\ (4)$$

This series of experiments was conducted only on FeS_2, since the pH measured during the previous experiments on FeS_2 was lower than those on FeS. A fixed quantity of FeS_2 (2g) was placed in a beaker with the oxidant solution selected in the previous steps (6.7 g of $Na_2S_2O_8$ in 0.25 L of deionized water). Different quantities of $NaHCO_3$ (99.5 % purity, Normapur) were added. These quantities, varying from 0 to 3 g, correspond to stoichiometry and off-stoichiometry molar $NaHCO_3/FeS_2$ ratios. The experiments were conducted at room temperature, under continuous stirring, for 48 hours. In order to evaluate the impact of the presence of $NaHCO_3$ on the extent of the reaction, the iron in the solution whose pH was maintained above 5 was dosed by atomic absorption spectroscopy. To make analysis possible, the solution was acidified beforehand with sulfuric acid in order to dissolve the iron. In fact, Fe^{2+} is eventually oxidized by $Na_2S_2O_8$ to Fe^{3+}, which at a pH above 2, is insoluble. The net reaction is:

$$2\ Fe^{2+} + S_2O_8^{2-} \rightarrow 2\ Fe^{3+} + 2\ SO_4^{2-}\ (5)$$
$$Fe^{3+} + 3\ H_2O \rightarrow Fe(OH)_3 \downarrow + 3\ H^+\ (6)$$

The orange color of the solution observed proved that these reactions actually occurred.

2.2. Results and Discussion
2.2.1. Experiments in Free pH Medium

Figure 2 shows the change in pH versus reaction time, for FeS and FeS_2. In the absence of any oxidant, the pH remained constant. In both cases, FeS_2 and FeS, and with every mass reactant ratio tested, the pH decreased with time to reach very low values after 48 hours of reaction.

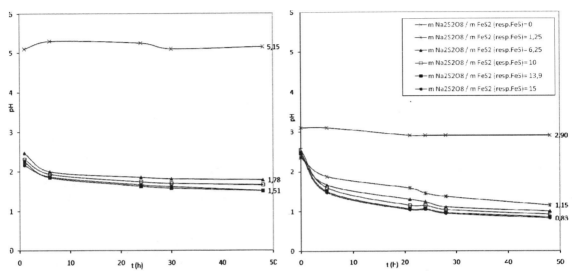

Figure 2. Change in pH with time in experiments conducted on commercial FeS (left graph) and FeS_2 (right graph) powders in different $Na_2S_2O_8$ solutions. Mass ratios $Na_2S_2O_8/FeS_2$ and $Na_2S_2O_8/FeS$ varying from 0 to 15 were tested.

This increase in acidity shows that oxidation occurred (formation of sulfuric acid). It may also be noted that the higher the mass reactant ratio (i.e. the more concentrated the oxidant solution), the lower the pH at each instant.

Figure 3, which reports the change in %Fe in solution versus time, confirms that oxidation occurred. With both sulfides, the %Fe in solution increased with time. The values reached were much higher in the case of FeS: nearly 70 % versus 30 % for FeS_2 after 48 hours of reaction in the case of the higher mass ratios. This difference is consistent with the fact that FeS is more unstable than FeS_2. In the case of FeS, the %Fe in solution substantially increased during the first 30 hours and then continued to increase but less quickly, whereas in the case of FeS_2, the graph shows a gradual rise over the 48 hours. Longer baths might have led to a higher final %Fe in solution, but for practical reasons it was preferred not to soak the archaeological artifacts any longer in the oxidant baths. After 48 hours, the oxidation efficiencies reached were quite acceptable in all cases. The final %Fe in solution increased with the mass ratio, but the values were quite close in the case of mass ratios higher than 6.25. A mass ratio of 10 would therefore be preferable since the same efficiency was obtained with a smaller quantity of oxidant.

The experiments performed in parallel to study the degradation of the wood showed that $Na_2S_2O_8$ seems not to cause significant damage. The wood was only slightly lightened and its structure did not seem to be weakened. However, as archeological wood is generally badly damaged and therefore very fragile, the impact of the oxidant could be stronger. That is why it was decided to supply the quantity of oxidant that had been defined as necessary to treat the artifact (calculated with a mass ratio of 10) in three successive baths instead of one single bath. The wood was thus immersed in a less concentrated and hence less aggressive medium.

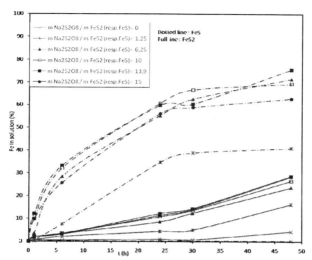

Figure 3. Change in %Fe in solution versus time in experiments conducted on commercial FeS (dotted line) and FeS_2 (full line) powders in different $Na_2S_2O_8$ solutions. Mass ratios $Na_2S_2O_8/FeS_2$ and $Na_2S_2O_8/FeS$ varying from 0 to 15 were tested.

2.2.2. Experiments in Buffer Medium

Figure 4 shows the change in pH versus time using different $NaHCO_3/FeS_2$ mass ratios and a fixed quantity of $Na_2S_2O_8$. In the case of ratios 0.7 and 1.05, the pH declines abruptly after about twenty hours. In the case of the higher ratios tested, the pH remained above 5 throughout the experiment. The final %Fe in solution was quantified for the lowest of these ratios. The result was very close to the value measured for the same oxidant solution in a free pH medium (see Table 1). $NaHCO_3$ therefore appeared to be efficient in buffering the medium and not to have any effect on the extent of the oxidation reaction. A slight decrease in oxidation efficiency might have been anticipated since the oxidation of FeS_2 can be catalyzed in an acidic medium. Indeed, with a pH under 2, Fe^{3+} ions, which can be formed by the reaction (4), can oxidize FeS_2 according to the followed reaction:

$$FeS_2 + 14\ Fe^{3+} + 8\ H_2O \rightarrow 15\ Fe^{2+} + 2\ SO_4^{2-} + 16\ H^+ \quad (7)$$

At the end of these experiments, $Na_2S_2O_8/NaHCO_3$ appeared to be an appropriate oxidant-neutralizing agent pair for extracting sulfur compounds from archaeological wood. It seemed to oxidize sulfides efficiently while preserving the wood texture.

3. Treatment of A Waterlogged Artifact From Tardinghen (Northern France)

3.1. Description of the Artifact

In November 2005, fragments of a Gallo-Roman shipwreck were discovered on Chatelet beach at Tardinghen in the north of France (see Figure 5a). All the fragments were found separated, but were originally fixed together with wooden plugs and iron nails, which are now totally corroded. The shipwreck was dated between the 1st and 4th centuries AD. Blackish mineral concretions were observed on the surface of several pieces. Two samples of these concretions were taken from two different fragments for X-ray powder diffraction analysis. In both cases, pyrite was found to be the major phase (80-90 %). The other phases detected were gypsum ($CaSO_4$) and silica (SiO_2).

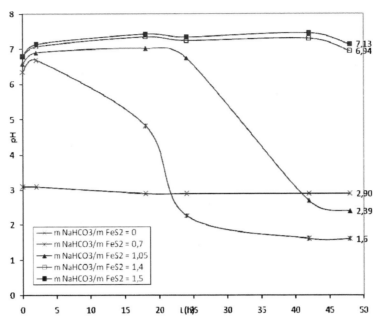

Figure 4. *Change in pH with time in experiments conducted on commercial FeS₂ powder (2g) in oxidant solution (fixed quantity of Na₂S₂O₈ : 6.7g) and with NaHCO₃ as buffering agent. Mass ratios NaHCO₃/FeS₂ varying from 0 to 1.5 were tested.*

Table 1. *Final pH and final %Fe in solution for experiments conducted on commercial FeS₂ powder (2g) in oxidant solution (fixed quantity of Na₂S₂O₈: 6.7g), in a free pH medium and in a buffer medium with a mass ratio NaHCO₃/FeS₂ of 1.4.*

	m NaHCO₃/ m FeS₂ = 0	m NaHCO₃/ m FeS₂ = 1,4
Final pH	1,22	6,94
Final %Fe in solution	20,9	20,5

Figure 5a (left): *Fragments of a Gallo-Roman shipwreck discovered on Chatelet beach at Tardinghen, in the north of France; b (right): Fragment of the shipwreck discovered in Tardinghen used for chemical oxidation.*

Table 2: *Results of the TGA conducted on two samples from a fragment of the Tardinghen collection (one from the surface and one from the core of the fragment) and on a modern wood. %wt are based on the waterlogged wood mass. Conditions of the TGA : Water loss: 2hr at 150°C in dry argon at 15mL/min. Cellulose decomposition: 1hr at 450°C in dry argon at 15mL/min. Combustion: 1hr at 650°C in dry argon at 10mL/min.*

	Initial mass of the water-logged sample (mg)	Water loss (%wt)	Cellulose decomposition (%wt)	Loss by combustion (%wt)	Total loss (%wt)	Ash content (%wt)
Sample 1 (core)	3	7.67	52.10	32.63	92.40	7.60
Sample 2 (surface)	12.6	9.61	47.67	25.68	82.96	17.04
Modern wood	135.3	7.34	68.23	24.37	99.92	0.08

One fragment of the shipwreck (see Figure 5b), featuring large concretions, was selected for treatment by chemical oxidation with $Na_2S_2O_8$ and $NaHCO_3$. In order to quantify the minerals present in the wood, thermogravimetric analysis (TGA, Setaram®, model Setsys Evo 2400) was conducted on samples from the surface and from the core of the fragment (see Table 2). The ash contents obtained for the samples from Tardinghen were much higher than those obtained for a modern wood, notably in the case of the surface sample: 17.04% of ash against 0.08% for a sound wood. The ash contents (based on the waterlogged wood mass) were used to estimate the quantity of sulfur compounds present in the wood (assuming that the minerals are mostly sulfur compounds, as was shown by X-ray powder diffraction analysis).

3.2. Treatment

Thanks to the experiments conducted on commercial sulfides and to the estimation of the quantity of sulfur compounds in the artifact (with the TGA results), the quantities of $Na_2S_2O_8$ and $NaHCO_3$ for the treatment could be estimated. These operating conditions were progressively adapted to the observations and results obtained during the treatment.

3.2.1. Operating Protocol

The artifact was soaked for 48 hours in a 50 L bath of the oxidant and buffer solution, at room temperature and under continuous stirring. Several baths were prepared. The pH of the solution was checked throughout the treatment. In this case, analyzing the iron concentration was not sufficient to monitor the oxidation efficiency. Indeed, the oxidation products were partly insoluble and stayed on the surface of the wood or at the bottom of the tank, so that samples of the solution were not representative. The changes in the appearance of the wood and in the state of the mineral concretion were considered to be the most important and significant indicators. Between two oxidant baths, the artifact was rinsed in a water bath to remove the oxidation products and allow better monitoring. At the end of the treatment, the object was rinsed in several water baths until the anion $S_2O_8^{2-}$ was detected in trace amounts in the solution, to be sure that no oxidant remained inside the wood.

3.2.2. Results and Discussion

Three baths were scheduled, but five were actually used to treat the object effectively. The quantity of $Na_2S_2O_8$ was kept the same for the five baths (1700 g, which corresponds to a concentration of 0.14 mol/L), but the quantity of $NaHCO_3$ was substantially diminished after the first bath. In fact, the first bath was not as efficient as expected. It is clear that the main cause of the difference in efficiency between the previous experiments and application to the artifact is that reduced sulfur compounds were here in a condensed form. The $Na_2S_2O_8$ oxidized the mineral concretions only superficially, so that little sulfuric acid was formed and the quantity of $NaHCO_3$ was overestimated. The pH stood at a rather high value (near 8, see Figure 6), which was likely to limit the efficiency of the oxidation reaction. A pH stabilized near 6 or 7 is preferable. The initial quantity of $NaHCO_3$ was thus reduced for the other four baths (from 700g to 100g, which corresponds to a decrease in concentration from 0.17 mol/L to 0.024 mol/L). This allowed the oxidation reaction to be initiated. Some $NaHCO_3$ was added during the two days of treatment if necessary. Figure 6 and Table 3 show the evolution of pH and the main results (bath, mineral surface concretions and wood aspects) for each bath.

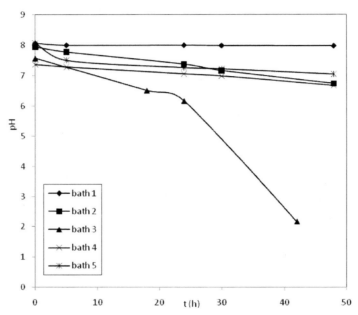

Figure 6. Change in pH with time during treatment of the artifact from Tardinghen collection. Five baths were used.

Table 3. Main observations (appearance of bath, mineral surface concretions and wood) for each bath.

Bath	Appearance of bath	Appearance of mineral surface concretions	Appearance of wood
1	Formation of few "reddish-brown insoluble products"	Slightly weakened	Slightly lightened
2	Formation of "reddish-brown insoluble products" in very large quantities	Weakened → possible to remove part of the concretions mechanically	Stable
3	Formation of "reddish-brown insoluble products" in very large quantities	Disappearance of large proportion of concretions	Stable
4	Formation of "reddish-brown insoluble product" on the remaining concretions	Disappearance of all concretions	Stable
5	-	-	Orange coloring

The pH was kept stable around 7, except for one bath during which the oxidation was really efficient and NaHCO₃ could not be added in time. During the second, third and fourth baths, some reddish-brown insoluble products, certainly iron oxides or hydroxides, were formed in large quantities at the surface of the wood. After 24 hours of immersion, the wood was completely covered with these products and after 48 hours the solution became totally reddish-brown, saturated with these products (see Figure 7). The $Na_2S_2O_8$ oxidant had a very pronounced effect. Since the concretions were weakened during the first bath and pH was maintained at a lower value, oxidation efficiency was bound to be increased. X-ray powder diffraction analysis of these insoluble products was carried out, but no phases could be detected precisely. A similar case has been mentioned by Kelsall et al. (1999), who investigated the oxidation mechanism of pyrite in aqueous electrolytes. They also observed reddish-brown film at the surface of pyrite, after oxidizing the surface electrochemically in pH 9.2 buffer solution. Using X-ray diffraction, a few weak lines matching FeO were found in the film product. However, since the film was reddish-brown in color, it was suggested that iron (III) was probably present in amorphous forms.

Figure 7: *Fragment of the Tardinghen collection soaked in an oxidant bath of $Na_2S_2O_8$ and $NaHCO_3$. Formation of oxidation products on the wood surface.*

During the four first baths, the mineral surface concretions were firstly weakened, allowing partial mechanical removal, and finally totally eliminated, while the wood was only slightly lightened (see Figure 8). However, at the end of the fourth bath, the wood had a blackish stain on some parts of its surface, which was probably due to the presence of sulfides at depth. A fifth bath enabled some of it to be removed. The blackish areas were lightened and the wood took on an orange coloring, which may have been an indication of oxidation at depth. However, the blackish color remained in some places, such as areas close to nail sites. Some mineral compounds probably remained in the object, but certainly in small quantities, not justifying a further bath. Unfortunately it was impossible to perform an additional analysis to quantify the sulfur remaining at depth, as this would have been too destructive for the artifact. It is therefore difficult to precisely determine the impact of the treatment in the bulk of the object. After several rinses in water the artifact became brown once again, suggesting that oxidation products remaining in the bulk of the object had been removed.

In this study, sodium persulfate appeared to be an appropriate oxidant for removing sulfur compounds from the archaeological wooden artifact. It oxidized pyrite efficiently while preserving the texture of the wood. No significant chemical or physical damage was observed and the extraction of most of the mineral compounds from the object enabled PEG impregnation and drying to proceed successfully. In addition, X-ray powder diffraction analysis of a sample from the surface of the dried artifact detected only silica; no sulfides remained. More than one year after drying, there are no efflorescences on the object. The wood seems to be stabilized.

Figure 8. Detail of the artifact: before treatment (top); after treatment (bottom). Mineral concretions and the blackish color of the wood have disappeared.

4. Treatment of an Artifact from Villefranche Sur Mer (Mediterranean Sea) Impregnated By PEG And Air-Dried

4.1. Description of the Artifact

Since the years 1999-2000, ARC-Nucléart has been in charge of a collection of wooden objects from the 16th century shipwreck *La Lomellina*, found at Villefranche sur mer, in the Mediterranean Sea. These objects were treated by PEG impregnation and then air-dried.

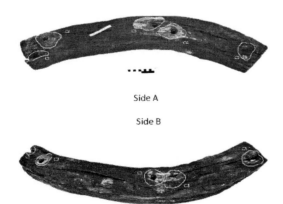

Side A

Side B

Figure 9. Artifact from the shipwreck La Lomellina (Villefranche sur Mer, Mediterranean Sea). Areas affected by the appearance of mineral efflorescences, caused by the oxidation of unstable sulfur compounds.

However, during their storage in air-conditioned rooms, several artifacts presented a number of crystalline efflorescences at their surface and suffered acid attack, due to the oxidation of iron sulfide compounds present in the wood. The efflorescences were first removed mechanically, but new ones reappeared in the same areas shortly after. It was therefore decided to proceed with chemical treatment in order to remove the sulfur compounds by forced oxidation and so avoid the future appearance of efflorescences and acidification of the wood by the formation of sulfuric acid. An artillery-type wheel fragment, presenting several efflorescences (see Figure 9), was treated by applying cellulose pulp poultices swelled by a solution of $Na_2S_2O_8$ and $NaHCO_3$ to the affected areas.

4.2. Treatment

4.2.1. Operating Protocol

A treatment was firstly conducted on only one affected area (area C2, side A) with a poultice swelled by a solution of $Na_2S_2O_8$ at 0.14 mol/L and $NaHCO_3$ at 0.17 mol/L. After few hours, the pH of the poultice decreased abruptly from 9 down to 2, so that it was decided to decrease the $Na_2S_2O_8$ concentration (from 0.14 mol/L to 0.047 mol/L) to limit the oxidation efficiency and hence the acidification of the wood. Moreover, while the treated efflorescence seemed to have been partially removed by this first poultice application, the other efflorescences had "grown" during the treatment. Afterwards, the affected areas were therefore all treated simultaneously (see Figure 10). Table 4 summarizes the treatments applied to each area.

Table 4. *Treatments applied to each area affected by mineral efflorescences.*

	Areas	C1	C2	C3	C4	C5
Side A	Number of poultice applications	2	2	2	2	2
	Time of each application	4-5h	4-5h	4-5h	4-5h	4-5h
Side B	Number of poultice applications	4	4	4	4	4
	Time of each application	4-5h	4-5h	4-5h	4-5h	4-5h

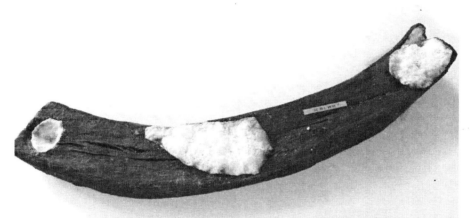

Figure 10. *Application of pulp cellulose poultices swelled by a solution of $Na_2S_2O_8$ and $NaHCO_3$ on areas presenting mineral efflorescences.*

4.2.2. Results and Discussion

At the end of the treatment, all the efflorescences had been removed (see Figure 11). With all the poultice applications, after 5 hours the wood surface had areas with different pH values: from 9 to 6, with a few areas having an acidic pH of 3. But, generally speaking, the wood did not seem to suffer serious damage. However, the appearance of PEG particles exuding at the surface of the wood was noted. After these PEG particles had been removed, the artifact recovered its initial appearance (just after drying) and was suitable for display in museums. The treatment was quite satisfactory. Moreover, one year after the treatment was carried out no new efflorescences have appeared, suggesting that the state of the wood is quite stabilized. However, X-ray powder diffraction analysis has revealed that some pyrite has remained in the wood, in rather high concentrations: from 10% to 70% in the treated areas, depending on the initial degree of sulfur contamination. These unstable sulfur compounds should be extracted to ensure that no problem occurs in the future.

435

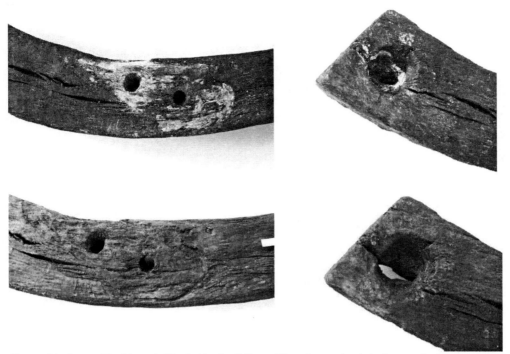

Figure 11. *Areas C3, C4 and C5 of side A of the artillery-type wheel, before and after poultice treatment. The efflorescences have been removed.*

5. Conclusion

These studies concerning the extraction of sulfur compounds from archaeological wood by chemical oxidation with sodium persulfate provided encouraging results, for both preventive and curative treatment. In the latter case, the application of poultices swelled with sodium persulfate and hydrogen carbonate removed the efflorescences from the surface of the treated artifact and, even though analyses revealed that a fairly large quantity of sulfur compounds have remained in the wood, no new efflorescences have appeared in a year. However the state of the wood needs to be monitored.

In the case of preventive treatment, which involves performing forced oxidation by soaking the waterlogged object in the oxidant solution, the results obtained were more conclusive. Successive oxidant baths removed all the surface concretions from the treated artifact and certainly a proportion of the compounds at depth, without significantly altering the color and

structure of the wood. PEG impregnation and drying could thus be carried out successfully. The stability of the wood more than one year after drying (no appearance of efflorescences) and analysis of a surface sample showing that no sulfides have remained prove the efficiency of the treatment.

Chemical oxidation with persulfate in an aqueous medium, buffered by hydrogen carbonate, seems to be a viable process for waterlogged archaeological wood. However, it is impossible to establish an optimum protocol for removing sulfur compounds from archaeological wood with sodium persulfate on the basis of this study only. Each artifact may require a different treatment, which must take into account several parameters, such as the degree of degradation of the wood, the sulfur compound content, the degree of contamination (surface, at depth), etc.

A research program concerning the problems of sulfur compound extraction from wet archaeological wood is currently

436

in progress, involving three French laboratories: ARC-Nucléart, ARC'Antique (Nantes) and LEMMA (Laboratoire d'Etude des Matériaux en Milieux Agressifs, La Rochelle University). This program intends to study these problems in detail by developing protocols for optimized and validated treatments, firstly using model samples impregnated with sulfur compounds and then using real archaeological samples infected by sulfur compounds. In order to improve the efficiency of the treatment, the program will also study a combination of two techniques: chemical and bacterial oxidation of the sulfides, followed by ionic extraction of the oxidation products by electrophoresis. The action of oxidation could be supplemented by an electrophoresis step in order to facilitate the migration of oxidized compounds, notably compounds at depth. In this way, the already satisfactory results obtained during this study are bound to be improved.

References

Bauchau F., (2008), Internship studies at ARC-Nucléart.

Block P.A., Brown R.A. and Robinson D., (2004), Novel Activation Technologies for Sodium Persulfate In Situ Chemical Oxidation, in Arun Gavaskar and Abraham S.C. Chen (editors), Proceedings of the Fourth International Conference on the Remediation of Chlorinated and Recalcitrant Compounds, Columbus, Ohio, USA, Battelle Press, 2004.

Fors Y., (2005), Sulfur Speciation and Distribution in the Vasa's Wood. Licentiate Thesis, Stockholm, Department of Structural Chemistry, Stockholm University.

Guinard M., (2006), Internship studies at ARC-Nucléart.
Kelsall G.H., Yin Q., Vaughan D.J., England K.E.R. and Brandon N.P., (1999), Electrochemical Oxidation of Pyrite (FeS$_2$) in Aqueous Electrolytes, Journal of Electroanalytical Chemistry, Vol. 471, 1999, pp 116-125.

Morlay M., (2007), Internship studies at ARC-Nucléart.

Pagel-Prevoteau A., (2006), Internship studies at ARC-Nucléart.

Sandström M., Fors Y. and Persson I., (2003), The Vasa's New Battle; Sulphur, Acid and Iron, Vasa Studies 19, Stockholm, The Vasa Museum.

Sandström M., Jalilehvand F., Damian E., Fors Y., Gelius U., Jones M. and Salomé M., (2005), Sulfur Accumulation in the Timbers of King Henry VIII's Warship *Mary Rose*: A Pathway in the Sulfur Cycle of Conservation Concern, Proceedings of the National Academy of Sciences, vol. 102, n° 40, 2005, pp 14165-14170.

Schuster I., Pécaut J. and Tran K., (2004), La Diffraction des Rayons X au Service de la Conservation des Bois Archéologiques Gorgés d'eau, J. Phys. IV France, Vol. 118, 2004, pp 377-384.

Tran K., Bertout N., Dalard F. and Magnin J.P., (2004), Trials on Chemical and Microbiological Processes for the Oxidation of Sulphur Compounds in Archaeological Wood, in P. Hoffmann, K. Straetkvern, J.A. Sprigs and D. Gregory (editors), Proceedings of the 9th ICOM Group on Wet Organic Archaeological Materials Conference, Copenhagen, 2004, Bremerhaven, The International Council of Museums, Committee for Conservation Working Group on Wet Organic Archaeological Materials, 2005, pp 227-241.

Werner C., (2009), Internship studies at ARC-Nucléart.

4.6

Re-Conservation of Wood Samples from the *Vasa* with Alkoxysilanes: Preliminary Assessment

Carlos Cabrera Tejedor*

MA Candidate, Nautical Archaeology Program, Department of Anthropology
243 Anthropology Building 4352 TAMU, College Station, TX 77843-4352, U.S.A.
*E-mail: carlos.cabrera.tejedor@gmail.com

Keywords: waterlogged wood, small objects, PEG, re-conservation, re-treatment, alkoxysilanes, silicone oil, MTMS.

Abstract

The purpose of this study was to explore the feasibility of re-treating artifacts previously conserved by PEG impregnation with alkoxysilanes. The study tried to evaluate pros and cons of re-conserving artifacts with this type of silanes. A series of experiments were conducted focusing on small, wood samples from the *Vasa* Museum Collection, to test different re-conservation methods. Three different procedures involving alkoxysilanes were implemented in order to re-conserve the samples. The study revealed the techniques are an efficient re-conservation method in which highly satisfactory results can be achieved. The re-treated samples present minimal volumetric distortion without significant collapse or shrinkage of the wood structures. Due to the negligible thickness of the polymer coating (a few microns), the samples acquire physical properties extremely close to the original, dry wood. In addition, microscopic anatomical and morphological diagnostic features of the wood are identifiable after treatment. Moreover, other physiochemical properties are obtained; the re-conserved wood becomes hydrophobic, chemically inert, resistant to chemical attacks (e.g. acids or bases), and resistant to ultraviolet light. Therefore, preventive conservation measures could be drastically reduced after this treatment. Despite the excellent results, the procedure is not reversible. Therefore, benefits and disadvantages should be assessed before applying this method.

1. Objectives

Three different re-conservation procedures were tested focusing on small, organic wood samples from the *Vasa* Museum Collection. The main objective was to explore the feasibility of re-treating small artifacts (previously conserved by impregnation with PEG) with alkoxysilanes. The three re-conservation procedures were: (1) a methyltrimethoxysilane (MTMS) treatment developed by Dr. Wayne Smith; (2) the method used by the Conservation Research Laboratory (CRL) using silicone oil and a crosslinker; and (3) a MTMS treatment variation developed by the author. The study was part of a *Vasa* Museum research program to examine different conservation methods on *Vasa* wood, including silicon oil (i.e. alkoxysilanes). In conjunction with the conservators from the *Vasa* Unit, in the *Vasa* Museum, three different wood samples were selected for an extensive research. The research constituted the core of a MA Thesis at Texas A&M University (TAMU) and, hence, falls outside the main research project initiated by the *Vasa* Museum. In this paper, however, only the results of one of the samples selected are presented; yet the three different re-conservation procedures are explained.

The *Vasa* pine wood sample presented in this paper (Figure 1) had been previously impregnated with PEG 3350 in the 1960s (Barkman 1975, 1976; Håfors 1993, 1998, 2001). The sample was divided into different sub-samples for applying the three different re-conservation

Figure 1. Two photographs of Vasa´s PEG sample (PS) pine wood: left, the sample with the original 1960s PEG treatment; right, the sample after being divided for this study

procedures. In this paper, each of the three re-conservation procedures are explained in detail, and the results obtained from each procedure are presented and compared

2. Re-conservation Methods

Since 1997 researchers at TAMU have investigated multiple applications of alkoxysilanes in the field of conservation of archaeological materials. These experiments have provided the foundation of knowledge from which different procedures with alkoxysilanes have been developed for conserving archaeological materials (Smith 2003, 2008).

2.1. MTMS re-treatment method

This procedure was developed by Dr. Wayne Smith of TAMU as a re-treatment method for previously conserved artifacts by impregnation with PEG (Smith 1998, 2003). Dr. Smith's procedure consists of immersing a previously PEG treated artifact in methyltrimethoxysilane (MTMS), a hydrolyzable multifunctional alkoxysilane polymer, at 70ºC. The procedure has two main goals: it removes the non-essential PEG from the wood and uses MTMS to cross-link the remaining PEG in the wood structure. By removing the non-essential PEG and crosslinking the remaining PEG and cellular structure, the wood cells are stabilized, thus preventing shrinkage or collapse of the wood structure (Smith 1998, 2003).

In this study, the original PEG treated sub-sample was placed into a beaker with MTMS. The container was then capped with aluminum foil to prevent the rapid evaporation of the MTMS. The beaker with the immersed sample was placed into a vented oven at 70ºC. The MTMS was replaced with fresh MTMS every 24 hours. After the fourth day of treatment, the MTMS was renewed every 48 hours. Throughout the process the temperature was maintained at 70ºC at which the non-essential PEG is melted and extracted from the sample (Smith 1998, 2003).

The PEG extraction process was monitored by measuring the differences in immersed weight of the sub-sample throughout the entire procedure. When the immersed weight of the sub-sample was stable over several days, the extraction process of the PEG was considered to be concluded. The immersed weight of the sample increased over time due the fact that the PEG coming out from the wood, and accumulating in the solution, is replaced by MTMS. Once the PEG extraction was concluded, the beaker containing the sub-sample was removed from the oven and was allowed to cool at room temperature. The sub-sample was then removed from the beaker and was allowed to dry under a fume hood for 48 hours. Differences in weight during the process were documented and compiled in Figure 2.

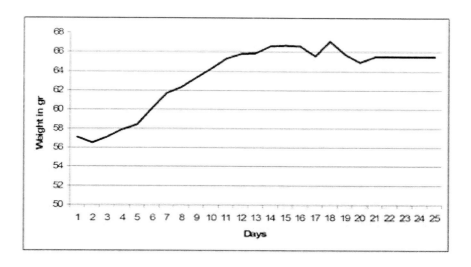

Figure 2. *Weight variation of pine sub-sample (i.e. PS6) during MTMS re-treatment method. The immersed weight of the sample increased overtime due the fact that the PEG coming out from the wood is replaced by MTMS*

During treatment, the heat melted the PEG from the sample, resulting in migration to the exterior of the wood and concentration on the bottom of the beaker (Figure 3).

Figure 3: *Beaker with used MTMS: on the bottom, the layer of extracted PEG*

The used MTMS acquired a slightly yellowish color probably due to the impurities and debris captured in the PEG and certainly from the tannic acid of the wood. These two separate layers are the result of the different viscosity and polarity of MTMS and PEG. The former is hydrophobic (i.e. tending not to or incapable of dissolving in water) and the later is hydrophilic (i.e. having a strong affinity for water). At room temperature, MTMS and PEG do not mix; thus when put together they form two separate layers in which PEG lies on the bottom due to its higher viscosity.

As a final step, the MTMS retained within the object is cured by vapor deposition catalysis with DBTDA catalyst as described below.

2.2. Silicone oil treatment
The silicone oil method uses a mixture of polymer and crosslinker to impregnate and consolidate artifacts, followed by the vaporization of a catalyst to finalize the polymerization process. This method used by the CRL can be summarized in five fundamental steps: desalination/PEG extraction, dehydration, forced impregnation, cleaning, and catalysis.

2.2.1. Desalination/PEG Extraction
In this study this step was not necessary because it was previously conducted. Yet, it is described as part of the general CRL method procedure where the waterlogged wood is recovered from a marine or saline environment. Objects are first desalinated in sequential water baths of tap water, reverse osmosis water, and deionized (DI) water until reaching low concentration levels of salts (e.g. less than 25-30 ppm of chloride). The desalination process is performed by the diffusion of salt through

441

the exchange of sequential water bath of lower salt concentration. Once the bulk of the soluble salts are removed from the object, the solvent dehydration process begins.

In this study PEG extraction was conducted instead desalination. The original 1960s PEG has to be removed from the samples in order to apply two of the re-conservation procedures (i.e. the silicone oil method and the author's variation of the MTMS method). Therefore, the extraction of the 1960s PEG was conducted as follows. The sub-samples were placed into a beaker with one liter of DI water. The beaker was placed inside a ventilated oven set at 60°C. The melting point of PEG 3350 is 54-58°C (Grattan and Clarke 1987); thus 60°C was enough to melt the PEG without damaging the wood structure. The DI water in the beaker was replaced every 24 hours.

The PEG extraction process was monitored by measuring the differences in the immersed weight of the sub-samples throughout the entire process. When the immersed weight of the sub-samples stabilized for several days, the extraction of the PEG was considered to be complete. The immersed weight of the sample increased overtime due the fact that the PEG coming out from the wood and accumulating in the solution, is replaced by water. The differences in the immersed weight during the entire process were documented and compiled in Figure 4.

2.2.2. Solvent Dehydration

Water extraction from the samples, or dehydration, is carried out by progressive solvent dehydration. Two solvents are used: ethanol and acetone. Solvent dehydration consists of replacing the water gradually by using more polar solvents in progressive sequence. The process starts by taking the object through sequential baths of water/ethanol, increasing the ethanol with each bath until reaching 100% ethanol. The ethanol is then replaced with sequential baths of increasing acetone concentration until 100% acetone is reached. Depending on the sample the increases in percentage of ethanol and acetone range from 5 to 25%.

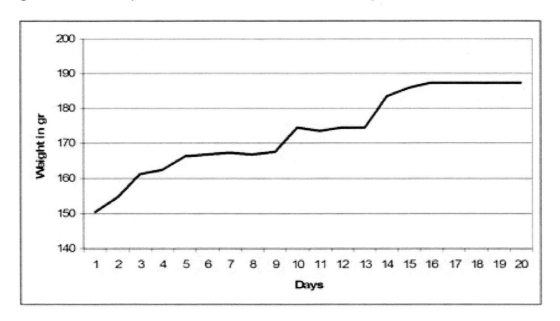

Figure 4. *Weight variation of PEG sample (PS) during PEG extraction. The immersed weight of the sample increased overtime due the fact that the PEG coming out from the wood is replaced by water*

442

2.2.2. Solvent Dehydration

Water extraction from the samples, or dehydration, is carried out by progressive solvent dehydration. Two solvents are used: ethanol and acetone. Solvent dehydration consists of replacing the water gradually by using more polar solvents in progressive sequence. The process starts by taking the object through sequential baths of water/ethanol, increasing the ethanol with each bath until reaching 100% ethanol. The ethanol is then replaced with sequential baths of increasing acetone concentration until 100% acetone is reached. Depending on the sample the increases in percentage of ethanol and acetone range from 5 to 25%.

For example, the initial solution, or first vat, is made of 75% deionized water and 25% ethanol. The second vat is made of 50% deionized water and 50% ethanol. The third vat is made of 25% deionized water and 75% ethanol. The fourth vat contains a solution of 100% ethanol. This process is repeated with another four vats and increments of 25%, but in this case, the acetone concentration is increased until it reaches 100% acetone concentration. Finally, an extra vat with 100% fresh acetone is used to complete the dehydration process. The process requires a sequence of nine baths that vary in 25% increments from the initial solution to the final bath.

Objects that are being dehydrated remain for variable lengths of time in the different dehydration vats. The length of time for dehydration is determined on a case by case basis based on the object's material nature, preservation status, and size.

2.2.3. Forced Impregnation

Prior to the forced impregnation, silicone oil which possesses the most convenient molecular weight for the object to be conserved (i.e. with an appropriate viscosity) must be selected. In this decision, the nature of the artifact, porosity of the material, and degree of preservation, among other factors, must be considered. As standardized procedure in the CRL, the method uses a mixture of the most desired molecular weight silicone oil and a 20% (by volume) of crosslinker.

The silicone oils commonly used in the method are dimethyl siloxane hydroxyl-terminated polymers. These silicones are produced by the chemical industry in many different types and different viscosities which all are applicable for archaeological conservation. The CRL utilizes non-commercialized polymers (i.e. SFD-1 silicone oil) manufactured by Dow Corning™ Corporation, which donates the polymers. However, polymers with similar characteristics to those used by the CRL (also made by Dow Corning™) could be purchased under the brand name of DC200® Fluid, which recently changed its commercial name to Xiameter® PMX-200 Silicone Fluid. Nonetheless, the CAS registry number of the polymer is 70131-67-8.

Two main polymers are used in the CRL which have similar composition, whereas their viscosity differs: a low viscosity oil SFD-1 (75 CST) and a medium viscosity oil SFD-5 (13,500 CST). The combination of these two oils provides a wide range of mixtures with different viscosities that allows the impregnation of diverse materials according to its specific necessities. In general practice, SFD-1 is the most versatile and is used most often. The crosslinker used in the CRL is methyltrimethoxysilane (MTMS), commercialized with the name DC® Z-6070 SILANE (1 CTS), which recently changed its commercial name to Xiameter® OFS-6070 Silane. However, the CAS registry number of the chemical compound is 1185-55-3.

Forced impregnation is carried out by transferring the object, coming from the last vat of 100% fresh acetone to a recipient container with the proper mixture of silicone oil and crosslinker (i.e. SFD-1 + 20% Z-6070). The object must be transferred quickly while it remains soaked in acetone in order to avoid undesired evaporation of the acetone and subsequent structural collapse. The object should remain immersed in the polymer solution during the forced impregnation. Throughout the exchange of acetone and polymer mixture, the object usually has a tendency to float due to the high viscosity of the silicone oil. To assure the immersion of the object in the mixture, a mesh, made of plastic or aluminum, can be used in combination with a weight. Once the object is kept immersed in the silicone oil mixture, the container is moved to a vacuum chamber to *force* its impregnation and to facilitate the acetone/polymer exchange.

If the object is small in size, glass desiccators can be used as a vacuum chamber. The pressure applied is just enough to facilitate the process (i.e. when small bubbles appear from the object), as the acetone vaporizes under vacuum around approximately 15 mm Hg and never more than 25 mm Hg. By applying vacuum, liquid acetone boils and evaporates to a gaseous state. In order to avoid uncontrolled boiling of the acetone, which could possibly damage the cellular structure of the samples, the vacuum is increased in progressive steps until the proper vacuum level is reached. The vacuum is also gradually decreased with the purpose of avoiding damaging the structure of the sample due to an uncontrolled release of pressure. In this process, the acetone vaporizes under vacuum coming out of the wood. As the acetone leaves the cells it facilitates the penetration of the oil into the cells. Then when the vacuum is lost the atmospheric pressure forces the oil into the wood. The wood is then impregnated with the silicone oil/crosslinker polymer solution. Finally, the object is left in the polymer solution at ambient pressure for a minimum period of 24 hours.

2.2.4. Cleaning

After completing the acetone/polymer exchange, the silicone excess (i.e. free-flowing polymer) must be extracted from the object. The removal of this non-essential polymer is a very important step in obtaining satisfactory results. If the excess of oil is left in the object a thick rubberized layer of silicone will be left on the surfaces. The cleaning of the object is addressed by several processes. First the object is placed on a mesh to allow the non-essential polymer to drain for at least 24 hours. It is important to note the silicone oil recovered can be recycled and reused for conservation of other objects similar in nature. If necessary, once the object is drained it can be immersed in crosslinker (i.e. MTMS) for periods up to 30 minutes. This step will help to dissolve, remove, and rinse the excess non-essential silicone oil. Finally, the object is cleaned and dried by blotting its surface with non abrasive tools such as: soft toothbrushes, paint brushes, cotton tipped applicators, lint free cloths, and paper towels among others.

2.2.5. Catalysis

As the final step, the silicone oil retained within the object is cured by vapor deposition catalysis. In the CRL, two possible catalysts are used: TPT Titanate or DBTDA. The former is a chemical reactive which is composed of tetra iso propyl *titanate* (99%) and isopropylic alcohol (1%); this product is commercialized as Tyzor® by Dupont® laboratories. The later is a tin derivate: dibutyltin diacetate. In vapor deposition catalysis, the object must be placed in a sealed plastic bag along with a container that holds several milliliters of catalyst for a minimum period of 24 hours. Alternatively, a small piece of wadded paper towel can be saturated with catalyst and placed in the container. The catalysis process must be repeated, replacing the catalyst with a fresh one, at least three more times in periods of 24/48 hours each. However, it is recommended to leave the object in the last catalysis step for a period of one week to assure a complete catalysis. Once the object has been totally catalyzed it is advisable to eliminate the residual vapors in the object from the catalyst. Thus, the object is placed into a fume hood for at least 24 hours to remove all possible residual vapors.

2.3. Alternative MTMS re-treatment method

The author developed an alternative MTMS re-treatment method combining two previous procedures. As explained above, Dr. Smith's procedure has two main goals: to remove the non-essential PEG from the wood and to use MTMS to cross-link the remaining PEG in the wood structure. These two goals are achieved by one single step, immersing the PEG treated artifact in MTMS at 70ºC (Smith 1998, 2003). The author of this paper expands upon Dr. Smith's study by achieving the same two main goals in separate steps instead of one.

Dr. Smith's idea of crosslinking the remaining PEG with MTMS has been demonstrated to be successful. However, there are better approaches for extracting PEG from the sample than immersing the wood sample in MTMS at 70°C. The different solubility of PEG and MTMS (i.e. the former hydrophilic, the later hydrophobic) means they do not dissolve each other, resulting in the creation of two separate layers, as previously seen in this paper. Their different solubility does not facilitate the diffusion of PEG out of the wood structure, but probably obstructs it. Hence, for the extraction of PEG from the wood, better results can be achieved by using DI water, which has the same solubility of PEG, at 60°C. This is the main difference between Dr. Smith's MTMS and the author's alternative MTMS re-treatment procedures.

The author's variation of the MTMS re-treatment method has four steps: first, the PEG is extracted from the wood with heated DI water at 60°C; second, the remaining water in the sample is removed through solvent dehydration; third, the sample is cross-linked with MTMS; and finally, the sample is catalyzed through vapor deposition.

The PEG extraction was conducted following the same method explained above and, as in the silicone oil sample, is documented and compiled in Figure 4. Once the PEG was removed, the water of the sub-sample was extracted through progressive solvent dehydration. After the dehydration, the sub-sample was transferred into a beaker with fresh MTMS (while thoroughly wet with acetone). The beaker with the MTMS and the sample were placed under a slight amount of vacuum for 24 hours. Then, the sample remained in the bath for a 24 hour period at ambient pressure. Finally, the sample was allowed to dry at room temperature under a fume hood for 48 hours. Finally, and to ensure total polymerization, the sample was catalyzed through vapor deposition with DBTDA as described above.

3. Re-conservation results

In order to evaluate the results of the different re-treatments, five physical parameters of the sub-samples were evaluated. The parameters were: color, texture, dimensional change, weight/size ratio, and microscopic status of the wood structure.

Differences in color were established by visual observations with the aid of a Munsell® Soil Color Chart (Munsell 1946). Linear measurements were controlled with the aid of a metric caliper and 3D modeling software Rhinoceros®. From each of the samples, linear measurements were taken of the longitudinal, radial, and tangential axis. The volume of each sample was recorded and calculated using 3D scanning

445

technology. The numerical volume values of the samples were obtained with the aid of 3D modeling software Rhinoceros® (Figure 5). The microscopic status of the wood structure was observed by scanning electron microscope (SEM) techniques.

Figure 5. 3D rendering, from Rhinoceros® software, of the three sub-samples resulting from the division of the PEG sample

3.1 Results of MTMS re-treatment method

3.1.1. Macroscopic results of PS6 (Figure 6)
Sample PS6: 1960s PEG conserved pine wood re-conserved with MTMS treatment as described by Smith (1998) and (2003).

1. After conservation, the color of the sample was, in general terms, slightly darker (i.e. it lost one degree of value on the Munsell® scale) and slightly more intense or saturated (i.e. it gained one degree of value on the Munsell® scale) from the original.

2. Average texture. The final texture was slightly waxy due to remaining PEG on the surface of the sample.

3. Shrinkage. Before the re-conservation treatment, the pine wood sample was impregnated with PEG and hence swollen. After re-conservation, dimensional changes were observed in the three axis measured within the average range expected (Hoadley 1980, Hamilton 1996); therefore, the results are considered good.

4. Despite the loss of PEG, the sample gained 10.5% from its original PEG treated weight. After treatment, the ratio weight/volume in comparison with the average value of oven-dry weight of fresh pine wood was very high. The specific gravity of the sample was increased by 12.1% after treatment. As a result, the final value was very high compared to the average value of oven-dry weight of fresh pine (Hoadley 1990), therefore the results are considered to be unacceptable.

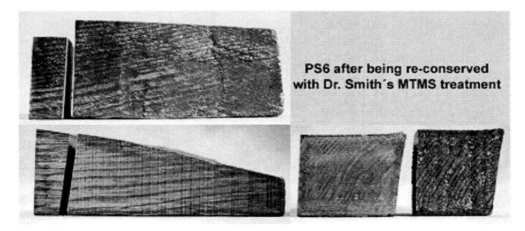

Figure 6. Three macroscopic photographs of pine sub-sample (i.e. PS6) after being re-conserved with MTMS procedure: Upper left, tangential plane; lower left, radial plane; lower right, cross-sectional plane

446

Table 1. *Summary of the physical characteristics of pine sub-sample (i.e. PS6) before and after its re-conservation with the MTMS procedure*

Color (Munsell® soil color chart reference # and color names)					
Pre-cons			Post-cons		
Exterior: 5Y 2.5/2; 10YR 5/1	Black; Gray		Exterior: 10YR 2/2; 10YR 4/4	Very dark brown; Dark yellowish brown	
Interior: 10YR 4/2; 10YR 7/4	Dark grayish brown; Very pale brown		Interior: 10YR 5/3; 10YR 6/3	Brown; Pale brown	

Linear measurements			
Axis	Pre-cons	Post-cons	% change
Longitudinal	85 mm	84.7 mm	- 0.3 %
Radial	37.5 mm	36.5 mm	- 2.7 %
Tangential	31.9 mm	30.2 mm	- 5.6 %

Weight			
Pre-cons (PEG)	Post-cons (Smith's MTMS)	% change	Same volume average weight of *Pinus sylvestris*
57.1 g	63.8 g	+ 10.5 %	29.4 g

Specific gravity			
Pre-cons (PEG)	Post-cons (Smith's MTMS)	% change	Average Specific Gravity of *Pinus sylvestris*
0.87 g/cm³	0.99 g/cm³	+ 12.1 %	0.46 g/cm³

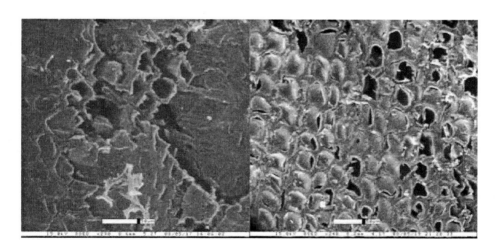

Figure 7. *Two ESEM micrographs of pine sub-sample (i.e. PS6): left, 1960s original PEG treatment; right, after being re-conserved with the MTMS procedure*

3.1.2. Microscopic Results of PS6 (Figure 7)
The two ESEM micrographs of the pine sub-sample taken before and after the treatment are shown below in Figure 7. As shown in the micrographs, the cell structure of the pine was saturated with PEG before the treatment. After treatment, the cells of the wood were filled by remaining PEG (especially on the surface of the sub-sample). Therefore, from the microscopic perspective the treatment result is poor.

3.2. Results of the silicone oil treatment
3.2.1. Macroscopic Results of PS5 (Figure 8)
Sample PS5:1960s PEG conserved pine wood re-conserved with silicone oil treatment.

1. After conservation, the color of the sample was, in general terms, slightly more intense or saturated (i.e. it gained one degree of value on the Munsell® scale) from the original.
2. Good texture. The final texture was dry and non-sticky.
3. Shrinkage. Before the re-conservation treatment, the pine wood sample was impregnated with PEG and hence swollen. After re-conservation, dimensional changes were observed in the three axis measured, within the average range expected going from swollen to dry wood (Hoadley 1980, Hamilton 1996), therefore the results are considered good.
4. The sample lost 0.2% of its original PEG treated weight. After treatment, the ratio weight/volume in comparison with the average value of oven-dry weight of fresh pine wood was very high. The specific gravity of the sample was increased by 2.2% after treatment. As a result, the final value was very high compared to the average value of oven-dry weight of fresh pine (Hoadley 1990), therefore the results are considered poor.

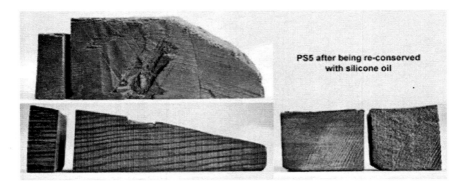

Figure 8. Three macroscopic photographs of pine sub-sample (i.e. PS5) after being re-conserved with silicone oil: Upper left, tangential plane; lower left, radial plane; lower right, cross-sectional plane

Table 2: Summary of the physical characteristics of pine sub-sample (i.e.PS5) before and after its re-conservation with silicone oil

Color (Munsell® soil color chart reference # and color names)					
Pre-cons			Post-cons		
Exterior: 5Y 2.5/2; 10YR 5/1	Black; Gray		Exterior: 10YR 3/2; 10YR 5/3	Very dark grayish brown; Brown	
Interior: 10YR 4/2; 10YR 7/4	Dark grayish brown; Very pale brown		Interior: 10YR 4/4; 10YR 5/4	Dark yellowish brown; Yellowish brown	
Linear measurements					
Axis	Pre-cons		Post-cons	% change	
Longitudinal	108 mm		107 mm	- 0.9 %	
Radial	43.2 mm		41.6 mm	- 3.8 %	
Tangential	34.5 mm		33.6 mm	- 2.6 %	
Weight					
Pre-cons (PEG)	Post-cons (Silicone oil)		% change	Same volume average weight of *Pinus sylvestris*	
87.6 g	87.4 g		- 0.2 %	45.4 g	
Specific gravity					
Pre-cons (PEG)	Post-cons (Silicone oil)		% change	Average Specific Gravity of *Pinus sylvestris*	
0.86 g/cm³	0.88 g/cm³		+ 2.2 %	0.46 g/cm³	

448

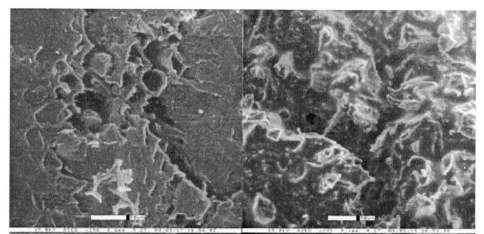

Figure 9. *Two ESEM micrographs of pine sub-sample (i.e. PS5): left, 1960s PEG treatment; right, after being re-conserved with silicone oil*

3.2.2. Microscopic Results of PS5 (Figure 9)
Two ESEM micrographs of the pine sub-sample taken before and after the treatment areshown in Figure 9. As evident in the micrographs, the cell structure of the pine was filled with PEG before the treatment. After treatment with silicone oil, the condition of the cell structure of the wood remained relatively unchanged, and little collapse is noted. However, there is an excess amount of silicone oil filling the cell structure of the wood. Therefore, from the microscopic perspective the treatment result is poor.

3.3. Results of author's alternative MTMS re-treatment method
3.3.1. Macroscopic Results of PS4 (Figure 10)
Sample PS4: 1960s PEG conserved pine wood re-conserved with the alternative MTMS treatment developed by the author.

1. After conservation, the color of the sample was, in general terms, slightly darker (i.e. it lost one degree of value on the Munsell® scale) and slightly more intense or saturated (i.e. it gained one degree of value on the Munsell® scale) from the original.
2. Good texture. The final texture was dry and non-sticky.
3. Shrinkage. Before the re-conservation treatment, the pine wood sample was impregnated with PEG and hence swollen. After re-conservation, dimensional changes were observed in the three axis measured within the average range expected (Hoadley 1980, Hamilton 1996), therefore, the results are considered good.
4. The sample lost 23.2% of its original PEG treated weight. After treatment, the ratio weight/volume was above the average in comparison with the value of oven-dry weight of fresh pine wood, thus satisfactory. The specific gravity of the sample was reduced by 19.4% after treatment. The final value was above the average value of oven-dry weight of fresh pine (Hoadley 1990), therefore, the results are considered good.

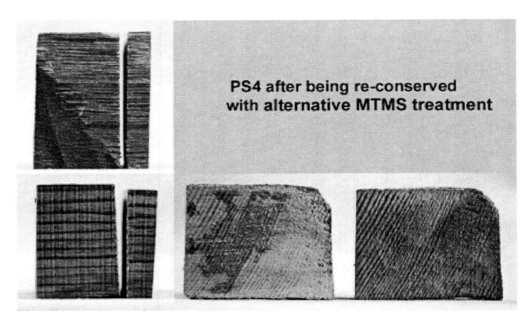

Figure 10. *Three macroscopic photographs of the pine sub-sample (i.e. PS4) after being re-conserved with the author's alternative MTMS treatment: Upper left, tangential plane; lower left, radial plane; lower right, cross-sectional plane*

Table 3. *Summary of the physical characteristics of pine sub-sample (i.e. PS4) before and after its re-conservation with the alternative MTMS procedure*

Color (Munsell® soil color chart reference # and color names)					
Pre-cons			Post-cons		
Exterior: 5Y 2.5/2; 10YR 5/1	Black; Gray		Exterior: 10YR 4/4; 10YR 5/4	Dark yellowish brown; Yellowish brown	
Interior: 10YR 4/2; 10YR 7/4	Dark grayish brown; Very pale brown		Interior: 10YR 3/3; 10YR 6/4	Dark brown; Light yellowish brown	
Linear measurements					
Axis	Pre-cons		Post-cons		% change
Longitudinal	34.3 mm		34 mm		- 0.8 %
Radial	43.7 mm		41.4 mm		- 5.5 %
Tangential	33.6 mm		33 mm		- 1.8 %
Weight					
Pre-cons (PEG)	Post-cons (Author's MTMS)		% change		Same volume average weight of *Pinus sylvestris*
36.6 g	29.7 g		- 23.2 %		18.8 g
Specific gravity					
Pre-cons (PEG))	Post-cons (Author's MTMS)		% change		Average Specific Gravity of *Pinus sylvestris*
0.86 g/cm³	0.72 g/cm³		- 19.4 %		0.46 g/cm³

450

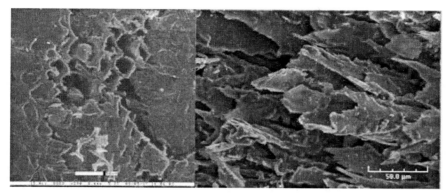

Figure 11: Two micrographs of pine sub-sample (i.e. PS4): left, ESEM micrograph of 1960s original PEG treatment; right, SEM micrograph after being re-conserved with the alternative MTMS procedure

3.3.1. Microscopic Results of PS4 (Figure 11)

Two micrographs of the pine sub-sample taken before and after the treatment are shown in Figure 11. As evident in the micrographs, the cell structure of the pine was completely saturated with PEG before the treatment. After treatment with MTMS, the cell structure of the wood is not collapsed. The cells were completely empty of any excess polymer. As a result, morphological characteristics of the wood structure are preserved in fine detail and identifiable. Therefore, from the microscopic perspective the treatment result is excellent.

4. Evaluation of Results

In order to evaluate the results of the different re-treatments, a matrix was created where five physical parameters of the sub-samples were evaluated by giving them numerical values. As explained above, several parameters were monitored: color, texture, dimensional change, weight/size ratio, and microscopic status of the wood structure. A numerical

value was assigned to each one of the parameters as follows: Undesirable = 0, Poor = 1, Average = 2, Good = 3, Excellent = 4. The grades were compiled in the matrix in order to obtain an overall evaluation (Table 4).

4.1. Evaluation of MTMS re-treatment method

As a result of several factors, the results were not satisfactory. The sample had a poor microscopic outcome, in which internal structures were saturated with polymer; the sample, despite having lost PEG, gained weight (+10.5%); and its specific gravity increased (+12.1%), high above the optimal. Therefore, the results for this sample were poor. As suggested by Dr. Smith the results could be improved by eliminating the layer of PEG formed on the exterior surfaces of the sample by wiping with lint-free cloths (Smith 1998, 2003). Due to the different solubility of PEG and MTMS, they create separate layers, and, in this case, PEG is deposited on the surface of the sample.

Table 4: Calculation key: 0 = Undesirable, 1 = Poor, 2 = Average, 3 = Good, 4 = Excellent

Re-conservation Treatment	Sub sample	Color	Texture	Dimensions	Weight	Specific Gravity	ESEM	Total
MTMS	PS6	3	2	3	0	0	1	9
Silicone Oil	PS5	3	3	3	1	1	1	12
Alternative MTMS	PS4	3	3	3	3	3	4	19

The increase in weight in the sample could have two hypothetical explanations: Nuclear Magnetic Resonance (NMR) spectrographic analysis conducted by Dr. Smith (Smith 2003) has demonstrated that silicone polymers are formed by the hydrolysis of the MTMS in an aqueous environment. Perhaps, these new polymers were the reason for the increase in weight. Also, the 70ºC applied in the procedure could have broken the PEG 3350 polymer chains into smaller molecular weight PEG polymer chains. Hence, despite losing PEG the resulting sample increases its weight because the resulting PEG absorbs more moisture from the ambient atmosphere. Another hypothesis came from the fact that since PEG has been partially removed, void cavities have been created due to the absence of PEG. These void cavities increased the specific surface area (i.e. the total surface area per unit of mass). Before treatment the sample was less hygroscopic because the specific surface area was smaller. The fact that the PEG (which is hygroscopic) has not been totally removed, and the fact that the specific surface area has been increased, could lead to a situation in which the resulting sample is more hygroscopic. However, in order to prove any of these hypotheses, further analysis should be conducted. The results obtained in this study applying the MTMS treatment differ from the results obtained by Dr. Smith (Smith 1998, 2003). This discrepancy could be the result of many factors. Since only one sample was tested in this study, the results have to be considered in relative terms. Nevertheless, further analysis should be conducted. From the three re-conservation procedures tested this offers the least desirable results.

4.2. Evaluation of the silicone oil treatment

In accordance with the poor microscopic outcome, in which internal structures were saturated with polymer, the sample barely lost weight (-0.2%), and its specific gravity increased (+2.2%), far above the desired optimum. Therefore, the results for this sample were average. However, the results could be improved. The slightly wet texture and slightly high weight due to the excess polymer could be avoided. The results could be improved by reducing the amount of silicone oil in the silicone oil/MTMS mixture employed to re-conserve the sample. Therefore, a mixture with less silicone oil and more MTMS would probably offer better results. Nevertheless, further tests should be conducted in order to establish a more suitable mixture. From the three re-conservation procedures tested this offers desirable results.

4.3. Evaluation of the alternative MTMS re-treatment method

Due to several factors, the results were extraordinary. The sample had a excellent microscopic outcome, in which internal structures were free of polymer, and it was possible to observe small diagnostic structural details of the wood; the sample lost PEG and decreased its weight (-23.2%) and its specific gravity also decreased (-19.4%), slightly above the optimum. Therefore, the results for this sample were extremely satisfactory. Of the three re-conservation procedures tested this offers exceptional results.

5. Discussion

Re-conservation with alkoxysilanes is the fusion of two approaches: solvent dehydration and consolidation. The main principle is similar to the other consolidation techniques: the incorporation of an agent into the wood which consolidates and confers mechanical strength while the water is removed (Grattan and Clarke 1987). Silicone oils act as a consolidant creating a three dimensional protective film of material over and in the structures of the wood; it confers plasticity and structural strength without filling the hollow cellular structures of the wood.

452

When the silicone polymer comes into physical contact with any organic material, in this case wood, it creates a protective film. The alkoxysilanes molecules in contact with the cell walls of the wood react by establishing covalent chemical bonds. Those molecules will remain adhered to the object, and they cannot be removed. This chemically bonded polymer molecule embodies what could be called the "essential polymer." Only the free-flowing or "non-essential polymer" (i.e. the one that did not form chemical bonds with the material) can be removed from the material by draining, rinsing, and cleaning, before the catalysis of the polymer.

After the removal of the non-essential polymer, the essential polymer has to be polymerized through catalysis. Once the essential polymer is catalyzed, it forms a film which protects the wood. The material's structure is coated by the formation of a hard yet flexible, non-reactive film that inhibits the treated material from further degradation. The material being coated with silicone polymer is *plasticized* on a microscopic scale.

If the silicone oil procedure is conducted properly, the amount of silicone oil retained in the object is negligible. The essential silicone polymer coats the surface of the structures of the wood without filling hollow structures of the wood. The polymer film's thickness is in the scale of micrometers, and can only be detected on a microscopic scale with the aid of scanning electron microscopy (Figure 12)

Because of the extreme thinness of the film that coats the wood, the physical characteristics (i.e. color, texture, weight) of the treated wood become very similar to those of the original wood. Without the aid of microscopic analysis, this polymer film is hardly detectable by organoleptic analysis (i.e. perceived by a sense organ).

Despite the thinness of the polymer film, it is able to maintain the conserved material's three-dimensional structure without collapse, shrinkage, or warping. This is because once the silicone is polymerized, it creates a highly cross-linked, stable, and flexible three-dimensional. polymer matrix which supports and confers mechanical strength to the conserved wood structure (Figure 13).

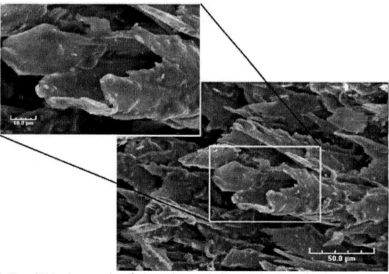

Figure 12. *Two SEM micrographs of pine sub-sample (i.e. PS4) taken after being re-conserved with author's MTMS procedure. Note the thinness of the silicone polymer coating*

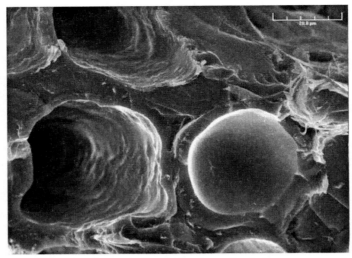

Figure 13. *SEM micrograph of pine sub-sample (i.e. PS6) taken after being re-conserved with Dr. Smith's MTMS procedure. Two vessels of the cellular wood structure are shown; the one on the right is completely filled with polymer and the one on the left is coated just by the essential polymer. Note the thinness of the silicone polymer coating*

If alkoxysilanes are applied correctly, the presence of polymer is so minimal that it allows analysis and identification of the morphological characteristic of the materials which compose the object. In the case of wood, the genus, species and subspecies can be determined because the structures are conserved, maintaining the lumina free of polymer. In the same way, in the conservation of textile or fabrics, fibers can be identified with the assistance of microscopic analysis.

Despite the interesting results that the use of alkoxysilanes offer, some significant drawbacks derived from this treatment should be addressed. The fact the procedure acts at a molecular level creating chemical bonds, means the use of alkoxysilanes modifies the wood's chemical composition and, more importantly, is irreversible.

Minimal intervention and reversibility are two of the four ethical principles any conservation procedure for waterlogged wood should follow (Grattan and Clarke 1987). However, despite common acceptance of these ethical principles, it has been proposed that there are some instances in which the ethical principle of reversibility could be made secondary for the sake of other needs or requirements (Horie 1982). The use of alkoxysilanes for the conservation of stone and other lithic materials is an example of this. Conservation of stone with alkoxysilanes has occurred since the 19th century and is widely used and accepted. The advantages of using alkoxysilanes can, in some instances, displace the ethical principle of reversibility to a secondary concern.

In the search for a good consolidant conservators of stone look for the restitution of structural strength. Hence, consolidants with strong adhesive properties are desired. In general, the more reversible a material is the weaker adhesive properties it has. Therefore, highly soluble (hence reversible) acrylic resins, such as Paraloid® B72, are not preferred for the conservation of stone. On the contrary, alkoxysilanes as a consolidant which have extremely good adherent properties despite their lack of reversibility are preferred (Wheeler 2005).

Those non-reversible consolidants are also desired due to their long lasting characteristics and life span. How long alkoxysilanes are expected to last in a material depend on many different and complex factors. However, the use of alkoxysilanes in the conservation of stone, in harsh outdoor environmental conditions, has proven to last long enough (i.e. at least 20 years) to validate their use (Wheeler 2005).

Studies have shown that despite the type of consolidant used (and its theoretical reversibility) no treatment is reversible at the molecular level (Horie 1982). Therefore, the definition of "reversibility" is complex and largely depends on which type of procedure is referred to (i.e. cleaning, consolidation, reassembly, etc). It has been proposed that it would be more accurate to classify treatments in degrees of reversibility (Jedrzejewska 1981, Appelbaum 1987, Horie 1987,). More particularly, when referring to consolidants, Appelbaum (1987) proposed the term re-treatability. The notion of re-treatability is one that is often more helpful in evaluating treatments than the idea of reversibility itself (Appelbaum 1987).

Due to the extreme thinness of the film formed over the conserved object, alkoxysilanes can be re-applied in the future; hence, its re-appliability (i.e. re-treatability exclusively with silanes) is high, thus expanding the time expectancy of the treatment and, consequently, expanding the life span of the treated object.

Dr. Smith conducted an accelerated ageing test of polymer durability on archaeological materials conserved with silicone oils with the aid of the accelerated weathering machine Atlas UV 2000. This experiment suggested that after four months of accelerated weathering, subjecting the samples to sharp variations of humidity and temperature, the silicone oil treated samples were comparable to other samples which had not undergone accelerated weathering (Smith 2003). Although this test does not provide detailed quantitative results, it does provide a qualitative evaluation. Another point of reference is that the first artifacts conserved by Dr. Smith at TAMU in 1997, currently present no degradation or discoloration, at the macroscopic level, after being on display for 13 years without the aid of any climatic or environmental preventive measures. Finally, in this conference (ICOM-WOAM 2010) a rigorous assessment of the condition of an elephant tusk conserved with silicone oil in 1998 has shown that after 12 years the tusk is stable and presents no significant deterioration (Godfrey et al. 2010).

Another important advantage to note is the fact that objects conserved with alkoxysilanes acquire the preventive characteristics of the silicone polymer. Because the object is coated with polymer, they become highly resistant to changes in temperature, chemical attacks from acid or bases, ultraviolet rays, and also turn hydrophobic in nature; therefore, they are less affected by environmental conditions changes (Wheeler 2005). These newly acquired characteristics are important to consider when the conserved artifacts are going to be exposed to the public because preventive conservation measures, during shipping or on display, can be drastically be reduced.

Finally, the use of alkoxysilanes do not required expensive equipment beyond the normal conservation laboratory tools; this is an advantage in comparison with the expensive requirements of other conservation procedures for waterlogged wood (e.g. heatable conservation tanks, freeze dryer unit, etc). Alkoxysilanes are relatively expensive chemicals. However, alkoxysilanes could be highly efficient consolidants due to two factors: the amount of polymer retained by the treated object is minimal, and the free flowing polymer can be re-used with a similar material. By re-using the polymer the amount of artifacts conserved by a given volume of polymer is very high when compared with other consolidants. Hence, alkoxysilanes can be considered inexpensive in the long term. The toxicity and fire hazard related with the solvents used are important factors to acknowledge and take into consideration.

6. Conclusions

In this study the feasibility of re-conserving small, wooden artifacts, previously conserved by impregnation with PEG, with alkoxysilanes has been tested. Three different wood samples from the *Vasa* Museum Collection were re-conserved with three different procedures involving alkoxysilanes.

The study demonstrated that the best way to remove PEG 3350 from an object is by reverse osmosis in aqueous solution at 60°C. The study showed that results vary depending on the selection of a different viscosity alkoxysilane (i.e. silicone oil *vs* MTMS). Better results are obtained with lower viscosity alkoxysilanes (i.e. MTMS). As in other consolidation techniques, the selection of a specific consolidant has to be *ad hoc* for each artifact or groups of artifacts. This selection will be largely based on the nature of the artifact, porosity of the material, and degree of preservation, among other factors.

Microscopic analysis of the samples demonstrated that the amount of polymer retained in the samples could be minimal. Micrographs have shown that, in the best cases, the thickness of the protective polymer film is in the scale of micrometers, yet is enough to support and confer mechanical strength to the conserved wood structure. Hence, the re-conserved samples acquire physical characteristics very close to those of natural wood. All resulting samples showed minimal shrinkage on the longitudinal, radial and tangential axis, within the average ratios

expected going from swollen to dry wood. The results also demonstrated that, in the case of the alternative MTMS re-treatment method it is possible to acquire values in weight and specific gravity very close to those of fresh dry wood. The presence of the polymer is so minimal that it allows analyzing and identifying diagnostic morphological characteristic of the materials.

The results obtained with the use of alkoxysilanes are very desirable but not reversible. However, it has been explained that in some instances reversibility is not necessarily a drawback. In these cases, re-treatability is an equally desirable quality. If the application of alkoxysilanes as a consolidant is performed properly, the technique is highly re-treatable.

The re-conserved samples obtain new added properties from the alkoxysilanes which could reduce the use of preventive conservation measures during display or storage. The stability of these alkoxysilane polymers is elevated due to the industrial formulation of the polymers. Therefore, the life span of small wooden artifacts previously conserved by impregnation with PEG could be significantly extended by their re-conservation with alkoxysilanes. Nevertheless, further detailed studies about the stability of archaeological wood conserved with alkoxysilanes should be conducted.

To summarize, this study demonstrated that the re-conservation of small, wood artifacts, previously conserved by total impregnation with PEG with alkoxysilanes is not only a feasible approach but it also offers quite significant results. Based on the results of the three re-conservation procedures tested in this study, the proposed author's alternative MTMS procedure is the most suitable re-conservation method for small wooden objects previously conserved by impregnation with PEG.

Nevertheless, and despite the significant results, the final responsibility in evaluating the pros and cons of using alkoxysilanes for the conservation or re-treatment of waterlogged archaeological wood lies with museum conservators and curators. They should study each particular case as a *unicum*, thoughtfully and in detail, taking into consideration the advantages and drawbacks of alkoxysilanes before applying this procedure.

Acknowledgements

The author wants to express his gratefulness to the following institutions for their generous support in conducting this study: *Vasa* Museum and the *Vasa* Unit; Department of Anthropology; Nautical Archaeology Program (NAP); Center for Maritime Archaeology and Conservation (CMAC); Conservation Research Laboratory (CRL); Archaeological Preservation Research Laboratory (APRL); Microscopy and Imaging Center (MIC); and Materials Characterization Facility (MCF) at Texas A&M University.

References

Appelbaum, B., (1987), Criteria for Treatment: Reversibility, Journal of American Institute for Conservation, Vol. 26, No. 2, 1987, pp 65-73.

Barkman, L., (1975), The Preservation of the Warship *Wasa*, in Oddy (editor), Problems in the Conservation of Waterlogged Wood, London, National Maritime Museum, 1975. Maritime Monographs and Reports 16, pp 65-105.

Barkman, L., (1976), The Conservation of Waterlogged Wood, in Grosso (editor), Proceedings of the Pacific Northwest Wet Site Wood Conservation Conference, Washington, 1976, Volume 2, pp 47-60.

Grattan, D. and Clarke, R., (1987), Conservation of Waterlogged Wood, in Pearson (editor), Conservation of Marine Archaeological Objects, London, Butterworths, 1987, pp 164-206.

Godfrey, I., Kasi, K., Lussier, S., and Smith, W., (2010), Conservation of Waterlogged Ivory, in Strætkvern (editor), Proceedings of the 11th ICOM Group on Wet Organic Archaeological Materials Conference, Greenville 2010, in press.

Håfors, B., (1993), Improvements of the Conservation Programme for Tank Treatment with Polyethylene Glycol at the *Vasa* Conservation Laboratory, in Hoffmann (editor), Proceedings of the 5th ICOM-CC Working Group on Wet Organic Archaeological Materials Conference, Portland/Maine, Deutsches Schiffahrtsmuseum, 1994, pp 51-62.

Håfors, B., (1998), Procedures in Selecting and Evaluating the Conservation Liquid for the *Vasa* Wooden Material, in Bonnot-Diconne et al. (editors), Proceedings of the 7th ICOM-CC Working Group on Wet Organic Archaeological Materials Conference = Actes de la 7e conférence du groupe de travail Matériaux archéologiques organiques humides, Grenoble, ARC-Nucléart CEA/Grenoble, 1999, pp 87-94.

Håfors, B., (2001), Conservation of the Swedish Warship *Vasa* from 1628, Stockholm, Vasamuseet.

Hamilton, D., (1996), Basic Methods of Conserving Underwater Archaeological Material Culture, Washington D.C., U.S. Dept. of Defense, Legacy Resource Management Program.

Hoadley, B., (1980), Understanding Wood: A Craftsman's Guide to Wood Technology, Newtown, The Taunton Press, Inc.

Hoadley, B., (1990), Identifying Wood: Accurate Results with Simple Tools, Newtown, The Taunton Press, Inc.

Horie, C., (1982), Reversibility of Polymer Treatments, in Tate et al. (editors), Proceedings of the Symposium Resins in Conservation, Edinburgh, Scottish Society for Conservation & Restoration, 1982, Chapter 3 pp 1-6.

Horie, C., (1987), Materials for Conservation: Organic Consolidants, Adhesives and Coatings, London, Butterworths.

Jedrzejewska, H., (1981), The Concept of Reversibility as an Ethical Problem in Conservation, in Járó (editor), Third International Restorer Seminar, Budapest, Institute of Conservation and Methodology of Museums (ICCROM), 1982, pp 27-32.

Munsell, A., (1946), A Color Notation, Baltimore, Munsell Color Co.

Smith, W., (1998), The re-treatment of two PEG-treated Sabots, in Bonnot-Diconne et al. (editors), Proceedings of the 7th ICOM-CC Working Group on Wet Organic Archaeological Materials Conference = Actes de la 7e conférence du groupe de travail Matériaux archéologiques organiques humides, Grenoble, ARC-Nucléart CEA/Grenoble, 1999, pp 155-162.
Smith, W., (2003), Archaeological Conservation Using Polymers: Practical Applications for Organic Artifact Stabilization, College Station, Texas A&M University Press.

Smith, W., (2008), Archaeological Preservation Research Laboratory (APRL), Reports, World Wide Web, URL, http://nautarch.tamu.edu/aprl/reports.shtml, Nautical Archaeology Program, Texas A&M University, College Station, Texas. Visited on May 2010.

Wheeler, G., (2005), Alkoxysilanes and the Consolidation of Stone, Los Angeles, Getty Publications.

Questions and answers

Gunnar Almkvist: I just have a stupid question on chemistry. Why did you want to replace the PEG with silicon oils?

Carlos Cabrera Tejedor: What I think that they did here, and please correct me if I'm wrong, was starting to explore the possibility of a feasible retreatment method because PEG has 50 years, if I'm not wrong, stability so at some point you can cross this ability. So that was his idea to see if it was possible.

Jim Spriggs: Dr. Smith during the barbeque last night told me that one of the phrases that he'd introduced to conservation was "retreatability" as opposed to reversibility. Now assuming this point about retreatability how retreatable is this wood now it has the silicone oils in it?

Carlos Cabrera Tejedor: Well, I have read an article in the *Journal of the American Institute of Conservation* from 1988 where the author was talking about retreatability specifically and she said with consolidants, because they are not reversible, it would be a better term to talk about how retreatable they are. In this scenario we will see that you can get really good results and really bad results within the same chemicals. Theoretically you get the really good results when the polymer is so thin that it's highly retreatable because you can extract again and add a few micrometers. But again to obtain these results needs practice and experience.

Suzanne Grieve: I wanted to know if anyone knows about the interaction of the sulfur with the silicone oil and is the premise that the silicone oil seals off the cells from any water or oxygen interaction?

Carlos, Cabrera Tejedor: I've never looked. I don't know what kind of reactions you can get. What I do know is that the polymer is really stable to any kind of heat reactions, chemicals, oxidation etc.

Ellen Carrlee: So, when you say retreatable do you mean retreatable with silicone oil or retreatable with something else? And if you can retreat it with something else what else can you use or has been tried?

Carlos Cabrera Tejedor: I mean retreatable with silicone oil. One of the drawbacks is the polymer is so...that's what I was referring to yesterday...it's so aggressive and so resistant that one of the problems is you may not be able to use any adherent on the pieces because the silicone is going to repel it. That's the drawback —you probably can't retreat it with anything other than silicone.

Shanna Daniel: With the MTMS did you try not catalyzing it? Or is it catalyzed to secure the PEG? Or the residual PEG?

Carlos Cabrera Tejedor: You don't need to catalyze it.

Shanna Daniel: Okay. That's where I was getting confused. Are you using it for the removal of PEG and then you retreat with the silicone process? Or were you just removing the PEG and then using the MTMS?

Carlos Cabrera Tejedor: A new treatment that will remove the PEG and then apply silicone polymer with MTMS catalysis upping the pace of reconservation. Better results are obtained. Not in my paper but in my thesis, I explain this because with the process of removing the PEG, you are just removing the PEG from the lumen, you are not removing the PEG from the cells. Naturally, this is the same even in plasticity as the wood, so it is perfect that you crosslink this PEG and this wood together. That's why, in my interpretation, you get such good results without using silicone oil. Use the silicone oil and you obtain a totally separate result because it's my understanding that you have too much polymer there – you don't really need it.

Shanna Daniel: Okay, thank you!

Johanna Rivera: Are you planning to do a long-term study on the stability of the silicone over time and also how it will react in different environments and not just in wood but in rope, textile and lead? And will you publish them?

Carlos Cabrera Tejedor: Well, I plan to do a stability aging test for wood samples but it has not been started yet. But you can get a good idea from the treatment of stone because the conditions are so hard. You have proof there that the chemical is really stable and again it's a different thing when you mix these chemicals with wood because it's going to react differently, but it does give you a good idea of how stable it is. Again Dr. Smith has conducted stability tests. The results are not published yet so therefore we cannot know the results. With other materials the results are quite similar. In textiles, the types of fiber could be identified by microscopy and in textiles another advantage is that you are giving elasticity – the elasticity of the polymer so it's quite impressive going from a material that decomposes when you touch it to a material that is actually dry and has elasticity.

Sarah Watkins Kenney: Just picking up on the comment that Carlos just made about the stone and saying that it's good for 20 years. I was just wondering how that might compare to other people in this group's thoughts on how long treatments should last? Are we thinking 20 years, or are we thinking 50 or 100? I'd just be interested to know because I'd be a bit worried if we had to retreat everything within 20 years when we're still going to be treating what's coming up in 20 years!

John Kenney: I had a few questions on this as well. That was a very nice talk on the silicone. It looks very promising. One question you mentioned, I think, if I heard you correctly, that you understand it was covalently bonded to the wood?

Carlos Cabrera Tejedor: Well, I asked a chemistry professor with the chemical formula with wood and that's what he explained to me. Again, I'm not a chemist.

John Kenney: Okay, the second question is (and it's really for the conservators as well): why not do the conservation where you actually include all the silicone in the void. That would make a heavier object but would that make it even stronger and more stable?

Carlos Cabrera Tejedor: It has been done, not in my studies. My study was a reconservation study but yes, Dr. Smith has treated artifacts just with silicone oil. Again the choices with polymer are good. If you have the right material, the right porosity and a little bit of luck, you can obtain really, really good results. It is true however, that if you don't obtain really good results, the results are terrible. So really, really good or really, really bad and there is no way back.

Shanna Daniel: I was going to answer John's question and Carlos feel free to pipe in. You were asking why not use all silicone oil. From my understanding, remember that silicone is just Si and O where you need to have a carbon to have it crosslink within the wood and the MTMS is your crosslinker which does have that carbon that makes it flow in there. So you do have to have something other than just that heavy silicone oil.

John Kenney: That wasn't my question.

Shanna Daniel: Oh. I thought it was.

John Kenney: I didn't explain it very well. My question was using the crosslinker why not make the voids completely full with the crosslinked silicone rather than leaving a thin layer. I mean, it's elegant to see a thin

layer and it means that you have a lighter piece of wood, but I was just wondering whether there would be an advantage to crosslinking the silicone so you completely fill the void. It would make it a heavier object but it might make it stronger.

Cliff Cook: Cost.

Carlos Cabrera Tejedor: Yes, but you'd have a totally plastified piece of silicone that I do believe is going to last 200 years but I don't think it is a good or desirable result. When you totally fill the structure the object just becomes really heavy and as Dr. Cliff mentioned it is expensive to use a lot of silicone.

Catherine Sincich: If I can add, one of the benefits, we feel, to the silicone oil is that you get the structural support without the weight of the bulking agent. Now if it's really decomposed, you might want to try PEG or use a heavier oil to actually give it more support but when you're talking about things that are bigger than a bread box that adds a lot of weight to things. We typically work with a lot of ship timbers and when you are talking about something that is that size it can add a lot of weight with PEG and silicone oil gives you that structural support without the extra weight, so when you go to display it or store it you don't have the support issues with it sagging. So that's one of the differences between the oil treatment and the PEG treatment. Just to go back to long-term stability, I just want to remind everybody, and hopefully this will come out in some of these studies if they want to look at it, is that since 1998 we've been working on La Belle artifacts and there's probably several hundred thousand organic pieces that were done through silicone oil, everything from rope to textile to even glass that had a carbon component, to bone. Any organic was there so we're now thirteen years out. They look really good but have we done scientific studies? No, they haven't been done yet. But there is no efflorescence, there's no powdering, there's no stiffness, there's no buckling. They are still flexible, when we wanted them to stay flexible. They still look like they were done yesterday. They need to be looked at obviously, it's a new procedure. So, we have a large bank of material that's actually been done so people can go back and look at that. It's all going to stay in Texas, in different museums. So, all that material's available, but the stuff looks really good. There is material to look at so those studies don't have to start right now.

Cliff Cook: Just a comment, many national labor laws require stringent health and safety conditions. If you are using significant quantities of a solvent you will have to have…well, in Canada, we have to have a laboratory that has 100% fresh and exhausted air separate from your building, breathable air connections on the wall. You are talking about significant capital structures here in order to safely work with the quantities of solvent you are looking at. So, it doesn't matter how good the treatment is, if the capital cost to outfit your lab to do it are prohibitive, you may never get a chance. When you are talking about the quantities of acetone to do a block, you are talking about several gallons of acetone, a lot of liters, here. There's no way it's going to fit in a fume hood, so extractives like elephant trunks, slot exhaust, the stuff we have in our normal lab operations, don't cut it. You need to have, literally, a room you can walk into at $100,000 maybe, I don't know. Huge Cost. You don't do the bunker out the back any more like we used to. You cannot get away with that any more, there's no way!

Mikkel Christensen: Just a quick addition to the whole plastification discussion. If you have an object and you fill every void, even if it's stable for 200 years, once that plastic block breaks down, there is no way to retreat it. We may want people to look at our ships or our wooden objects in a

thousand years. So if we leave some kind of open structure, it may be possible to retreat and restrengthen them. So paranoia is, I would say, very much the reason why we won't fill anything completely.

461

4.7

Possible Use of Chelates of Calcium to Remove Iron from Bone, Ivory, Teeth and Antler

Anthony Crawshaw* and Margrethe Felter
Conservation Laboratory, York Archaeological Trust, 47 Aldwark, York, YO1 7BX, UK.
*E-mail: acrawshaw@yorkat.co.uk

Abstract
This paper examines the possible use of the calcium complexes of ethylenediaminetetraacetic acid (EDTA) and diethylenetriaminepentaacetic acid (DTPA) to remove iron from bone, ivory, teeth and antler. The usual iron removal agents, sodium EDTA and diammonium citrate, tend to strip calcium from the substrate. Our idea was that our reagents, having the calcium already present in the chelate, would reduce the loss of calcium from the objects. We used archaeological bone and teeth samples for the tests, analyzing the resulting solutions and solid residues. The results showed that our reagents were much slower and less effective than sodium EDTA and diammonium citrate but damaged the substrates less. Synthesis of the reagents will be described.

Keywords: iron removal, bone, ivory, antler, EDTA, DTPA

1. Introduction
This project is concerned with exploring the possibility of removing iron from materials such as ivory, bone, antler and teeth using the calcium complex of ethylenediaminetetraacetic acid (EDTA) or diethylenetriaminepentaacetic acid (DTPA). All of these substrates are composites of an inorganic phase, largely a calcium phosphate – hydroxyapatite - in an organic matrix, mainly collagen. The removal of iron during conservation is desirable because the iron can cause acidification if chlorides are present and can catalyze oxidation of organic materials under some circumstances. In addition reduction of iron staining is often thought desirable on aesthetic grounds. A *caveat* is that there has been some evidence (Godfrey et al. 2002) that there is sometimes better preservation in the areas of metal staining – such better preservation does however refer to the conditions before recovery of the object, not necessarily afterwards.

1.1. Previous work
Godfrey et al. (2002) looked at the effects of EDTA, and other compounds, on iron-stained bone and ivory from a marine site. Although some iron was removed from the objects the results were far from satisfactory as there was clear evidence of degradation of both mineral and organic components, taking the form of softening and weight loss. In addition the ivory turned more orange in color. EDX spectra showed that calcium, in addition to iron, was being removed from the surface layers of the samples and FTIR indicated that phosphate was also being lost. There was a residual gelatinous layer left on the surface of many of the samples.

O'Connor (1987) states, when describing bone, antler and ivory that both cations and anions in their structures may exchange with species from the environment. As a result iron may have substituted for calcium in the structure of the inorganic phase, so that the removal of the iron could result in damage to the structure of the mineral. The same source says that demineralization of bone will occur at pH values of 5 or less, whilst collagen consuming bacteria thrive at pH values around 7-8.

1.2. Chemistry

EDTA has four acidic protons and is capable of forming a stable chelate complex with many metal ions, in which six groups from the EDTA (four carboxyls and two amines) bind to the metal. We will here denote the unreacted acid as $H_2[H_2EDTA]$, whilst the disodium salt of commerce is $Na_2[H_2EDTA]$. Calcium and ferrous iron complexes of the latter will be written as $Na_2[CaEDTA]$ and $Na_2[FeEDTA]$, respectively. If a metal ion is written inside the square brackets, we mean that it is held as a chelate by the EDTA.

1.3. Proposed Treatment

EDTA is a non-selective chelating agent, which was reflected in the demineralization noted by Godfrey et al. (2002). These authors do not mention the pH values of the solutions used, but we found that a 0.1M solution of $Na_2[H_2EDTA]$ had a pH of 4.4, which is outside the safe zone for bone. The present proposal is to use a calcium complex of EDTA to try and remove the iron from the object being treated and to adjust the pH to within the range 5 – 9. The driving force for the removal of the iron would be the much greater stability of the iron complex of EDTA, by comparison with the calcium complex. From Bell (1977) we note that the stability constant of the calcium complex of EDTA is 11.0, that of ferrous iron is 14.3, whilst ferric iron is 25.1. Stability constants are logarithmic values, so for example, the ferrous/EDTA complex is between 1000 and 10,000 times more stable than the calcium/EDTA complex. The ferrous iron complex of EDTA is readily oxidized to the ferric complex by atmospheric oxygen, so we can expect to see any removed iron as the ferric complex. The hope is that the iron removed would be replaced by the calcium carried by the EDTA reagent, reducing the degradation of the mineral component of the substrate. Near neutral pH values should also assist in preservation of both inorganic and organic components, provided that bacterial growth can be kept

in check. An important requirement of any treatment is that the object should not be highly colored by the treatment; in this context we note that the ferric iron complex of EDTA is described by Garvan (1964) as pale yellow.

Jones (1983) notes that when EDTA is used medicinally, to remove heavy metals from the body, it is injected as the calcium complex, $Na_2[CaEDTA]$. The reason for using the calcium complex, rather than $Na_2[H_2EDTA]$, is that the latter rapidly removes calcium from the blood serum, with serious consequences. The same author states that DTPA is more effective than EDTA for removing heavy metals from the body, as the stability constants of its salts are higher than those of EDTA. The iron complex of DTPA is yellow (Sandström et al. 2003) whereas iron complexes of chelating agents with aromatic groups close to the chelate-forming groups may be expected to be highly coloured. An example of the latter type of compound is ethylenediaminobis(2-hydroxy-4-methylphenyl)acetic acid (EDMA), as examined in the *Vasa* research (Almkvist et al. 2005). For our purposes a highly colored iron complex would only be acceptable if there were no residual colored iron complex remaining in the object after treatment.

Bell (1977) states that the ferric complex of EDTA is not stable in solutions of pH 8 or above, precipitating iron hydroxides. Ullmann's Encyclopaedia of Industrial Chemistry (1987) states that pH values greater than 5.5 lead to precipitation of ferric hydroxide, $Fe(OH)_3$, from iron EDTA complexes, whilst a commercial website says that that complex was stable in the pH range 1.5 to 6.5. Garvan (1964) states that the addition of two equivalents of alkali to $H[FeEDTA]$ leads to the formation of deep orange $[FeEDTAOH]^-$. As iron hydroxide is also orange, either or both of these pH-dependent reactions may be responsible for the orange colors noted by Godfrey et al. (2002). In any case these comments suggest that we may well have to control the pH of EDTA treatment solutions carefully, or use a complexing agent other than EDTA.

A possible problem with the idea is that although the displacement of the calcium from $Na_2[CaEDTA]$ by iron is favored by the much greater stability of the iron complex, the reaction will require the breaking of several bonds to the chelated calcium, before it can proceed. Such coordinated bond breakage may be difficult. In chemical terms, the reaction is thermodynamically favored, but may be kinetically prohibited. That said, the medical use of $Na_2[CaEDTA]$ evidently overcomes the same problem, without using extreme temperatures, so we shouldn't give up just yet.

2. Experimental
2.1. Samples
York Archaeological Trust is fortunate in having a large urban excavation underway at Hungate in York, which has yielded quantities of unstratified animal bone and teeth. This meant that we could use archaeological samples for our destructive investigations, without being concerned about their unique nature. The bulk of our tests were carried out on a ground archaeological bone which we had shown contained about 1% of iron in the ash. It was not possible to powder teeth, with the equipment available to us, because of their hardness. Consequently we cut teeth up into three pieces, each of which could be immersed in different test solutions. This approach has the disadvantage that each particular tooth probably contains different iron levels, but if there is a common test solution between different teeth then we may be able to draw up a qualitative ranking order for the different test solutions.

2.2. Methodology
When examining the extraction of iron from bone, 100mgs samples of ground

bone were treated with 10mls of each test solution. The solutions were always the same strength, 0.1M, so that we were comparing the chemical effects of the different solutions, at the same concentrations. Such would not have been the case if we had always used, for example, a 2% weight/volume solution, due to the differing molecular weights of the compounds involved (if expressed as % weight/volume our solutions fell in the range 2 – 5%, depending on the compound being tested). The quantities of solution and bone used meant that there was about a two-hundredfold excess of reagent to iron for each test, i.e. the solution could have complexed two hundred times as much iron as was actually present, were complete reaction to occur. All tests were carried out at room temperature.

An attempt to monitor the extraction of iron from the samples, by examining the solutions with a UV/Visible spectrometer, gave results inconsistent with those from ashing the residues. Analysis by ashing was carried out using a method adapted here (Crawshaw and Humphrey 2002) from standard wet chemical methods. We concluded that the problem with the spectrometric method was the growth of organisms in the solutions leading to erroneous absorbances, evidenced by the solutions being turbid, even after centrifuging. Consequently the results reported below were all derived by ashing (TAPPI 1958), followed by wet chemistry. We also tried taking color measurements on the dry powdered samples used using a Minolta Chromameter. The results were not very reproducible, probably due to variations caused by the powdered nature of the samples, so this approach was not pursued further.

3. Results
The first ground bone sample that we tried contained less than 0.2% Fe_2O_3 in the ash, which meant that the analytical procedure was working at the low end of its

sensitivity, with consequent reduction in accuracy. (All results for iron analyses in this paper are reported in terms of Fe_2O_3 for easy comparisons – this does not mean that the iron is necessarily present in that form). Three different portions of the sample were treated with water, diammonium citrate and $Na_2[CaEDTA]$. Qualitatively, diammonium citrate extracted more iron than $Na_2[CaEDTA]$ but with greater loss of bone.

A second ground bone sample contained 1.2% Fe_2O_3 in the ash, so this sample was used in subsequent experiments, the results of which are reported in Table 1. The first column lists the treatment solution and the next three numerical columns in this table are the extraction time in days, and the initial and final pHs. The remaining columns and their significance are discussed below.

Column 4 gives, for the bone samples only, the percentage of dried bone sample recovered. These percentage recoveries are generally in the 80% – 90% range, which probably reflects losses on handling and some loss of bone matter either to bacterial action or solubility. The two exceptions are the treatments with diammonium citrate and $Na_2[H_2EDTA]$, with 40% and 16% recovery, respectively. We suspect that this loss of bone material reflects attack on the bone mineral content by these two more aggressive reagents.

Column 5 gives the percentage loss of weight on ashing the solid residue, again for the bone samples only. These weight loss figures are in the 27% – 29% range, again with the exception of the treatments with diammonium citrate and $Na_2[H_2EDTA]$, with 37% and 99% weight loss, respectively. The higher weight losses on ignition of the residues from these two solutions reflect higher organic content in the residues, as a result of demineralization of the bone.

The sixth and seventh numerical columns give the percentage of Fe_2O_3 in the ash from the bone residues, together with the weight of recovered iron, the latter as mgs of Fe_2O_3. It is evident (column 7) that there is some reduction in iron content of the ash for all solutions. Only diammonium citrate and $Na_2[H_2EDTA]$ seem to give results markedly better than water, but at the expense of loss of calcium from the substrate.

The solutions recovered from each treatment were evaporated down and columns 8 and 9 in the table give the percentage of Fe_2O_3 in the ash from the dried solutions, together with the weight of recovered iron, the latter as mgs of Fe_2O_3. Because most of the test solutions will themselves give some ash, from the calcium or sodium present, the amount of recovered iron (column 9) has more significance than the percentage of Fe_2O_3 in the ash. All of the test solutions had extracted some iron, by comparison with the water used as a control, whilst diammonium citrate and $Na_2[H_2EDTA]$ extracted the most. Since the diammonium citrate should not give any ash, being entirely organic, the 38 mgs of ash recovered testifies to the demineralizing powers of that reagent.

The final numerical column (column 10) gives the total weight of recovered iron, from both residue and solution. The result should, in theory, equal the weight of iron in the original bone sample and thus will act as a check on our procedures. The recovered weights are reasonably close to the 1.2 mgs expected, the one exception being line five. Test five was the first stage in a two-stage treatment, the second stage being retreatment of the same bone sample with fresh solution. The idea behind this experiment was to see if iron extraction was being limited by a solution equilibrium being set up between iron extraction and redeposition. This situation would be similar to that which occurs when salts are being extracted from marine objects, when repeated water changes are needed. Line six in Table 1 gives the result of the second stage, from which it can be seen that further iron was indeed extracted by the second solution. We do not know whether this continued extraction was due to the use of fresh reagent or the longer total extraction time. The fourth experiment with $Na_2[CaEDTA]$ as the treatment solution used a solution of lower starting pH than the other three. The reason for this variation was that the stability of the iron complex of EDTA is known to decrease with increasing pH (Bell 1977) and our treatment solutions generally become more basic during treatment. There seems to have been a slight increase in iron extraction with this more acidic solution.

The last two tests on bone, using our calcium complexes, were with DTPA complexes, as opposed to EDTA complexes. Both DTPA reagents contained the $[CaDTPA]^{3-}$ ion, differing only in the positive counter-ions. In one case the counter-ions were sodium and in the other calcium. This latter was synthesized in the hope that the excess calcium would render the reagent even less likely to remove calcium from the object. In practice the complex with the calcium counter-ion was less efficient at removing iron from the bone, possibly because the excess calcium in solution opposed further release of calcium by the desired reaction.

Turning to the tests on sheep teeth, cut into thirds, we can only show relative rankings of the various reagents within any one tooth. This is because we were unable to powder the teeth, so the iron content of the test samples was not constant. The results of the tests on teeth are reported in Table 1 and enable us to derive a crude ranking order of extraction efficiency. Like the bone samples, $Na_2[H_2EDTA]$ was similar to ammonium citrate and both were better than $Na_2[CaEDTA]$, $Na_3[CaDTPA]$ and $Ca_{1.5}[CaDTPA]$. All of the test solutions were more efficient than water.

The teeth were treated in the solution by suspending them from the rim of a test-tube so that approximately half of the fragment was immersed (Figure 1). The teeth were examined in terms of condition before and after treatment to determine, on a purely observational basis, if the solutions had the desired effect of removing part or all of the iron staining, or if they caused damage to the surfaces or structure of the teeth.

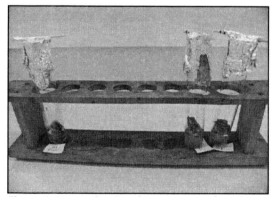

Figure 1. *Image showing the treatment of tooth A in the different solutions*

Table 1. Results of Iron Extraction Experiments on Bone and Teeth - Iron Analyses.

Numerical Column Number	1	2	3	4	5	6	7	8	9	10
Solution	Extraction Time, Days	Initial pH	Final pH	Solid Residue Remaining, %	Loss on Ignition, %	% Fe_2O_3 in Ash	Fe_2O_3 from Residue, mgs.	% Fe_2O_3 in Ash from Solution	Fe_2O_3 from Solution, mgs.	Total Recovered Fe_2O_3, mgs.
Bone (100 mgs. treated with 10 mls. of 0.1M solution)					28	1.18	1.18			
RO Water	39	6.3	7.7	92	29	1.15	0.75	~30	0.03	0.79
Diammonium Citrate	4	5.2	5.8	40	37	1.58	0.40	1.65	0.64	1.04
$Na_2[H_2EDTA]$	13	4.4	4.3	16	99	n/a	n/a	0.52	0.91	0.91
$Na_2[CaEDTA]$	39	6.4	8.6	93	29	1.03	0.68	0.08	0.13	0.81
$Na_2[CaEDTA]$ - First	9	7.6	8.4	(Used for Second Extraction)				0.07	0.13	0.13
$Na_2[CaEDTA]$ - Second	50	7.5	8.5	81	27	1.33	0.79	0.09	0.12	0.91
$Na_2[CaEDTA]$	49	5.3	7.7	80	28	0.96	0.55	0.17	0.30	0.86
$Ca_{1.5}[CaDTPA]$	45	7.5	7.9	89	27	1.6	1.04	0.06	0.12	1.16
$Na_3[CaDTPA]$	35	7.2	8	89	28	1.42	0.91	0.13	0.28	1.19
Teeth (Not Quantitative)										
A						??				
RO Water	32	6.3	7.8	n/a	n/a	n/a	n/a	~35	0.05	0.05
Diammonium Citrate	32		8.5	n/a	n/a	n/a	n/a	10.5	2.00	2.00
$Na_2[CaEDTA]$	32	6.4	8.3	n/a	n/a	n/a	n/a	0.15	0.23	0.23
B						??				
$Na_2[CaEDTA]$	44	7.5	8.6	n/a	n/a	n/a	n/a	0.37	0.46	0.46
$Ca_{1.5}[CaDTPA]$	44	7.5	7.8	n/a	n/a	n/a	n/a	0.14	0.27	0.27
$Na_2[H_2EDTA]$	44		5.7	n/a	n/a	n/a	n/a	2.46	~2.5	~2.5
C						??				
$Ca_{1.5}[CaDTPA]$	28	7.9	7.9	n/a	n/a	n/a	n/a	0.07	0.15	0.15
$Na_2[CaEDTA]$	28	5.2	7.8	n/a	n/a	n/a	n/a	0.04	0.07	0.07
$Na_3[CaDTPA]$	28	7.3	7.7	n/a	n/a	n/a	n/a	0.07	0.16	0.16

A more detailed study of the effects could be done using the Scanning Electron Microscope to see if the damage/stain removal is visible under higher magnification, this was not possible here due to time constraints.

The teeth were also photographed before and after treatment, both in their wet state and after they had been allowed to dry out. The observations were made by one of the authors without knowing which solutions were being used on which part of the tooth, to avoid bias. The results, by comparison with the untreated state, have been laid out in Table 2 below (with the solutions given, for ease of reference).

As can be seen from Table 2, very few of the solutions had a noticeable effect on the iron staining of the teeth. Only fragment A2 (diammonium citrate) and C2 (Na_2 [CaEDTA]) had showed a marked color change, but this seemed to be accompanied by a dry, chalky appearance to the surfaces, which would be undesirable in a conservation context, although in the case of the latter this was less apparent. The calcium complex of EDTA with a lower starting pH seems to have been much more effective than those with a higher pH. It is possible that some of the solutions which had a slight effect on the iron staining might be more effective over a longer period of time.

Table 2. Effects of solutions on teeth

Tooth A	Wet	Dry
A1 (RO water)	No change	No change
A2 (Diammonium citrate)	Effective stain removal, still some orange specks. Enamel surface is still hard but part of the interior of the tooth is damaged and soft. Some areas of white accretions.	Some pieces have become detached from the interior of the tooth. Bleached areas have a dry, chalky look. White accretions.
A3 (Na_2 [CaEDTA])	Very little change in color, surface is hard. No burial accretions on outer enamel surface.	Very slight change in color to cut surface.

Tooth B	Wet	Dry
B1 (Na_2 [CaEDTA])	No change	No change
B2 ($Ca_{1.5}$[CaDTPA])	Some slight stain removal. Some removal of accretions.	Very little change visible on drying.
B3 (Na_2 [H_2EDTA])	Slight softening of the surface. Very slight stain removal. Burial accretions still attached. White powdery accretions on surface, some fungal growth.	Very little change visible on drying.

Tooth C	Wet	Dry
C1 (Na_3[CaDTPA])	Outer surfaces chalky and fragile, slightly soft surface. Some stain removal.	Outer surface still slightly soft. Slight stain removal.
C2 (Na_2 [CaEDTA]) (low starting pH)	Effective stain removal, slightly soft surface.	Marked color change, slightly dry, chalky appearance to the surface.
C3 ($Ca_{1.5}$[CaDTPA])	Very little change. Some very slight, uneven stain removal.	Very little change.

469

4. Discussion

All of our test complexes were much less efficient, and slower, at removing iron than ammonium citrate and $Na_2[H_2EDTA]$, but seemed to result in less damage to the substrate. The poor results might be due to the difficulty in breaking the several bonds from the chelate to the calcium, as suggested in the last paragraph in section 1.3.1. above. Another possibility might be that the iron in the tooth or bone may be held more tightly than the calcium with which we seek to replace it. This would have the effect of opposing the driving force for the desired reaction, which is the greater stability of the chelate-iron complex than the chelate-calcium complex, hence reducing the speed.

Given the reduced efficiency of our complexes at removing iron, vis-à-vis ammonium citrate or $Na_2[H_2EDTA]$, it is probably not worth pursuing the idea further. In addition, we are not certain if the limited quantity of iron we can remove will result in an improved appearance or assist in protecting the objects from iron-induced deterioration.

5. Further Extensions

Further substrates that this technique might be applicable to are calcium containing minerals such as limestone and marble. Other metal ions, e.g. copper, might be removed with the same compounds as we are considering from calcium containing substrates. Bell (1977) gives the stability constant of the Cu^{2+} EDTA complex as 18.8, so if the object contains equal amounts of iron and copper staining the iron would be removed first. Since cream and yellow colors of stonework may well be due to traces of iron incorporated in the stone, the area of treatment may need to be limited with poultices in order to stop bleaching of the stonework. In this context we note that Stambolov (1968) discusses the use of chelating agents such as EDTA in conjunction with absorbent material such as chalk to form a paste. Although Stambolov does not state that the mixture would generate a calcium EDTA complex, in situ, of the type we are discussing in this paper, such is very likely to occur.

The solutions might be used in conjunction with the usual pH 7.0 buffer solution when treating ivory, bone, antler or teeth, in order to maintain a neutral pH, as that buffer is based on phosphate salts, so the combination may be even less likely to change the object's chemical structure.

Reagents

Water was purified by reverse osmosis.

EDTA acid was obtained from ABM Chemicals, under the name 'Nervanaid B Acid'.

$Na_2[CaEDTA]$ is available commercially from Sigma-Aldrich, but at an increased price by comparison with $Na_2[H_2EDTA]$, so it was made in-house. A 0.1M solution of $Na_2[CaEDTA]$ was made by dissolving 3.72gms of $Na_2[H_2EDTA]$ (Prestons) in about 50ml of reverse osmosis water, followed by 1.00g of calcium carbonate (Fisons) with stirring, and making up to 100ml. 0.74g of calcium hydroxide (Sigma-Aldrich) could also be used, instead of calcium carbonate.

The 0.1M low pH solution of $Na_2[H_2EDTA]$ was made by stirring 2.92g of $H_2[H_2EDTA]$ with 60ml of water and adding 0.74g of calcium hydroxide. A solution of 0.8g of sodium hydroxide, dissolved in 20ml of water, was then added dropwise, until the pH reached 5.2, when the solution was filtered and made up to 100ml.

A 0.1M solution of $Na_3[CaDTPA]$ was made by stirring 50ml of water with 3.93g of DTPA (Sigma-Aldrich) and 0.74g of calcium hydroxide. 1.22g of sodium hydroxide (Fisons) dissolved in 25ml of water was then added, with stirring. The resulting solution was then filtered and made up to 100ml.

The 0.1M solution of $Ca_{1.5}[CaDTPA]$ was made in a similar way to $Na_3[CaDTPA]$, but substituting 1.11g of calcium hydroxide for the sodium hydroxide solution.

Acknowledgements

We would like to thank Ian Panter, Head of the Conservation Laboratory, for facilitating this research and Pete Connelly, Hungate Project Director, for supplying the samples tested, together with those of our colleagues who have made helpful comments.

References

Almkvist G., Dal L. and Persson I., (2005), Extraction of Iron Compounds from Vasa Wood, in P. Hoffmann et al. (editors), Proceedings of the 9th ICOM Group on Wet Organic Archaeological Materials Conference, Copenhagen, 2004, Bremerhaven, The International Council of Museums, Committee for Conservation Working Group on Wet Organic Archaeological Materials, 2005, pp 203-211.

Bell C.F., (1977), Principles and Applications of Metal Chelation, Oxford, Clarendon Press.

Crawshaw A.J.G. and Humphrey A., (2002), Simple Analyses for Iron Content in Archaeological Wood, in P. Hoffmann et al. (editors), Proceedings of the 8th ICOM Group on Wet Organic Archaeological Materials Conference, Stockholm, Bremerhaven, The International Council of Museums, Committee for Conservation Working Group on Wet Organic Archaeological Materials, 2001, pp 309-317.

Garvan F.L., (1964), in F.P. Dwyer and D.P. Mellar (editors), Chelating Agents and Metal Chelates, New York, Academic Press, 1964, pp 310-311.

Godfrey I.M., Kasi K., Schneider S. and Williams E., (2002), Iron Removal from Waterlogged Ivory and Bone, in P. Hoffmann et al. (editors), Proceedings of the 8th ICOM Group on Wet Organic Archaeological Materials Conference, Stockholm, 2001, Bremerhaven, The International Council of Museums, Committee for Conservation Working Group on Wet Organic Archaeological Materials, 2001, pp 527-553.

Jones, (1983), Therapeutic Chelating Agents, in H. Sigel (editor), Metal Ions in Biological Systems, Vol. 16, New York, Marcel Dekker,1983, p 60.

O'Connor T.P., (1987), On the Structure, Chemistry and Decay of Bone, Antler and Ivory, in Archaeological Bone, Antler and Ivory, Occasional paper No. 5, UKIC, 1987, pp 6-8.

Sandström M., Jalilehvand F., Persson I., Fors Y., Damian E., Gelius U., Hall-Roth I., Dal L., Richards V.L. and Godfrey I., (2003), The Sulphur Threat to Marine Archaeological Artefacts: Acid and Iron Removal from the Vasa, in J.H. Townsend, K. Eremin and A. Adriaens (editors), Conservation Science 2002, London, Archetype Press, 2003, pp 79-87.

Stambolov T., (1968), Notes on the Removal of Iron Stains from Calcareous Stone, Studies in Conservation, Vol. 13, pp 45-47.

TAPPI (Technical Association of the Pulp and Paper Industry), (1958), Ash in Wood, Standard T15 m-58.

Ullmann's Encyclopaedia of Industrial Chemistry, (1987), in W. Gerhartz et al. (editors), Weinheim, VCH, 1987, Volume A10, p 96.

Questions and answers

Shanna Daniel: I have a question. What were the percentages that you used?

Anthony Crawshaw: All the percents were 0.1 molar. It will be in the paper but it worked out to something like 2 – 4%.

Gordon Turner Walker: This isn't necessarily a question for the speakers but for anyone. If you have a reasonably small and reasonably porous object - not necessarily ivory - perhaps bone with a fairly open pore structure. Is there any sense in washing or flooding the specimen with oxygenated water? So you'd try to oxidate out all the most susceptible, whether it is pyrite or anything else, you try and get rid of the most reactive species in a solution where the reaction products can just diffuse out. Does that make any sense at all? I should add that I've done that and it seems...I mean, would you expect it to work?

Anthony Crawshaw: I think it's more up to somebody else to answer the query.

Vicki Richards: I'd just be worried maybe about the molar volume change in the oxidation of inner pyrites. They're a lot smaller and then you oxidize them and their molar volume gets larger.

Gordon Turner Walker: That's less of a problem with bones where it's not so collapsed.

Vicki Richards: Point taken.

Anthony Crawshaw: Can I answer Jim's question? Well Jim's question for anyone who didn't hear was how you make the stuff. It's in the paper but it's ridiculously easy. You just weigh out the EDTA, put it in a beaker of water, stir in calcium hydroxide or calcium carbonate and there you are. And if you want to - check the pH.

4.8

Removal of Alum from Iron-Age Wooden Objects by an Applied Electric Field

*Iben V. Christense and, Lisbeth M. Ottosen
Department of Civil Engineering, Technical University of Denmark, Brovej building 118, DK-2800 Lyngby, Denmark
*E-mail:ivch@byg.dtu.dk

Poul Jensen and Inger Bojesen-Koefoed
Department of Conservation, National Museum of Denmark

Hartmut Kutzke, Susan Braovac and Mikkel Christensen
Department of Conservation, Museum of Cultural History, University of Oslo, Norway

Tom Sandström
Swedish National Heritage Board

Abstract

In this paper removal of potassium, sulfate and aluminum ions from waterlogged alum treated wood with the use of an applied electric field is described. An electric DC field was applied across the wood for 4-20 days. At the end of the experiments sulfate had moved as expected towards the anode and potassium had moved towards the cathode. One experiment showed that after 20 days only 10% of the sulfate and 8% of the potassium was left in the wood. Aluminum tended to be removed more slowly and even after 20 days only minor amounts of aluminum were removed from the wood. Total removal of alum was not obtained in the experiments reported here, but the high conductivity and the transport of the measured ions due to the electric field indicates that an applied electric field as a method for removal of alum and other unwanted ions from treated wooden objects warrants further investigation.

Keywords: wood conservation, alum, electromigration, potassium, sulfate, aluminum

1. Introduction

Alum is not used for conservation of waterlogged wood today, but it was widely used in Denmark, Norway and Sweden up until 1960. This means that many important finds have been treated with alum, including the Hjortspring find, an Iron Age find from Denmark and the Norwegian Oseberg find, considered the most richly ornamented Viking Age find in the world.

In alum treated wood, the ingress of alum into the wood may be limited to the outermost few millimeters, whilst the inner part of the object is left unimpregnated. The shape of the object may thus be preserved, but the untreated wood in the center has often shrunk during drying, causing internal cracking. Even after drying, the crack formation is ongoing and this may be attributed to mechanical tension and ongoing degradation of the untreated wood. The alum treatment made the wood heavy and brittle, but the strength of the wood was not improved. Alum treated wood is also subject to structural powdering which may eventually cause the total destruction of the artifact. The disadvantages of the alum treatment method have resulted in different attempts at re-conservation. At the Danish National Museum this is presently done by extraction of alum in water at room temperature and elevated (80°C) temperature, followed by re-conservation with PEG. The water is changed multiple times during the extraction until no more can be removed (monitored by conductivity measurements).

473

A Nordic collaboration, involving the Technical University of Denmark, the National Museum of Denmark, the University of Oslo, and the Swedish National Heritage Board, is currently working across borders in an attempt to solve the problems of the alum-treated wood. One attempt is to investigate the possibilities of removing alum from the wood by electromigration. In this method a DC electric field is applied across the wood sample and the alum ions (K^+, Al^{3+} and SO_4^{2-}) are transported by the electric field out of the wooden object.

At the Technical University of Denmark the use of a DC electric field to transport ions in porous materials has been a research area for the last 15 years. Initially the method was developed for removal of heavy metals from polluted soils, but it has also been used for e.g. removal of copper, chromium and arsenic from impregnated waste wood (Christensen et al. 2006) and in-situ impregnation of wood with boron or copper (Ottosen et al. 2010)

When an electric field is applied across a moist porous material, the electric current is carried by ions in the pore water of the material. This is known as electromigration. The ions will move according to their charge, positively charged ions (cations) will move towards the negatively charged electrode (cathode) and negatively charged ions (anions) will move towards the positively charged electrode (anode). At the anode oxidation takes place and at the cathode reduction processes occurs. The transported ions takes part in these redox processes and with inert electrodes, oxidation and reduction of water also takes place. At the anode acid is produced:

$$H_2O \rightarrow 2H^+ + \frac{1}{2}O_2 + 2e^- \qquad (1)$$

and at the cathode alkali is produced:

$$2H_2O + 2e^- \rightarrow 2OH^- + H_2 \qquad (2)$$

The electrode processes (1) and (2) will result in pH changes near the electrodes and the ions produced will also move in the electric field, so an acidic front will emerge from the anode and an alkaline front from the cathode unless actions are taken to prevent this. In the experiments reported here the electrodes were placed in a clay poultice designed at DTU (Rörig-Dalgaard 2008). The poultice contains both kaolin and $CaCO_3$. The key purpose of the carbonate is to neutralize acid produced at the anode. The kaolin itself may also be able to act as an ion exchange resin, taking up H^+- ions and instead releasing other cations from the clay. However, given the fact that kaolin is a 1:1 clay with relatively low CEC (cation exchange capacity), the main pH control is expected to be due to $CaCO_3$. In addition to controlling pH, the poultice also serves as a reservoir for the removed alum ions and ensures an optimal contact between the electrodes and the wood without damaging the wood.

2. Experimental Conditions

The wood used for these experiments were alum treated samples from the Hjortspring find. The experimental setup is shown in figure 1. The wood is placed between two mesh electrodes, which are placed in the clay poultice. The anode (to the right) is an inert titanium electrode and the cathode (left electrode) is stainless steel. A DC power supply (HP3612A) is used and a constant current is applied to the electrodes.

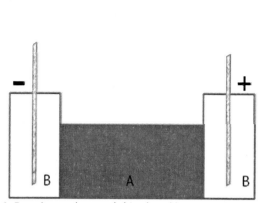

Figure 1. Experimental setup. (A) is placed between two electrodes placed in poultice (B). Right picture: experimental setup of experiment A1.

The wood sample is orientated with the length of the sample between the electrodes, e.g. with the grain aligned with the flow of current. This has shown to be the optimal position for transport of ions in wood (Ottosen et al. 2010). In some of the experiments the wood was presoaked in water before the current was applied.

During the experiment current and voltage drop were monitored and in some cases the current adjusted to optimize the process. The clay poultice was changed during the experiments to evaluate the transport rate of potassium, sulfate and aluminum during the experiments and also the change of poultice was used if the voltage drop (and thereby resistance) of the system increased drastically. High resistance was sometimes due to lack of contact between wood and poultice and by changing the poultice the contact was reestablished. The experimental conditions are summarized in table 1. A1 was the longest running experiment (20 days) and A2 was a reference experiment to A1 with no current applied. In A3 the current was increased to initially 5 mA and later 3 mA. Experiments A1-A3 was all wrapped in plastic to avoid drying out the samples during the experiments. Experiment A4 was instead placed in a sealed glass vessel, above water (RH close to 100%). In A5 we

used same setup as in A4, but without soaking the sample in water first. In A6 the sample was placed outside the vessel and only slightly covered with a piece of plastic to protect the setup from spills, etc. from the work in the laboratory. Samples A1-A4 was soaked prior to the experiment, whereas samples A5 and A6 were not.

At the end of the experiments each wood piece was divided into four slices and dried at 40°C for 48 hours and pulverized before further analysis. The slices were numbered 1-4 with slice 1 being closest to the anode and slice 4 closest to the cathode. The clay samples were dried at 103°C for 24 hours and pulverized before subsamples for analysis were taken. Concentrations of aluminum, potassium and sulfate were measured in the wood, clay poultice and in experiment A1-A4 also in the soaking solution.

Aluminum and potassium were measured after pressurized digestion of 0.25 g wood in 10 ml concentrated nitric acid. Aluminum was measured with ICP and potassium by AAS. Sulfate in the wood samples was measured by ion chromatography after extraction of the wood sample in distilled water for 1 hour with a wood: water ratio of 1:8 w/w. These

Table 1. Experimental conditions

Experiment	Dimensions [1](l,w)/mm	soaking	Current /mA	Duration/days	Set up	Poultice change
A1	50,35	45 min.	1	20	Wrapped in plastic	Day 1, 8, 15
A2	46,35	1.5 hour	0	20	Wrapped in plastic	None
A3	53,23	3 hour	3-5	4	Wrapped in plastic	Day 1
A4	32,32	1,5 hour	2	9	unwrapped, above water	Day 7
A5	37,28	None	1-2	7	unwrapped, above water	Day 5
A6	42,24	None	2	9	On table	Day 2, 5

[1]length and width of the sample. The height was between 10 and 18 mm.

extractions were also used when measuring pH of the samples. Aluminum, potassium and sulfate were measured in clay samples after extraction of the clay sample in distilled water. No acid digestions were made.

Due to limitations in the amount of sample material, all analyses were made as single measurements. In most cases the amount of wood in each slide was between 0.5 g and 2.0 g. Of this 0.25 g was used for the acid digestion and the remaining was used for extraction in distilled water.

3. Results and Discussion

In table 2 the distribution of sulfate and potassium after the experiments are shown. In calculating the distribution, the recovered amount of the element (in the wood and the clay) is set as 100%. A source of error here may be the presence of potassium in the clay used. Potassium is often found as a counter ion in clay, but given the fact that kaolin has low CEC and thereby low concentration of counter ions, the error is considered to be negligible here. However this is to be investigated in future experiments.

The recovered amount in clay and wood is based on one analysis of each wood slice and the anode- and cathode clay. The measured concentration of the subsamples were then taken as representative for the whole sample. This was considered to be acceptable as almost all the wood and more than 50 % of the clay was actually analyzed.

The distribution is shown with the charge- and energy consumptions of the experiments. The charge consumption is an expression of how much charge was moved in the experiment and the energy consumption is an expression of how difficult it was to move the charge. In two experiments with the same charge consumption, higher energy consumption is a sign of higher resistance in the system. The lowest energy consumption was seen in A1 and this was also the experiment with the highest charge transfer. The removal of aluminum, however, was not successful. Even though aluminum was removed by soaking (between 11-28 mg in experiment A1-A4), the applied electric field seemed to have very little effect in the experiments presented here. The best result was obtained in experiment A6, where 1.5 mg aluminum was removed. The removal seems to be towards the cathode, indicating aluminum being present as cations. However, higher removal to either side is preferred before the speciation may be identified.

Due to difficulties with the analytical equipment all measurements of sulfate, potassium and aluminum were done at the same time; after the end of experiment A6. This made it impossible to design a setup for later experiments based on the removal rate of sulfate and aluminum in the previous experiments. The results imply that it would have been possible to obtain higher removal rates of both potassium and sulfate if the duration of the experiments had been prolonged. This is being taken into consideration in the ongoing research.

As shown in table 2, the removal of sulfate is dominantly towards the anode and potassium towards the cathode. This is expected since sulfate ions are negatively charged and potassium are positively charged. For no obvious reasons sulfate is only measured in the anode clay and not also in the cathode clay in experiment A2. This was not expected, since no current was applied in this experiment, and the transport here from the wood into the clays is due to passive diffusion alone. It seems unlikely that the sulfate was present in the clay from the beginning, as previous analyses of the same type of clay

(reference sample) showed no content of sulfate and also the clay used in both the anode and cathode side of the experiment came from the same batch. It is, however, seen that the removal is six times higher in A1 where current was applied. The highest removal of both sulfate and potassium was obtained in experiment A1, where only 72 mg and 31 mg respectively were left in the wood after the experiment. It is highly likely that even higher removal could have been obtained if the duration of the experiment was prolonged. In figure 2 the voltage drop of the experiments are seen and for experiment A1 the voltage drop did not exceed 4 V at any time during the experiment. This implies very low resistance in the system and therefore a longer duration would be possible as current could still be passed without any problems. In experiment A3 a current of 3 mA was applied initially, and since the voltage drop was low, the current was increased to 5 mA the next day. This however was too high and the voltage drop increased considerably during the next three days. A reduction of the current to 3 mA decreased the voltage drop, but only for a few hours and the experiment was therefore ended. The removal of sulfate to the anode was lower than in A1 even when

Table 2. Results from experiment A1-A6

	Charge trans-fer (C)	Energy consumption (Wh)	Distribution of SO$_4$ at the end of the experiments (mg/% of total)				Distribution of K at the end of the experiments (mg/% of total)			
			Soaking	Anode clay	Cathode clay	Wood	Soaking	Anode clay	Cathode clay	Wood
A1	1686	1.6	187 (26%)	400 (56%)	57 (8%)	72 (10%)	45 (12%)	47 (12%)	258 (68%)	31 (8%)
A2	-	-	260 (26%)	66 (7%)	0	681 (68%)	73 (23%)	36 (11%)	43 (13%)	170 (53%)
A3	533	7.4	232 (24%)	93 (10%)	9 (1%)	640 (66%)	21 (13%)	0	99 (29%)	169 (50%)
A4	1509	8.4	121 (14%)	102 (11%)	9 (1%)	660 (74%)	26 (9%)	0	175 (58%)	101 (34%)
A5	1091	11.7	0	84 (17%)	1 (0%)	398 (82%)	0	0	105 (46%)	124 (54%)
A6	1453	13.5	0	180 (14%)	31 (2%)	1048 (83%)	0	0	128 (29%)	320 (71%)

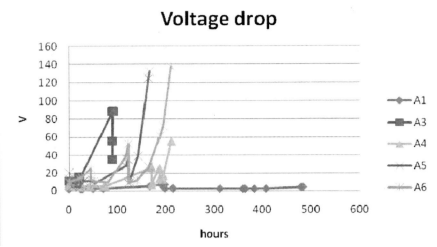

Figure 2. *Voltage drop in experiment A1 and A3-A6.*

it is taken into consideration that the charge transfer was lower in A3. This is often seen in electrokinetic experiments of this type, where the stressed situation caused by too high a resistance, may not be fully reversible. In A4 the lower current and the change of setup to the glass vessel resulted in a lower resistance in the system. The resistance increased significantly after nine days (see figure 2) and the experiment was ended. The low removal rate of sulfate (11%) is discouraging since the charge consumption is in the same range as A1, but it is likely that a higher removal of sulfate could have been obtained if the clay poultice was replaced with a new one instead of simply ending the experiment.

In A5 and A6 the objective was to investigate the possibilities of removing alum from wood without presoaking. A5 was the first step, where the wood sample was placed in high RH (in a glass vessel above water). The results showed that it was possible to apply the field without presoaking and at the end of the experiment 84 mg (17%) of the sulfate was found in the anode poultice and 105 mg (46 %) of the potassium was found in the cathode poultice. As in experiment A4 a higher removal seems likely if the poultice clay was replaced instead of ending the

experiment after seven days. Since the electric field was easily applied to the sample that had not been pre-soaked in experiments A5, where the sample was placed in a glass vessel above water, A6 was made with the intention to investigate if a high humidity was necessary for the success of the experiment. In A6, the setup was placed directly on a table in the laboratory and the results were very promising. It was possible to remove 180 mg (10%) of the sulfate and 128 mg (29%) of the potassium in this experiment and with poultice replacement additional removal is foreseen.

Both in the wood and in the poultice, pH was measured after extraction in distilled water. The results are presented in figure 3.

In experiment A2 no current was applied and this may be used as a reference for A1, since the samples for A1 and A2 were cut from the same piece of wood. In A2 pH is between 3 and 4 throughout the length of the wood. In the rest of the experiments the initial pH is unknown, however a series of pH measurements were made on different pieces of alum treated wood and using the same method for pH measurements, values between 2 and 4 were measured.

478

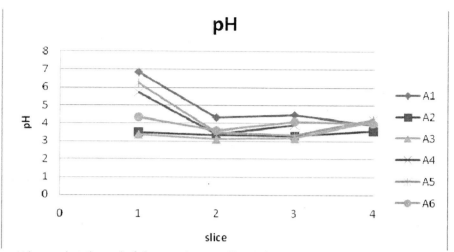

Figure 3. *The pH in wood at the end of the experiments. Slice 1 closest to the anode, slice 4 closet to the cathode.*

In experiment A1, A4 and A5 a significant increase of pH is seen in the wood near the anode. The reason for this is not clear; however it seems evident that the clay poultice is capable of neutralizing any acid being produced at the anode. It is most likely caused by redistribution of ions in the wood. Further investigations are needed to evaluate why the increase in pH is seen in these experiments and not the others.

4. Conclusions

The objective was to investigate the possibility of using an applied electric field to remove alum (aluminum, potassium and sulfate) from treated wood.

A series of six experiments are reported here and in all the experiments where current was applied, both potassium and sulfate were removed to some degree. The removal of potassium was towards the cathode, in agreement with potassium ions being positively charged. The removal of sulfate was towards the anode, in agreement with sulfate ions being negatively charged. The removal of aluminum was very low and insignificant. The exact reason is not known. Aluminum may be present as an oxide, either charged or uncharged or precipitated. More information of the aluminum speciation is needed to establish this.

In experiments where presoaking was used, a significant amount of sulfate and potassium were removed in the soaking step. This may be the preferred method, since the current then targets the more unavailable ions in the wood. However there may be situations where soaking of the wood is unwanted and the results from experiments A5 and A6 shows that removal is also possible using the electrokinetic method without presoaking. Research is ongoing and experiments with longer duration and more frequently poultice clay replacements are planned.

References

Christensen I.V., Pedersen A.J., Ottosen L.M. and Ribeiro A.B. (2006) Electrodialytic remediation of CCA-treated waste wood in a 2 m³ pilot plant. *Science of the Total Environment.* Vol 364, 2006, pp 45-54.

Ottosen L.M., Block T., Nymark M., Christensen I.V. (2010) Electrochemical in-situ impregnation of wood using a copper nail as source for copper. *In press: DOI: 10.1007/s00226-010-0325-7*

Rörig-Dalgaard I. (2008) *Preservation of murals with electrokinetic- with focus on desalination of single bricks.* PhD thesis, The Technical University of Denmark, Department of Civil Engineering (DTU Byg).

Questions and answers

André Bergeron: Just one comment really. We know that there are a lot of objects that are dry today that are filled with iron. I know that it was not the focus of your research but I think that it would be very interesting to see if you could achieve some sort of iron removal in the dry state. We do it all the time when it's wet using electrophoresis for the treatment of our wet artifacts. It works very well but it would be very interesting to see if you could come up with some sort of research or a way to implement iron extraction in the dry state on objects that we cannot rewet.

Hartmut Kutzke(presenting the paper on behalf of Iben Christensen) : Yes, I really agree with you. I thought about this because we are thinking of removing other ions. Susan (Braovac) will talk about our Oseberg find where we have a lot of screws and metal pins in it and this means also that there are copper and zinc and iron in it. Maybe it's possible to remove this metal also. Maybe it's also possible to remove sulfur ions.

Magnus Olofsson: What would happen if the objects were PEG treated?

Hartmut Kutzke: We haven't tested it but I think it is probably one of the next steps to test how it works if the objects are treated with something.

Lars Elding: When you have regularly frame test specimens like a box I can understand that the current distribution is efficient but when you have an irregular piece of wood, I have a feeling that the current would choose the easiest way and you might have an incomplete separation. Is that the case?

Hartmut Kutzke: We did not test it but, yes, I actually had the same concern as you that the migration front of the ions is not a complete plane but it follows and especially if the objects are not regular I think maybe it's one possibility to solve this problem is to apply the electrons very flexibly so that maybe we apply it at one point and then move the electrode to another part but I think this is something we have to test on actual objects. I think it isn't possible to say in general but I agree with you. It's a potential problem.

Khoi Tron: What are your electrodes made of?

Hartmut Kutzke: The anode was made of titanium and the cathode was made of silver.

Khoi Tron: Titanium? It's very expensive! You can use stainless steel. I presented on this.

Harmut Kutzke: So, I cannot really say why they have used titanium. I am not so familiar with electrochemistry so I don't know whether there is some special reason some overvoltage or whatever. I can't really say what the reason for selecting these materials is.

Lars Elding: Just a comment. Titanium is a good electronic conductor, of course, and it is very chemically resistant so that's an okay elect rode material.

4.9 (Sc PR)

Past Conservation Treatments and their Consequences – the Oseberg Find as a Case Study

Susan Braovac and Hartmut Kutzke
Museum of Cultural History, University of Oslo PB 6762 St. Olavs plass, 0130 Oslo, Norway
E-mail: susan.braovac@khm.uio.no; hartmut.kutzke@khm.uio.no;

Abstract

The wooden objects from the Oseberg find, conserved over 100 years ago with aluminum potassium sulfate salts (alum), are used as a case study for unstable historical treatments. Recent surveys show that the objects are actively deteriorating and are highly acidic. By repeating the alum treatment on freshly excavated waterlogged wood, the state of the objects at the time of treatment could be reconstructed and compared to those treated 100 years ago. The samples were analyzed with ATR-FTIR, SEM-EDX, XRD and neutron tomography. Alum salts are not uniformly absorbed within the wood structure and the elements Al, K and S are not evenly distributed within the alum-treated wood, indicating a decomposition of the salt. Reconstruction experiments simulating the original treatment demonstrated that at least one reason for the wood's high acidity is the high temperature used during the alum treatment. Alum is decomposed and releases sulfuric acid. Newly alum-treated archaeological wood is not as degraded as that from Oseberg, implying that the high acid content remaining in the wood after treatment will slowly degrade remaining wood components. The results of this ongoing project will be used as a foundation to develop a suitable preservation strategy for these unique finds.

Introduction

The consequences of past conservation treatments are becoming an increasingly important issue regarding the future preservation of objects. Damage and degradation caused by previous treatments provide challenges for conservators and conservation scientists, stimulating further research into deterioration mechanisms, possible stabilization methods and suitable re-treatment procedures.

The wooden objects from the Oseberg find, conserved over 100 years ago, may be considered a model case regarding the problem of historical conservation methods. The most deteriorated, waterlogged wood from this find was conserved by soaking it in hot concentrated baths of alum salts (aluminum potassium sulfate 12-hydrate). The objects were then restored from hundreds of fragments.

In the past decade, surveys carried out by several museums have shown that alum-treated wood is unstable and highly acidic (Braovac 2001, Child 2002, Lindahl 2006). One of the preservation challenges is that the wood that has been treated by what is today an obsolete method; we simply do not know enough about it. This paper will describe the original alum treatment applied to the Oseberg find, its present condition and suggest deterioration mechanisms by focusing on the origin of the acidity in the wood. Our understanding was increased by applying the 'Oseberg alum treatment' method to recently excavated archaeological wood and comparing it to that from the Oseberg collection. Analytical methods include FTIR, SEM-EDX, XRD and tomographic imaging using neutrons. The results of this ongoing project will form the basis for developing stabilization methods for the Oseberg finds.

1. The Oseberg find

The subject of this case study, the Oseberg find, represents one of the richest finds of wooden objects from the Viking Age. The objects, excavated in 1904 from a grave mound situated at the Oseberg farm near Tønsberg, Norway (ca. 100 km south of Oslo) were part of a burial ritual for two women of high standing. The burial was dated to 834 AD. The mound contained – in addition to the Oseberg ship and a number of metal artifacts and textiles – a collection of ornately carved wooden objects such as a ceremonial wagon, three sleds, and animal head posts which lay together with cooking kits, weaving tools and looms, agricultural implements and ship gear.

1.1 The alum conservation method

The wooden objects from Oseberg were recovered in a highly fragmented and waterlogged state. They were also in varying states of degradation, depending on wood species. Oak, yew and pine were the most well-preserved and could be dried without treatment. Other species, such as birch/alder and maple – which involved hundreds of artifacts – had to be impregnated before drying.

At the time of excavation of the Oseberg mound in 1904, several methods were already in use to conserve degraded waterlogged wood. After a study trip to conservation laboratories in Zurich, Copenhagen and Berlin, Gabriel Gustafson, the archaeologist leading the excavations, chose to treat the most degraded wood in hot baths of alum salts. This method was developed by C.B. Herbst in the 1850's and first applied to the highly degraded waterlogged wooden finds from Viemose, Denmark (Christensen 1970). The treatment gave acceptable results, and therefore gained recognition in museums worldwide (e.g. Rathgen 1898). The method was in use until the late 1950's when it was replaced by polyethylene glycols as an improved alternative. During the 100-year use of the alum method several variations are documented in older journals, including using different concentrations of the alum salt and the addition of compounds, such as glycerol (Christensen 1970, Brøgger 1917). At the Museum of Cultural History, it appears as though only the Oseberg finds were treated with alum, without the addition of glycerol.

Based on literature (Brøgger 1917, Rosenqvist 1959) and descriptions in archival material, the alum treatment used on the Oseberg finds involved immersion in large tanks of concentrated alum solution (aluminum potassium sulfate dodecahydrate), heated to ca. 90°C from 2-36 hours. The impregnation times can be generally related to fragment thickness. For objects greater than 1 cm thick, the average impregnation time was 24 hours. The solution penetrated the wood, where the alum salts recrystallized and supported the degraded wooden fabric, allowing the artifacts to be dried with minimal dimensional change. Maintaining the fragment's dimensions allowed the pieces to be fitted together. After treatment with alum, fragments to be reassembled were impregnated with linseed oil. Objects were reconstructed from the fragments using adhesives, metal screws, pins, fills and modern wood. The reconstructed object was finally coated with synthetic resins. Objects treated in this way include those with spectacular carvings such as the three sleds and the wagon now displayed at the Viking Ship Museum in Oslo, in addition to hundreds of smaller finds.

1.2 Consequences of the alum treatment

Recent collection surveys reveal an alarming situation. Many of the objects can barely support their own weight, new cracks and breaks are observed on their surfaces and inner cores lack structural integrity [1]. In addition, the wood is highly acidic (pH ca. 1).

Minimal penetration of alum salts (ca. 5 mm across the grain) at the time of treatment has resulted in mechanical weakness due to the formation of inner voids and cracks upon drying, only visible on X-ray images. The high concentrations of alum solution used (ca. 4.1M) have also contributed to the formation of interior collapse and cracking due to osmotic shock. The current condition of the Oseberg finds is comparable to that reported in condition surveys of alum-treated wood in collections in Denmark and Sweden (Jensen 2009, Sandström 2009, Lindahl 2006), including the low pH values. The source of acidity, however, has only recently been studied.

Here we present preliminary results of experiments elucidating the origin of the low pH measured in the wood, which also aids in understanding its current deteriorated state.

2. Experimental

Archival research and technical contemporary literature informed on how the finds were treated and the nature of chemical understanding at the time of treatment. Literature searches were complemented by reconstructing the alum treatment in the laboratory, which was applied to fresh wood and archaeological wood that was recently excavated. The procedure used was based on general contemporary descriptions by Brøgger (1917), but without the addition of linseed oil or lacquer. Variation of the temperatures and concentrations of alum salts relative to the published method were also investigated. The newly treated wood was then compared to alum-conserved wood from Oseberg, treated in the period 1904-1913. Chemical changes due to treatment were analyzed using ATR-FTIR. Elemental distribution within the wood was investigated using SEM-EDX on ashed and unashed samples. To study the distribution of alum salts in the wood, neutron tomography was used.

An alum solution at room temperature has a pH value of 3.5 – 4, whereas the Oseberg wood treated with alum solution has a pH of ca 1. To investigate possible sources of this high acidity alum salts were heated in both the solid state and in solution, simulating the original treatment. X-ray diffraction (XRD) was used to monitor the changes in the alum salts due to heating and to characterize decomposition products.

2.1 Sample description

The samples used in this study included fresh poplar, recently excavated archaeological poplar, alum-treated alder/birch from the Oseberg find and cellulose chromatography paper as a simple indicator for the released acid. Wood samples were identified by light microscopy.

The fresh poplar was taken from a reference set, measured about 1 cm^3 each. The archaeological poplar samples, originating from the Viking Age, were excavated in 2005 and stored in water at 4°C. Samples were cut into 1 cm thick discs from a branch 20 cm long and 3 cm in diameter. Each disc was quartered before treatment.

The samples from Oseberg used to compare with the archaeological poplar were identified as best as possible to be either birch or alder. They were treated with alum without the addition of linseed oil and originated from the same object, a weaving loom (cat.no. C55000/185). The samples are only from a part of the loom, and consist of six separate 'slices' that fit together. Each slice showed a distinct visible increase in deterioration relative to the one beside it. Based on archival information, it is assumed that the fragments were treated at the same time, but this is not certain.

The basic density of wood samples was measured by comparing the oven dried weight to the waterlogged volume according to Jensen and Gregory (2006). The average density for archaeological poplar was found to be 0.125 g/cm^3, comparable to that previously measured for alum-treated Oseberg wood (0.1 g/cm^3). Fresh poplar had a density of 0,436 g/cm^3.

Selected wood samples from Oseberg, fresh wood and archaeological poplar were ashed at 575°C for 30 hours to determine inorganic content.

2.2 Repeating the Oseberg alum-treatment in the laboratory

Treatment solutions with 2:1 and 4:1 parts by weight aluminum potassium sulfate salts (Merck p. a.) to distilled water were mixed. For each concentration, treatment was carried out at room temperature and at 90°C for 24-hours and then air-dried. pH values of the alum solutions and of treated woods were taken at both room temperature and 90°C (after cooling), using pH strips for the range 0-6.

Two samples of archaeological poplar were treated with each concentration – temperature combination (2:1 at room temperature; 2:1 at 90°C; 4:1 at room temperature; 4:1 at 90°C), totaling 8 samples. One sample of fresh poplar was treated in each concentration – temperature combination, totaling four samples.

2.3 Analysis of the alum-treated wood
Treated and untreated wood samples were analyzed using infrared spectroscopy (ATR-FTIR) and scanning electron microscopy with an energy dispersive X-ray analysis attachment (SEM-EDX).

Infrared spectroscopic measurements were carried out on a Perkins Elmer Spectrum One ATR-FTIR unit, containing a ZnSe/diamond hybrid crystal, at a resolution of 4 cm^{-1}; 32 scans and one spectrum were taken from each sample.

The freshly treated wood was sampled by removal of thin flakes from the radial face with a scalpel. The Oseberg wood was also sampled with a scalpel, yielding coarse crumbs. To avoid overlapping of bands from wood and sulfate groups, all alum-treated samples were rinsed in distilled water before analysis with FTIR in the air-dried state. No further manipulation of the samples, such as grinding, was carried out.

Untreated fresh wood was used as the reference for alum-treated fresh wood. However, due to the heterogeneity of the 12 untreated archaeological poplar samples, it was difficult to choose one as a reference for the treated archaeological samples. Archaeological poplar treated with alum at 90°C were therefore compared with those treated (with alum) at room temperature, since they originated from the same disc. Samples from Oseberg analyzed by FTIR were compared with spectra obtained from the newly treated samples at 90°C.

Inorganic elemental distribution was studied using a Jeol scanning electron microscope equipped with an Oxford detector system. An acceleration voltage of 20 KeV and a filament current of 80 mA was used, data evaluation was performed using Link software. Elemental distribution of ashed and unashed wood samples from treated as well as of untreated wood. Samples were taken from fresh wood, archaeological poplar and Oseberg objects.

Tomographic imaging using neutrons allowed visualization of the distribution of alum salts in a sample of alum-treated Oseberg wood. Imaging was carried out at the ICON facility of Paul Scherrer Institute (PSI), Switzerland.

2.4 Studies on change in acidity
Strips of cellulose chromatography paper were partly immersed in 4.1 M alum solution and heated to 90-95°C for 10-72h. Alum solutions (4.1 M) were also heated for 8-30 hours. XRD patterns of alum salts and crystalline precipitations were recorded using a Siemens D5000 powder diffractometer.

3. Results and Discussion
3.1 pH of alum solutions and alum-treated wood
At room temperature, alum solutions are acidic, with pH values between 3.5 - 4. The pH of cooled solutions which had been heated to 90°C had a broader range, from pH 0-2.5, regardless of start concentration used in these experiments. If we compare pH values of archaeological wood samples treated with alum at 90°C – the same temperature under which the Oseberg finds were treated – with that of untreated archaeological wood there is a large difference: the alum-treated archaeological poplar has a pH value of approximately 2.5, while the untreated samples had a pH value of 5 (untreated fresh poplar had a pH value of 4). pH values of the six Oseberg slices were similar (0,5-1) and did not reflect the variation in visible states of deterioration.

3.2 Repeating the Oseberg alum-treatment in the laboratory
According to experiments reported by various authors, wood samples treated with a 2:1 alum solution at 90°C, gave the best results in terms of dimensional stability upon drying and little change in color of the

treated wood (e. g. Brøgger 1917). Based on these observations, it is understandable that this procedure was chosen to treat the Oseberg finds, even though it leaves the finds in a brittle state (Christensen 1970). At room temperature for both 2:1 and 4:1 solutions, there was very little penetration of alum salts into the wood, which resulted in significant shrinkage upon drying. The 4:1 solutions at 90°C gave similar results as the 2:1 solutions (at 90°C) but there was more collapse that was visible, likely due to an even greater osmotic shock than for the 2:1 solutions.

3.3 Analysis of the treated woods

3.3.1 FTIR analyses of newly treated woods

After baseline correction and normalization to 1505 cm^{-1}, spectra from untreated and treated fresh poplar were compared (not shown). The alum-treated samples all show a slight reduction in absorbance at the band assigned to hemicellulose at 1734 cm^{-1} relative to sound poplar at all temperatures and concentrations. This is likely due to the hydrolysis of these polymers due to the acidic conditions created by dissolution of alum salts. Otherwise, changes are mainly seen in the C-O and C-H stretching regions, between 1185-925 cm^{-1}. The greatest difference between treatment temperatures occurs at 1031 cm^{-1}, where samples treated at 90°C have higher absorbances relative to the samples treated at room temperature. Bands at 1031 cm^{-1} are due to C-O stretches of primary alcohol (carbohydrate) and C-H stretches of guaiacyl lignin (Pandey 1999). The increase in absorbance may indicate that both lignin and carbohydrate oxidation have occurred.

For untreated archaeological poplar (Fig.1), the main constituent is lignin when comparing to band assignments from other studies (Mohebby 2005, Pandey 1999, 2003, Hedges 1985). There are likely carbohydrate remains left, but characteristic bands for hemicellulose (1734 cm^{-1}) and cellulose (1371, 1158, 897 cm^{-1}) are not prominant (Fig.1). A peak at 1122 cm^{-1} becomes visible in the archaeological poplar, which is only a shoulder in the fresh poplar. This peak is due to aromatic skeletal

and C-O stretches of lignin (Pandey 2003) which will become enhanced as carbohydrate content is reduced, as in this case.

Bands from untreated archaeological poplar was compared to that which was alum-treated after baseline correction and normalizing to 1505 cm^{-1}. However, Fig.1 shows spectra after basedline correction in split view, since it is easier to visualize in black and white. The archaeological poplar samples treated with alum at 90°C were compared with the sample treated at room temperature from the same disc. That is, 4A (2:1 alum: water at room temperature) is compared to 4B (2:1 alum: water at 90°C), where 4A and 4B originate from the same disc cut from the branch. The most notable differences between treatments at different temperatures occur in the C-O and C-H stretching regions of the spectrum. At 1122 cm^{-1} there is a slight increase in absorbance and at 1027 cm^{-1} there is a slight decrease in absorbance for samples treated at 90°C regardless of solution concentration.

Signals at 1122 cm^{-1} correspond to combined aromatic and C-O stretches from lignin, and bands at 1027 cm^{-1} are due to C-O stretches of primary alcohol (carbohydrate) and C-H stretches of guaiacyl lignin (Pandey 1999). As the carbohydrate content is somewhat depleted in the archaeological samples, it is assumed that the signal at 1027 cm^{-1} is mainly due to lignin.

The observed increased absorbance at 1122 cm^{-1} for samples treated with alum at 90°C implies increased oxidation (a greater number of C-O bonds). The decrease in absorbance at 1027 cm^{-1} may also be attributed to increased oxidation of the guaiacyl lignin at the C-H bonds.

Increased oxidation should also be reflected by a corresponding increase in the region between 1615-1770 cm^{-1}, if oxidized to C=O. However this is not observed in our experiments either because full oxidation to C=O did not occur or because the samples were washed before analysis with FTIR to remove alum salts (due to interference from sulfate groups), which may have also removed other components in the wood.

3.3.2 FTIR analyses of Oseberg samples

Each of the six 'slices' from Oseberg were sampled and analyzed by FTIR separately. Visual inspection shows that each slice gradually increases in deterioration relative to the one beside it, with slice 1 in the best condition, and slice 6 in the worst condition. This was also reflected in the FTIR spectra of these slices, but not in the same order as that ranked visually. In the spectra, the samples are collected into two groups: slices 1, 2, 3 were in better shape than slices 4, 5, 6.

All spectra were baseline-corrected and normalized to 1505 cm^{-1} before comparing bands. Figure 2 shows the spectra in a split view after baseline correction, since it is easier to visualize in black and white. As with the recently excavated archaeological samples, spectra of Oseberg wood are also dominated by signals from lignin. Characteristic bands for carbohydrates are more heavily depleted in all Oseberg samples (1734, 1371, 1159, 897 cm^{-1}) compared to untreated archaeological poplar. In the region between 1820-800 cm^{-1}, all Oseberg samples have much broader, less-defined bands than the newly alum-treated archaeological wood, indicating a general reduction in regularity of remaining polymer structures due to deterioration. Between 1820-1176 cm^{-1} absorbance by slices 4, 5, 6 is higher than that for slices 1, 2, 3. At 1712 cm^{-1} and 1701 cm^{-1}, new bands are present in slices 4, 5, 6, while slices 1, 2, 3 show the development of a band at 1712 cm^{-1}. Both 1712 cm^{-1} and 1701 cm^{-1} are assigned to unconjugated C=O stretches (Pandey, 1999) and their presence indicates that part of the remaining lignin exists in an oxidized state. The band at 1222 cm^{-1} in slices 1, 2, 3 is shifted to 1218 cm^{-1} in slices 4, 5, 6. The band at 1222 cm^{-1} is assigned to C-O stretches for both syringyl lignin and xylans (hemicellulose) (Mohebby, 2005), while that at 1218 cm^{-1} is assigned to C-O of guaiacyl lignin units (Pandey, 1999). As the

band for hemicellulose at 1734 cm^{-1} is not present, it is assumed that 1222 cm^{-1} is mainly due to syringyl lignin. This shift indicates the preferential deterioration of syringyl lignin relative to guaiacyl lignin. Syringyl lignin's C-O vibration is also represented at 1327 cm^{-1} (Pandey, 2003) and here slices 4, 5, 6 show a significant broadening of this band and greater absorbance, compared to slices 1, 2, 3. Band broadening here likely indicates deterioration of the syringyl structure.

At about 1074 cm^{-1} the absorbance of slices 4, 5, 6 becomes less than that of slices 1, 2, 3. The band at 1030 cm^{-1} shows a significant reduction in absorbance for 4, 5, 6. This is assigned to C-O of primary alcohols (associated with carbohydrates) and C-H of guaiacyl lignin. As carbohydrate signals are depleted, the absorbance recorded in the spectra are mainly due to the guaiacyl units. This reduction in absorbance in the more deteriorated slices (4, 5, 6) indicates that the guaiacyl lignin has undergone structural changes, which decrease the signals due to C-H. This may be due to the conversion of C-H bands to that of C=O during oxidation reactions, reflected in the 1712 cm^{-1} and 1701 cm^{-1} bands (Pandey 2003).

Generally, the spectra from the Oseberg samples show severe depletion in carbohydrate polymers and the remaining lignins have also undergone deterioration, where syringyl units appear to be more deteriorated than the guaiacyl units. Deterioration is in the form of both polymer breakdown products, reflected in the broadening of bands, and of oxidation products, seen at 1712 cm^{-1} and 1701 cm^{-1}.

Based on FTIR spectra, the slices can be divided into two distinct groups: slices 4, 5, 6 are more deteriorated than slices 1, 2, 3. This confirms the visual observation that as the wood darkens in color, it becomes more deteriorated. Darkening can therefore, in this case, be associated with lignin breakdown. The newly alum-treated archaeological samples are a light, wood-color, however over time, it will likely become as deteriorated as the Oseberg samples, and show an increase in darkening. Sample color, therefore, if recorded systematically, may provide information about extent of deterioration. More work in this area will allow for better correlation between condition measured by FTIR and visual observations.

Table 1 gives an overview of the main bands examined in the FTIR spectra. Wavenumbers from spectra in this study are given in parentheses when they differ from references.

Wave number (cm^{-1})	Assignment	Reference
1734	Unconjugated C=O groups in lignin and carboxylic acid ester hemicellulose	Mohebby, 2005
1712 (1701)	Unconjugated C=O stretch	Pandey, 1999
1665	C=O conjugated aldehyde and ketone	Stewart 1997
1650	Adsorbed O-H; conjugated C-O cellulose	Pandey, 2003
1592	Conjugated C-O; Aromatic skeletal vibration, lignin	Pandey, 1999
1502 (1505)	Aromatic skeletal vibration, lignin	Pandey, 1999
1462	C-H deformation, lignin + carbohydrate	Pandey, 1999
1425	C-H in-plane deformation combined with aromatic ring stretch; C-H deformation in carbohydrate + lignin;	Pandey, 1999
1371	Symmetric C-H deformation carbohydrate + C-H bending carbohydrate	Mohebby,2005
1330 (1327)	O-H in-plane deformation and C-H deformation, cellulose; C-O vibration syringyl lignin;	Mohebby,2005
1319	C-H vibration, cellulose; C$_1$-O in syringyl lignin;	Mohebby,2005
1226 (1222)	C-O xylan (hemicellulose), syringyl lignin	Mohebby, 2005
1218	C-O guaiacyl lignin	Pandey, 1999
1158	Asymmetric C-O-C vibration carbohydrate	Pandey, 2003
1122 (1119)	Aromatic skeletal and C-O stretch	Pandey, 2003
1112 (1102)	Glucose ring stretch	Pandey, 1999
1026 (hardwood); 1030 (softwood) (1028, 1027)	C-O primary alcohol (carbohydrate); C-H guaiacyl lignin	Pandey, 1999
898 (897)	C$_1$ group frequency in cellulose + hemicellulose; C-H deformation cellulose; Glucose ring stretch, cellulose	Pandey, 1999

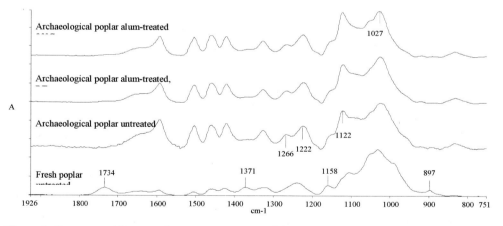

Figure 1. *Deteriorated lignin is the main constituent of the archaeological poplar, especially apparent at 1266,1222 and 1122 cm^{-1}. Characteristic peaks for cellulose (1371, 1158, 897 cm^{-1}) and hemicellulose (1734 cm^{-1}) are not visible in infrared spectra (FTIR-ATR).At room temperature, alum solutions have pH values 3.5 - 4. The pH of cooled solutions which had been heated to 90°C are more acidic, pH 0 – 2.5. At both room temperature and 90°C, alum-treated archaeological samples showed increased deterioration relative to untreated wood, with greater deterioration at 90°C, likely due in part to increased acidity.*

Comparing the Osberg samples to those from newly alum-treated archaeological wood (treated in the same way as the Oseberg finds), we find that the newly treated samples do not show the broadening of bands seen in Oseberg samples, nor do they show signals at 1712 and 1701 cm⁻¹ (Fig. 2 and 2b). This indicates that severe deterioration of the wood polymers due to the alum-treatment has not occurred. The newly-treated samples also have significantly higher absorbance at 1029 cm¹ than all Oseberg samples when normalized to 1505 cm⁻¹. Over time, however, it is postulated that this newly-treated acidic wood will likely become as deteriorated as the Oseberg samples, due to the acidic environment present inside the wood created during the alum-treatment at 90°C. However, why the alum-treated wood exists in such variable conditions, as seen with the six slices from Oseberg, remains to be investigated.

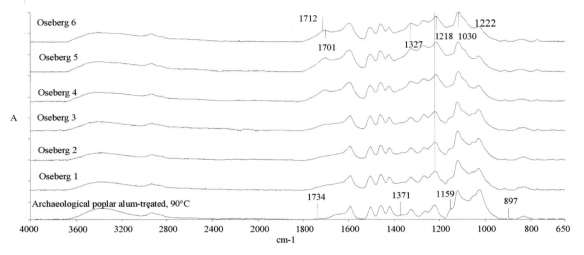

Figure 2. *Absorbance FTIR spectra of the six slices of Oseberg alum-treated wood show a gradual increase in peak broadening from slices 1 to 6. Spectral data generally correlate with visible deterioration, which also increases from slice 1 to 6. Sample 4B, newly alum-treated archaeological poplar is included for comparison.*

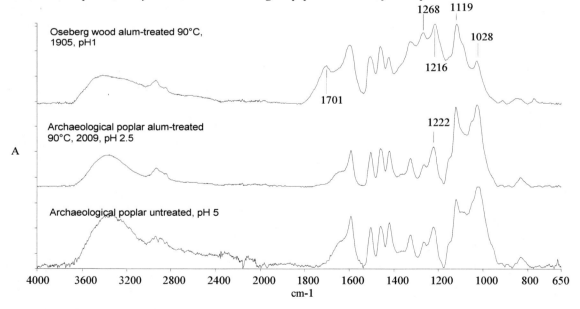

Figure 2b: *Absorbance FTIR spectra from a sample of alum-treated Oseberg wood, treated ca 1905, show significantly broader peaks than in the newly alum-treated archaeological wooden sample ('archaeological poplar alum-treated'), as well as a new peak at 1701 cm⁻¹, corresponding to an increase in oxidized lignin products due to its deterioration. Increasing band widths, especially in the regions of 1268, 1222/1216, 1119 and 1028 cm⁻¹ (shaded areas), correspond to increased degradation. The broad peaks in the Oseberg wood may be due to the long-term exposure of remaining wood polymers to the acidic environment in the wood, created during the alum treatment. Untreated archaeological poplar is shown as a reference.*

488

Although the mechanisms involved in the breakdown of alum-treated wood cannot be elucidated through these experiments, the effects of acidic-related deterioration over time which have caused the current state of deterioration of the Oseberg wood are clearly reflected in infrared spectra when comparing to newly alum-treated wood.

3.3.3 Ashed and unashed wood: comparison of inorganic content

The inorganic elemental content was compared between ashed and unashed samples of alum-treated wood using SEM-EDX. Samples of alum-treated wood that were washed out prior to ashing were also analyzed for elemental composition. It was found that ashed samples yielded greater weight % for aluminum than in unashed samples, shown by the decrease in the K/Al ratio from 1.4 to 1.05 (Table 2). Samples of alum-treated wood that had been washed out before ashing yielded a very high weight % of aluminum relative to potassium, shown by the decrease in the K/Al ratio in ashed samples. A greater number of other elements were also detected in washed, ashed samples. For example, in unwashed, ashed samples of alum-treated wood other elements include Ca, P, Cu, while in washed, ashed samples elements detected include Mg, Si, P, Ca, Ti, Fe, Cu, Zn. Washing out the wood prior to ashing has removed what is most soluble, which in this case seems to be the potassium, while the aluminum and sulfur remained in the wood. This may be due to the aluminum ion's affinity for lignin (Vance 1996) while still binding to sulfur. Ashing the wood exposes more elements to the electron beam by removing organic material that normally would shield it, resulting in an improved picture of the elemental content, since SEM is effective at the surface (and a few microns below it).

3.3.4 Neutron tomography

The distribution of alum salts within the wood is difficult to visualize due to its brittleness. Alum treated wood cannot be sliced without first impregnating with another medium, for example paraffin, and risking alteration of the sample. Tomographic imaging using neutrons is a non-destructive method of exploring alum distribution within a sample. The light areas on the image are due to attenuation of the neutron beam by hydrogen in the water associated with alum salts. As can be seen in Fig.3, the alum salts are not evenly distributed within the wood. The spatial resolution (ca. 40 microns) was not high enough to associate salt distribution with wood structure. However, the information obtained from the images confirms that alum salts were not evenly absorbed by the wood even on a microscale, and may partly explain the varying states of degradation observed in alum-treated woods.

Table 2 compares the inorganic elemental content of ashed and unashed samples of alum-treated wood. %weights are averaged from 3 spectra and are normalized to sulfur.

Sample	% weight Al	% weight S	% weight K	ratio K/Al
C55000-185-6, alum-treated Oseberg, unashed.	0.1	1	0.14	1.4
C55000-185-6, alum-treated Oseberg, Ashed.	1	1	1.05	1.05
Fragment 5, alum-treated, Oseberg, washed out, unashed	0.15	1	0.34	2.3
Fragment 5, alum-treated, Oseberg, washed out, ashed	0.75	1	0.12	0.16

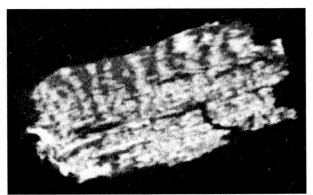

Figure 3. Neutron image of alum-treated wood Oseberg, longitudinal section (sample size:ca 1.5 cm). The light areas represent alum salts and the dark areas are archaeological wood.

3.4 The behavior of alum salts during heating

Alum-conserved wood from Oseberg exhibits a pH of ca 1, whereas a previously unheated solution of alum at room temperature has a pH of ca 3.5. The increasing acidity indicates that during treatment and/or during storage (additional) acid has been formed. To understand the source of acidity, the alum treatment as used on the Oseberg finds was applied to chromatography paper, which can be considered to be pure cellulose.

Strips of cellulose paper were partly immersed in an alum solution with a concentration as used in the original treatment (2 parts alum: 1 part water), and heated to 90-95°C. The part of the paper above the solution was blackened and destroyed, indicating the action of strong acid (Fig.4). This observation initiated a closer consideration of the effect of heat on alum salts in solid form and in solution.

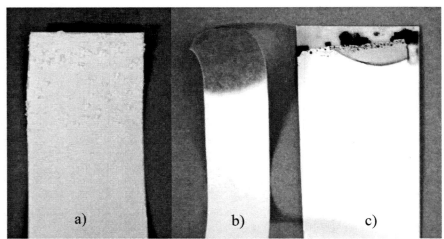

Figure 4. Formation of sulfuric acid by decomposition of alum is illustrated by the reaction with cellulose paper. a) alum-treated at room temperature; b), c) alum-treated at 90°C.

3.4.1 Heating of alum solutions
A solution with a concentration of 5g/50ml was heated up to 95°C for 30 hours. A white precipitate formed, which after drying was identified by means of XRD as potassium aluminum sulfate hydroxide, $KAl_3(SO_4)_2(OH)_6$ [PDF 47-1885] (Fig.5). The pH value of the solution after heating

had decreased from 3.5 to 2. What is the mechanism causing a decrease in pH after heating?

At room temperature, the dissociation of alum in solution can be described approximately by the net equilibrium

490

reaction (without considering the $SO_4{}^{2-}$ / $HSO_4{}^-$ equilibrium):

$$2KAl(SO_4)_2 + 3H_2O \leftrightarrow Al(OH)^{2+} + Al(OH)_2{}^+ + 3H^+ + 4SO_4{}^{2-} + 2K^+ \quad (2)$$

Heating the solution likely promotes the following reaction of precipitate formation:

$$3KAl (SO_4)_2 + 6H_2O \rightarrow KAl_3(SO_4)_2(OH)_{6\downarrow} + K_2SO_{4(aq)} + 3H_2SO_{4\ (aq)} \quad (1)$$

Precipitation of $KAl_3(SO_4)_2(OH)_6$ is quite a slow process; nevertheless, one has to take into account that the original treatment took up to 36 hours, and that the same bath was used for several treatments. This leads to an enrichment of aluminum hydroxide precipitate, which results in increased acidity.

Further investigations have to be carried out to evaluate whether aluminum hydroxide compounds cause changes in equilibrium over time by reacting with lignin or other wood components, which would result in an increase in acid content of the wood. The diffusion behavior of different aluminum hydrate and aluminum hydroxide species has also to be considered.

3.4.2 Heating of crystalline alum

As the salt concentration within the wood increases during treatment, it may be possible that the crystallization process already begins within the wood while it is still in its 90°C bath, if salt concentrations reach their saturation point. Therefore the effect of heat on solid alum salts should also be considered.

Heating of crystalline alum leads to a loss of crystal water. However, in the literature, descriptions of the dehydration process between 20 -100°C and identification of hydrates formed in this temperature range are inconsistent and contradictory. Aside from the maximally hydrated $KAl(SO_4)_2 \cdot 12\ H_2O$ and the water-free $KAl(SO_4)_2$, the existence of different intermediate hydrates, containing 3-, 4-, 6-, 7-, 8- and 9- water molecules as defined chemical species are given in different sources [2] (Müller-Erzbach 1888a, 1888b, Krauss 1929, Schischkin 1930, Kohler 1965).

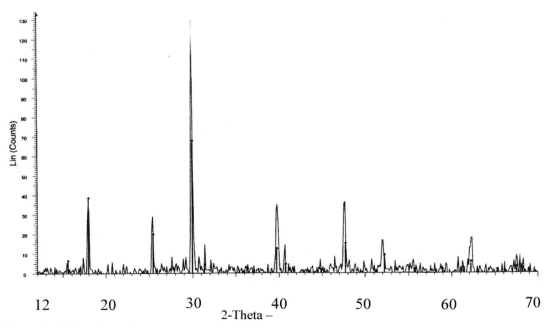

Figure 5. *XRD confirms the precipitation of $KAl_3(SO_4)_2(OH)_6$ from hot alum solution.*
Alum solution heated, precipitate
◆ Reference 00-047-1885 (I) - Potassium aluminum sulfate hydroxide $KAl_3(SO4)_2(OH)_6$

491

At 92°C alum melts and the remaining crystal water evaporates. 'Burnt Alum' (*alumen ustum*) is formed, a porous, amorphous mass, which was used as a drug in earlier times. Further heating leads to recrystallization of water-free alum, steklite $KAl(SO_4)_2$ (Vegard 1929).

Whereas the formation of 'burnt alum' and steklite is confirmed by our experiments, the question of the existence of different hydrates in the temperature range between 20 -100°C needs re-consideration. Initial XRD measurements indicate the presence of such compounds in alum-treated wood from Oseberg as well as from newly alum-treated wood made in reconstruction experiments. Knowledge of identity and properties of the salts existing in the Oseberg wood are important for the understanding of the behavior of alum-conserved objects in museums at different RH levels and under fluctuating climate conditions.

4. Conclusion

Because conservation using alum salts is obsolete today, details of the treatment procedure and their consequences have to be revealed through a combination of studying written sources, such as contemporary technical literature and laboratory journals, and laboratory experiments to reconstruct the historical treatment and to investigate its consequence. Although the alum treatment clearly gives good results in terms of dimensional stability and color, laboratory experiments also demonstrate the drawbacks of the treatment, such as brittleness and high acidity.

Neutron tomography images show an uneven distribution of alum salts. This may be caused by a different diffusion behavior of the various ions in the wood structure or reactions between wood compounds and the penetrating ions. Further studies are on the way.

FTIR proves that alum solutions, at both room temperature and 90°C, are capable of degrading cell wall material in archaeological wood and fresh wood. Extent of degradation is increased at higher temperatures, in this case 90°C, rather than at increased concentrations.

Greater differences are observed in FTIR spectra of newly alum-treated archaeological wood than that of alum-treated fresh wood, likely due to the fact that degraded wood is more susceptible to further deterioration. Specifically, the greatest difference in spectra occurs at 1028 cm^{-1}. It is suggested that the acidic milieu in the wood created by heating of alum solutions causes the oxidization of the C-H bonds of lignin, resulting in a decrease in absorbance relative to both untreated archaeological wood and that treated with alum at room temperature.

Comparing the newly alum-treated wood with those from the Oseberg find, FTIR analyses confirm that samples from the Oseberg find have even less little cellulose, and have a greater number of oxidation products. This is likely due to a greater degree of lignin oxidation from acid attack over a 100 year timeframe.

The inorganic elemental distribution was compared between ashed and unashed samples of wood using SEM-EDX. Analyses of ashed wood showed higher content of aluminum relative to potassium than in unashed samples. Ashing of alum-treated wood after washing out also showed a large increase in aluminum relative to potassium when compared to the washed out, unashed sample. This may be due to the polyvalent aluminum, iron, copper ions complexing with the cell wall material, such as lignin, preventing their removal during washing and which may not be accessible to the electron beam until the organic material has been removed by ashing. Possible reactions between metal ions and lignin are under consideration.

SEM-EDX analyses on unashed wood also showed that elements making up the alum salts, Al, K and S, are unevenly distributed in the wood, and may exist in different forms (potassium sulfate, for ex). This seems to be confirmed by XRD results; however, a lack of suitable reference data in the literature has initiated a still ongoing study on decomposition products of alum. Nevertheless, the initial results presented in this study show that 'alum conservation' does not mean that all the salts present in the wood are solely comprised of alum $(KAl(SO_4)_2 \cdot 12H_2O)$.

One species of an aluminum hydroxide precipitated from heated alum solution was identified by means of XRD analyses. During the treatment procedure, aluminum is likely partially precipitated as aluminum hydroxy salts in the solution vessel and inside the wood. Removal of aluminum by precipitation leads to an increasing formation of sulfuric acid. Heating of solid alum also leads to its decomposition and formation of sulfuric acid. Therefore, it is suggested that heating during the alum conservation treatment is one important reason for the formation of sulfuric acid. These results are in accordance with a study by Vance (1996) who stated that higher temperatures increase the reaction rate of the aluminum ion with water, forming aluminum hydroxides and hydrogen ions. Other mechanisms may also be involved but have not yet been identified.

Today's highly degraded condition of the Oseberg alum-treated wood may illustrate the effect of an acidic environment over a 100-year period causing breakdown of the remaining wood polymers, leading to a drastic decrease in mechanical strength (Hoffmann, 2002).

Further work has to be carried out to clarify whether the acid generated during treatment in alum solutions is the only source of acidity in the wood. This will involve characterization of the salts in the Oseberg wood (e.g. identity, solubility, hygroscopicity, pH sensitivies), and investigation of their behavior in the museum environment. If the salts prove to be stable in relation to the future stabilization procedures applied to the wood, it is not imperative to remove them,

mitigating a risky step towards the stabilization of these fragile finds.

Based on the knowledge obtained from further identification of degradation products and salts in alum-treated wood, the next steps will focus on testing possible consolidants and neutralization agents to strengthen and stabilize these finds to develop a sustainable preservation strategy. Retreatability is a criterion that will be used to assess treatments applied to the objects, to ensure future needs of the finds will not be compromised. An associated project aims in developing new materials, such as consolidants forming an open, airy structure in the wood, which would minimize weight and allow a future retreatment without removal of the consolidant. We hope that the results of this research will also be useful for treatment of waterlogged wood in general.

Acknowledgements:
This work was partly a result of the authors' participation in COST Action IE0601, Wood Science for Cultural Heritage. We would like to thank participants of this COST action for stimulating discussions. Eberhard Lehmann, Stefan Hartmann and Anders Kæstner, Paul Scherrer Institute, Switzerland, gave valuable guidance and assistance in performing neutron imaging experiments. The Department of Archaeology, Art History and Conservation, University of Oslo, provided access to their FTIR instrument. Mikkel Christensen (KHM), contributed with helpful discussions, and Helge Høeg (KHM) provided guidance in the identification of wood samples. We would like to thank all of them.

Notes
1. It should be emphasized that a relatively large proportion of the alum treated wood from the Oseberg find was fortunately surface-treated with linseed oil. In contrast to the powdery, disintegrating mass of 'wood' beneath it, this coating (which has penetrated at the most ca 5 mm across the grain) has ensured the survival of the finely carved surfaces, due to its consolidating

493

effect. Whether this coating proves to be a potential barrier to neutralizing and strengthening agents remains to be tested, but so far its preserving effect is unquestionable.

2. In 1929, Krauss et al. stated that publications on alum salts and their hydrates are '*außerordentlich zahlreich [und] sich oft widersprechend*' (very numerous and often contradictory) – this situation continues today. Powder data references exist in the ICDD data base, but they are marked as 'questionable'.

References

Braovac, S. (2001), An Evaluation of the Condition of the Viking Age Collections at the Viking Ship Museum. Internal report. University Museum of Cultural Heritage, Oslo.

Brøgger, A.W., Falk, H.J., Schetelig, H. (1917), Osebergfundet Bind I. Utgitt av den norske staten, Kristiania.

Child, N., (2002), From wood to what? From the Oseberg find: Gustafson's sled, Documentation of its condition and changes in its structural fabric and composition. UKM skrifter 1, 49-63.

Christensen, B.B. (1970), Studies in Museum Technology 1: The Conservation of Waterlogged Wood in the National Museum of Denmark, The National Museum of Denmark, Copenhagen.

Daniel, G. (2003), 'Microview of Wood under Degradation by Bacteria and Fungi', in Wood Deterioration and Preservation Advances in Our Changing World, ed. B. Goodell, D.D. Nicholas, T.P. Schultz, ACS Symposium Series 845, American Chemical Society, Washington DC, 34-72.

Hedges, J.I., Cowie, G., Ertel, J.E., Barbour, J., Hatcher, P. (1985), Degradation of carbohydrates and lignins in buried woods, Geochimica et Cosmochimica Acta 49, 701-711.

Hoffman, P., Schwab, E., Bonde, N. (2002), Report on strength tests performed on wood samples from the Gokstad Ship and boats, and from the Oseberg finds complex, and some observations on strakes from the Gokstad, Oseberg and Tune ships, Vikingskipsseminaret 14. og 15. februar 2002, University of Oslo, 71-85.

Jensen, P. (2009), Presentation at the Meeting of Scandinavian representatives from National Museum of Denmark, Danish Technical University, Swedish Heritage Board, Museum of Cultural History, Univ. of Oslo.

Jensen, P., Gregory, D.J. (2006), Selected physical parameters to characterize the state of preservation of waterlogged archaeological wood: a practical guide for their determination. Journal of Archaeological Science 33, 551-559.

Krauss, F., Fricke, A. and Querengässer, H. (1929), Über die Alaune des Aluminiums und des Chroms. Zur Kenntnis der Doppelsulfate und ihrer Komponenten V. Zeitschrift für anorganische und allgemeine Chemie 181, 38-54.

Kohler, K., Franke, W. and Henning, G. (1965): Der thermische Abbau einiger Aluminium- und Chrom-Alaune. Zeitschrift für anorganische und allgemeine Chemie 340, 68-74.

Lindahl, K., Sahlstedt, M., Sandström, T., Wikstad, E. (2006), Saving alum-treated archaeological wood – report from a research project underway. Delrapport för FoU-projektet Riksantikvarembëtet, Sverige.
http://raa.siteseeker.se/?q=alunkonservert+tre

Mohebby, B. (2005), Attenuated total reflection infrared spectroscopy of white-rot decayed beech wood. International Biodeterioration & Biodegradation 55, 247-251.

Müller-Erzbach, W. (1888a), Dissociation einiger Alaune und des essigsauren

Natrons. Berichte der Deutschen Chemischen Gesellschaft 21, 2222-2224.

Müller-Erzbach, W. (1888b), Das Krystallwasser des Alauns. Berichte der Deutschen Chemischen Gesellschaft 21, 3538-3540.

Pandey, K.K. (1999), A Study of Chemical Structure of Soft and Hardwood and Wood Polymers by FTIR Spectroscopy. Journal of Applied Polymer Science 71, 1969-1975.

Pandey, K.K and Pitman, A.J. (2003), FTIR studies of the changes in wood chemistry following decay by brown-rot and white-rot fungi. International Biodeterioration & Biodegradation 52 (3), 151-160.

Rathgen, F. (1898), Die Konservirung von Alterthumsfunden, Berlin, 135f.

Rosenqvist, A.M., (1959), The Stabilizing of Wood found in the Viking Ship of Oseberg, Parts I, II, Studies in Conservation 4, 13-21 and 62-72.

Sandström, T. (2009), Presentation at the Meeting of Scandinavian representatives from National Museum of Denmark, Danish Technical University, Swedish Heritage Board, Museum of Cultural History, Univ. of Oslo.

Schischkin, N. (1930), Wasserfreie Aluminiumalaune. Zeitschrift für anorganische und allgemeine Chemie 189, 289-296.

Stewart, D, Yahiaoui, N., McDougall, G.J., Myton, K. Marque, C., Boudet, A.M. and Haigh, J. (1997), Fourier-transform infrared and Raman spectroscopic evidence for the incorporation of cinnamaldehydes into the lignin of transgenic tobacco (Nicotiana tabacum L.) plants with reduced expression of cinnamyl alcohol dehydrogenase, Planta 201, 311-318.

Vance, G.F., Stevenson, F.J. and Sikora, F.J. (1996): Environmental Chemistry of Aluminum-Organic Complexes, in Sposito (editor), The Environmental Chemistry of Aluminum, 2nd edition, Boca Raton, Lewis Publishers, 169-220.

Questions and answers

Suzanne Grieve: This question is for Susan and Hartmut: did you find that the ion migration was affected at all by linseed oil or the lacquer that you said was used or was this a different sample from the sleds? And secondly, is there any concern in the future that the iron nails will act as an anode if this treatment is applied?

Hartmut Kutzke: So, this experiment was electromigration not with specimens from the Oseberg find but with samples from the Hjortspring find, and these fragments, these wooden fragments, were not treated with any lacquer or anything else. But I agree totally with you that the next step is to see how this lacquer affects the electromigration and if it can be applied to such objects.

4.10

Re-conservation of wood treated with alum in the 1920s – challenges and strategies

Inger Bojesen-Koefoed
The National Museum of Denmark, Department of Conservation, Archeology, Organic Materials, I.C. Modewegsvej,DK-2800 Kgs. Lyngby
E-mail: inger.bojesen-koefoed@natmus.dk

Abstract

This article deals with re-conservation of wooden objects previously conserved with alum. As derived subjects the ethical problem of re-conservation as well as the history of conservation is of interest. The initial practical work of packing the objects before re-conservation is described.

Keywords: Alum, re-conservation, history of conservation, packing.

Introduction

In the Scandinavian countries there is much focus on wooden objects previously conserved with alum. In Denmark we have during the last 40 years been doing a good deal of re-conservation of these objects. As the standard methods of conservation have changed, the methods of re-conservation have followed. When working on re-conservation it is not only the practical aspects of the work that occupy one, some related considerations inevitably arise.

The ethics

When working with re-conservation, it is inevitable to think about the concept of re-conservation itself. What allows one to interfere with our predecessors' work? In the development of conservation treatments each generation of conservators probably finds that its methods are better, and that the results are closer to the ideal, than the ones of previous generations - they probably are. However, conservators are hopefully also aware that they have not yet found the perfect method of conservation - the final solution.

It is important to remember that each generation does its absolute best. Our knowledge and our methods are based on the work of our predecessors and thus the stage of present knowledge could hardly have left out their experiences, we must remember to respect their work - even if we see defects and deficiencies in the conserved objects.

As the methods changes so do the looks of the conserved objects. The cultural history of any object is linked with tits excavation - and thus its conservation history. It is a part that cannot be removed but rather we should consider it as an extra dimension and I would urge that re-conservation is only to be done if absolutely necessary, if it is a prerequisite for the survival of the object.

In museums the objects are exhibited to the audience as representatives of the time during which they were created and used, for example from the Bronze Age, the Iron Age, etc. Finds from the same period, but excavated and conserved at different times are often shown together in the museum exhibitions (see figure 1) but unfortunately the audience is not told that the reason why the objects differ so much in character is because of the different times that they happened to be conserved.

497

Figure 1. To the left: Bowls from the Iron Age bog Viemose, conserved with alum in the 1860'ies. To the right: Bowls from the Iron Age bog Nydam Mose conserved with PEG 2000 and vacuum freeze drying in the 1990s.

A short history of the tradition of conservation in Denmark

The alum method was invented around 1859 and was used in Denmark for about a 100 years. It was the first method that managed to stabilize waterlogged wood in such a way that the objects, when dried, still looked like themselves. The method had some shortcomings, however. Shrinkage and collapse might occur and the surfaces of the objects could be dry and powdering. To avoid this, the conservators throughout its period of use tried to improve the method. From around 1900 onwards, attempts were made by adding increasing quantities of glycerol to the impregnation bath. This turned out to be a big step backwards and the disastrous consequences gave the whole method a bad reputation. But we must remember that using the alum method objects were conserved with fine results and it is the reason why we now have many fine objects preserved in our collection, which we would otherwise not have had.

In the 1960s when the alum method was replaced by full impregnation with PEG 4000, it was a major innovation in Denmark. The method was used for the conservation of the five Viking ships now exhibited in Roskilde, and the method was subsequently also used to re-conserve objects, that previously had been conserved with alum. In the enthusiasm for a new method one can be tempted to reject all the methods and results of one's predecessors, and thus the plan at the National Museum from the 1970s and onwards was that all objects conserved with alum should be re-conserved with PEG over time – no matter whether they needed it or not. The decision was so clear, that it was not considered as important for all parts of an object to follow along, the plan was the same for all, it was only a matter of time and number of processes before all the alum conserved objects of the museum would be treated. Fortunately the practice changed before it went too far for the following the reason. Today in the museum magazines there are objects where one half is conserved with alum and the other half is re-conserved by full impregnation with PEG 4000 - i.e. one part brown and one part black, see figure 2.

Figure 2. A stick from the Viking Age site Jelling, originally conserved with alum. The piece to the left has been re conserved. The alum salts leached from the wood and the piece full impregnated with PEG 4000. The piece to the right is still in its alum conserved condition.

498

Maybe we are no better in our approach today? Anyway, one can be tempted to do something about these black and shiny PEG treated objects when they are to be used in an exhibition. At least it has been proved possible to clean them so they turn from black to brown and from shiny to matte.

But the ideal of conservation in the '70s and '80s was that there should be a surplus of PEG on the surface of the object, it was the fashion of the time. Therefore, this was the ideal look of successfully conserved archaeological wood. Consequently, the ability to conserve implies the ideal of beauty in the conserved artifact. The joy of having found a new method changes aesthetics - and the archaeologists have nicely adopted it. Today you will meet many archaeologists who have difficulties getting used to our results of conservation using freeze drying.

The Hjortspring find

For the time being we are going to start a new process of re-conservation, Most of the objects currently being processed belong to the Hjortspring find. It is a pre-Roman Iron Age weapon sacrifice site dating from the 4th century before Christ. The find consists of an almost 20 meters long boat, weapons, tools and utensils. It was excavated in 1921-22 and conserved in the following years. This is a very important find in Denmark. The boat is the oldest plank built boat we have and the only one of the type seen on the rock engravings. When such a find turns up you naturally wish to improve your methods as much as possible.

Denmark's legendary conservator Gustav Rosenberg was the archaeologist, the conservator and the publisher of the find. As the result of many experiments Rosenberg improved the alum method by adding glycerol to the impregnation bath. Specifically, in the conservation of the boat more than 15 % glycerol was added to the alum solution. Rosenberg was fully aware that this required that once the conservation was finished, the objects should be kept in a stable and dry climate. Unfortunately, his recommendations were overruled and the find was put on exhibition in a damp cellar. After spending nearly 30 years in this exhibition area the find was almost destroyed. This is, I believe, the disaster that gave the alum method its bad reputation in Denmark. Most of the find was re-conserved in the 1960s by full impregnation with PEG 4000 and it is now on exhibition appearing with the character of full impregnation with high molecular weight PEG (see figure 3).

Figure 3. To the left, the Hjortspring boat on exhibition shortly after re conservation, to the right, details of boat timbers.

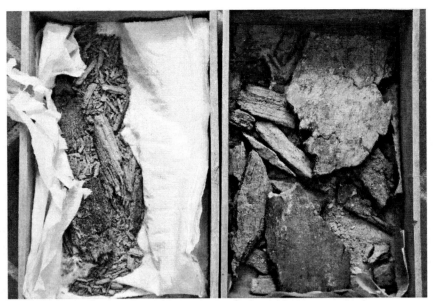

Figure 4. Alum – Glycerol treated pieces from the Hjortspring find awaiting re-conservation.

The task of re-conservation was huge and that is probably the reason why a number of smaller objects were left in their alum conserved state, and are now in urgent need of re-conservation (see figure 4).

The current process of re-conservation, the packing

Some parts of the find consist of hundreds of small fragments of shields, in a way you might say - these objects will never come to any use, but re-conserved they shall be.

The fragments are packed by welding inside perforated PE film only. Previous tests have produced fine results with this approach. The sheets with their many fragments are fixed by sewing onto perforated plastic boxes. Bigger objects and objects of more importance, especially parts of the boat, are wrapped in sheets of 2 mm thick rubber foam before being welded in the PE folio (see figure 5), in this case a folio with bigger holes in it.

Figure 5. The fragments to the left are packed in PE folio only, the fragments to the right are wrapped in rubber foam before welding in PE folio

Objects which are more difficult to handle are encased with cyclododecane before being handled at all. The layer of cyclododecane is added to the surface of the object and provides a brace which

makes it possible for it to be handled. The cyclododecane is either used melted or as a spray. The melted approach gives a much stronger and longer-lasting layer than the spray, but the conditions differ. On some

500

occasions it is good to have different alternatives to choose from. All the packed objects are put into perforated plastic boxes and are fixed to the box by sewing, so that nothing can float around. Depending on the depth of the vat in which the re-conservation is going to take place, a number of boxes are fixed together in a stack. The stacks are put in the vat, subsequently water is added and the leaching begins. When the alum salts have been removed, the objects will be impregnated with PEG 2000 gradually raised to a concentration of about 50 %. When the impregnation is finished, the objects will be vacuum freeze dried.

Identification

As circumstances are now, not only the objects themselves are in danger of getting lost but also their identity. Their numbers stamped in metal or written on labels and notes are also disappearing due to the glycerol and the alum salts, leaving the objects more or less meaningless. Some of the old numbers stamped in tablets of lead or iron/bronze from the 1920s can still be read, but some cannot. Those which cannot are X-radiographed to try to decipher their meaning. The pieces of paper are cleaned, put together and read - if possible, see figure 6.

Figure 6. To the left are two very degraded lead labels, to the right a deteriorating paper label in boxes containing pieces of alum conserved wood.

The 1920s

The boxes in our magazine filled with the Hjortspring find contain not only the objects; they also contain much archaeology - and conservation - history. The archaeologist and conservator Gustav Rosenberg published the find in 1937. In his book he describes in detail how the excavation and the conservation work were done. Reading his book you will find the words "lead numbers" and "metal numbers" and the ones in these boxes are the only ones which have survived until today.

We will in this re-conservation seek to preserve not only the wooden objects themselves but also what is left of the

excavation and conservation history. One can say: we will also seek to preserve the little that is left of what might be described as a spirit of its time, the "find – accessories", the once so common things – ephemera – that are not being used any more. For example a cigar box containing some small twigs found in the boat. Cigar boxes were in those days very common as a packing material - today only a few have survived, see figure 7.

The cigar box will be conserved by our paper conservator, together with all the written notes on paper and cardboard, while the metal numbers will be conserved by the metal conservators.

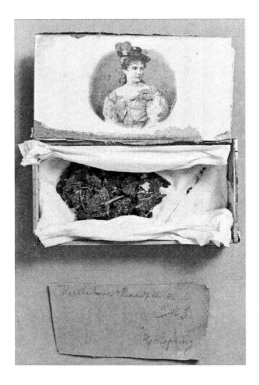

Figure 7. Original storage box and id label from the 1930s.

Another curious item to mention are the little bricks of Rosenberg's raw material for filling parts of missing objects - a mixture of rye bread and bees wax, which he had invented for the purpose. The common conservation practice of the time was to some extent to complete the objects where parts were missing. There are collections of the resin, once part of the caulking, which Rosenberg - for some unknown reason - removed from the planks. In some pieces of resin you can see imprints of the cords which once tied the planks together. In order to see a positive imprint of how the cords were tied, Rosenberg made castings in plasticine® of the negative imprints in the resins and these small casts are also preserved.

Conclusion

When looking at an object and working with its re-conservation, it is of vital importance not only to think of the period of time in which it was made but also to take into consideration when it was excavated and conserved. In regard to the objects from the Hjortspring find that are now to be re-conserved, we hope that they will look more as they did after their first conservation treatment in the 1920s, than those from the find that were re-conserved in the1960s. We further hope that the preserved "accessories" will be valued by the persons who will work with the finds in the future.

References

Herbst C.F., (1861), Om bevaring af Oldsager af Træ fundet i Tørvemoser, København, *Antiquarisk Tidsskrift* 1858 – 60

Rosenberg, Gustav, (1937), *Hjortspringfundet*, København, Nordiske Fortidsminder III

Accelerated Ageing of Recent Oak- Impact of Iron Ions and Oxygen on Mechanical Properties in Longitudinal Direction

Gunnar Almkvist* and Charles Johansson
Swedish University of Agricultural Science,
Department of Chemistry, Uppsala,
Sweden.
* E-mail: Gunnar.Almkvist@kemi.slu.se

Ingela Bjurhager
Royal Institute of Technology, Department
of Fiber and Polymer Technology,
Stockholm, Sweden

Iron catalysis in waterlogged wood

The Swedish 17th Century warship *Vasa* has faced a new challenge since it was salvaged in 1961. The present exposure to the atmosphere, corroded iron from bolts, nails, guns and cannons as well as sulfur compounds from sewage dumped at Stockholm harbor during 19th and 20th centuries all play a crucial role for the future of this unique ship (Almkvist and Persson 2008a).

Mechanical testing of the wood shows that the tensile strength of *Vasa* oak is generally lower compared to fresh oak. The two main explanations for this behavior are the changed wood properties due to the polyethylene glycol (PEG) treatment and the chemical degradation (Bjurhager 2008). The latter is highly correlated to the presence of iron compounds in the wood which implies that iron-catalyzed processes have taken place engaging reactive oxygen species, such as hydroxyl radicals (Almkvist and Persson 2008b).

Accelerated ageing

In order to mimic the wood of the *Vasa*, fresh oak wood was impregnated by iron(II) and iron(III) solutions followed by an exposure to different environmental conditions. After the treatment, the tensile strength of dog-bone shaped (see Figure1) samples (170 x 2 mm) were measured in the axial direction by an *Instron universal testing machine*.

Results

A reduction of the tensile strength was observed among all the iron impregnated samples after one week. The effect was significant when exposing iron(II) impregnated samples to air or pure oxygen. 39% decrease of the strength has been observed (see Figure 2).

A closer analysis by scanning electron microscopy-energy dispersive spectroscopy (SEM-EDS) showed that the iron compounds had accumulated in the same way as in *Vasa* wood on the cell lumina and cell walls (see Figure 3).

Untreated

Iron(II) impregnated

Figure. 1. The dog bone shaped oak wood in the untreated and iron treated format.

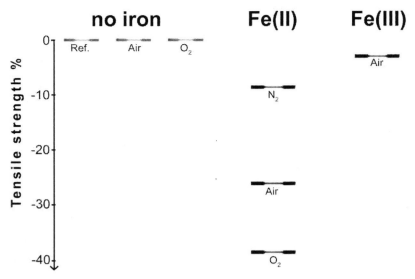

Figure 2. Reduction of tensile strength due to different treatment of the oak wood. A significant strength reduction was observed with those treated with iron (II) solutions and subsequent exposure to oxygen from 0 - 100

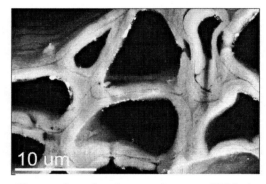 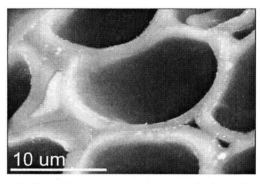

Figure 3: Scanning electron microscopy (SEM) pictures from Vasa (left) and iron impregnated recent oak (right). The light dots in the lumen and cell walls are accumulated iron compounds.

Conclusions

These preliminary results show that the iron compounds affect the strength of oak wood. The combination of oxygen and iron(II) compounds in organic materials has a devastating effect especially in the case of *Vasa* which is contaminated by iron compounds in ship hull. Nevertheless the crucial question remains: are the processes related to iron chemistry and their subsequent degradation of the wood influencing the mechanical stability and the future preservation of the hull?

References

Almkvist, G. & Persson, I., Holzforschung 62, 694-702 (2008a).

Almkvist, G. & Persson, I., Holzforschung 62, 704-708 (2008b)

Bjurhager, I. Effects of polyethylene glycol treatment on the mechanical properties of oak, Lic. Thesis KTH, (2008), Stockholm.

Acknowledgments

This project is part of The Swedish National Maritime Museums' research program "A Future for Vasa". Financial support from The Swedish Science Research Council (VR), The Swedish Foundation for Strategic Research (SSF), The Swedish Research Council for Environment, Agricultural Sciences and Spatial Planning (FORMAS), The Swedish Agency for Innovation Systems (VINNOVA) and the National Maritime Museums is gratefully acknowledged.

Removing Iron Compounds from a Waterlogged Wooden Gun-carriage using the Chelating Agent Diethylenetriamine pentaacetic acid (DTPA)

Ebba Phillips* and Inger Nyström Godfrey
Studio Västsvensk Konservering (SVK), Västarvet, Gamlestadsvägen 2-4, 41502 Göteborg, Sweden.
*E-mail: ebba.phillips@vgregion.se

Abstract

The use of DTPA has been studied as a method for extracting iron from degraded wood from the Swedish warship Vasa. The results have been promising, but the method has not been applied to waterlogged non-impregnated archaeological wood to any large extent. An opportunity to do this came with the conservation treatment of a 16th century wooden gun-carriage that started at Studio Västsvensk Konservering (SVK) in 2008. Today, the gun-carriage has been treated for 6 months in a 20mM solution of DTPA adjusted to pH 5-8. The extraction of iron has regularly been analyzed by the Swedish University of Agricultural Sciences (SLU) and a total of 2,4 kg iron, corresponding to 4,6 kg $Fe(OH)_3$, has been extracted so far.

Object

In 2008 a wrought iron gun with a 5 meter long wooden gun-carriage was lifted from the seabed outside Visby on the Swedish island of Gotland. The gun originates from the wreckage of the Danish-Lübeck fleet 1566 and it is unique due to its size, age and condition. The marine archaeological excavation was performed by AquaArkeologen within the Huma-project (Huma-Gotland website) and the gun was brought to SVK for digital documentation and conservation.

The gun is a complicated composite artifact. The degraded wrought iron gun had corroded to the oak carriage and was covered with thick marine concretions. The gun and gun-carriage had to be separated mechanically to make the conservation treatment possible. Both parts will be reassembled when the treatment is finished (Figure 1 and 2).

The average density of the wood in the gun-carriage is 0.44 g/cm^3 and the average maximal water content (Umax) is 160%. In other words, the wood is in relatively good condition. Microscopical analyses of the degradation indicate a very low surface degradation (<2 mm) caused by soft rot (Björdal 2008).

It was obvious that the wood was contaminated with a lot of iron and probably also sulfur; therefore four samples were taken for elemental analyses (ICP-AES) at ALS Scandinavia in Luleå. The sulfur speciation was determined by X-ray absorbtion spectroscopy (XANES) at MAX laboratory in Lund. The results showed that the wood was highly contaminated with both iron and sulfur and that the reduced sulfur compounds(iron sulfides and thiols) are dominating (table 1).

Figure 1. The gun and gun-carriage at SVK before treatment. *Figure 2.* Removing the crust of marine concretions.

Table 1. *Wooden samples analyzed for iron and sulfur. Different organic- and inorganic sulfur compounds were present in the wood and the dominating species are listed above.*

Sample / Analyses and depth in the wood	Fe (mg/g dry wood)			S (mg/g dry wood)		
	2 mm	10 mm	40 mm	2 mm	10 mm	40 mm
1: Rear end of carriage	9	-	-	23 $(S_8, R\text{-}SH)$	-	-
2: Area of powder charge	7	131	-	3 (S_8, SO_4^{2-})	183 (S_8, Fe_{1-x}, S)	-
3: Below gun barrel	197	57	37	92 (Fe_{1-x}, S, S_8)	8 (S_8, FeS)	3 $(R\text{-}SH, SO_4^{2-})$
4: Bottom, center (sample taken in-situ)	14	-		6		-

An extraction treatment to reduce the amount of contaminants was started, since research has shown that inorganic sulfur oxidate into sulfuric acid and an iron content above 1 mg /g dry wood can cause severe damage of the object in the future (Almkvist 2008).

To remove as much as possible of the inorganic sulfur compounds, the storage water was kept saturated with oxygen and changed every week during 17 months. This extraction treatment was not monitored, but the result of the treatment will be analyzed when the whole process is finished. The extraction of iron with DTPA started in September 2009

Iron removal
The chelate DTPA was chosen for the extraction treatment because it is meant to be more powerful than the more commonly used chelates, such as oxalate, citrate and EDTA. There is a lot of iron in the wooden structure of the gun-carriage and with a stronger chelating agent more iron should be more efficiently removed. Another advantage is that the solution, in the concentration and pH we use, is environmentally friendly and can be poured down the drain. This is quite an important factor, since about 5000 liter will be discharged. The drawback is that it is a new and relatively unproven method for treating waterlogged wood.

DTPA is produced by Akzo Nobel – Functional Chemicals and can be bought in a 40%-solution with pH 10. Based on a discussion about earlier research preformed at SLU (Almkvist, Persson 2006), a 20mM (1% w/v) solution of DTPA was used for the treatment of the gun-carriage. The pH was regularly adjusted with concentrated HCl and kept between 5 and 8. The treatment was performed in a 1000 liter tank with circulation and kept at room temperature.

The progress of the extraction treatment was monitored by regularly analyzing samples of the solution and the DTPA was changed then it was close to saturated with iron (20mM). The analyses were done by Dr. Gunnar Almkvist and Ph.d. student Charles Johansson at SLU. The iron and sulfur content in the wood will again be analyzed after one year of iron extraction treatment.

 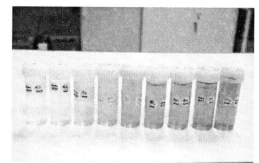

Figure 3. The gun-carriage in the treatment tank. *Figure 4.* The samples of the DTPA solution during 11 days of extraction

Results and discussion

Today the iron extraction treatment has been in progress for 6 months and a total amount of 2.4 kg iron, which means approx. 42mg/cm^2, has been extracted so far (the surface area of the gun-carriage is around 57000 cm^2). The speed of extraction has gradually slowed down. The first solution removed 1 kg iron in about 40 days, while the second solution removed the same amount in over the double amount of time. The curve in the figure 5 also indicates an even slower extraction rate in the third solution and the speed has totally been reduced by 73%. A reason for this is probably the initial removal of the easily accessible iron situated at the surface of the wood. Another reason could be that it takes longer time for the chelating agent to reach further into the wooden structure.

The efficiency of different chelates used for iron extraction is being studied at the Western Australian Museum (Richards, Kasi and Godfrey 2010) and SLU. If we compare their results for the DTPA extractions with our results they do not seem to correspond. More iron is removed from the gun-carriage than from the WAM and SLU samples in the same amount of time (table 2). The reason for this is probably the differences in shape, size and degree of contamination of the objects being treated.

The final result of the treatment of the gun-carriage has not yet been analyzed, but it is clear that a lot of iron has been removed and that the appearance of the wooden surface is much nicer than before. A positive result of the extraction treatment is also that the thin hard layer of marine concretions and corrosion products at the surface of the wood was partly dissolved and could easily be removed with a soft brush. Time consuming mechanical cleaning of the surface of the wood could thereby be much less.

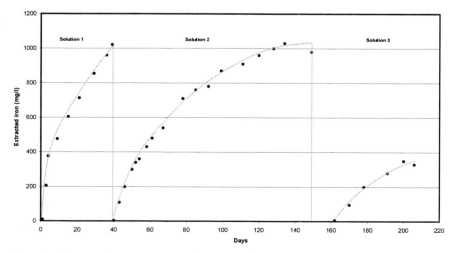

Figure 5. Results from the Fe extraction treatments. The DTPA solutions were changed when they were close to saturated with iron (20mM).

507

Table 2. *The amount of extracted Fe in mg/cm² in treatments performed by SVK, WAM and SLU*

Solution No.	Days of extraction	Extracted amount of Fe (mg/cm²)	Concentration and pH of the DTPA solution
1. SVK	38	17.9	20 mM (1% w/v) with pH 5-8
2. SVK	94	18	20 mM (1% w/v) with pH 5-8
3. SVK	45	6.1	20 mM (1% w/v) with pH 5-8
WAM	45	1.7	2% (w/v) DTPA with pH 6
SLU	45	3.7	20 mM DTPA with pH 9

Unfortunately, the extraction treatment of the gun-carriage has to be stopped after about one year. The reason is that the object needs to go on display and there are still a few steps, such as PEG impregnation and vacuum freeze drying, left to complete the conservation treatment. The amount of iron left in the wood will probably still be too high and could possibly constitute a threat for the long term preservation of the object, but the gun and gun-carriage will be placed in a controlled display cage with nitrogen gas, which will hopefully keep it stable.

References

1. Project website: http://www.magotland.se/eng

2. Björdal, C., Analyses performed at the Swedish University of Agricultural Science, 2008

3. Almkvist, G., The Chemistry of the Vasa – Iron, Acids and Degradation, Faculty of Natural Resources and Agricultural Sciences, Uppsala, 2008

4. Almkvist, G., Persson, I., Extraction of iron compounds from wood from the Vasa", in Holzforschung, Vol 60, 2006

5. Richards, V., Kasi K., Godfrey, I., (this volume) Iron removal from waterlogged wood and the effects on wood chemistry, in Proceedings of the 11th ICOM Group on Wet Organic Archaeological Materials Conference, Greenville, North Carolina, USA, 2010

End of theme 4:
General discussion on removal of iron and other inorganic compounds:

Shanna Daniel: I have a general question. Have there been any studies about the reaction of PEG after it has been freeze-dried with the iron? Is it stable?

Ian Godfrey: You are asking if residual iron causes problems for the PEG?

Shanna Daniel: Yes. Let's say you don't remove the iron and you freeze-dry it is there any reaction with the PEG and the iron even though it has been freeze-dried? Or is it stable?

Ian Godfrey: No, I think you need to remove the iron if you can because one of the problems and I think of the latest work that Lars Ivar Elding referred to that Tommy Iversen has done showing the presence of iron II in the inner regions on the wood and Fe II will catalyze oxidation reactions so you're going to speed up this oxidative breakdown, if you like, of cellulose probably also of PEG...so it will be a problem.

Ellen Carrlee: I'm wondering if the iron content of the soil can cause similar problems in wood?

Vicki Richards: It would depend on what form it's in. I haven't done a lot of work on that. Are you talking about land stuff?

Ellen Carrlee: Some of it is land, well stuff dug out of a river bank for example.

Vicki Richards: If they are there as iron corrosion products they will still be iron corrosion products, so it doesn't really matter where the iron's actually come from. It's still going to be a problem. There's Fe3+, Fe2+ and they cause problems with oxidative degradation of materials so I don't think it really matters. You'll probably get a lot less iron from a river bank than you will say from cellulosic

materials that have been subjected to iron corrosion products in the marine environment but it would still have the potential to be the same problem.

Henning Matthiesen: I just wondered... all the presentations we have heard about trying to remove the water or the iron. Has anyone tried to remove the oxygen? Either by storing in nitrogen or coating the artifacts? And have there been any studies where there has to be some solid?

Vicki Richards: We haven't.

Henning Matthiesen: Then another question for you about removing the iron. Do we know exactly what level is low enough? How low should we go? What's the safe level?

Vicki Richards: That's always the question. No, I don't know what a safe level is. I think with cellulosic materials maybe the lower the better, however with proteinaceous materials that have collagen in them, we've been finding and you'll see with Lars' talk and with some leather that we've done that we actually find that the iron can protect the collagen from degradation so then you have to find out what level is right. I think that would be another really good experiment to have a look at – to see what a safe level is if there is one. It's a bit like having chloride in your iron artifacts – what's the safe level of chloride? It's a great question – I can't answer it!

Lars Elding: It's also a matter of how deep the extraction liquids can penetrate into the wood for instance. I mean we say that we have chemical reactions taking place rather deep inside the wood but the iron extraction methods using EDMA or DTPA are active in the surface regions and maybe a few centimeters down but it's not yet clear how efficient they are in the deep timbers. You need very long extraction times – up to 30 months I've seen in some of the protocols for the DTPA or EDMA extractions in order to get good penetration. That's quite a hard treatment for the piece of wood at a pH level between 8 – 9. So the long-term efficiency of iron extraction methods using DTPA or EDMA is still an open question.

Vicki Richards: Yes, we're taking core samples and we're analyzing the total amount of iron in the outer regions versus the inner regions. It's just that the experiment is not finished yet. So hopefully we'll get more information about the penetration but my chocks aren't very thick either. They are maximum maybe 3 cm. So we're not talking about a timber that's 50 cm or so.

Anthony Crawshaw: Not so much a question as a comment – we had a log boat from the Bronze Age from a fresh water site that was extensively iron filled and I think it probably was because the log boat was lying at the layer where you've got a transition. So we've got an iron pan formed or heavy iron encrustations in this log boat. We didn't realize at the time but it was entirely fresh water.

Sarah Watkins-Kenney: Just one comment to add to this interesting concept of how much iron is safe iron. I think we also need to remember that it depends on the environment that it's going to go into afterwards because if it's going to go to an 80% RH environment then your level of iron is going to have to be a lot lower, whereas if you can be sure your levels are below the critical humidities for those chemical reactions to occur, then maybe your artifact can tolerate higher levels of iron. So, we won't really get a simple answer.

Emma Hocker: OK. It sounds as if we just have to take the whole life of the object into question when we treat it.

Vicki Richards: Anybody with any questions about any other burning subjects?

Kristiane Straetkvern: I just think it would be nice to conclude our discussion... When you look at today's presentations and those on the other days, I think Inger's presentation was really good because it told us how we have to be aware of what we do when we treat our objects. If we put something new into it or we try to remove anything, what's it for, what's the purpose? And I think it also came to my mind regarding the *Vasa*, what do you really want to do? Do you want to reconserve everything? You said there was a difference between the smaller objects and the ship. And I think it's the same sort of situation with the Oseberg. How do we decide what to reconserve and how to do it? Do any of you have comments on that?

Hartmut Kutzke: To answer your question – some thought about this concerning the Oseberg project. The situation is that we do know we have Alum treated wood, the consequences and the possibility of reconservation and so the aim of our electro project is not to find the only one solution but to evaluate different options and then decide what is the best conservation strategy and this way may not be the same for all objects. We are in a research stage where we have to find out what are actually options and as you saw in Susan's presentation it's the same as the *Vasa*. It's not only the wood, it's the metal, it's the lacquering and all this and how it interacts. So there is a lot of basic research before we come to the stage of deciding what we want to do.

5.1 (Sc. PR)

A New Approach to Excavating and Handling Waterlogged Textiles from the American Civil War Submarine *H.L. Hunley*

Johanna Rivera*, Maria Jacobsen, Paul Mardikian ,and Michael Scafuri
Warren Lasch Conservation Center. School of Materials Science and Engineering. Clemson University. 1250 Supply Street. North Charleston, SC 29405. USA.
*E-mail: jrd123@clemson.edu.

Philippe de Vivies
A-Corros expertises. 23 Chemin des Moines. 13200 Arles. France.

Abstract

During excavation of the American Civil War submarine *H.L. Hunley*, archaeologists uncovered skeletal remains of the eight-man crew along with fragile, waterlogged fragments of their clothing and personal possessions. Due to their fragility, the textiles could not be excavated *in situ*, but were instead block lifted and brought to the laboratory for documentation and excavation. Most of the block lifts removed were composite in nature and contained a combination of textiles, skeletal remains, and other artifacts. This paper addresses the methodologies used to document and handle the blocks in general, describes the immersion technique developed to excavate them, and presents in detail how the textile remnants in one particular block were further processed.

Keywords

H.L. Hunley, block-lift excavation, immersion technique, waterlogged textile.

Introduction

On February 17, 1864, the Confederate submarine *H.L. Hunley* sank off the coast of Charleston, South Carolina. The hand-cranked submarine and her ill-fated crew vanished that night and remained lost for well over a century. In 1995 the *H.L. Hunley* was discovered, subsequently raised, and brought to the Warren Lasch Conservation Center. This laboratory was specifically designed to accommodate the excavation and conservation of the submarine and its associated artifacts (Mardikian 2004, Conlin 2005). This 12-meter-long time capsule from the American Civil War represents a unique find in the fields of maritime archaeology and conservation. In the years following recovery, a multi-disciplinary team excavated the interior of the submarine and uncovered skeletal remains of the eight-man crew along with fragile, waterlogged fragments of their clothing, personal belongings, and miscellaneous boat gear. The waterlogged textiles were found to be too fragile to handle or excavate *in situ*. For this reason, most of the textile material was lifted in blocks, along with associated artifacts and the surrounding sediment, and brought into the clean lab for documentation and excavation (Jacobsen 2005). A total of 49 block lifts were removed from the interior of the hull.

Laboratory Setting

Immediately after recovery the *H.L. Hunley* was transported to the Warren Lasch Conservation Center and placed in a large tank filled with refrigerated tap water and stabilized with an impressed-current protection system (see Figure 1). This was done to minimize corrosion of the metal components and avoid the use of any chemical corrosion inhibitor that might adversely affect any organic content of the submarine such as human remains, fabrics, wood, and leather items (Mardikian 2004). Before the excavation of the crew compartment started, the laboratory and equipment needed for the excavation were prepared in advance and a protocol was developed to document and handle human remains and artifacts (Neyland 2000).

Removal of four plates along the top of the hull provided access to the interior and revealed that the submarine was completely filled with sediment. During the excavation of the crew compartment (see Figure 2), the disarticulated skeletal remains of the crew were exposed and found to lie along the bottom of the compartment intermingled with remnants of their garments, artifacts, and boat gear. The scenario was somewhat different in the forward part of the crew compartment where the remains of the commander Lt. George E. Dixon were located. His body was found in a semi-articulated state and a good portion of his garments were still located on and around his skeleton.

Figure 1. *H.L. Hunley submarine in its conservation tank (©FOTH)*

Figure 2. *Senior archaeologist Maria Jacobsen and conservator Philippe de Vivies excavating the Hunley's crew compartment.*

Block Lift Assessment and Methodology
Once the first remnants of waterlogged textiles were exposed, it was clear that they were too fragile to be manipulated and separated from the human remains. They could, therefore, not be excavated *in situ*. Those remains were mapped and block lifted to be documented and excavated in a more controlled laboratory setting (Jacobsen 2005).

The block-lifting technique consisted in probing the sediment using wood skewers and dividing the blocks along major bones groups and artifacts. Galvanized steel plates were slid under the blocks and used to separate each block from the rest of the sediment. Each block was delineated and treated differently based on a case-by-case decision. In all, 49 sediment blocks supported by metal plates and wrapped in translucent polyethylene film were removed from the crew compartment; of these, eight contained the remains of Lt. Dixon (see Figure 3).

The first critical step in handling these blocks was to ensure their safe transport from the submarine to the laboratory. The wrapped blocks were raised from the excavation tank onto the mezzanine, the staging area attached to the edge of the tank, using a tray suspended from an overhead crane. A scissor lift was then used to lower the trays to floor level and onto a trolley to carry them to the lab. Once in the lab, the blocks were stored in containers filled with water to 4°C in a walk-in cooler.

All the blocks were x-rayed using digital radiography. Each block was analyzed to map the position of the human remains and artifacts. This critical assessment provided a road map for the excavation and proved to be the imaging technique of choice to analyze and excavate this material (Mardikian 2004) (see Figure 4)

At this stage, a number of the more complex block lifts were transported to the Medical University of South Carolina for Computer Tomography (CT) scanning (Jacobsen 2005). The CT images provided a good three-dimensional picture of the layout of the skeletal remains but the CT technology was not always adapted to imaging the very dense metallic objects that were sometimes imbedded in some of the blocks.

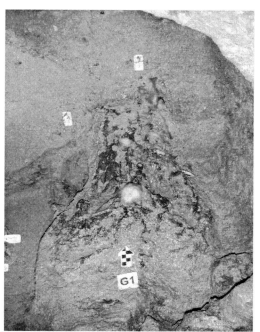

Figure 3. Remains of Lt. Dixon in the submarine prior to block-lifting. Details of his torso and the textile draped over it. (©FOTH)

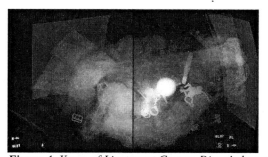

Figure 4. X-ray of Lieutenant George Dixon's lower torso. The image shows block lift 36 and 37 after removal from the submarine. Artifacts such as a pocket watch, a pocket knife, suspender buckles, and buttons were identified. (©FOTH)

In order to understand the matrix in which the human remains were buried the sediments were analyzed and they were found to range from silt to very fine silty sand with traces of organic detritus and finely disseminated carbonates (Harris 2009). In addition, sediment samples were taken for bacteriological analysis by Mary Ballard, senior textile conservator at the Smithsonian's Museum Conservation Institute (MCI). Fortunately, no infectious bacteria were found in the sediment from the *Hunley* (Ballard 2001).

Development of an Immersion Technique to Excavate Block Lifts

The scientific team was requested to recover the skeletal remains of each crew member in a timely manner, to conduct a forensic study, and eventually rebury the remains of the crew. However, the degraded fabric was somewhat of a limiting factor during the excavation of the skeletal remains. Unfortunately, there was no known precedent or reported technique that could have been applied to the excavation of the blocks. Attempts to manipulate waterlogged textile out of the water and to remove the bones proved to be next to impossible and very destructive. As a consequence, conservators had to develop a less invasive approach to excavate the blocks without literally destroying them. (see Figure 5).

The team noticed that the sediment would slowly dislodge without disturbing the fragile fabric when the block is placed in a gentle flow of running water. A number of ideas were discussed on the way to improve this cleaning effect using, in a certain manner a modified underwater excavation techniques. When nautical archaeologists excavate a shipwreck the waterlogged timbers are exposed by hand-fanning over the burial matrix suspending the sediment particles in the water column above the timbers. The suspended sediment is then sucked away with an airlift or dredge. This same principle was utilized here in a scaled-down version.

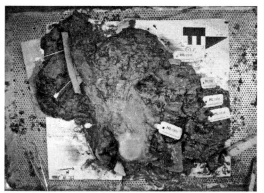

Figure 5. Lt. Dixon's Block Lift prior to excavation in water. (©FOTH)

513

Each block selected for excavation was placed in a tray in the bottom of a translucent-white polyethylene vat. The vat rested on a sturdy table with wheels for added mobility (see Figure 6). The vat was slowly filled with tap water until approximately 15 cm above the block. A clamped hose connected to the city water supply, was attached to the vat and used to keep the water level constant at all times. The plastic wraps encasing the exposed face of the block lift were carefully cut away and the exposed block was photo documented (through the water) prior to the start of the excavation. Articulated lights were positioned in such a way that would not create glare. The photographs were taken with a Nikon® D60 digital camera manually focused so the block could be photographed through the surface of the water.

A water-filled syringe fitted with a long needle was used to generate a gentle water current over the exposed surface of the block. Sediments suspended in the water were siphoned off with a half-inch clear polyvinyl chloride vacuum hose. Once the initial suction was established in the water-filled hose, it was kept primed by having the other end of the hose attached to a screen near the floor drain (i.e. at a lower elevation than the excavation vat). The level of suction through the hose was regulated by pinching the tube. With this simple but effective technique the sediment was gradually dislodged from the block revealing the fragile remains.

Excavation Phase One: Documentation and Removal of Human Remains and Artifacts

The objectives of the first phase of the block lift work were to excavate, document and remove any human remains and artifacts contained within the blocks. The project's overseeing authority, the South Carolina Hunley Commission, had decided that the identification of the crew and repatriation of their remains would be a priority. Therefore, block lifts that contained skeletal remains were selected first for excavation. Using the immersion technique described above, the excavators would remove the overburden of sediment and gradually expose remnants of waterlogged textiles, skeletal remains, and other artifacts. Stainless steel pins were used to secure the unfolded layers of fabric while excavating. The entire process was documented with sketches and photographs. Any exposed objects were then mapped *in situ* using a 3D point mapping system (Scafuri 2005, Jacobsen 2007). This system allowed archaeologists to reconstruct the position of artifacts found within the blocks and place them in a three-dimensional Rhinoceros-based site plan (see Figure 7). Hundreds of skeletal remains and artifacts were thus documented and removed. Among the most important personal possessions found in the blocks were those associated with Lt. Dixon's semi-articulated torso. They included field glasses, a folding ruler, a pocket knife, a diamond ring and brooch, a gold pocket watch, suspender buckles and miscellaneous buttons.

Figure 6. *Senior conservator Paul Mardikian and Philippe de Vivies excavating one of the blocks. (©FOTH)*

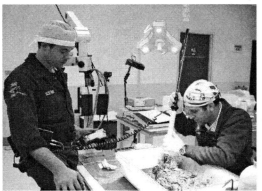

Figure 7. *Archaeologists Michael Scafuri (left) and Shea McLean mapping artifacts using the Vulcan Measurement System. (©FOTH)*

Following the removal of the skeletal remains and artifacts from the exposed half of the block, a fiberglass protective mold was put in place to support the block and allow for turning the block over. To accomplish this task, the excavating tank was drained. Polyether foam was used to fill the gaps produced due to the artifact removal. A transparent film (clingy polyethylene film) was used to cover the surface of the block in multiple layers, followed by a fiber glass wrap for added support (DuraPower Inc., Pipe and Hose repair kit). This long fiberglass tape (10 cm wide), impregnated with polyurethane resin, was moistened with water to activate the resin and laid on the block. The block was wrapped several times with the tape overlapping. The resin cured in an hour providing a rigid form-fitting support to the block. Once cured, the block could be turned over and the excavation continued in the other side. There are not major safety concerns associated with the resin. The use of gloves is highly recommended.

Once all skeletal remains and artifacts were removed from the block all that remained were the waterlogged textiles. These textile blocks were then rewrapped and stored in a water-filled tank in the cooler. Further processing of the textile blocks resumed in 2006.

Excavation Phase Two: Handling of Waterlogged Textiles from Block Lift 36, a case study.

Working with waterlogged textiles is problematic as these materials are often in a severe state of physical and chemical degradation (Peacock 2005). This was the case with most of the textiles recovered from the *H.L. Hunley*. Due to the decomposition of the crew member's bodies, the environment inside the submarine was very aggressive to textiles. In particular, it was observed that cotton fibers had hydrolyzed to such an extent that they were not retrievable. Only two samples of cotton were positively identified on the *H.L Hunley*: one sample in block lift 36 and one in a ferrous concretion from the hull. Enzymatic hydrolysis as well as fungi and

cellulose-digesting bacteria are known to participate in the breakdown of cotton fabrics in such an environment (Peacock 2005). Proteinaceous materials such as wool have shown to survive better than cellulosed-based materials and are the most abundant textile materials retrieved from the submarine

Figure 8. Top image: creating a fiber glass support. Bottom image: surface of the block lift wrapped in fiber glass tape (©FOTH).

Excavation of block lift 36 (Dixon's block) revealed three types of fabric-like materials: a finely, woven brown-black wool, a very thin reddish colored fabric, and thick fragments of a pink material scattered throughout the block. The initial assessment of block lift 36 indicated that the brown-black wool was the major constituent of the textile block (see Figure 9). This material was identified as cashmere using a Scanning Electron Microscope (SEM) and a Fourier Transform Infrared Microscope (FT-IR) (Ballard 2001).

The wool was so severely degraded that it could not support its own weight out of the water. Based on the results of the

515

Smithsonian's sediment and fiber analysis by culturing and SEM (Ballard 2001), it was confirmed that wool had suffered bacterial degradation. In addition, iron corrosion products and a number of mineral contaminants in the wool fibers apparently contributed to its decay (Ballard 2001, Rivera 2009).

During the excavation of this block lift it was determined that the wool could be easily manipulated underwater using brushes without damaging the fabric. Thanks to this technique it became possible to expose, document, and safely remove small and large fragments of textile (see Figure 10). Mylar©, a polyester film, was the only material found to be helpful in supporting the fragments as they were lifted from the block. Mylar was flexible enough to slide underneath the textile, strong enough to lift it and did not float in the water during this process.

Figure 9. Block Lift 36, resting in the fiber glass support, was mainly comprised of cashmere wool. (©FOTH)

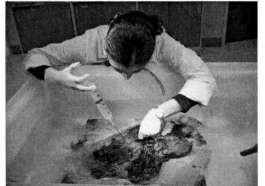

Figure 10. Conservator Johanna Rivera excavating Lt.Dixon's textiles. (©FOTH)

During removal of the wool fragments dozens of long pink threads were revealed. The threads ran diagonally across the block and did not appear to be woven fibers. Analysis using SEM and FT-IR revealed that these were rubberized materials belonging to Dixon's suspender straps (Mardikian 2006). The fabric that previously held the rubberized threads in place had completely disintegrated leaving behind only the rubber strings with the imprint of the original fiber.

Lifting of the rubberized strings was a very difficult task as the strings were brittle. Each string was approximately 30 cm long and covered by a textile mass. The first step was to "open up" and unfold the textile covering the strings to gain better access to the underlying strings. During this process, netting (tulle), polyether foam and stainless steel pins were used to keep the wool layers open and aligned with the suspenders. Circular Mylar tags were cut and slid under the suspenders to separate them from the rest of the block (see Figure 11). The suspenders were then lifted, placed in refrigerated water, and covered with a black film.

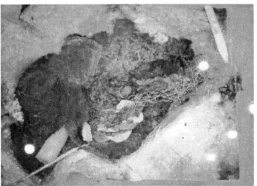

Figure 11. Rubberized strings being lifted using Mylar tags. (©FOTH)

After the removal of the suspenders from the block, very degraded reddish woven fragments were revealed (see Figure 12). A decision to lift these fragments was made knowing that greater damage would occur if they were left in place during the rest of the excavation. All the fragments were removed using the techniques previously mentioned, resulting in some unavoidable

516

further disintegration. It was noticed that, upon exposure to light, these fragments would fade and change from a bright red to a dark brown.

Figure 12. *Reddish material was uncovered during the sediment removal (©FOTH)*

Following excavation, the reddish-colored fabric was subjected to material analysis (see Figure 13). A sample was air-dried and examined using SEM and FT-IR. During the drying process, however, this specimen exhibited an unusual drying pattern. It shrank by almost 50% and an organic film covered the surface of the textile obscuring the underlying fibrous matrix. It was hypothesized that the presence of the film and unusual degradation pattern of the textile may be due to the presence of adipocere (hydrolyzed fatty tissue) from Dixon's remains. This may have contaminated the fibers (Jacobsen 2008) and resulted in an accelerated bacterial activity. Due to these problems it has not been possible to make a positive identification of this material yet or stabilize it in any manner other than keeping it waterlogged and refrigerated (Rivera 2009).

As the excavation continued on the reverse side of the block one large piece of wool was revealed (see Figure 14). Using soft brushes the piece of the wool was carefully unfolded and laid flat. As work progressed the remains of a vest were revealed. All the edges and stitches became clearly visible indicating that this was the inside surface of the vest. In addition, a large opening across

the vest appeared to be the hole of a pocket (see Figure 15).

Figure 13. *Photomicrographs of a sample from the reddish material at a 150x magnification. The main image shows the wet sample. The top right image shows the sample after drying. (©FOTH)*

Figure 14. *Unfolding of Dixon's Block Lift 36. (©FOTH)*

The vest consisted of three layers of fabric: an outer panel, an interior layer or padding (that was very degraded and without cohesion) and lining. While most of the sediment covering the vest was removed using the immersion technique, the very fine sediment that had penetrated the waterlogged fibers and yarns of the fabric could not be removed with this technique. A decision was made to remove the interior fabric since it was otherwise impossible to eliminate the sediment trapped between the layers. Although some stitching was observed on the surface of the vest, these were not found to penetrate the rest of the layers.

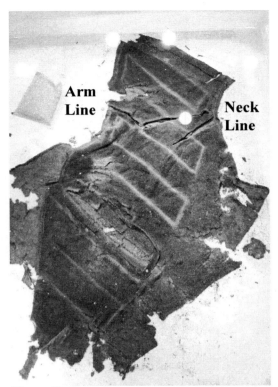

Figure 15. Vest after removing most of the surface sediment. The pattern of a rectangular stitching and a pocket can be seen. (©FOTH)

Since the exterior panel of the vest appeared to be in better condition, fine gauze was placed on top of it and the textile rolled back until the interior layer could be examined. This layer was then lifted, stored separately and the exterior panel of the vest placed back in its original position. Small fragments of wool and red textile, which became detached during this process, were also removed. The vest remnants were lifted using large Mylar sheets, gauze, and a glass support and were transported to another container. The transfer of the vest was necessary to begin the process of cleaning and conserving the fabric.

Of the materials recovered from block lift 36, the brown-black wool was the only fabric that could withstand the subsequent cleaning process. The rest of the materials were so severely degraded that they could not be cleaned any further.

Much work remains to be done on the *Hunley* textiles. Only a portion of the blocks have been excavated, cleaned and stabilized. The full identification of the different fibers found in Dixon's blocks, as well as the conservation techniques used to clean and stabilize the textiles have been reported (Rivera 2009).

Conclusion

Waterlogged textiles recovered during the excavation of the crew compartment of the *H.L. Hunley* submarine, were found combined with skeletal remains and were so severely degraded that they could not be excavated and manipulated using traditional excavation techniques. Instead, these remains were block lifted so the excavation could continue in the laboratory in a controlled environment. An interdisciplinary team developed a series of techniques that enabled them to document and excavate the blocks successfully. The immersion technique allowed the excavators manipulate the textiles underwater while keeping the water clear. This facilitated photography and viewing of the fabrics and associated objects during the entire excavation process. In addition, handling and air drying were minimized as the textiles were kept waterlogged at all time and were efficiently cleaned and manipulated by brushes without damaging the degraded textiles. Providing the blocks with fiberglass shells was also an important tool for containing the materials and retaining their shape during the excavation and turning over of the blocks. The added benefits of the system are that the set-up is relatively cheap and quite flexible. It can be moved around the laboratory if needed and can be easily adjusted to fit specific needs (by changing vat sizes). These techniques specifically designed for the handling of the textiles from the *Hunley* may be useful to other projects facing similar challenges.

References

Ballard M., (2001), Personal communication, Smithsonian Center for Materials Research and Education, Museum Conservation Institute, Washington DC.

Conlin D.L., (2005), USS Housatonic Site Assessment, Underwater Archaeological Branch, Naval Historical Center, Washington, DC.

Harris S., (2009), Personal communication, Department of Geology and Environmental Geosciences, College of Charleston, Charleston, South Carolina.

Jacobsen M., (2005), H.L. Hunley Project: 2004 Archaeological Findings and Progress Report, Department of Defense Legacy Resource Management Program, Project 04-106, 2005, pp 1-18.

Jacobsen M., (2007), Strategies and Mapping Techniques Used to Reconstruct and Interpret the American Civil War Submarine H. L. Hunley, in 35th Annual Conference of Computer Applications and Quantitative Methods in Archaeology, Layers of Perception: Advanced Technological Means to Illuminate Our Past, Berlin, Deutches Archäologishces Institut, 2007, pp 26-27.

Jacobsen M., (2008), Personal communication, Clemson Conservation Center, School of Materials Science and Engineering, Clemson University, Charleston, South Carolina.

Mardikian P., (2004), Conservation and Management Strategies Applied to Post-Recovery Analysis of the American Civil War Submarine H.L. Hunley (1864), in The International Journal of Nautical Archaeology, Portsmouth, Blackwell Publishing, 33 (1), 2004, pp 137-148.

Mardikian P., (2006), Personal communication, Clemson Conservation Center, School of Materials Science and Engineering, Clemson University, Charleston, South Carolina.

Neyland R.S., Jacobsen M., Mardikian P., Pecorelli H., (2000), Operations Plan for the Underwater Excavation of the H.L. Hunley, North Charleston, Warren Lasch Conservation Center and the Department of the Navy.

Peacock E., (2005), Investigation of Conservation Methods for a Textile Recovered From the American Civil War Submarine H.L. Hunley (1864), in

Proceedings of the 9th ICOM Group on Wet Organic Archaeological Materials Conference, Copenhagen,2005, pp 497-512.
Rivera J., Mardikian P., Cretté S., (2009), Waterlogged textile recovered from the Civil War submarine H.L.Hunley: Identification and conservation of textile belonging to Lieutenant George Dixon, American Institute for Conservation, 37th Annual Meeting, Los Angeles, California, 2009, in press.

Scafuri M., (2005), The H.L. Hunley Project 2004: Recent Developments in the Analysis and Mapping of the Civil War Submarine and its Crew, in Society for Historical Archaeology's 38th Annual Conference on Historical and Underwater Archaeology, York, England, 2005.

Questions and answers

Elizabeth Peacock: I have a question regarding your red fabric. Has dye analysis been done to determine the dye that was used to create the red?

Johanna Rivera: That's something that I didn't mention here. We did analyze the red fabric using SEM and it had this film covering the fabric. We had a big piece under the microscope which allowed us to analyze it wet because when it dries it shrinks and it changes colors and crumbles. We thought that using an environmental SEM we could analyze what it is but we realized that it has this film that you cannot go through the sample so it is very hard to analyze the dye. We did analyze the cashmere and we weren't able to find any dye but we did find a chromate, which might be a mordant for a dye so we have to work on that.

Elizabeth Peacock: There are a lot of finds from wet environments, both on land and underwater but also from burial degradation studies where madder dye in textiles are better preserved than undyed textiles or textiles dyed with other dyestuffs, so that's why I was curious.

519

Johanna Rivera: Yes, we are still trying to analyze it because of this slime that is formed and by the way the slime is either fungal or the other theory is it's the soft tissue from Dickson's body. We have found soft tissue or adipocere so that may be covering the textile as well. So we did analyze it dry, we did analyze it wet, we did EDS but we still cannot figure it out.

Elizabeth Peacock: There are other types of techniques that are used for dye analysis. So I was curious about whether you'd used them because there are lots of examples where red woolen textiles are well preserved but you have a situation where it was less pristine, less well preserved than the other textiles

.

5.2

Preliminary Investigation for the Conservation Plan of a Marine Composite (Copper/Textile) from the 19th Century Shipwreck 'Patris' in Greece

Stavroula Rapti[*], Christina Margariti, Stavroula Golfomitsou, Stamatis Boyatzis, Panayota Pitsiri, Vasilike Argyropoulos

Department of Conservation of Antiquities and Works of Art, Technological Educational Institute of Athens, Ag. Spyridonos, Egaleo, 12210 Athens, Greece

*email corresponding author:
srapti@teiath.gr

Abstract

In October 2006 the famous shipwreck "Patris" was visited off the coast of the Greek island Kea, and several artifacts were removed and taken for exhibition at the Ermoupolis Industrial Museum in Syros. Many of these objects were composites, and difficult to treat due to the fact that the organic component could not be separated from the metal. Collaboration between the Museum and the TEI of Athens has resulted in the conservation of the finds removed from the shipwreck. This paper discusses the analysis and conservation considerations of a copper alloy fire hose with textile and remnants of wood attached to the surface of the metal. A detailed examination and assessment of this object was carried out using SEM-EDX, XRF, and FTIR analyses. Analyses enabled weave, yarn and fiber identification of the textile, and also identified the chemical and mineralogical composition of copper alloy and its corrosion products. Results obtained clearly showed the presence of organic matter within the textile fibers. Understanding the technology and condition of the different components of the object will help in planning a suitable conservation treatment, which should be effective and at the same time preserve the different components of the object.

Keywords: Composite, copper alloy, textile, waterlogged, benzotriazole

Introduction

The paddle-wheel steamship *Patris* (initially named *Othon*) was launched at the order of King Othon of Greece in 1859, at the shipyard of C. Lungley & Co, Deptford, on the Thames River in England. Its dimensions were 66.14×8.38×4.88m and it was equipped with a 180 HP steam engine. *Patris* was employed by the Hellenic Steamline Company, until 1868 when it sank off the reef Koundouros, off Kea Island in the Aegean Sea. It was officially located in 1979 and the lifting of the paddle wheel and some objects took place in 2006 by the Ermoupolis Industrial Museum in Syros, the National Hellenic Research Foundation, the Ephorate of Underwater Antiquities, and the Underwater Film Research Team.

After it sank, *Patris* broke in two and it is located at two different depths. A number of finds, mainly ship fittings and utilitarian objects, were recovered. These included one of the two paddle-wheels of the ship, two cannons, an anchor and various small objects mainly made of metal, china and glass, most of which were composite. Conservation of composite artifacts is challenging given that the treatment of the textile and wood components could result in corrosion of metals and vice versa.

A co-operative agreement between the Ermoupolis Industrial Museum and the TEI of Athens has resulted in the conservation of some of the objects removed from the shipwreck. Among them was a copper alloy and textile fire hose fitting with traces of wood on its surface. Fire hoses, originally made of leather, were fashioned in 1673 by Jan van der Heiden and his son Nicholaas. James Boyd patented a rubber-lined and cotton-webbed fire hose in 1821 (Hashagan 2005). Unlined, tightly-woven linen was also used. Swelling of the flax fibers when water passed over them made the hose watertight (Couvillon 2006).

Figure 1. *Fire hose before treatment: iron corrosion products and calcareous concretions cover the whole surface.*

The *Patris'* fire hose was originally covered with calcareous concretions which varied in thickness (from 0.4-2 cm) and iron corrosion products, which lead to the assumption that the object was made of iron and treated accordingly (see figure 1). To remove the concretions, compresses of 10% (v/v) formic acid in deionized water were applied locally following which the object was immersed in 1% (v/v) Hostacor IT® in deionized water to halt the iron corrosion processes. Partial removal of the concretions revealed the presence of textile and wood, and revealed that the object was a copper alloy so it was removed from the inhibitor solution and immersed in deionized water. The previous actions were carried out prior to this investigation.

The aim of the investigation was to better understand the condition of the object so as to plan a suitable conservation strategy. Different diagnostic techniques were carried out for identification and compositional analysis of the materials and evaluation of the extent of their decay.

Description of the object

The object is a piece of tubular metal, which attaches the fire-hose to the fire hydrant. The diameter of the main tubular body narrows towards the bottom and has a screw top. Below the threaded top part there is a metal ring with two grips placed transversely. The lower part is where the textile hose is fitted. There is an additional metal wire, which holds the hose in place. The hose is 120mm long and 132mm wide (see figure 2).

Figure 2. *Note the screw top, the metal ring with the two grips and the metal wire which hold the textile hose into the lower part.*

Methods of examination

The fire hose was visually examined with a stereomicroscope, yarn analysis was carried out using Fourier Transform Infrared micro-spectroscopy (FTIR) and Scanning Electron Microscopy (SEM) coupled with Energy Dispersive X-ray analysis (EDX) and compositional analysis of the metal was performed using a portable X-Ray Fluorescence Spectroscopy (XRF).

Initially, visual examination in conjunction with a WILD M3B stereomicroscope at 20x magnification revealed information about the weave and the amount of the textile present on the object. Two yarn samples were removed from different areas of the object indicative, microscopically, of different states of preservation. They were dehydrated gradually using ethanol. The samples were immersed consequently in solution of ethanol in deionized water where the ethanol was increased 10% resulting in three final immersions in absolute ethanol. Each immersion lasted 20 min.

FTIR micro-spectroscopy using a Perkin Elmer Spectrum GX[1] equipped with AutoImage was performed on the samples in order to characterize the chemical alteration and the presence of organic matter within the fibers.

Figure 3. Detail of the threaded top part of the fire hose. Wood traces are evident on the metal surface.

For SEM examination and EDX elemental analysis the yarn samples were coated with palladium/gold using the High Resolution Sputter coater Polaron SC7640 and with graphite in BAL-TEC/CED 030 Carbon Evaporator. They were both examined using a JEOL JSM 5310 SEM. Elemental analysis was carried out on both samples with Pentafet 6587 Detector (INCA analysis system, Oxford Instruments). EDX was performed at an acceleration voltage of 15 kV.

A handheld XRF spectrometer was designed under the framework of the Educational and Initial Vocational Training Program – Archimedes for the study of characteristic corrosion products found on outdoor bronze monuments. The spectrometer consists of a low power (3W), cool cathode, transmission anode (Ag) X-ray tube, and a Si-PIN detector. Portable X-Ray Fluorescence Spectroscopy carried out in order to identify the metal component.

Very little wood is preserved so sampling was not possible (see figure 3).

Results
Identification and compositional analysis
The technical analysis of the textile revealed a plain weave (1/1), Z yarn twist, 1 ply, 5x8/10mm^2 (count warp/weft per 10mm^2) (see figure 4). The width of the

yarns is distinctly uneven. SEM examination showed the presence of cross markings and dislocations at the majority of the fibers. This morphology is characteristic of bast fibers, such as flax and hemp. A small number of fibers with the characteristic convolutions of cotton were also detected (see figure 5).

Figure 4. *Textile detail*

Micro-reflectance FTIR analysis showed that the fibers are made of carbohydrates. The characteristic peaks of cellulose (e.g. 1425, 1369, 1338, 1315, 1152 cm^{-1}), hemicellulose (xyloglycans e.g. 1368, 1132 cm^{-1}) and pectin (e.g. 1743, 1458, 1379, 1237 cm^{-1}) were detected (see figure 6). Based on the analytical results and a literature review (Hashagan 2005, Couvillon 2006) it was presumed that the fire hose was a mixture of flax and cotton fibers.

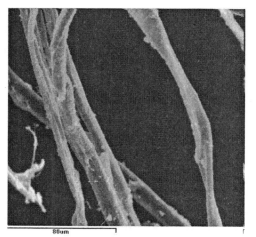

Figure 5. *Presence of cross markings and dislocations characteristic of bast fibres, and convolutions characteristic of cotton. SEM, magnification 750x.*

---

[1] Resolution is 4cm^{-1} Range is 4.000 to 700cm^{-1}

XRF analysis of different areas of the metal revealed that the fire hose was made of leaded brass. Antimony and traces of iron were also detected.

Condition assessment upon receiving

The surviving textile covers approximately 55% of the total surface of the object and is found mainly on the lower part. The textile is waterlogged, and the fibers appear to be fragile and brittle. The surface of the textile is partially covered with very fine clay silt which has also penetrated the interstices of the yarns and fabric weave. In addition,

SEM examination of those fibers which were in poor condition showed loss of their cell wall, as well as surface cracks and fractures running longitudinally (see figure 7). Hyphae (indicative of biodeterioration) were also observed.

FTIR analysis of the samples showed that the organic matter has reached various stages of mineralization. In some areas the fiber has been totally replaced by copper corrosion products forming pseudomorphs

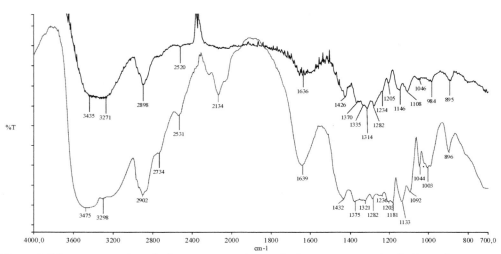

Figure 6. *Fiber spectrum from the better preserved area, the bottom spectrum is of a flax reference sample. Comparison of the two spectra showed that the former gave the characteristic peaks of cellulose, hemicellulose and pectin. Both spectra have been acquired by FTIR microscopy in reflectance mode*

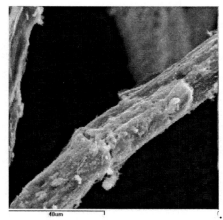

Figure 7. *Fibers show the presence of surface cracks and loss of their cell wall. SEM, magnification 1500*

The spectrum of the more poorly preserved sample showed no peaks indicative of

organic matter, such as cellulose. This was also corroborated by KBr pellet analysis of powder-ground sample, which produced spectral features typical of metal oxides (see figure 8). SEM-EDS analysis confirmed the fibers are impregnated with iron and copper corrosion products, at different grades, depending on the area. The morphology of the fibers from the better preserved area shows the characteristic microscopic features, whereas the morphology of the fibers from the poorly preserved area appears heavily masked by metal corrosion products. The textile is also encrusted with carbonates, gypsum and metal corrosion products (see Figure 9-12).

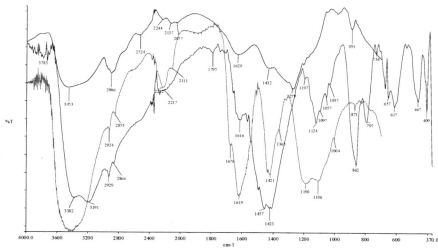

Figure 8. The top spectrum is FTIR micro-reflectance of the sample from the better preserved area. The middle spectrum is that of a sample from the worst preserved area, ground to a KBr pellet for FTIR analysis. The bottom spectrum is of a sample from the same area examined by FTIR micro-reflectance. A comparison of the top with the middle and bottom spectra indicated the fibers from the different areas have reached different stages of mineralization.

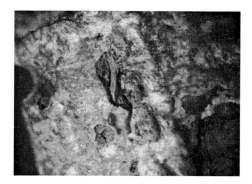

Figure 9. Detail of the textile encrustation. Textile fibers are evident underneath

Figure 10. Fibers from the better preserved area. SEM, magnification 750x.

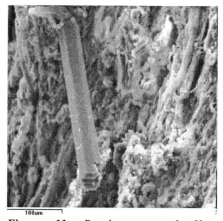

Figure 11. Poorly preserved fibers heavily impregnated by metal corrosion products and

As far as the metal is concerned, the threaded top part is partially covered with concretions. The copper alloy hose is generally in a good state of preservation with most of the metal core remaining intact. There is mechanical deformation on the lower part of the pipe. The metal was covered with thin layers of corrosion underneath the concretions with the original surface preserved in the greater part (see figure 13). In some areas (such as the threaded part and the ring) the corrosion layer has been removed by the formic acid and the exposed metal surface appears porous and is covered with copper crystals as a result of secondary deposition of copper and a newly formed layer of cuprite (see figure 14). On several areas there are spots of active corrosion ('bronze disease') (see figure 15). The copper alloy wire found around the textile appears to be totally mineralized.

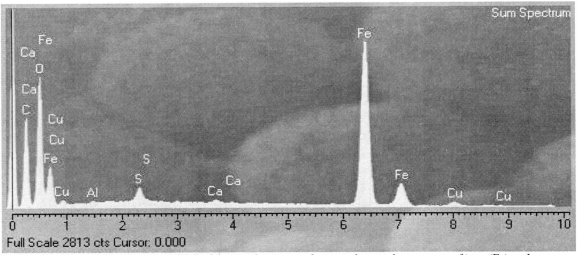

Figure 12. *Elemental analysis with EDS of the poorly preserved area indicates the presence of iron (Fe) and copper (Cu) corrosion products, gypsum (CaSO₄), as well as clay (Al).*

Figure 13. *Detail of the threaded part of the top of the fire hose. Concretions partially cover the surface.*

Figure 14. *Detail of the grip of the fire hose revealing the exposed metal surface which is porous and covered with copper crystals as a result of secondary deposition of copper.*

Figure 15. *Detail of the threaded part of the top of the fire hose. Spots of active corrosion ('bronze disease') are present.*

Discussion

After the thorough examination and the condition assessment of each component of the object, it became clear that due to the object's complex nature, an interdisciplinary approach was necessary to achieve an efficient conservation treatment. Separation of the textile from the metal was ruled out because of the partial fiber mineralization that would result in damage and/or loss of the textile, affecting the object's integrity. The research carried out to date makes it clear that any conservation treatment should address the object as a whole, emphasizing its composite nature.

The aim is to develop a treatment strategy that achieves a balance between the stabilization requirements of each component of the composite object. All standard conservation methods used for composite artifacts were taken into account for the treatment of the fire hose. However, often treatments used commonly for metals can be destructive for the organic parts and conversely (Hawley 1989).

It was decided that cleaning of the object should be avoided. The waterlogged textile has stains and mineral accretions, as iron hydroxides, iron oxides, which tend to accelerate the deterioration process of the fibers (Jenssen 1987) but at the same time they act as stabilizers for the cell walls of the fibers.

The main purpose of waterlogged textiles conservation treatment is to maintain the flexibility and stability, while avoiding collapse of the cell fibers, fracture of the textile fibers and shrinkage of the textile (Jenssen 1987). This involves the removal of water using different drying methods, such as air drying, controlled air drying, solvent drying, critical-point drying, vacuum and non-vacuum freeze-drying (Jakes and Mitchell 1992, Mumford 2002, Mathias et al. 2004). The aim of these drying processes is to maintain flexibility by achieving an appropriate Equilibrium Moisture Content (EMC) (Timar-Balazsy and Eastop 1998). Problems have been reported with air drying techniques. In some cases, the cells may collapse during air drying (Peacock 1992, Timar-Balazsy and Eastop 1998), while in other cases no shrinkage was observed, but the fibers become so weak that they could not support their own weight (Jenssen 1987). Freeze drying (vacuum and non-vacuum) has been successfully used for removing water (Peacock 1992), sometimes without any distortion (Jenssen 1987). In such cases, textiles are first pre-treated with water-soluble consolidants, such as polyethylene glycols (PEG), glycerol and cellulosic ethers, (Jenssen 1987, Watson 2004). These consolidants, which impregnate the porous structure of the wet textile and remain in situ once the water has been evaporated, can be used without freeze-drying to good result (Peacock 1990). The addition of the consolidant to the textile adds strength and preserves the existing flexibility and the dimensions of the dried textile. Glycerol has been used on waterlogged textiles in order to avoid brittleness and retain moisture content within the fibers (Jenssen 1987, Tarleton and Ordonez 1995).

Copper alloy objects recovered from the sea usually suffer from active corrosion because of the reactions taking place between copper and chlorides. The active corrosion observed on the object makes the stabilization process necessary. Given that textile is the more fragile component for this object and the low RH required to store copper alloys suffering from active corrosion will lead to desiccation of the textile (Timar-Balazsy and Eastop 1998), it is imperative to carry out stabilization of the active corrosion before drying the object. Depending on the deterioration of the fibers, textiles could be affected by the pH, the temperature and the duration of the stabilization solution applied. Cellulosic textiles like that of the fire-hose could safely be treated at a pH above 6.5 (Jenssen 1987). Additionally, the use of alkaline solutions can lead to textile and wood destruction, as the hemicellulose can be dissolved (Selwyn et al. 1993). Stabilization of marine copper alloys usually includes the use of sodium sesquicarbonate and/or a corrosion inhibitor. Sodium sesquicarbonate treatment (pH-10) is based on the chemical conversion of cuprous chloride (CuCl) into cuprite (Cu_2O) with simultaneous release of chlorides into the solution as shown in equations 1 and 2 below (Scott 2002).

$$2CuCl + 2OH^- = Cu_2O + H_2O + 2Cl^- \quad (1)$$
and
$$4CuCl + O_2 + 8HCO_3 = 4(Cu(CO_3)_2)_2^- + 4H^+ + 4Cl^- + 2H_2O \quad (2)$$

Prolonged use of sodium sesquicarbonate solutions can lead to the alteration of copper corrosion products such as chalconatronite ($Na_2Cu(CO_3)_2.3H_2O$), malachite ($CuCO_3Cu(OH)_2$), cuprite (Cu_2O) or tenorite (CuO) (Pollard et al. 1990) and may damage the remaining pseudomorph or textile.

Another dechlorination technique for copper alloys involves the use of cathodic polarization in neutral solutions. However, it requires further investigation. Electrolysis even in neutral solutions may damage any adhering layers of organic material and may not prove to be the best option.

The application of corrosion inhibitors used to stabilize copper corrosion is another option. The pH of such compounds varies from acidic to alkaline. The pH of the inhibitor to be used in this case should be near pH 7 to avoid damaging the textile. Triazole derivatives have been used as photostabilizers in the conservation of wool, silk and cotton fibers (Waters and Evans 1978, Waters and Evans 1983). Benzotriazole ($C_6H_5N_3$), a common corrosion inhibitor with a pH around 6 has been investigated in PEG 400 solutions and was found to preserve the copper corrosion layer or patina without diminishing the efficacy of the PEG treatment (Guilminot et al. 1998, Guilminot et al. 2000). PEG 400 by itself is slightly acidic and can result in further corrosion of the copper alloy (Selwyn et al. 1993).

However, treatment of a composite object in PEG solutions with BTA followed by air-drying without dechlorination of the heavily corroded copper alloy object may effectively stabilize the copper alloy. Research into the use of non-toxic corrosion inhibitors for PEG treatment of copper alloy composite artifacts has, to the best of our knowledge, not been carried out.

Air-drying without copper stabilization would also accelerate corrosion processes. Controlled drying by gradually reducing the humidity should also be avoided, as prolonged wetting of the metal surface particularly at the metal/textile interface in combination with increased oxygen could accelerate copper corrosion.

Conclusion

Conservators and scientists of different specializations collaborated in order to address this project. The conservation of composite artifacts is complex and raises numerous concerns. From the results of the examination and of the analyses carried out, as well as the review of current methods and materials, it is apparent that more research on alternative techniques is necessary. In terms of metal conservation, stabilization of active corrosion is one of the most important stages whilst for the textile the maintenance of its flexibility and stability through either drying or bulking techniques is paramount. This project will form the basis for further research on the conservation of composite artifacts. This research will be supported by experiments on the efficacy of selected treatments and the effect they may have on the components of such objects.

Acknowledgements

The authors wish to thank Athanasios Karabotsos conservator, TEI of Athens, for performing the SEM analysis; Kalliopi Kamani, conservator, TEI of Athens, for providing historical information about the *Patris* wreck; Kostis Bitsanis Director of the Ermoupolis Industrial Museum of Syros, for permission to publish this paper.

References

Couvillon A. R., (2006) (4th edition). *Entrance Fire Fighter Written Exams Study Guide*. USA: Information Guides.

Guilminot E., Degrigny C., Hiron X. and Dalard F., (1998) Protection d'un cuivre archéologique par le benzotriazole (BTA) en milieu aqueux de polyéthylène glycol (PEG), in: W. Mourey and L. Robbiola eds, Proceedings of ICOM-CC Metal conference, 1998, London, James & James, 234-241.

Guilminot E., Rameau J-J., Dalard F., Degrigny C. and Hiron X., (2000), Benzotriazole as inhibitor for copper with and without corrosion products in aqueous polyethylene glycol. Journal of Applied Electrochemistry, 30, 1, pp.21-28

Hashagan P., (2005), The Development of Fire Hose, [online]. Available at: http://www.firefightercentral.com/history/development_of_fire_hose.htm. [Accessed 12 April 2010]

Hawley J.K., (1989), A Synopsis of current treatment for waterlogged wood and metal composite objects, in J.D. MacLeod ed., Proceedings of ICOM-CC WOAM and METALS, Fremantle, 1987, Perth, Western Australian Museum, pp. 223-243.

Jakes K. A. and Mitchell J. C., (1992), The recovery and drying of textiles from a deep ocean historic shipwreck, Journal of the American Institute for Conservation, 31, 3, pp. 343-353.

Jenssen V., (1987), Conservation of wet organics artefacts other excluding wood, in: Pearson ed. *Conservation of Marine Archaeological Objects*. Oxford, Butterworth, pp.122-163.

Mumford L., 2002, The conservation of the Llangorse textile, in P. Hoffman, J. A. Spriggs, T. Grant, C. Cook and A. Recht eds, Proceedings of the 8th ICOM-CC WOAM Group Conference, Stockholm, 11-15 June 2001, Bremerhaven, Druckerei Ditzen GmdH und Co, pp.471-491.

Mathias C., Moffatt E. and Murray A., (2004), Technical analysis of textile remains from a 17th-century English plantation at Ferryland, Newfoundland and Labrador, Canada, Journal of the Canadian Association for Conservation, 29, 26-41.

Peacock E., (1990), Freeze –drying of Ancient Textiles: the need for basic Research, Archaeological Textiles, UKIC Occasional Paper No 10, ed. O' Connor, S and Brookes M., pp.22-31.

Peacock E., (1992), Drying Archaeological Textiles, In Bender Jorgensen, L. and Munksgard, E. eds Archaeological textiles in Northern Europe: report from the 4th NESAT symposium, 1-5 May 1990 in Copenhagen, Copenhagen, Konservatorskolen, det Kongelige Danske Kunstakademi, pp. 197-207.

Pollard A.M., Thomas R.G., Williams P.A., (1990), Mineralogical changes arising from the use of aqueous sodium carbonate solutions for the treatment of archaeological copper objects, Studies in Conservation, 35, 3, 148-152.

Scott D.A., (2002), Copper and Bronze in Art: Corrosion, Colorants, Conservation, Los Angeles, Getty Conservation Institute.

Selwyn L.S., Rennie-Bissaillion D.A. and Binnie N.E., (1993), Metal Corrosion rates in Aqueous Treatments for Waterlogged Wood-Metal Composites, pp.180-197.

Timar-Balazsy A. and Eastop D. (1998), Chemical principles in textile conservation, Oxford, Buterworth

Tarleton K. S. and Ordoñez M. T. (1995), Stabilization methods for textiles from wet sites, Journal of Field Archaeology, 22, pp. 81-95.

Watson J., (2004), The freeze-drying of wet and waterlogged materials from archaeological excavations, Physics Education, 39, 2, pp. 171-176.

Waters P.J. and Evans N.A., (1978), The Effect of Phenylbenzotriazole Derivatives on the Photoyellowing of Wool, Textile Research Journal, 48, 5, pp.251-255.

Waters P.J. and Evans N.A., (1983), The abrasion-resistance of ultra-violet-irradiated wool: the effect of a benzotriazole photostabilizer, Journal of the Textile Institute, 74, 2, pp.99 – 100.

5.3

A Neolithic Shoe from Sipplingen –Technological Examination and Conservation

Ingrid Wiesner
Regierungspräsidium Stuttgart, Landesamt für Denkmalpflege, Berliner Straße 12, 73728 Esslingen am Neckar, Germany
E-mail: Ingrid.Wiesner@rps.bwl.de

Jakob Beirowski
Universität Erlangen-Nürnberg, Lehrstuhl für Pharmazeutische Technologie, Cauerstrase 4, 91058 Erlangen, Germany

Abstract
A fragment of a rep-woven Neolithic shoe of bast fiber, preserved in waterlogged conditions, was excavated in Sipplingen, Germany in 2008. Generally waterlogged archaeological textiles are immersed in aqueous solutions of low molecular weight polyethylene glycol (PEG) before freeze-drying. Prior to conservation the use of different molecular weight PEGs was investigated by Scanning Electron Microscopy (SEM) and the critical freeze-drying temperatures were determined with Differential Scanning Calorimetry (DSC). The results confirmed the disadvantages of low molecular weight PEG such as its low critical freeze-drying temperature and its low solidification point.

Keywords: conservation, waterlogged, textile, polyethylene glycol, freeze-drying, shoe

1. Introduction
The locality of Sipplingen plays a key role in the archaeological research of Neolithic settlement and economy in the area of Lake Constance, Germany. On the bottom of the lake lots of organic remains have been preserved. These areas are endangered by erosion. Both in-situ preservation and archaeological research is supported by the "Landesamt für Denkmalpflege Baden-Württemberg". In 2008, several areas were excavated to improve dendrochronological data. In occupation layers of the "Horgner Kultur" stone blades and objects made of antler, bone and teeth from bears were found and dated to 2900-2860 BC. At the base of a burnt layer, when it is supposed that the settlement had been burnt, a large fragment of a shoe was found (Matuschik et al. 2009: 47).

In this paper the technology of the shoe, which was analyzed during the conservation process, is described. The standard conservation method in Baden-Württemberg consisted of impregnation with an aqueous solution of low molecular weight PEG before freeze-drying. The use of high molecular weight PEG was investigated as a conservation treatment because of the brittleness of the fibers, especially of the carbonized finds.

2. Description of the Neolithic Footwear
2.1. Archaeological Background
The find from Sipplingen belongs to the oldest European shoes. Fragments of Neolithic footwear were already discovered in Germany (Feldtkeller and Schlichtherle 1987, Körber-Grohne and Feldtkeller 1998), Switzerland (Winiger 1981, 1995, Egloff 1989, Hochuli 2002), Spain and Portugal (Feldtkeller and Schlichtherle 1987). The most famous shoes are those of the Iceman (Goedecker-Ciolek 1994) which date from 3900 BC. Because of the few examples of Neolithic footwear archaeological research is rudimentary and statistical tools cannot be employed. Each piece is very important and has to be regarded individually.

2.2 Condition

Three main fragments of the textile were preserved (see Figure 1). Because of the shape of the fragments they likely belong to a sole section. The length of the fragmented shoe is 25 cm and the width is 10 cm. The toe and the upper parts are missing. One bigger void is seen in the internal part of the shoe in the area of the waist. The appearance of the fragmented heel seat differs from the rest of the shoe. The structure is loose. This fact may be due to the non-carbonized condition and more strain on the area caused by walking.

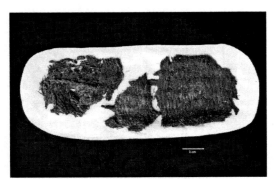

Figure 1. *Shoe after conservation (Mühleis, LAD)*

As already mentioned the footwear was found in a burnt layer and it is partially carbonized, mainly on the upper side of the shoe. These carbonized bast fibers are black, stiff and brittle. The underside of the tread, the waist, the heel seat as well as some regions on the insides of the bast strips are not carbonized. The non-carbonized fibers are soft and very weak.

2.3. Technological Analyses
The shoe is made of a network of strips of bast fibers that are woven in rep (see Figure 2). The edge of the shoe is turned up. No torsion of the strips could be detected. The strips from system 1 proceed along the shoe and consist of thick, stable strips (system 1 has a thickness of 7-10 mm). This system is not visible in intact areas because it is covered by system 2. The strips of system 2 have an average thickness of 4-6 mm. The strips of bast are, especially in the area of the sole, flatter and thinner. The whole shoe is woven very

closely and it has a very compact character. Therefore it seems that the structure is very strong and resilient. The orientation of the bast strips in the area of the heel centre is slightly circular and concave. A perpendicular folded lace (sZ-direction) lies in a diagonal direction on the heel centre and is probably a fastening. Laces are documented on finds by Feldtkeller and Schlichtherle (1987), Körber-Grohne and Feldtkeller (1998) and Egloff (1989). After Feldtkeller and Schlichtherle (1987) laces were probably tied around the leg.

Lime (*tilia*) was used for every component of the weave as is evident by microscopical examination of several samples [1]. Anatomical features proved that the fibers were retted before processing to make the fibers flexible. Different information about the need for retting bast fibers before processing are given by Krünitz (1807), Anon (1830) and Reichert (2005).

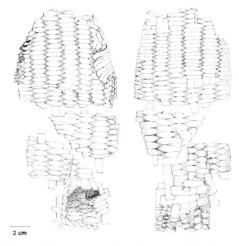

Figure 2. *Conventionalized drawing of the front and backside*

3. Material and Methods
The use of bulking cryoprotectants, consolidants, plasticizers or humectants before freeze-drying for the conservation of archaeological textiles is reported by Peacock (1990). Most of the finds in Baden-Württemberg were conserved

according to the methods of Elmer (1973) and Feldtkeller (1989), respectively. After cleaning the finds were soaked in an aqueous solution of 8% PEG 400, 5% Luviskol K30™ [2], and 2% borax before freeze-drying. The drawback of the method is the low pH value of Luviskol K30. A 1% concentration has a pH of 3,95 (Peacock 1990, Timar-Balaszy and Eastop 1998). Finds that were treated 20 years ago seem to be brittle. Carbonised finds in particular need to be consolidated in order to save the original structure.

Bojesen-Koefoed et al. (1993) reported the use of high molecular weight PEG for more degraded waterlogged rope. The use of PEG of different molecular weights was investigated in order to sufficiently stabilize the degraded bast structure of the Neolithic footwear. In this study measurements of the physicochemical properties were carried out with Differential Scanning Calorimetry (DSC) to better define the freeze-drying process in relation to the conservation material. Additionally the structure of bast fibers conserved recently and 20 years ago was compared using the Scanning Electron Microscope (SEM).

3.1. DSC Analyses
Specific information about freeze-drying such as the physicochemical behavior and the definition of the critical freeze-drying temperatures are necessary to control a freeze-drying process (Beirowski and Gieseler 2008). These specifications are missing in the conservation literature. Therefore aqueous solutions of PEG (concentration = 10% (w/w)) with different molecular weight (400, 600, 800, 1500, 2000, 3350) were analyzed by DSC.

In a DSC the quantitative exchange of energy (heat) of a sample with its surrounding is measured using a sample and a reference sample. These samples undergo the same time-temperature program. The difference of the heat flow rates between the sample and the reference sample is measured as a function of temperature which is proportional to the specific heat capacity of the sample (Atkins and de Paula 2006). These differences in the heat capacity reveal exothermic or endothermic reactions like a chemical reaction or a physical modification in the sample. Endothermic properties like the eutectic temperature (T_E) or the glass transition temperature of the maximally concentrated phase ($T_{g'}$), crucial factors for freeze-drying, are detected and documented in a thermogram.

The measurements were carried out using a calibrated Mettler Toledo DCS 822e differential scanning calorimeter [3]. Thirty µL of the test solution was pipetted in an alum pan which was hermetically sealed. The samples were cooled in liquid nitrogen and afterwards the samples were heated (details of the monitoring program are listed in Figure 3).

3.2. SEM-Analyses
The micro structure of bast fibers treated with the method after Feldtkeller (1989) were investigated in the Scanning Electron Microscope to estimate the long term effect of the treatment. Samples were taken from another non-carbonized Neolithic shoe of bast fibers from the same locality of Sipplingen which was treated 20 years ago. These samples were compared with recently conserved bast fibers to get an idea of the alteration of the structure. The immediate impact of different PEGs on the structure of fixed and un-fixed fibers was investigated. Both carbonized and non-carbonized bast fibers were separated and soaked in a solution of 10% PEG 400, 800, 1000, 1500, and 2000 for one week. After conservation each fiber was placed on a glass slide and frozen at -50 °C and freeze-dried at 0,38 Pa. After drying the samples were investigated in a SEM (EVO 60, Carl Zeiss) at low vacuum. No sputter coating was necessary (Ackermann 2003).

The impact was recorded at about 200 Pa with an acceleration voltage of 10-12 kV. A QBSE detector was used to analyze the structure of the sample.

4. Results and Discussion

DSC measurements showed an eutectic melting of the PEG-water mixtures for PEGs with an average molecular weight at or above 600 g/mol. For example, the thermogram of an aqueous solution of 10% PEG 1500, as seen in Figure 3, confirms that aqueous solutions of PEG 1500 will not fully crystallize when cooled at a rate of -10 °C/min to -80 °C. During heating (5°C/min) an exothermic peak, the cold crystallization at ~-45 °C, was detected, where metastable crystals were formed due to molecular movement (Huang and Nishinari 2002). As incomplete crystallization inevitably leads to freeze-drying problems, a thermal treatment (annealing) of the samples was necessary to ensure complete crystallization (see Figure 3). The samples were heated (5 °C/min) to -25°C for 45 minutes, a temperature above the glass transition temperature of the maximally concentrated glass phase (-72 °C) but below the eutectic temperature where the amorphous parts in the solution were crystallizing. Then the samples were re-cooled to -80°C (rate -5°C/min) and after 3 min reheated to 5 °C (rate 5 °C/min). After annealing both the glass transition and cold crystallization were prevented. The eutectic composition started to melt at about -19 °C, before the water began to melt (data not shown). Therefore freeze-drying of aqueous solutions of PEG 1500 has to be performed below -19 °C.

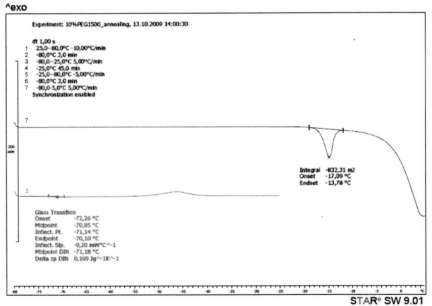

Figure 3. *Thermogram of an aqueous solution of 10% PEG 1500. Step 1-7 of the monitoring program are listed in the top of the figure. The initial heating to -25 °C is not visualized in the lower graph (step number 3 of the monitoring program); the second heating procedure after the thermal treatment (annealing) is documented in the upper graph (step number 7 of the monitoring program).*

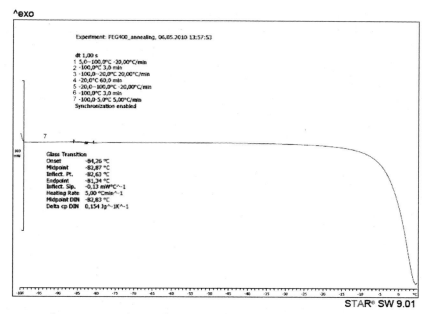

^exo

Experiment: PEG400_annealing, 06.05.2010 13:57:53

dt 1,00 s
1 5,0~100,0°C -20,00°C/min
2 -100,0°C 3,0 min
3 -100,0~-20,0°C 20,00°C/min
4 -20,0°C 60,0 min
5 -20,0~-100,0°C -20,00°C/min
6 -100,0°C 3,0 min
7 -100,0-5,0°C 5,00°C/min
Synchronization enabled

7

Glass Transition
Onset   -84,26 °C
Midpoint   -82,87 °C
Inflect. Pt. -82,63 °C
Endpoint   -81,34 °C
Inflect. Slp. -0,13 mW°C^-1
Heating Rate 5,00 °Cmin^-1
Midpoint DIN -82,83 °C
Delta cp DIN 0,154 Jg^-1K^-1

STAR® SW 9.01

Figure 4. *Thermogram of an aqueous solution of 10% PEG 400. Step 1-7 of the monitoring program are listed in the top of the figure. The solution was annealed for 60 minutes at −20°C but no crystallization could be detected. A glass transition is revealed at −83 °C.*

Figure 4 shows the thermogram of an aqueous solution of 10% PEG 400. The frozen solution remains amorphous and no crystallization could be detected even after annealing at -20 °C for 60 minutes (step 4 of the monitoring program). According to Huang and Nishinari (2002) and Jablonski (2002) no eutectic phase can be established between water and PEG 400 because the interaction between water and PEG is not strong enough. At -80 °C a glass transition is visible. To maintain an aqueous solution out of 10% PEG 400 in a frozen and stable state it would be necessary to freeze-dry at temperatures below -80 °C. Therefore it is impossible to freeze-dry the mixture. The solution will remain liquid and the drying time will extend. The low critical freeze-drying temperature makes PEG 400 unsuitable for freeze-drying.

Table 1. *Critical freeze-drying temperature of PEG of different molecular weight*

Material	c (w/w)	Critical freeze-drying temperature
PEG 400	10%	-83 °C
PEG 600	10%	-38 °C
PEG 800	10%	-31 °C
PEG 1500	10%	-19 °C
PEG 2000	10%	-18 °C
PEG 3350	10%	-17 °C

As mentioned, the critical freeze-drying temperature of PEG of a molecular weight of 600 g/mol or higher is defined as the temperature where the eutectic mixture starts to melt. According to Jablonski (2002) the eutectic temperature of aqueous solutions of PEG is dependent on the molecular weight. The lower the molecular weight the lower the eutectic point and the higher the eutectic concentration. Aqueous solutions of PEG 400 solidify as an amorphous glass phase and no crystallization of the eutectic phase can be detected (Jablonski 2002, Huang and Nishinari 2001, Bogdanov and Mihailow 1985). In summary, the measurements of the critical freeze-drying temperatures of PEG of various molecular weights are listed in Table 1.

The micro structure of the bast fibers was documented in the SEM. A freeze-dried and untreated carbonized bast fiber is seen in Figure 5. Big voids in the tissue indicate the reason for the brittleness of the fibers (see above). Bast fibers that were treated recently with 10% PEG 400 before freeze-drying have a good appearance and they are very flexible. As can be seen in the micrograph, a diffuse substance with no structure is evenly distributed over the whole surface. This substance was interpreted as PEG 400 which is liquid at room temperature (see Figure 6). In contrast, the structure of a fiber treated in the 1980's looks very different. No PEG 400 could be detected on this sample and the sample was brittle (see Figure 7). This fact may be caused by the low solidification point of PEG 400 (Tg at 4-8 °C). It is liquid at room temperature and stabilizes the structure because of its high viscosity. In addition, PEG 400 is hygroscopic. Juling (2001) simulated the mobility of PEG 200 with increasing humidity during SEM analyses. It can be assumed that the reason for the differences in the microstructure is the mobility of the low molecular weight PEG. It is questionable if PEG 400 is able to support the fragile and degraded fiber structure in perpetuity.

The samples that were treated with PEG 800 and 1000 seemed to be very homogenous but voids in the structure were visible (see Figure 8). In the sample pre-treated with 10% PEG 1500 however the interspaces in the fiber structure were filled. It seemed to stabilize and support the structure homogeneously (see Figure 9). Fibers conserved with 10% PEG 2000 seemed to be too hard and thick deposits on the surface of fibers were visible (see Figure 10).

5. Conservation
The waterlogged shoe was covered with sediment and roots had grown through the structure during burial. The shoe was rinsed in demineralized water and cleaned mechanically. Following Feldtkeller (1989), Elmer (1973) and Rothenhäusler and Cevey (2009), a mould of paper and plaster bandage was made. With the aid of the mould the shoe was turned to the other side and cleaned.

As discussed, PEG 1500 is more suitable for stabilizing the degraded structure of the bast fiber. Therefore the footwear was conserved with an aqueous solution out of 8% PEG 1500 for 10 days. The find was supported on the underside by a mould of plaster bandages. The upper side was covered with tissue paper and polyester wadding to avoid excess conservation material on the surface of the object.

10μm   EHT = 10.00 kV   Signal A = QBSD   WD = 6.5 mm   Mag =   503 X

Figure 5. *Carbonized fiber with no treatment*

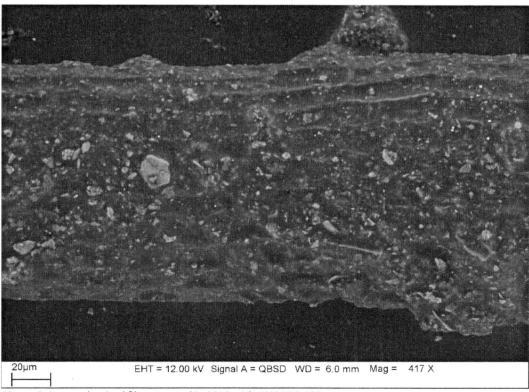

20μm   EHT = 12.00 kV   Signal A = QBSD   WD = 6.0 mm   Mag =   417 X

Figure 6. *Non-carbonized fiber, treated in 2010 with 10% PEG 400*

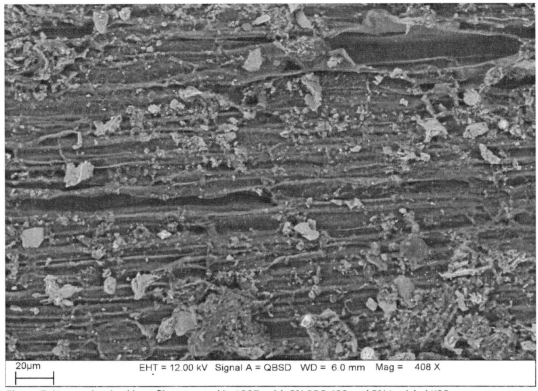

| 20μm | EHT = 12.00 kV Signal A = QBSD WD = 6.0 mm Mag = 408 X |

Figure 7. Non-carbonized bast fiber, treated in 1987, with 8% PEG 400 and 5% Luviskol K30

| 20μm | EHT = 12.00 kV Signal A = QBSD WD = 5.5 mm Mag = 535 X |

Figure 8. Carbonized fiber treated with 10% PEG 800

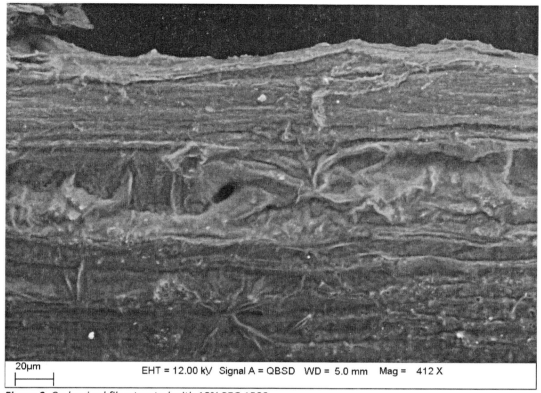

Figure 9. *Carbonized fiber treated with 10% PEG 1500*

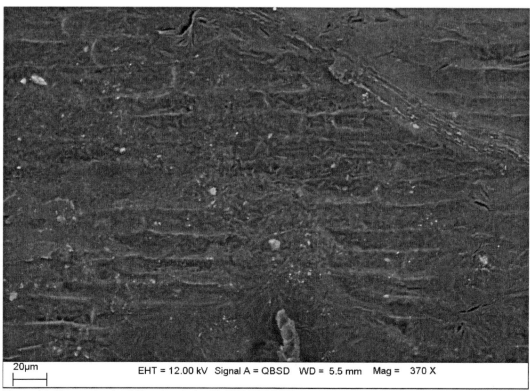

Figure 10. Non-carbonized fiber treated with 10% PEG 2000

In order to prevent dimensional breakdown due to its own weight, the whole solution was placed into the freeze-dryer where it was frozen at -30 °C. Afterwards the find was freeze-dried as a block (Bojesen-Koefoed et al. 1993). Freeze-drying was carried out at 10 Pa and -30 °C. After drying the excess conservation material was removed with a brush and ethanol. Methocel A4C 0,5% to 3% in an ethanol : water (1:1) solution and was used to consolidate brittle parts and to fix loose fibers.

A support for the presentation and handling was manufactured of a starch-based cotton tape from the bookbinding market. The support was covered with Japanese paper Kozo 15g/m² (see Figure 1).

6. Conclusion

Statistical methods cannot be used for archaeological research in the field of Neolithic footwear because of its rarity and therefore every object must be analyzed in detail. PEG 400 is used in conservation to consolidate, bulk and/or plasticize archaeological textiles. During impregnation the conservation material will disperse into the degraded fiber structure. Freeze-drying is applied to maintain the shape, appearance and state of the object. This study confirmed that during freeze-drying with common freeze-drying facilities and storage at room-temperature PEG 400 is in a liquid state and therefore it is questionable if the fragile and degraded structure is sufficiently stabilized. An alternative to low molecular weight PEG is the use of a higher molecular weight PEG as reported by Bojesen-Koefoed et al. (1993). The critical freeze-drying temperature of an aqueous solution of 10% PEG 1500 is -19 °C so freeze-drying should be performed below -19 °C. Further research is necessary to determine the impact on the structure of the object caused by incomplete crystallization of the PEG- water system.

SEM pictures proved that PEG 1500 is lining the structure of a bast fiber after freeze-drying. The ability of high molecular weight PEG to bulk the cell wall, as is reported from low molecular weight PEG, could not be evidenced. So far, it can be claimed that PEG 1500 is able to stabilize the degraded structure much more than low molecular weight PEG. The conserved structure of the Neolithic shoe underlines the suitability of high molecular weight PEG for the conservation of waterlogged bast fibers. Additionally, statistical studies on conserved objects are needed to evaluate past-treatments more precisely.

7. Acknowledgements
The experimental work is part of a PhD dissertation to be submitted to the State Academy of Art and Design Stuttgart (Objects Conservation) and the authors wish to thank Prof. Dr. Gerhard Eggert and Prof. Dr. Christoph Krekel. The authors also gratefully acknowledge Dr. Henning Gieseler, University of Nürnberg-Erlangen; Annemarie Feldtkeller, Dr. Johanna Banck-Burgess and Dr. Helmut Schlichtherle both Landesamt für Denkmalpflege Baden-Württemberg for technological analyses and discussion. The authors wish to thank COST Action 0601, Poul Jensen, Ph.D., senior researcher and Inger Bojesen Kœfod, both from the Danish National Museum Denmark Department for Conservation in Brede for lots of information, discussion and advice regarding the drying process.

Notes
[1] Analyses were carried out by W. H. Schoch, Labor für Quartäre Hölzer, Tobelhof 13, CH-8134 Adliswil.
[2] Polyvinylpyrrolidone (PVP), BASF
[3] Iridium was used for calibration

References
Ackermann, J., (2003), Handbuch für die Rasterelektronenmikroskope LEO 14XX(VP), Oberkochen, LEO Elektronenmikroskope GmbH, 2003.

Anon (1830), Gesammelte Abhandlungen zur Verfertigung der Strohhüte nach italienischer, englischer und deutscher Art, Ulm, Ebner, pp129-135.

Atkins, P.W. and J. de Paula, (2006), Physikalische Chemie, Weinheim, WILEY-VCH Verlag GmbH & Co. KgaA.

Beirowski, J. and H. Gieseler, (2008), Application of DSC and MDSC in the Development of Freeze-dried Pharmaceutics. European Pharmaceutical Review, 6, 2008, pp 63-70.

Bogdanov, B. and M. Mihailow, Melting of Water/Poly(ethylene oxide) Systems, Journal of Polymer Science, 23, 1985, pp 2149-2158.

Bojesen-Koefoed I.M. et al., (1993), Conservation of Wet Archaeological Rope. In: Bridgland (Editor), ICOM-CC 10th triennial meeting. Washington DC. ICOM Committee for Conservation, 1993, pp 262-265.

Egloff, M., (1989), Des premiers chasseurs au début du christianisme. In: Egloff (editor) Histoire du Pays de Neuchâtel, volume 1, Gilles Attinger – Hauterive, Suisse, 1989, pp 13-160.

Elmer, J.T., (1973), Gefriertrocknung neolithischer Gewebe und Geflechte. Arbeitsblätter der Restauratoren 1, 1973, pp 17-22.

Feldtkeller, A., (1989) Zur Festigung vorgeschichtlicher Textilfunde. Arbeitsblätter der Restauratoren 2, 1989, pp 130-133.

Feldtkeller, A. and H. Schlichtherle, (1987) Jungsteinzeitliche Kleidungsstücke aus Ufersiedlungen des Bodensees. Nachrichten aus Baden 38/39, 1987, pp 74-84.

Hochuli S., (2002) Teil eines neolithischen Schuhs aus Zug. Jahrbuch der Schweizerischen Gesellschaft für Ur- und Frühgeschichte 85, 2002, pp 45-54.

Huang, L. and K. Nishinari (2001), Interaction between Poly(ethylene glycol) and Water as Studied by Differential Scanning Calorimetry, Journal of Polymer Science, 39, (2001), pp 496-506.

Jablonski P., (2002), Kalorimetrische Untersuchungen des Systems Polyethylenglykol/Wasser. Dissertation Duisburg, 2002.

Juling, H. (2001) http://www.mpa-bremen.de/forsch/for0028.php

Körber-Grohne, U. and A. Feldtkeller (1998), Pflanzliche Rohmaterialien und Herstellungstechniken der Gewebe, Netze, Geflechte sowie anderer Produkte aus Neolithischen Siedlungen Hornstaad, Wangen, Allensbach und Sipplingen am Bodensee. Siedlungsarchäologie im Alpenvorland V, Forschungen und Berichte zur Vor- und Frühgeschichte in Baden-Württemberg 68, 1998, pp 131-242.

Krünitz, D.J.G., Ökonomisch technologische Enzyklopädie 79, 1807, pp 256-259.

Matuschik, I. et al., (2009), Besiedlungsgeschichte und –dynamik der jungsteinzeitlichen Pfahlbausiedlungen in Sipplingen "Osthafen", Bodenseekreis. In: Archäologische Ausgrabungen in Baden-Württemberg 2008. Stuttgart, Konrad Theiss Verlag, 2009, pp 45-49.

Peacock, E.E., (1990), Freeze-drying archaeological textiles. The need for basic research. Occasional Papers 10, (1990), pp 22-30.

Reichert A., (2005), Be- und Verarbeiten von Lindenbast. Anzeiger der Arbeitsgemeinschaft für experimentelle Archäologie der Schweiz, (2005), pp.5-7.

Rothenhäusler U. et al., (2009), Mounting Systems for Fragile Water-Degraded Artefacts. In: H. Huisman and K. Strætkvern (editors), Proceedings of the 10th ICOM Group on Wet Organic Archaeological Materials Conference, Amsterdam 2007, Drukkerij Stampij Amersfoort (2009) pp 455-463.

Tímár-Balázsy, A. and D. Eastop, (1998), Chemical principles of textile conservation, Oxford, Butterworth-Heinemann.

Wiesner, I. and C. Krekel, (2009), Low Vacuum Scanning Elelectron Microscopy of Waterlogged Archaeological Leather. In: H. Huisman and K. Strætkvern (editors), Proceedings of the 10th ICOM Group on Wet Organic Archaeological Materials Conference, Amsterdam 2007, Drukkerij Stampij Amersfoort (2009) pp 741-760.

Winiger, J., (1981), *Feldmeilen*-Vorderfeld. Der Übergang von der Pfyner zur Horgener Kultur. *Antiqua 8,* 1981.

Winiger, J., (1995), Die Bekleidung des Eismannes und die Anfänge der Weberei nördlich der Alpen, In: Spindler (editor), Der Mann im Eis. Neue Funde und Ergebnisse, Wien, Springer Verlag 1995, pp. 119-187.

5.4

Analyses of Plant Fiber Artifacts from a Shipwreck: Application of Material History Methodology

Runying Chen, Department of Interior Design and Merchandising, East Carolina University, Greenville 27858
E-mail: CHENR@ecu.edu

Abstract

The purpose of this study was to identify the structure of textile artifacts recovered from the claimed *Queen Anne's Revenge* (QAR) shipwreck site, to explore their possible applications aboard ship, to provide complimentary data for other studies of QAR shipwreck, and to gain further understanding about sail and rigging through history. The investigation was based upon a material history methodology reported in Material History Bulletin 22 of 1985. The research process followed through four steps, step 1 of observable data, step 2 of comparative data, step 3 of supplementary data, and step 4 of conclusions. The findings at each step of investigation were reported by answering the questions about material, construction, function, provenance and value of the artifacts.

Keywords: sail cloth, sail seam, cordage structure, rigging, and boltrope.

Introduction

Among the numerous artifacts retrieved from North Carolina shipwreck site 31CR314, identified as the early 18th century English pirate vessel *Queen Anne's Revenge (QAR)* and formerly the French slaver *La Concorde,* are some fabric and cordage fragments. The purpose of this study was to identify the structure of textile artifacts recovered from the claimed *Queen Anne's Revenge* (QAR) shipwreck site, to explore their possible applications aboard ship, to provide complimentary data for other studies of QAR shipwreck, and to gain further understanding about sail and rigging through history. A material history methodology (Smith, 1985) was applied as a guide to this investigation.

Due to the very specific and important roles that sails and cordages play on a ship, some basic but essential information can be obtained about the ship from these artifacts. For example, the size of the rope or cordage varies with their specific applications in a ship's rigging and also with the ship's size; the same goes with the grades and weights of the cloth used for sails on a ship. Furthermore, variations also exist in the rigging details practiced between ships of varying nationalities over the course of history. For example, the French sail cloth is narrower and longer than the English sail cloth, and certain grades of the French sail cloth is made of hemp and cotton rather than hemp or flax alone (Marquardt, 1992). Therefore, the structural analysis of textile artifacts may reveal some of the details about the overall ship structure, and may be also useful for analysis in conjunction with other related artifacts. As indicated by Sanders (2010), there is a lack of 'comparative background data' of rigging materials from different shipwrecks to realize the potential of understanding the history of rope making and rigging mechanics. The author of this study hoped to add more detailed data to the study of historical or archaeological sail and cordage.

Methodology

The material history methodology was a group discovery through a graduate history seminar taught by Smith (1985). This methodology could be conceptualized as a process consisting of four steps of investigation, including observation data, comparative data, supplementary data, and conclusion. Each of the first three steps seeks answers to five questioning categories including material, construction, provenance, function, and value of an historic object. The last step is to draw conclusions. This investigation grid of interpreting and understanding a historical object emphasizes careful and thorough examination of the object itself before referring to other information sources; therefore, bias or 'preconceived notions about the artifact' could be kept at minimum. This methodology also encourages the investigator to re-examine the object at each step and during each data inquiry when new information is available. As recommended by Pearce (1994, p.5), this methodology along with others related to object interpretation should be 'regarded as a guide, not a set of rules'.

Methods of data collection and definition

To obtain the observable data (step 1 analysis), material and structure of the fabric and cordage fragments, several instruments were applied besides eye observation, such as microscope and fabric counter. The fabric artifact's structure analysis included fabrication type, fabric count, yarn type used, seam and stitch type or assembly method when applicable.

In this study, the term cordage was used and applied to describe collectively "rope, together with all the other flexible string like materials such as cord, twine and cable" (Weber-Partenheimer and Lenzburg AG., 1971. p.3). The observable structural data of all the cordage artifacts was based on the cordage structure levels or stages recommended by Dixon (1957) and some terminologies recommended by Osborne and Osborne (1954). Although Dixon's framework and Osbornes' terms were criticized by Sanders (2010) as un-usable in referring the varying methods of rope making and terminology through history and geography, the author felt that they are still useful generic tools for the samples

investigated in this study, at least in the observable data requisition process. Then, the appropriate terms and techniques may be discussed in the following comparative and complimentary data requisition steps. The English rope-recording form by Sanders (2010) is very comprehensive and can be used for complex cordage materials. The author also felt that to a certain degree, the form by Sanders assumes the knowing date and origin of the rigging materials, which, in some cases, are not known yet during the early investigation time.

The comparative data in this study included comparison with other similar objects found in the same shipwreck site, and reported from other shipwrecks. The supplementary data were obtained from descriptions found in articles or books as well as experts' opinions or knowledge in the subject area.

Step 1: Observable data
Material
Through light microscopic examination of the fiber samples, taken from both fabric and cordage samples, it can be concluded that these textiles are made from bast fibers, either flax or hemp. The cordage fibers are in rough texture of bundles, while the fabric fibers are much more refined. Figure 1 shows the typical morphology of fibers from the studied fabric fragments, which presents the dislocation marks of flax fiber as well as the biodegradation occurred to the fibers.

Construction and function
The construction of the fabric fragment themselves consists of the following structure levels, fabrication or weave structure, fabric count, and yarn type. Furthermore, when two or more pieces of fabrics are assembled, both the seam type and stitch type are examined as construction data. Besides data about fabrics and cordages, an artifact which contains both fabric and cordage elements

was also studied, thus how the two elements are constructed together is also observed and reported.

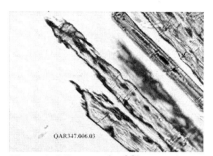

Figure 1. *Micrograph of fiber specimen at 400x by DIC*

Table 1 is a summary of all observation data of the textile fragments examined in this study. Two types of fabrication or weave structure were identified, 2x1 half basket weave and 1x1 plain weave. The 2x1 half basket weave is the most common

fabrication structure when the cloth is used for making heavier sails. It is a variation of the basic plain weave with one weft yarn interlacing over and under every two warps instead of one warp yarn. Basket weave fabric is more flexible than the corresponding plain weave fabric due to the lower frequency of interlacing between warp and weft yarns. Though the breaking strength of basket weave fabric is less than that of equivalent plain weave fabric, its tearing strength is higher than that of plain weave. In addition, basket weave allows higher fabric count in comparison with plain weave therefore heavier fabric, which in turn can compensate the breaking strength of the fabric.

Table 1. Fabric construction identification

Inventory number	Fabrication structure	Fabric Count cm (inch)	Yarn information and other observation note
QAR 347.006(1)	2x1 basket	20x9 (51x23)	Yarns – Z twist
QAR 347.006(2)	2x1 basket	21x9 (53x24)	Two pieces are sewed together. Sewing twine – plied yarn. Z twist yarn from S elements.
QAR 387.017	2x1 basket	16-20x8 (40-50x20)	A plain weave cloth was found: 10x10 (25x25) fabric count
QAR 344.017	2x1 basket	20x8 (50x20)	Fabric concrete with nail
QAR 366.086	2x1 basket	19x9 (48x24)	Yarns: weft – Z twist Warp – S twist.
QAR 387_???	1x1 plain	13x9 (33x23)	Yarns: about 3/100 inch in width, low twist level
QAR 345.014	1x1 plain	13x11 (32x28)	Weft yarn – Z twist Warp yarn – S twist
QAR 347.004	1x1 plain	17x15 (43x38)	There are mixed fabric fragments; one piece seems to be 2x1 basket weave. Weft yarn: Z twist, and finer size, less than 1/100 inch in width.
QAR 247.006	1x1 plain	Warp: 14 (Warp: 35)	Yarns: Z twist

Fabric count is expressed as number of warp by number of weft per cm and per (inch)

The data presented in Table 1 can be viewed as rough estimates due to the sampling and measurement limitation of small fabric sizes and their wet condition. According to standard measurement, fabric count is obtained by averaging several measurements from different locations of

a fabric sample. Fabric count determines a fabric's weight and strength as well as its cost. Usually, the higher is the fabric count, the better quality is the fabric.

QAR 347.006 (Figure 2) consists of two pieces of canvas sewed together by a flat seam (author's opinion) with three rows of stitches. The seam width is about 1.125 in or 2.86 cm. The stitch density was measured of 5 stitches in 1.5 inch length, which is about 97 stitches per yard or 131 stitches per meter. As to the middle stitching, its stitch density is two stitches in 0.86 inch length seam, which is equal to about 84 stitches per yard or 91 stitches per meter. The seam observed here reveals its application or function on the ship as part of a sail.

The structure characteristics of the retrieved cordage artifacts are analyzed by the stages of cordage formation and its twist angle and direction, plus the size of the cordages measured by their circumferences. All the observation data of cordage constructions is summarized in Table 2.

According to the framework recommended by Dixon (1957), the first stage is yarn formation by fiber bundles, followed by strand formation by two or more yarn or stage I elements, then the third stage of rope formation by two or more strands or stage II elements, and the last stage is cable formation by two or more rope or stage III elements. Here as emphasized by Dixon (1957), the terms of yarn, strand, rope and cable refer to their structures rather than their sizes and usages.

Among the cordage artifacts examined in this study, complete cordage stage structures were only observed and obtained from *QAR* 050.001 (Figure 3) as they had been cleaned and dried already. They have the following structure characteristics: 3 stages of cordage formation that result in 3-strand rope with Z-S-Z twist sequences; twist angle of the strand falls in the hard range between 30° to 50°. In another word, they are not shroud-laid or 4-strand rope with one strand forms the core in the middle of the rope.

As to 3-strand rope, there are two terms being used to describe them, one is plain-laid (Weber-Partenheimer and Lenzburg AG., 1971) and the other is hawser. The definition of hawser given in Boteler's Dialogue states that "it is a three-strand rope, of that thickness as it may be called and held for a little cable, and it serveth for many uses; as to warp a ship over bar, and for the like occasions. And with these kinds of ropes also, the main and fore shrouds are made fast" (Perrin, 1929, p.170). However, the term hawser-laid is defined by Marquardt (1992) as "Three strands laid in right (clockwise) turns formed a hawser, and this was the most common type of rope" (p.255). Sanders (2010) provided this definition for hawser "a rope, usually of three strands laid together, usually in a Z-twist. Plain or 'hawser-laid rope is rope which follows this covention" (p.8).

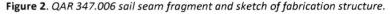

QAR347.006

Figure 2. *QAR 347.006 sail seam fragment and sketch of fabrication structure.*

Table 2. *Cordage artifacts and their structure identification*

Inventory No.	Cir. m (Inch)	Stages	Twist angle and direction	Note
QAR 050.001 - A	0.071 (2.83)	Yarn, strand, and 3-ply rope (Z-S-Z)	50-55° (hard) Z or right-laid	Plain-laid rope
QAR 050.001 - B	0.063 (2.48)	Yarn, strand, and 3-ply rope (Z-S-Z)	45° (hard) Z or right-laid	Plain-laid rope,
QAR 5.02	0.073 (2.87)	Yarn, strand, and 3-ply rope (?-S-Z) Fiber element in yarn within strand seems to be parallel with the rope axis	45° (hard) Z or right-laid	Plain-laid rope
QAR 418.085	0.053 (2.09)	Yarn (not visible), Strand, 3-ply rope? (not visible)	42° (hard) Z or right laid	Covered with rust and difficult for detailed analysis.
QAR 387.13 Several pieces	0.060 (2.36)	3-ply rope	40-45° (hard) Z or right laid	Covered by rust and black deposit, and difficult for detailed analysis
QAR 366 C4 hook		Single strand cordage wrapped on an iron hook	30° Z twist	The inside curve area of the hook appears to be intact with tightly aligned ropes served on the hook.

Figure 3. *Dried cordage sample of QAR 050.001*

As to the degree of twist angle, it affects the strength of the cordage. The tensile strength of the cordage increases with the twist angle but decreases when twist angle is too high. The stiffness of the cordage also increases with the twist angle. Another factor which affects the strength of a cordage is the twist direction sequence among the stages of cordage formation. The cordage with alternating twist direction sequence, such as Z-S-Z or S-Z-S, has a higher tensile strength than the sequence of S-S-Z or Z-Z-S which tends to have a higher friction resistance (Weber-Partenheimer and Lenzburg AG., 1971).

Besides the fabric and cordage artifacts, another type of artifacts included in this study contains both fabric and cordage elements. Both *QAR 387.017* and *QAR 387.018*, from the same concretion *QAR 387.000*, are parts of the ship's sail due to the fact that they have boltrope marled on (see Figure 4). The size of the boltrope is about 3.5 inches or 0.089 m in circumference. Two types of fabric were identified, 2x1 basket canvas which is the main fabric wrapped around the boltrope, and small 1x1 plain weave fabric fragment on top of the basket weave above the boltrope. Visual examination revealed that the boltrope had been served by oakum or old rope yarns – parallel wrapping bundles perpendicular to the rope axis direction are visible. It is also noticed that at one end of QAR 387.018 fragment there are six layers of the fabrics stacked on top of each other.

The other detail found with *QAR 387.017* and 387.108 includes a smaller plied twine other than that of the marling twine. This smaller twine could either be the worming twine or the twine to lace or sew other sail components. Another detail is how the edge of the sail is finished. It is a double round seam formed by two pieces of canvas with each piece canvas fold once inside the seam (Figure 5), and the stitches are about 0.7 inch apart, which is equal to about 53 stitches per yard. In sail making, the sail edges are usually finished as a broad hem called tabling.

Figure 4. *QAR 387.017 and QAR 387.018 object contains both fabric and cordage elements.*

 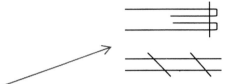

Figure 5. *Sail edge and stitch from QAR 387.018, folding principle of edges, seam and stitch.*

Provenance and value

At the observation step, the provenance (where, when and who) information about these artifacts cannot be obtained yet. As to value, it has two levels of meaning in this study; one being their importance to this shipwreck itself, and the other being the historical significance of these artifacts to the understanding of sails and rigging in general. The two artifacts examined above, *QAR 347.006* (Figure 2) and *QAR 387.018* (Figures 4 &5), have more construction details, thus, they have the potential of revealing more information about the ship itself, such as their provenance and value when compared with other shipwreck records and literature information.

Step 2: Comparative data

In this study, comparative data was first obtained by comparison among the artifacts themselves in the same categories, such as comparison among all the fabrics and comparison among all the cordages. The next comparison was made between these artifacts and those reported and found in other shipwrecks.

Comparison of material

The sail cloth fragments explored in this study was identified as flax or linen based on its morphological appearance and the fineness (fiber bundle) in the yarns of these cloth fragments. However, it seems that QAR 347.006 has distinct color appearance from the others, that the yarns of the cloth have both white and brown colored fiber bundles. Further investigation is necessary to examine if the two elements are the same type of fibers. The sail cloth reported in other shipwreck studies includes the woolen square sails used by the Vikings (Cooke, et al., 2002), the hemp sail on *Vasa* and linen sail on *Victory*.

Comparison of construction and function

The structural data reported in Table 1 indicates at least four different types of cloth, including two types of half-basket weave and two types of plain weave. The

548

main difference in fabric structure between the two types of half-basket weave is the twist direction of the warp and weft yarns; one has Z-twist yarn in both warp and weft directions and the other has S-twist warp yarn and Z-twist weft. However, all the half-basket weave fragments have similar fabric count of 50 (warp) by 23 (weft) per inch or 20 by 9 per centimeter (cm), which results a near 2:1 ratio between warp and weft yarn density. The two different plain weave fragments have different fabric count with one being higher than the other one.

When compared with other known sail cloth, it was found that the sail of the *Vasa* (1628) is a plain woven structure (Bengtsson, 1975) and both warp and weft yarns have a Z-twist (Cooke, et al., 2002). The fabric count of the *Vasa* sail cloth is 10/12 warp by 7/8 weft per centimeter or 11/14 warp by 9/11 weft per centimeter. It seems that both of the sail cloth compared here have similar weft yarn density but the warp yarn density of the sail cloth reported in this study doubled that of the *Vasa* sail cloth as the fabric structure changed from plain weave to half-basket weave. When compared with the fore topsail of *HMS Victory* (1805), it was found that the sail cloth of *Victory* is a half-basket weave, having a fabric count of 21.6 (warp) by 8.3 (weft) per centimeter (Garside and Wyeth, 2005). These data are very close to those obtained in this study. The yarns' twist direction of the *Victory* sail cloth, however, was not reported or found.

The sail seam fragment examined in this study was also compared with those reported from *Vasa* and *Victory* mentioned above. When it was observed, the author felt that the seam seems to be a flat seam due to the existence of the middle stitching line. The seams of the *Vasa* sail is reported to be double round seam in which each of the two stitching lines is sewn at edge by folding down one piece of cloth about one inch with the other piece topping the

folding end – the details of double round seam construction were illustrated and explained by Bengtsson (1975). The width of the seam or fold is about one inch, which is not too much different from the 1.125 inch seam width measured in this study. However, there is no middle stitching line through the double round seam on the *Vasa* sail and no stitch density data was reported. Different from the *Vasa* sail seam, the fore topsail of *Victory* is assembled by a flat seam (Bartos, 2005). Its seam allowance or width is 1-3/4 inch, and the flat seam stitch density ranges from 120 to 150 per yard, while the middle stitching or stuck has a density of 78 stitches per yard.

When cordage or roping elements were compared, it was observed that Z-twist boltropes were employed on *Vasa* (based on the image presented in Bengtsson, 1975). However, Bengtsson described "the cordage used was three-stranded, left hand laid and of tarred hemp, with a 3-1/2 in (0.08 m) circumference in the larger sails and a 2 in (0.05 m) one in the smaller" (p.35). It is obvious that 'left hand laid' refers the Z-twist, which differs from the definition used in this study, right hand laid or plain laid. Three-strand hawser with Z-twist appeared often in the study by Sanders (2010).

Comparison of provenance and value
Based on the above comparative construction data between the sailcloth and cordage fragments of *QAR* shipwreck and those from other shipwrecks, i.e. *Vasa and Victory*, it seems that the shipwreck investigated is of similar European origin. The material type of the *QAR* sail cloth showed that the ship was from a later period than that of *Vasa*. However, similar marlin hitch was observed from both of them. The seam type of the small fragment from *QAR* resembles that of *Victory* sail rather than that of *Vasa* in terms of the number of stitch lines. This is another indication of European origin of the ship

questioned in this study. The identification of the shipwreck can eventually help to add knowledge as to when the center stitching method started for the purpose of increasing the durability of the sail's seam. The boltrope fragment described and compared above is of greater importance to the ship itself due to the more detailed structural elements presented. More functional details and values of the sail seam and the boltrope fragments can be revealed through supplementary data investigation by referring to related descriptions in literature and opinions or information provided by experts in the area of study.

Step 3: Supplementary data

Marquardt (1992) provided following details of seam construction about 18th century of rigs and rigging practices:

> When sailcloth was joined, the double flat seams were supposed to be sewn together with 108 to 116 stitches per yard of length. The widths of these flat seam were $1^1/_2$in for the fore, main and topsails in ships with more than 50 guns, and under $1^1/_4$in for these sails in ships of 44 guns. All other sails had flat seams of 1 inch width. The middle of the seams of courses and topsails were also stitched over the whole length with double seaming twine with sixty-eight to seventy-two stitches per yard. In merchant ships it was common to give each seam two rows of stitches when the sail was half worn, which would last until sail wore out. (pp.173-174)

The above supplementary data seems to support the QAR347.006 seam fragment's construction identification presented above. Louie Bartos however, a sail maker and historian, suggested that the QAR sail seam seems to be a double round seam rather than a flat seam due to the ridge observed at one side of the seam fragment (Focht, 2008). However, center stitching

was not known to be used on double round seam, by either writing or recovered sails dated in the 17th century or earlier. If this is confirmed, then the QAR seam sample may serve as the transition example between 17th century and 18th century sail making.

It is also known that the size of foot rope is the largest, leech rope is a little smaller, and the head rope is much smaller. According to all the boltrope sizes used on different sails mentioned by Marquardt (1992), the size of head ropes on different sails are rarely larger than 3 inches. According to Goodwin (1988), the 20-gun ship *Blandford*, a similar ship to QAR (personal communication with Chris Southerly), has the largest boltrope of 3.5 inches used on the main course foot and leech, and all the head ropes are 1.5 inches to 1 inch. As to the boltrope found in QAR 387.017 and 387.018, its size is about 3.5 inches. Thus, the sail fragments from QAR 387.000 are very possibly from either the foot rope or leech rope adjacent to the crew rather than from the head rope of a sail, similar identification was also given by Mr. Bartos from his expert's opinion (Focht, 2008). The concrete of QAR 387.000 was found at the shipwreck location N43 E76, which is considered as the aft deck hosting the mizzenmast near the officer's quarters (personal communication with Wendy Welsh). If this is confirmed, there is a possibility that the sail fragments with boltropes are from the mizzen sail which is the largest sail with the largest blot ropes for its foot and leech. All other mizzen sails are smaller with smaller boltropes.

Conclusions (Step 4)

After completing the investigation or data collection through the above three steps, observation, comparative and supplementary, the following conclusion remarks could be reached in regarding to both the methodology applied and the artifacts studied in this study. First, the material history methodology seems to be very helpful as a systematic guide for data collection and inquiry. Although most of the research studies on historical objects do have content resembling the steps and data elements included in this method, such as literature review, the steps and the data elements of this material history methodology have the advantage of keeping the researchers go through the data collection systematically while minimizing the pre-conceived notions or bias. The author of this study felt that this guide should be taken as a fluid process in which the data collections can happen at several steps simultaneously.

The *QAR* textile artifacts, although small and fragmented, revealed a lot of important information about the shipwreck. The fabrics investigated can be concluded as sail cloth, either the sail itself or the sail's lining fabric. The interesting question that needs to be investigated further is the warp and weft yarn's twist direction of the sail cloth, especially when different twist directions between the warp and weft yarns being identified. The data collected from the sail seam fragment QAR 347.006 revealed its unique value to the history of sail construction if it can be further confirmed as a double round seam but with middle stitching. If it is a true double round seam, it can serve as first example of its kind in the study of sail history reported so far. The cordages, all being three-strand hawser type with Z-twist, are similar to the cordages often used and applied to a ship's rigging of European origin from 17th to 18th century. The sizes of the cordages investigated in this study, except the boltrope of *QAR* 387.018, are all between 2 to 3 in or 0.05 to 0.076 m in circumference. The size of the boltrope along with its attached sail cloth layers and the marlin hitch pointed its particular sail location as well as possible sail in specific when all the data were considered.

The results reported in this study also support the argument or comment by Sanders (2010) that as far as rigging elements are concerned, there is a lack of understanding about their recording or description method. The author of this study felt the same way when going through the three steps of data collection. There are confusions as to the terms or structural elements of cordage and sail cloth applied in different studies. Hopefully, the data provided in this study, although from very small sail and cordage fragments from this particular *QAR* shipwreck, could add some information about our understanding of sail construction and rigging through history. In addition the information could be useful when being compared and analyzed with other findings of *QAR* shipwreck studies.

References:
Bartos, L. (2005). David steel's *The Art of Sailmaking & HMS Victory*'s fore topsail. *Sea History*, 111 (summer), 10-13.

Bengtsson, S. (1975). The sails of the Wasa. *International Journal of Nautical Archaeology and Underwater Exploration* 4: 27–41.

Cooke, B.; Christiansen, C.; and Hammarlund, L. (2002). Viking woolen square-sails and fabric cover factor. *The International Journal of Nautical Archaeology*, 31(2), 202-210.
Dixon, K. A. (1957). Systematic cordage structure analysis. *American Anthropologist* 59(1): 134-136.

Focht, A. (2008). Blackbeard sails again? Conservation of textiles from the Queen Anne's Revenge shipwreck (31CR314). *Unpublished independent study research draft*. East Carolina University, Greenville of NC.

Garside, P. and Wyeth, P. (2005). Assessing the physical state of the Fore-topsail of

HMS Victory. In R. Janaway, and P. Wyeth, (eds.) *Postprints First Annual Conference of the AHRC Research Centre for Textile Conservation and Textile Studies, Scientific Analysis of Ancient and Historic Textiles: Informing Preservation, Display and Interpretation.* London, UK, Archetype, 118-125.

Goodwin, P. (1988). *Anatomy of the ship: the 20-gun ship Blandford.* Maryland: Naval Institute Press.

Marquardt, K. (1992) *Eighteenth Century Rigs and Rigging.* Conway: Maritime Press.

Osborne, D. and Osborne, C. (1954). Twines and terminologies. *American Anthropologist* 56: 1093-1101.

Pearce, S. M. (1994). *Interpreting Objects and Collections.* London: Routledge.

Perrin, W. G. (1929). *Boteler's Dialogures.* London: Navy Records Society.

Personal communication with Chris Southerly (2006), *QAR Project Archaeology.* Address: Underwater Archaeology Branch, 1528 Ft. Fisher Boulevard South, Kure Beach, NC 28449. Email: chris.southerly@ncdcr.gov

Personal communication with Wendy Welsh (2005), *QAR Project Conservation Laboratory.* Address: 1157 VOA Site C Road, West Research Campus, East Carolina University, Greenville, NC 27834. Email: wendy.welsh@ncdcr.gov

Sanders, D. (2010). Know the ropes: The need to record ropes and rigging on wreck-sties and some techniques for doing so. *The International Journal of Nautical Archaeology*, 39(1), 2-26.

Smith, S. (1985). Towards a material history methodology. *Material History Bulletin*, 22, 31-40.

Weber-Partenheimer, W. and Lenzburg AG., A. (1971). Ropemaking, then and now: Enough rope? *CIBA-GEIGY Review* 1971/1: 2-15.

5.5 (Sc. PR)

Polyethylene Glycol Treatments for Basketry on the Northwest Coast of North America

Ellen Carrlee* and Dana K. Senge
Alaska State Museum, 395 Whittier Street,
Juneau AK 99801 USA
*E-mail: ellen.carrlee@alaska.gov

Abstract

Basketry artifacts discovered in wet sites have been routinely treated with polyethylene glycol (PEG) since the 1960's. Although the vast literature on PEG treatment of shipwrecked wood informs the treatment decisions for this material, basketry treatments often do not behave in the manner expected for waterlogged wood. This is in part due to the size and geometry of the material, as well as the parts of the tree used, such as bark and root. A group of waterlogged archaeological baskets at the Alaska State Museum provided the basis of an investigation into better PEG protocols for treatment of this material. Ancient baskets treated with 20% PEG 400 and 5% PEG 4000 were not adequately stabilized for exhibition and study. Testing suggests 55% PEG 3350 is a better solution for the remaining baskets in this group still in need of treatment, and consolidation with 10% Butvar B-98® in ethanol is effective in stabilizing the fragile baskets that had previously been treated with PEG.

Keywords: polyethylene glycol, PEG, basketry, consolidation, Butvar, waterlogged, archaeological

1. Introduction to PEG Treatment For Basketry

Basketry artifacts discovered in water saturated archaeological sites (wet sites) on the Northwest Coast of North America have been routinely treated with polyethylene glycol (PEG) since the 1960's. These artifacts range in age from a few centuries to more than five thousand years old. The vast literature regarding PEG treatment decisions focuses on the needs of shipwrecked wood. Basketry treatments utilizing PEG often do not behave in the predicted manner of waterlogged wood. This is in part due to the size of the woven elements of the basketry structure, as well as the parts of the tree processed for the fabrication of these artifacts, such as bark and root. The cellular structure of some basketry material, such as inner bark, differs enough from trunk wood to require a variation in treatment (Florian 1982, Purdy 1996).

The ideal approach to treatment of archaeological basketry would be to assess the degree of degradation before treatment and apply the proper PEG protocol. This can be more challenging for basketry than for wood. One simple method is to air dry a small sample fragment and observe shrinkage and deformation. Dramatic changes in dimensions from wet to dry can be expected to correlate to a more deteriorated the cellular structure. Since the complex small shapes made by the basketry weave can be difficult to measure accurately for comparison before and after drying, photographing on graph paper can be useful technique. McCawley (1977) has reported that waterlogged wood in sound or slightly degraded condition shows variation in shrinkage in the three major directions: 0.5% longitudinally, 3-6% radially, and 5-10% tangentially. For more deteriorated waterlogged wood, these differences are less distinct.

Another method to determine degree of degradation involves comparing the density of the archaeological wood to the density of sound, non-waterlogged wood. Archaeological and waterlogged wood is expected to be less dense because of the structure lost in deterioration. Methods of quantifying this include the computer program PEGCON (Cooke and Grattan 1990), and moisture content readings (Boone and Wengert 1998, Hamilton 1998).

However, these methods are less accurate with basketry than with wood. Measuring density is easiest with a solid chunk of wood. Tiny woven basketry elements are challenging to measure accurately because of the small size and geometry of the warps and wefts. Moisture content readings cannot be considered accurate using equipment in a typical conservation laboratory because the sample size available is so much smaller than recommended. For example, Boone and Wengert (1998) recommend 100g of oven-dry sample to be used for measuring moisture content. While this may be possible for waterlogged ship's timbers, 100g is far greater than the sample permitted for analyzing a basket, particularly since the analysis is destructive. The weight of a generous basketry sample that might be available for testing is a mere 0.1 g dry weight (0.5g fully waterlogged.) In addition to the tiny size, basketry is often made of root or bark, while the reference standard is trunk wood.

Light microscopy has been used extensively to identify deterioration mechanisms in archaeological wood. While conservators are trained in the principles and use of the polarized light microscope, successful analysis of archaeological basketry can be difficult without specialized training and practice. Most of the important references in the conservation literature are authored by scientists with considerable backgrounds in plant anatomy and pathology. In order to examine archaeological wood, familiarity with the structures present in sound wood of the same species and part of the tree (root, branch, trunk) is needed (Friedman 1978, Florian et al. 1990). Techniques used by experienced microscopists, such as examination under half polarized light or fluorescence, and the use of staining may also be helpful (Florian et al. 1990, Bjordal and Nilsson 2002).

In addition to a firm grasp of wood anatomy, an understanding of the various factors contributing to archaeological degradation is needed to successfully interpret the images under the microscope.

Micromorphological changes include deterioration of layers in the cell wall, fungal decay, bacterial attack, impregnation with foreign substances or staining from the burial environment, missing or eroded structural elements, and even problems with sampling and mounting techniques (Florian 1990, Hedges 1990, Blanchette et al. 1990, Blanchette and Hoffmann 1994). It is difficult for a conservator who does not regularly work with wood anatomy and archaeological material to make a confident analysis of archaeological basketry with light microscopy. For example, secondary cell wall can sometimes look present when in fact only amorphous granular residue remains (Hoffman and Jones 1990, Bjordal and Nilsson 2002). Caution is in order for determining degree of deterioration from light microscopy alone.

The conservation literature on the use of PEG to stabilize waterlogged wood indicates several variables affect PEG treatment: deterioration of the basketry elements due to age, use and burial environment, species, anatomical structure of the wood (bark, trunk, root etc), concentration of PEG used, molecular mass of PEG used, duration of soaking, and heating during impregnation. Low molecular mass PEG (PEG 200-600) is thought to penetrate more deeply into the secondary cell wall and the smaller spaces in the wood than higher molecular mass PEG. It is also more mobile and hygroscopic. If too much is used, the surface of the artifact will look wet, feel moist and soft, attract dust, and be humidity-sensitive. High molecular mass PEG (PEG 1500-6000) does not penetrate the secondary cell wall because the molecule is too large, but it acts like a filler, impregnating the lumens and interstices between the cells. Too much high molecular mass PEG can leave white crusts on the surface, result in a heavy artifact, and be more difficult to dry. Higher molecular mass PEG is thought to cause structural damage if used on wood with fairly intact cell wall structure, perhaps from the osmotic pressure as the hygroscopic PEG pulls water out of the smaller structures where the larger PEG molecule cannot penetrate. (Grattan 1986, Hoffmann 1990). A combination of high and low molecular masses of PEG is often the solution (Hoffmann1986, Johns 1998, Hoffmann *et al.* 2004) but it can be tricky to determine the right mixture for solid wood, and basketry is even more challenging.

A review of the PEG literature and previous treatments at the Alaska State Museum suggests a bias that basketry materials surviving in the archaeological context have intact secondary cell wall structure that is available to be bulked. This bias would lead to treatment with low molecular mass PEG. However, the results indicate that use of predominantly low molecular mass PEG was not enough to impart the stability needed for study and exhibition.

2. PEG Treatments at The Alaska State Museum

Much of the past PEG based treatment for waterlogged basketry on the Northwest Coast has followed the lead of Gerald Grosso's 50% PEG 1500 used on Ozette site material. PEG 1500 is a combination of 41/59 weight percent mixture of PEG 300 and PEG 1450, with an average molecular mass of 500-600. The name of the product was changed to PEG 540 Blend after 1976. At the Alaska State Museum, several PEG combinations have been attempted, and comparison is informative, but limited. Caution is needed when comparing the results of basketry that may be made of different materials, have differing degrees of deterioration, or suffering from the all-too-frequent challenge of poorly documented treatments.

The Castle Hill Basket (Figure 1, 49-SIT-002) is thought to be spruce root and was excavated damp but not fully waterlogged from a site dating to the Russian-American period (at least 150 years BP) in Sitka, Alaska in 1998. It was not impregnated but slowly air-dried in a refrigerator with good results. It has an easily readable surface, slightly flexible woody feel and can be easily handled or flipped for study.

The Tawah Creek Basket (Figure 2, 49-YAK-019) is thought to be spruce root and was removed from a waterlogged freshwater site in 2004 in the Yakutat area with fish weir stakes that were radiocarbon dated approximately 130 years BP. It had a three-dimensional structure when found, and retained that shape though treatment with 50% Carbowax PEG 540 Blend at 60°C for one month. It was slowly dried at -35°C in a non-vacuum freezer. Surface appearance and flexibility are adequate, although the broken edges could benefit from some additional consolidation.

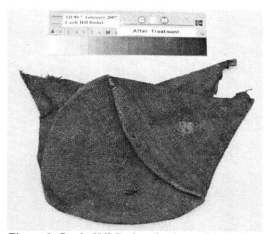

Figure 1. *Castle Hill Basket slowly air-dried without impregnation with PEG*

Figure 2. *Tawah Creek Basket treated with 50% PEG 540 at 60°C for one month*

The Montana Creek Fish Trap (Figure 3, 49-JUN-453) was found eroding from a riverbank near Juneau, Alaska and excavated in 1989-1991. It was radiocarbon dated at 400-600 years BP. The trap has sizable hemlock and spruce elements, but also basketry-like spruce root lashings.

Treatment notes suggest the trap was impregnated unheated over several months with 10% PEG 200, 5% PEG 1000 and 10% Carbowax Compound 20M. Polyethylene glycol Compound 20M has an average molecular mass between 15,000 to 20,000 and is not typically used in conservation. Its use at the Alaska State Museum was experimental based on a recommendation and free sample from Dow Chemical Company. Due to its size, the trap was slowly air-dried after impregnation. The trap materials fared very well, with no darkening, but the spruce root was rather brittle and broken in many places. Small wads of Japanese tissue saturated with a mixture of wheat starch paste and a small amount of polyvinyl acetate emulsion provided support and adhesion for the spruce root lashings (Carrlee 2005).

Figure 3. Spruce root lashings, 0.5cm wide, on the Montana Creek Fish Trap. Likely impregnated with low concentrations of low, medium and very high molecular masses of PEG. Five of the diagonal strips are painted Tyvek® reinforcing bands adhered with Acryloid B-72®.

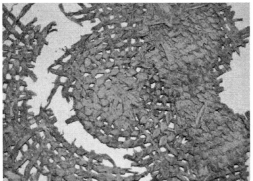

Figure 4. Detail of the Thorne River Basket under-treated with 20% PEG 400 and 5% PEG 4000 in need of supplementary consolidation.

The Thorne River Basket (Figure 4, 49-CRG-433) was found as one large fragment in a waterlogged site on Prince of Wales Island, Alaska in 1994 and radiocarbon dated 5450 years BP. It was confirmed spruce root and treated with unheated 20% PEG 400 and 5% PEG 4000 over 6 months, then slowly dried at -35°C in a non-vacuum freezer. The basket has a pleasing appearance but a soft, spongy rubbery quality. It sheds fibers readily and cannot be handled without risk of breakage or unraveling the weave at the edges.

Figure 5. Detail of one of the South Baranof Island baskets under-treated. with 20% PEG 400 and 5% PEG 4000 in need of supplementary consolidation.

The South Baranof Island baskets from a waterlogged site in Southeast Alaska (49-XPA-78) were radiocarbon dated at 4,550 years BP. Only one of the six baskets (Figure 5) from this site has been treated; the other five remain waterlogged pending results of this study. The treated basket was impregnated with the same protocol as the Thorne River Basket, with similar results. Surprisingly, this basket was identified by plant anatomist Mary-Lou Florian as mountain hemlock *Tsuga heterophylla* root instead of the expected spruce root. There is no known tradition of weaving with hemlock root (Henrikson and Criswell 2009). The basket is in two large fragments and about a dozen smaller fragments. Three of the smaller fragments were used in this investigation to determine an appropriate consolidant for the under-treated Thorne River and South Baranof Island baskets. Another waterlogged item from the 49-XPA-78 group, a semi-rigid knotted netting artifact, provided sample material for exploration into a better impregnation protocol.

3. Testing Higher Molecular Mass PEG For Basketry

3.1 Objectives of Testing

The shortcomings of the PEG treatment used for the Thorne River and South Baranof Island baskets revealed the need for a better PEG treatment technique for the remaining baskets found at the South Baranof Island site. A knotted spruce root netting artifact recovered in hundreds of fragments provided sample material for testing various concentrations of high molecular mass PEG. Reconstruction of this artifact is unlikely, and the large number of similar small fragments gives good comparative study samples. All fragments had been stored in distilled water in a refrigerator since their discovery in 1995. Limited biological growth had occurred in the past. Water was rarely changed. Since 2006, little biological growth has been noted. All fragments were fragile. Extreme shrinkage and distortion to an air-dried fragment (figure 7) suggested advanced deterioration. The testing aimed to answer the following questions:

- Can we develop a PEG protocol that will make the waterlogged artifacts in group 95-12 stable enough for study and exhibition?
- What are the optimum concentrations of PEG for this basketry?
- What are the optimum molecular masses of PEG for this basketry?
- Will increasing the amount of high molecular mass PEG help?
- Does heating during treatment provide a benefit?
- Will the treated artifact be vulnerable to high humidity?

One set of samples was impregnated in a lab oven at 60°C to evaluate the potential advantages and disadvantages of heating. Heating may speed and enhance penetration as well as the solubility of high molecular mass PEG (Grattan and Clark 1987). However, heating was thought to contribute to undesirable darkening for the objects treated at the Ozette site (Cooke, Cooke and Grattan 1994). Heat is an accelerant to deterioration and PEG treatments for leather in the literature have mostly eliminated heat altogether for that reason. Heat is also thought to break down the PEG molecule, and some sources have advised against heating PEG during the impregnation (Bilz et al 1994). Christensen (1970) found less osmotic collapse of oak using PEG 4000 at room temperature than he did with heating. In both cases, no impregnation of the oak core took place, but collapse only occurred in the hot bath. The Tawah Creek basket at the ASM was heated with good results. (Carbowax PEG 540 Blend at 50% concentration for a month at 60°C).

3.2 Selection of Concentrations and Molecular Masses

Samples fell into three main groups: samples treated at room temperature, samples treated at 60°C, samples treated briefly in a 160°C oven and then at 60°C. (This third grouping was the result of an error that led the samples to be overheated for approximately 12 hours). Each group had five fragments treated with various concentrations and molecular masses:

20% PEG 400, then 20% PEG 3350
Rationale: PEG 400 should enter the secondary cell wall and bond there, while the 3350 will fill in the larger voids and give strength. This is slightly higher than the concentration of 3350 PEG used previously on the South Baranof Island material, but that treatment did not give enough strength. PEG 400 is kept at 20% to hopefully prevent excess from oozing out. Ozette site material that was re-treated with 15% PEG 200 and 10% PEG 4000 was the subject of additional consolidation tests with POLYOX® coagulant, suggesting the PEG treatment was not adequate (Cooke *et al.* 1994).

20% PEG 400, then 35% PEG 3350
Rationale: High molecular mass PEG is supposed to perform well on highly degraded wood (Hoffmann, 1984). The South Baranof Island basketry is very old

and treatment with mostly low molecular mass PEG was not fully successful. This suggests the basketry may be more degraded than predicted, and may respond better to high molecular mass PEG.

20% PEG 400, then 55% PEG 3350
Rationale: Some references suggest avoiding the eutectic, but others (Jensen et al. 2002) seem to suggest that aiming for the eutectic is desirable for even distribution. Theoretically, ice crystals form in a way that blocks even distribution of the PEG unless the eutectic is used. Apparently, concentrations lower than the eutectic also expand on freezing, causing cracks. At the eutectic, the 9% expansion of ice is counterbalanced by 7% volumetric contraction of PEG. A medieval log house in Oslo was treated successfully with 50-55% PEG 4000 (Astrup 1994). The successful Tawah Creek basket treatment by Scott Carrlee (unpublished, Alaska State Museum) used PEG 540 near the eutectic.

55% PEG 3350 alone
Rationale: Since the Jensen et al. article (2002) seems to suggest PEG near the eutectic is optimal if an even distribution is the aim, even though other articles specifically indicate the eutectic should be avoided, it would be worthwhile to isolate the PEG 3350 to test this. Perhaps it simplifies the freezing process to only use one molecular mass of PEG. In addition, Astrup (1994) and Hoffman (1990) found some success in their treatments with around 50% PEG 4000 in degraded softwoods. Strætkvern (2001) reported compression strength of wood is greater for high molecular mass PEG treatments done without low molecular mass PEG.

20% PEG 400, then 75% PEG 3500
Rationale: Several sources report success with high concentrations of high molecular mass PEG for highly degraded wood (DeJong 1978, Keene 1982, DeWitte et al. 1984, Jover 1994, Kaenel 1994).

3.3 Testing Protocol
Fragments of similar size with no obvious joins to other fragments were selected for testing and photographed. Each sample was sewn between layers of nylon mesh screening with polyester thread to hold the fragment securely, allow good circulation of solution around the fragment, and permit handling. Each PEG concentration was increased incrementally approximately every two weeks. PEG 400 was increased in 5% increments, PEG 3350 was increased in 5 or 10% increments. In each case, the concentrations were increased gradually to minimize the risk of osmotic shock from pressure differentials between the fluid inside the fragile wood and the fluid in the container. The time to reach desired concentration took between 3 and 6 months. PEG 3350 was supplied as a powder and was dissolved in a bit of the test solution using a hotplate before adding it to the unheated and heated sample containers. For the unheated samples, the addition of the warm PEG 3350 caused them to be cloudy for two to three minutes before becoming clear again. All samples were removed from solution at the same time. Each sample was dipped in a beaker of distilled water to rinse excess PEG from the surface and gently tamped with KimWipes® to remove as much water as possible before freezing. Fragments were weighed and placed in a non-vacuum freezer (-35°C) to drive off the excess water through sublimation (solid ice directly to vapor). Air drying without the freezer would send liquid water to water vapor, and the strong surface tension of liquid water contributes to collapse of cell structure as the water evaporates (Grattan 1986). Samples were regularly weighed to determine the end point of drying (when weight no longer decreased,) and fragments were all removed from the freezer at the same time. Concern about shrinkage or distortion during final air drying required a method to compare the fragments at this stage to the final result. After removal from the freezer, fragments were taken out of the nylon mesh and photographed on graph paper immediately. They were photographed on graph paper again a week later to check for possible distortion from the evaporation of residual water at room temperature (Figure 6). One month after they were removed from the

freezer, they were subjected to several 12 hour cycles of 80% humidity to determine if the treatment rendered the fragments vulnerable to changes at high RH. While the Alaska State Museum has stable RH, there are less stable locations in Alaska that may wish to exhibit the artifacts after treatment. Exhibition and storage in uncontrolled humidity is a reality for many PEG treated archaeological baskets.

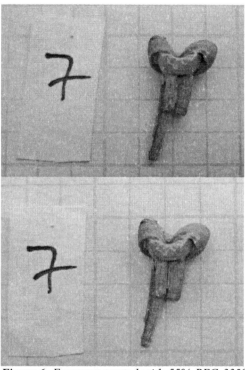

Figure 6. Fragment treated with 55% PEG 3350 at room temperature. Photographed on graph paper immediately out of the freezer (top) and one week later (bottom) to check for distortion.

3.4 Results and Interpretation:

In this experiment, the percent weight loss in the freezer is used to interpret water loss and possible impregnation with PEG (Table 1). Theoretically, in comparison to the air-dried control, lower percent weight loss during drying means less water left in the system, indicating PEG molecules replaced water molecules during treatment, reducing the amount of water that could be lost from the structure during drying. According to this theory, all the room temperature fragments had about the same amount of water loss after drying, and therefore a similar amount of PEG penetration. At

higher concentrations, the heated fragments had less water loss, indicating better penetration of PEG 3350 than the room temperature samples. Possible explanations of this greater penetration of molecules that may include: size variation through thermal breakdown, better diffusion, possible expansion of wood structure with heat to allow better penetration, or the enhanced solubility of heated PEG. Weight loss in the freezer for the treated fragments ranged from 10% to 33%, compared to the air-dried untreated fragment which lost 40% of its weight.

The samples with lowest concentrations were distinctly spongier to the touch than those concentrations of 55% 3350 and higher, in spite of similar amounts of weight loss. Surprisingly, results for 20% PEG 400 with 55% PEG 3350 were nearly the same as the results for 55% 3350 alone. Most of the samples showed very little dimensional change after final drying as revealed by before and after photographs on graph paper. All were within a range acceptable for successful treatment.

The waterlogged basketry elements (identified as spruce root) were dark brown in color when waterlogged before treatment. After treatment, the samples treated at room temperature all appeared a very pale beige-gray or driftwood-like color, with no obvious color difference with higher concentrations. The samples treated at 60°C were all pale yellow ochre-grayish in color, but still much paler than most historical basketry. The samples treated at 160°C then 60°C were a rich brown burnt umber color, ironically more like historical spruce root basketry in color, and samples treated with higher concentrations of PEG were darker in color. The untreated air-dried control sample was the darkest of all (dark burnt umber in color) and extremely brittle, shrunken, and deformed (Figure 7). Almost all samples had some whitish powdery PEG residue/crusts in the crevices. This did not seem to increase with concentration, but was more pronounced on the samples impregnated at room temperature. The waxy PEG could not easily be brushed from the surface (the brush tended to drag it around) but localized application of ethanol with a brush under magnification seemed to drive the PEG below the surface and improve the appearance. All impregnated samples were placed in the humidity chamber and raised to 80% RH for 12 hours to evaluate effect of high RH on the concentrations and molecular weights of PEG used. No oozing or surface changes were observed on the samples or on the blotter paper below them during this first test. However, when the RH test was repeated, the unheated and the heated to 160°C samples that had been treated with the 75% PEG solution in water turned dark and waxy, oozing PEG-like material. This did not revert back upon stabilization of the RH, and did not seem to get worse with repeated RH tests. The sample treated with 75% PEG heated to 60°C did not ooze or get dark, even on repeated RH fluctuations.

Table 1. Percentage weight loss

PEG Concentration	Results of treatment at room temperature	Results of treatment at 60°C	Results of treatment at 160°C (12hours) and 60°C
20% PEG 400 20% PEG 3350	20 days at -35°C 22% weight loss in non-vacuum freezer	65 days at -35°C 22% weight loss in non-vacuum freezer	40 days at -35°C 33% weight loss in non-vacuum freezer
20% PEG 400 35% PEG 3350	40 days at -35°C 23% weight loss in non-vacuum freezer	90 days at -35°C 21% weight loss in non-vacuum freezer	40 days at -35°C 25% weight loss in non-vacuum freezer
20% PEG 400 55% PEG 3350	65 days at -35°C 23% weight loss in non-vacuum freezer	90 days at -35°C 23% weight loss in non-vacuum freezer	20 days, at -35°C 22% weight loss in non-vacuum freezer
55% PEG 3350	90 days at -35°C 23% weight loss in non-vacuum freezer	65 days at -35°C 18% weight loss in non-vacuum freezer	20 days at -35°C 22% weight loss in non-vacuum freezer
20% PEG 400 75% PEG 3350	90 days at -35°C 20% weight loss in non-vacuum freezer	20 days at -35°C 10% weight loss in non-vacuum freezer	65 days at -35°C 18% weight loss in non-vacuum freezer

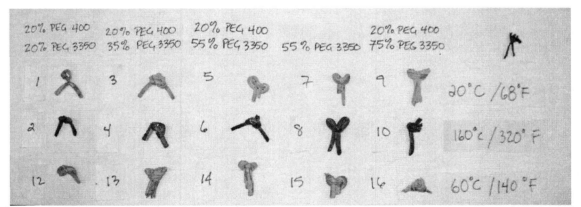

Figure 7. *These waterlogged archaeological basketry samples test increasing concentrations of PEG 3350. Concentrations increase from left to right, with top row representing unheated, middle row heated to 160°C then 60°C, and bottom row heated to 60°C. Untreated air-dried sample in upper right.*

4. Testing Consolidants for Under-PEGed Baskets
4.1 Objectives of Testing
Identifying a good consolidant for the undertreated baskets was challenging because materials that might consolidate wood well are not the same as ones that are expected to bond well to a waxy surface such as PEG. A review of the literature indicated that many of the adhesives said to

bond well with PEG are not conservation-friendly. These included casein glues, hide glues, hot-set phenolic resin, cold-set urea resin and resorcinol resin (Stamm 1959, Mitchell 1972). Empirical testing was carried out to examine various potential consolidants commonly available to conservators and archaeologists.

4.1.1 Testing Protocol

The testing done was empirical in nature, meant to narrow down the possibilities to test on fragments of the under PEGged basketry. Rice (1990) thinks that PEG chemically interferes with the formation of bonds between the wood and the adhesive and that PEG gets in the way of further consolidation with polymers such as acrylics. Testing the bond of potential consolidants with PEG was one aspect of the empirical testing. PEG 3350 was placed in a disposable aluminum weighing pan on a hotplate over low heat. Patches of molten PEG 3350 were brushed onto the ends of two glass microscope slides and allowed to cool. The two patches were then adhered with a drop of test adhesive. The free end of the top slide was supported by a blank slide. After drying overnight, the supporting slide was pulled out to cause slight stress on the join and identify the weakest bonds. Then one slide was picked up and shaken manually to test the strength of the bond. Finally, the slides were manually pulled apart. Under magnification, each adhesive was picked at with a sharp tool to test how easily it might peel off the PEG. The test on glass slides was repeated a second time. An identical test was done with molten PEG 3350 on the surface of flat wooden sticks. Several products were tested that are not ideal for conservation but may be tempting to archaeologists. Hide glue, cyanoacrylate, wood glue, and cellulose nitrate were tested because they are mentioned in the hobbyist literature concerning PEG and green wood and they are more widely available than adhesives which have good aging properties and are readily reversible. Of those four adhesives, only cellulose nitrate (Duco®) performed at the level of the final samples.

Results narrowed the field of choices to seven: Acryloid B-72®, AYAT®, Butvar B-98®, BEVA D-8 dispersion®, Acrysol WS-24®, Lascaux Medium for Consolidation®, and POLYOX® WSR coagulant. These seven were then tested on silk crepeline and gossamer nylon fabrics by both pipette dropper and brush application to see how the consolidants might penetrate small spaces in the textile weave and to reveal qualities of flexibility and glossiness. The final five consolidants were applied by brush on five small fragments of the South Baranof Island basket that had been under-treated with PEG. Samples needed to be flipped frequently during drying to avoid pooling of consolidant on the underside.

4.1.2 Results and Interpretation

Samples that failed at the bond between the two patches of PEG on the glass slides and the wooden sticks were interpreted as weaker than samples that failed at the PEG/substrate bond. Samples that did not penetrate into the PEG but formed a skin were considered poor candidates. Consolidants tested on the fabric were examined for gloss, penetration, and flexibility. On the archaeological basketry, samples were examined for gloss, darkening, and flexibility in addition to stabilizing the fragile structure.

4.2 Promising Consolidants Tested on Basketry Fragments

4.2.1 Butvar B-98®

Several sources (Grattan 1980, Sakuno and Schniewind 1990, Schniewind 1990, Spirydowicz et al. 2001) suggested Butvar B-98® might be successful on archaeological wood not treated with PEG. Tímár-Balázsy et al. (1998) reports that on textiles, polyvinyl alcohols and polyvinyl butyrals can get stiffer and the textiles are said to suffer frictional damage from the sharp edges of the particles when the adhesive become aged, rigid, and cracked. Sakuno and Schniewind (1990) found the adhesive strength of Butvar B-98® higher than Acryloid B-72® and AYAT® but less than PVA emulsion.

Figure 8. South Baranof Island basket fragments under-treated with PEG. Top fragment consolidated with Butvar B-98® 10% in ethanol and bottom fragment unconsolidated.

Schniewind and Carlson (1990) also mention that Butvar B-98® is better than Acryloid B-72® for strength. In the Alaska State Museum testing, 10% Butvar B-98® in ethanol was the best consolidant choice (Figure 8). It had among the strongest bonds of all adhesives tested, although weaker on the wooden stick than on the glass slide. It did seem stronger than Acryloid B-72® when manipulated with the fingers. It penetrated the fabric well, looked slightly glossy, and was flexible without being brittle, but not as flexible as Lascaux Medium or Polyox. No noticeable darkening occurred, and the physical appearance of the basketry was the best of the five consolidants tested on basketry. Butvar B-98® is a polyvinyl butyral resin manufactured by Monsanto and available through Talas in the U.S.

4.2.2 Acryloid B-72®

Acryloid B-72® has been recommended as a consolidant for deteriorated archaeological wood not treated with PEG by several sources (Grattan 1980, Wang and Schniewind 1985, Sakuno and Schniewind 1990, Schniewind 1990). It also performed well in the reconstruction of an archaeological fish trap treated with PEG (Carrlee 2005).

10% Acryloid B-72® in 50:50 acetone and ethanol was tested empirically at the Alaska State Museum and seemed to be the strongest of all consolidants tested on the PEG-treated basketry (Figure 9). It

penetrated the fabric well, looked slightly glossy, and was flexible without being brittle, but not as flexible as Lascaux Medium or POLYOX. Some darkening occurred and the surface of the basketry was slightly glossy. Acryloid B-72® is an ethyl methacrylate (70%) and methyl acrylate (30%) copolymer manufactured by Rohm and Haas and available through Talas in the U.S.

Figure 9. South Baranof Island basket fragments under-treated with PEG consolidated with 10% Acryloid B-72® in 50:50 acetone and ethanol.

4.2.3 AYAT

Grattan (1980) did not test AYAT®, but listed AYAC® as his third choice of consolidant for dry and degraded wood (not PEG treated) after polyvinyl butyrals and acryloid resins. Schniewind (1990) tested AYAT® on degraded archaeological wood (not PEG treated) and felt it was not hard enough, only penetrated the surface layer, and caused a notable deepening of color. In the Alaska State Museum testing, 10% AYAT® in ethanol was one of the better consolidant choices (Figure 10) and had the best handling properties, flowing smoothly off the brush and wicking visibly into the basketry fibers during application. On the glass and wood mock-ups, it was almost as strong as Acryloid B-72® or Butvar B-98® and penetrated into the PEG. It also penetrated the fabric well, looked slightly glossy, and was flexible without being brittle, but not as flexible as Lascaux Medium® or POLYOX®. No noticeable darkening occurred, and the physical appearance of the basketry was similar to the excellent appearance of Butvar B-98® tested on the basketry. The AYAT® tested was part of the series of polyvinyl acetate resins manufactured by Union Carbide until recently, and the same as the product mentioned by Grattan (1980) and Schniewind (1990). However, the products marketed today through Conservation Support Systems and Talas in the U.S. may not be the same AYAT® available in the past (Alderson 2008). Investigating the performance of the new AYAT® may be an avenue of future research.

Figure 10. South Baranof Island basket fragment under-treated with PEG consolidated with AYAT® 10% in ethanol

4.2.4 Lascaux Medium for Consolidation®

Lascaux Medium for Consolidation® has not been mentioned in the literature for this application, but behaved well during the empirical tests. It was used in full concentration as supplied, and penetrated the fabrics very well. It dried with slight gloss, and was one of the few samples to fail at the PEG-glass bond instead of the PEG-adhesive bond. However on the basketry samples it was unacceptably dark and glossy with a rubbery, plastic-like quality when manipulated with the fingers (Figure 11).

Figure 11. South Baranof Island basket fragment under-treated with PEG and consolidated with Lascaux Medium for Consolidation®.

It also formed a skin in some interstices of the basketry, and formed some areas of glossy pooled excess in spite of frequent

flipping of the fragments during drying. Lascaux Medium for Consolidation® is an aqueous dispersion of acrylic co-polymers based on acrylic ester, styrene, and methacrylate ester manufactured by Lascaux Colours and Restauro in Switzerland and available through Talas in the U.S.

4.2.5 POLYOX® WSR Coagulant

POLYOX® has been used on archaeological material with good results (Bilz *et al.* 1991, Cooke *et al.* 1993). During testing, POLYOX WSR coagulant 2% aqueous solution formed a stringy mess with very poor handling properties. It was not sticky but made long slimy strings that could not easily be broken. However, it seemed to penetrate well into the PEG and form a moderate bond on both wood and glass samples. It also penetrated the fabric very well and dried with little gloss. On the basketry, POLYOX® darkened the surface slightly, had a slight gloss and formed a distracting skin in some interstices of the weaving (Figure 12). The POLYOX® fragment was still very flexible and felt the most fragile of the three fragments tested on basketry fragments when manipulated with the fingers. The product literature suggests mixing in a 1% solution, which may have better handling properties, but as a 2% solution was still too fragile a 1% solution was not attempted. POLYOX® WSR coagulant is a non ionic polyethylene oxide with a molecular mass of 5,000,000 g/mol manufactured by Dow Chemical and provided as a free sample.

Figure 12. South Baranof Island basket fragment under-treated with PEG consolidated with 2% POLYOX® WSR coagulant.

4.3 Other Consolidants Examined

Acrysol WS-24® took a long time to fully dry, but had moderate penetration of PEG and a moderate bond. When tested on fabrics, it was glossy, formed bubbles that dried in place, and formed a stiff film that cracked when flexed. Acrysol WS-24® is often used on archaeological bone.

BEVA D-8® dispersion made a moderate-to-weak bond, and formed a skin that separated readily from the PEG. Further testing on fabric revealed good flexibility but poor penetration, with drops made by the pipette drying in place as droplets on the surface.

Carbowax PEG 3350 failed to bond well on both glass and wood tests, although molten high molecular mass PEG has been frequently mentioned as a surface treatment for artifacts stabilized with PEG (Grattan 1982, Grattan and Clarke 1987, Singley 1988, Muncher 1991, Rodgers 1992).

CM Bond M-4® formed a moderate bond and seemed to partially penetrate into the PEG but also formed a skin that separated readily from the PEG.

Jade 403® PVA emulsion was part of the treatment used by Carrlee (2005) for spruce root lashings of a fish trap treated with PEG. In the current testing, it formed a moderate bond and seemed to partially penetrate the PEG, but did not dry well.

Klucel G® penetrated well but was weak in all tests at both 2% and 20% in ethanol. It has been mentioned in treatment of archaeological wood not treated with PEG by Caple and Murray (1994) and Park (1997).

Lascaux 498 HV® penetrated into the PEG and did not form a separate skin but had a moderate-to-weak bond.

Rabbit skin hide glue gave a poor bond, did not penetrate well, and was noticeably yellow. Hide glues had been mentioned in the literature by Stamm (1959) and Rice (1990).

Super Glue® (cyanoacrylate) did not penetrate well and formed a separate skin. It made a moderate but brittle bond. It has been mentioned in the literature by Zumpe (1981).

Titebond II® wood glue penetrated little, had a poor bond, was slow to dry fully, formed a separate skin that readily slid off the PEG and was noticeably yellow. Mitchell (1972) did not think PVA's worked well to bond wood treated with PEG and Stamm (1959) thought they gave decreasing strength with increasing PEG concentration. Grattan and Clarke (1987) suggested PVA emulsions with a little bit of PEG aided bonding PEG treated wood.

Duco® (cellulose nitrate) made a moderate bond on the glass and wood samples and penetrated well, but lacks good aging properties (Stark 1976).

5. Conclusions

For the ancient waterlogged basketry from the South Baranof Island site, 55% PEG 3350 is the best solution for stabilization. The idea that high molecular mass PEG at around 55% concentration is useful for highly degraded softwoods is in harmony with the conclusions found by others (Astrup 1994 and Hoffmann 1990). This may indicate that these basketry pieces are more degraded than previously thought, with little secondary cell wall available for bonding with low molecular mass PEG. The survival of this material may be due in part to the tenacity of the lignin. Lignin is often the predominant structural element in archaeological wood (Hedges 1990). In addition, lignin content is typically higher in softwoods than in hardwoods (Bidlack *et al.* 1992) and softwood lignin is less easily degraded (Hedges 1990). Ideally, degree of deterioration ought to be determined before treatment in order to guide the proper protocol, but this can be difficult and treatment is often done based on previous examples from other sites. The diminutive size, irregular geometry, and very light weight of basketry fragments make accurate measurement of density and moisture content difficult. In cases where PEG treatment has not afforded adequate stability, 10% Butvar B-98® seems to offer enhanced stability without brittleness or changes in surface appearance. Acryloid B-72® and AYAT® resins may also hold promise. One of the few references on adhesives for PEG (Rice 1990) recommends solvent-borne systems that can dissolve into the surface of the PEG, and solvent borne systems did perform better in the testing on the basketry fragments than aqueous systems. Ongoing research by the authors seeks to determine if examination of archaeological spruce root and cedar bark basketry with light microscopy is adequate to determine degree of degradation and predict correct treatment strategies with PEG. The authors are also compiling a reference of archaeological basketry treatments one the Northwest Coast of North America to help inform future treatment of this material. This work will be presented at the 2010 annual conference of the American Institute for Conservation. An annotated bibliography of articles relevant to PEG basketry conservation is available at http://ellencarrlee.wordpress.com

7. References

Alderson, S., (2008), Posting to the American Institute for Conservation Objects Specialty Group discussion list 12/4/2008. Accessed December 2008.

Astrup, E.E., (1994), "A Medieval Log House in Oslo - Conservation of Waterlogged Softwoods with Polyethylene Glycol", In Proceedings of the 5th ICOM Group on Wet Organic Archaeological Materials Conference, Portland, Maine, 16-20 August 1993, pp 41-50.

Bilz, M., L. Dean, D.W. Grattan, J.C. McCawley, and L. McMillen, (1994), "A Study of the Thermal Breakdown of Polyethylene Glycol", Proceedings of the 5th ICOM Group on Wet Organic Archaeological Materials Conference, Portland, Maine, 16-20 August, 1993, pp 167-197.

Bilz, M, D.W. Grattan, J.A. Logan, C.L. Newton, (1991), "An Investigation of Polyox for the Conservation of Wet Archaeological Textiles and Other Fragile Fibrous Materials", Proceedings of the 4th ICOM Group on Wet Organic Archaeological Materials, Bremerhaven, Germany, 1990, pp 189-208.

Björdal, C. and T. Nilsson, (2002), "Decomposition of Waterlogged Archaeological Wood", Proceedings of the 8th ICOM Group on Wet Organic Archaeological Materials, Stockholm, Sweden, 2001, pp 235-247.

Blanchette, R.A. and P. Hoffmann, (1994), "Degradation Processes in Waterlogged Archaeological Wood", Proceedings of the 5th ICOM Group on Wet Organic Archaeological Materials, Portland, Maine, 1993, pp 111-142.

Blanchette, R.A., Nilsson, T., Daniel, G., and A. Abad, (1990), "Biological Degradation of Wood", in R.M. Rowell and R.J. Barbour (editors), Archaeological Wood Properties, Chemistry and Preservation, Advances in Chemistry Series 225, Washington D.C., American Chemical Society, 1990, pp 141-174.

Boone, R.S. and E.M. Wengert, (1998), "Guide for Using the Oven-Dry Method for Determining the Moisture Content of Wood", Forestry Facts, Department of Forest Ecology and Management University of Wisconsin-Madison, No. 89, June 1998.

Caple, C., and W. Murray, (1994), "Characterization of a Waterlogged Charred Wood and Development of a Conservation Treatment", Studies in Conservation, Vol 39, No 1, 1994, pp 28-38.

Carrlee, E. (2005),"Conservation and Exhibit of an Archaeological Fish Trap", In American Institute for Conservation Object Specialty Group of the American Institute for Conservation Postprints Vol 13, 2005, pp 117-129.

Carrlee, E. and D.K. Senge, (2010),"Annotated Bibliography of Articles Relevant to PEG Treatment of Basketry", http://ellencarrlee.wordpress.com/2009/04/04/peg-bibliography-annotated/, Accessed January 3, 2010.

Cooke, V., D. Cooke, and D.W. Grattan, (1994), "Reversing Old PEG Treatments of Objects from the Ozette Site", In Proceedings from the 5th ICOM Group on Wet Organic Archaeological Materials Conference, Portland, Maine, 16-20 August 1993, pp 92-109.

Cook, C. and D. Grattan, (1990), "A Method of Calculating the Concentration of PEG for Waterlogged Wood", Proceedings of the 4th ICOM Group on Wet Organic Archaeological Materials, Bremerhaven, Germany, 1990, pp 239-252.

Christensen, B.B, (1970), The Conservation of Waterlogged Wood in the National Museum of Denmark, Copenhagen, National Museum of Denmark.

DeJong, J., (1978), "The Conservation of Shipwrecks", ICOM Committee for Conservation 5th Triennial Meeting, Zagreb, Yugoslavia,1978, 78/7/1.

DeWitte, E., A. Terfve, J. Vynckier. (1984),"The Consolidation of the Waterlogged Wood from the Gallo-Roman Boats of Pommeroeul", Studies in Conservation, Vol 20, No 2, 1984, pp 77-83.

Florian, M.L.E., (1990), "Scope and History of Archaeological Wood", in R.M. Rowell and R.J. Barbour (editors), Archaeological Wood Properties, Chemistry and Preservation, Advances in Chemistry Series 225, Washington D.C., American Chemical Society, 1990, pp 3-32.

Florian, M.L.E., D.P. Kronkright, and R.E. Norton, (1990), The Conservation of Artifacts Made from Plant Materials, J. Paul Getty Trust.

Florian, M.L.E. and R. Renshaw-Beauchamp. (1982),"Anomalous Wood Structure: A Reason for Failure of PEG in Freeze-Drying Treatments of Some Waterlogged Wood from the Ozette Site", In Proceedings of the 1st ICOM Group on Wet Organic Archaeological Materials Conference, Ottawa, Canada, 15-18 September 1981, pp 85-98.

Friedman, J. (1978), "Wood Identification by Microscopic Examination: A Guide for the Archaeologist on the Northwest Coast of North America", Heritage Record No 5, British Columbia Provincial Museum.

Grattan, D.W. and R.W. Clarke,(1987), "Conservation of Waterlogged Wood", In C. Pearson (editor), Conservation of Marine Archaeological Objects, London, Butterworths, 1987, pp 164-206.

Grattan, D.W., (1986) "Some Observations on the Conservation of Waterlogged Wooden Shipwrecks", Australian Institute for the Conservation of Cultural Material, Vol 12, No 3 and 4, 1986.

Grattan, D., (1982), "A Practical Comparative Study of Treatments for Waterlogged Wood Part II: The Effect of Humidity on Waterlogged Wood", In Proceedings of the 1st ICOM Group on Wet Organic Archaeological Materials Conference, Ottawa, Canada, 15-18 September 1981, pp 243-252.

Grattan, D.W. and R.W. Clarke, (1987), "Conservation of Waterlogged Wood", In C. Pearson (editor), Conservation of Marine Archaeological Objects, London, Butterworths, 1987, pp 196-197.

Grosso, G. (1976), "Volume Processing of Waterlogged Wood at a Remote Archaeological Site: Modification of old Techniques, Identification of Special Problems and Hopes for Their Solution", In Pacific Northwest Wet Site Wood Conservation Conference, September 19-22, 1976, Vol 1,Neah Bay, WA.

Hamilton, D.L., (1998), Methods of Conserving Archaeological Material from Underwater Sites, Nautical Archaeology Program Department of Anthropology, Texas A&M University.

Hedges, J.I., "The Chemistry of Archaeological Wood", in R.M. Rowell and R.J. Barbour (editors), Archaeological Wood Properties, Chemistry and Preservation, Advances in Chemistry Series 225, Washington D.C., American Chemical Society, 1990, pp 111-140.

Henrikson, S. and J. Criswell, (2009), personal communication. Steve Henrikson is the curator of collections at the Alaska State Museum and Janice Criswell is a Tlingit-Haida weaver. They are both instructors of Northwest Coast art and culture at the University of Alaska Southeast.

Hoffmann, P., A. Singh, Y.S. Kim, S.G. Wi, I.J. Kim, U. Schmitt, (2004), "The Bremen Cog of 1380: An Electron Microscopic Study of the Degraded Wood Before and After Stabilization",Holzforschung, Vol 58, No 3, 2004, pp 211-218.

Hoffman, P., (1990), "On the Stabilization of Waterlogged Softwoods with Polyethylene Glycol (PEG). Four Species from China and Korea", Holzforschung, Vol 44, No 2, 1990, pp 87-93.

Hoffmann, P., (1986), "On the Stabilization of Waterlogged Oakwood with PEG II Designing a Two-Step Treatment for Multi-Quality Timbers", Studies in Conservation, Vol 31, No 3, 1986, pp 103-113.

Hoffmann, P. and Jones, M.A., (1990), "Structure and degradation Process for Waterlogged Archaeological Wood", in R.M. Rowell and R.J. Barbour (editors), Archaeological Wood Properties, Chemistry and Preservation, Advances in Chemistry Series 225, Washington D.C., American Chemical Society, 1990, pp 35-65.

Jensen, P., G. Jørgensen, U. Schnell, (2002), "Dynamic LV-SEM Analyses of Freeze Drying Processes for Waterlogged Wood", In Proceedings of the 8th ICOM Group on Wet Organic Archaeological Materials Conference, Stockholm, Sweden,11-15 June 2001, pp 319-333.

Johns, D.A., (1998) "Observations Resulting from the Treatments of Waterlogged Wood Bowls in Aoteroa (New Zealand)", in K. Bernick (editor), Hidden Dimensions, WARP Occasional paper No.11, Vancouver, University of British Columbia Press, 1998, pp 319-328.

Jover, A., (1994), "The Application of PEG 4000 for the Preservation of Palaeolithic Wooden Artifacts", Studies in Conservation, Vol 39, No 3, pp 193-198.

Kaenel, G., (1994), "PEG Conservation of a Gallo-Roman Barge from Yverdon-les-Baines (Canton of Vaud, Switzerland)", In Proceedings of the 5th ICOM Waterlogged Archaeological Materials Conference, Portland, Maine 16-20 August 1993, pp 143-165.

Keene, S., (1982), "Waterlogged Wood from the City of London",In Proceedings of the 1st ICOM Group on Wet Organic Archaeological Materials Conference, Ottawa, Canada,15-18 September 1981, pp 177-180.

McCawley, J.C., (1977), "Waterlogged Artifacts: the Challenge to Conservation", Journal of the Canadian Conservation Institute, Vol 2, 1977, pp 17-26.

Mitchell, H.L., (1972), "How PEG Helps the Hobbyist Who Works with Wood", US Dept of Agriculture Forest Service Forest Products Laboratory, Madison Wisconsin, 1972.

Muncher, D.A., (1991), "The Conservation of WLF-HA-1: the WHYDAH Shipwreck Site", The International Journal of Archaeology, Vol 20, No 4, 1991, pp 335-349.

Park, J., (1997), "The Barton-on-Humber Project. A Large Collection of Waterlogged Wood: Data, Retrieval, Storage, Pre- and Post- Treatment Methods", In Proceedings of the 6th ICOM Group on Wet Organic Archaeological Materials Conference, York, England,1996, pp 503-516.

Purdy, B., (1996), How to Do Archaeology the Right Way, Gainesville, University of Florida Press.

Rice, J.T., (1990), "Gluing of Archaeological Wood", in R.M. Rowell and R.J. Barbour (editors), Archaeological Wood Properties, Chemistry and Preservation, Advances in Chemistry Series 225, Washington D.C., American Chemical Society, 1990, pp 373-398.

Rodgers, B.,(1992),ECU Conservator's Cookbook: A Methodological Approach to the Conservation of Water Soaked Artifacts,Chapter 2: Waterlogged Wood,Herbert P. Paschal Memorial Fund Publication, Greenville, East Carolina University.

Sakuno, T. and A.P. Schniewind, (1990), "Adhesive Qualities of Consolidants for Deteriorated Wood", Journal of the American Institute for Conservation, Vol 29, No 1, pp 33-44.

Singley, K. (1988), The Conservation of Archaeological Artifacts from Freshwater Environments, South Haven, Michigan, Lake Michigan Maritime Museum.

Schniewind, A.P., and P.Y. Eastman, (1994), "Consolidant Distribution in Deteriorated Wood Treated with Soluble Resins", Journal of the American Institute for Conservation, Vol 33, No 3, 1994, pp 217-255.

Schniewind, A.P., and S.M. Carlson, (1990), "Residual Solvents in Wood Consolidant Composites", Studies in Conservation, Vol 35, No 1, February 1990

Schniewind, A.P., (1990), "Consolidaiton of Dry Archaeological Wood by

Impregnation with Thermoplastic Resins." in R.M. Rowell and R.J. Barbour (editors), Archaeological Wood Properties, Chemistry and Preservation, Advances in Chemistry Series 225, Washington D.C., American Chemical Society, 1990, pp 361-372.

Spirydowicz, K.E., E. Simpson, R.A. Blanchette, A.P.Schniewind, M.K. Toutloff, and A. Murray, (2001), "Alvar and Butvar: The Use of Polyvinyl Acetal Resins for the Treatment of the Wooden Artifacts from Gordion, Turkey", Journal of the American Institute for Conservation, Vol 40, No 1, 2001, pp 43-57.

Stamm, A.J., (1959), "Effect of Polyethylene Glycol on the Dimensional Stability of Wood", Forest Products Journal, Vol 19, No 10, 1959, pp 373-381.

Stark, B.L., (1976), "Waterlogged Wood Preservation with Polyethylene Glycol", Studies in Conservation, Vol 21, No 3, 1976 pp 154-158.

Strætkvern, K. (2002), "Freezing of Polyethylene Glycol: Compressions Strengths and Freezing Curves for High-Molecular Weight PEGs with and Without Low-Molecular Weight PEGs Added", In Proceedings from the 8th ICOM Group on Wet Organic Archaeological Materials Conference, Stockholm, Sweden, 11-15 June 2001, pp 335-352.

Tímár-Balázsy, Á., D. Eastop, M. Járo, (1998), Chemical Principles of Textile Conservation,

London, Butterworth-Heinemann.

Wang, Y., and A.P. Schniewind, (1985), "Consolidation of Deteriorated Wood with Soluble Resins", Journal of the American Institute for Conservation, Vol 24, pp 77–91.

Zumpe, R., (1981), "Die Konservierung von Feuchtholz mit Polyethyleneglycol (PEG)", Neue Museumskd 24, 1981, pp 129-137.

Questions and answers

Jessica La France: I'm just wondering if you used a high molecular weight PEG? I'm not sure how much would actually get inside the wood because it's so hard to penetrate some of these woods. I've had success treating basketry with a local (?) and then using a consolidant after. But I'm not sure how so much consolidation will get to the edges which are often friable.

Tara Grant: I can make a comment on the coagulant you were using, the PEG coagulant – Polyox. We played with it a while ago. It is very viscous and when you put it on it strings out like mozzarella cheese and if you have little objects and you put it on, the object will go flying off the surface of the table. So we actually ended up putting a layer of it out on a piece of Mylar and let it wick in. But we found it really wasn't that useful. It's too difficult to control.

Carlos Cabrera Tejedor: It's just a general comment for the treatment of basketry and textiles. Silicone oils, although they are not reversible, are a method that is worth studying for these objects because they are so structurally disintegrated. If you use a silicone oil you can plastify the material. It's definitely going to look nice. Without SEM microscopy you're not going to see the plastic but if you do use it you'll see with the textiles that there will be more flexibility so people will think "Wow, that's remarkable!" So I think it's worth… again it's not reversible. If you just have one try you have to think is it worth it, is it not worth it? And you have to test it but I think it's worth the effort to know that this can be actually used.

Ellen Carrlee: The silicone oil treatment has been tried on three baskets in Alaska that came from Castle Hill site and all three of them were destroyed in the process completely. Unfortunately, it was a treatment done by an archaeologist and I think that something went wrong with the treatment and it's very delicate to ask him what has gone wrong even though he went to Texas A & M and got training and thought that he knew what he was doing. I wish he hadn't done all three at the same time so at least we'd had two of the three. So it's one of those situations that if it goes wrong it goes very wrong and you don't have an artifact at all so because of that experience in Alaska, I've been very hesitant about the silicone oil but I still think it's a tool in the toolbox and one we need to keep considering.

Johanna Rivera: I'm just wondering if the formula that you use for wood is the same that you use for fabrics and cordage and things like that. There are really different morphologies between wood and fabrics for example. You have plant based fabrics and animal based fabrics.

Carlos Cabrera Tejedor: I never treated textile. I've treated rope and what has been done…I can speak about what I did. We have noticed that since there is a different structure and morphology in the case of rope, it's highly permeable and you can eliminate the step with the acetone. You don't really need the step with the acetone because it is to facilitate the polymer getting inside the wood structure. In the case of rope, and therefore textile, the polymer is going to go inside the structure pretty easily so theoretically you can eliminate the acetone step, you just need to go ethanol and that would be the theoretical difference in the process.

Kate Singley: Ellen, which Lascaux was it? Do you know which product number it was?

Ellen Carrlee: It might be in the article. It's the one that's marketed right now as "Lascaux medium for consolidation." That's how it's marketed. It's not marketed with a number or a code.

Kate Singley: Okay, because I've had very good results with the dispersion as a secondary in an emergency.

Ellen Carrlee: So you were using a different Lascaux product that was working well for you?

Kate Singley: Yes, it's old age...I can't remember which one it is. It's the dispersion. I'll email you.

Ellen Carrlee: There were other waterbased consolidants that tested out but that didn't perform as well during those early cruder tests so in general it seemed that the solvent based consolidants were working better than the water based ones just in my situation.

Kristiane Straetkvern: In baskets there may be some cordage and rope and other similar structures that are a problem and of course it is a problem because what is holding these fibers together is in fact the soil in between and as soon as you start to remove that, it can get difficult. What we have been doing is that again we avoid the low molecular weight PEG. So we started with high molecular PEG – PEG 2000 – approximately 10% and we did freeze-drying. We took the ropes and immersed them in the solution, then they were frozen, sealed in plastic and then the plastic was removed and had evaporation. This gave the rope the right shape during the drying process and I think this was published in Portland many years ago. Still, after freeze-drying, they tend to be brittle. After treatment we use Paraloid F-10 which is flexible and very nice to work with.

Carlos Cabrera Tejedor: Just one comment about the unsuccessful trial of basketry in Alaska. But first of all I would like to thank everyone with all their questions about silicone oil. Catherine and I are flattered and again we aren't trying to sell any kind of chemicals we are just trying to say this is another tool that has been tested and these are the results and it could work. So thank you very much for your questions and I just agree with what Cliff Cook said yesterday, I believe this is more art than pure science so even though you can theoretically know you need only 20% polymer and crosslinker and it will work there are many many variables and I think is why for many techniques you need to work both with a chemist who is going to tell you the theoretical background and a conservator who is going to have the feeling, the experience and the knowledge to know whether this will be a good approach or not. And perhaps that's what happened [in Alaska]. The problem with silicone oil is that unless you know exactly step by step what you are doing you can get very bad results.

5.6 (Sc PR)
Assessing the Physical Condition of Waterlogged Archaeological Leather

Ekaterini Malea*
Technological Educational Institute of Athens, Dept. Conservation of Antiquities & Works of Art, Ag. Spyridonos str. GR – 122 10 Egaleo, Greece,
*E-mail: kmalea@teiath.gr

Thelxiopi Vogiatzi
Moraitini 8, GR-142 32 Athens, Greece,

David E. Watkinson
School of History and Archaeology, Cardiff University, Cardiff CF10 3EU, U.K.

Abstract

The aim of the present study was to determine the condition of waterlogged archaeological leather by a series of simple visual and physical examinations testing the flexibility, strength and coherency of the fibers, and then correlate these assessments with the condition of leather as determined by various chemical and physical analyses. Fifteen waterlogged archaeological leather samples from Great Britain and Greece were examined under the Scanning Electron Microscope and analyzed. The methods of analyses were measurement of the acidity (pH), measurement of the Shrinkage Temperature (Ts), and amino acid analysis of collagen by means of High Performance Liquid Chromatography. Finally the results were statistically elaborated by using Logistic Regression, Principal Components and Discriminant Analysis.

In conclusion, this study has revealed the problems associated with the analysis of waterlogged archaeological leather and has shown that the analytical approach needs to be refined and many more samples should be examined to facilitate statistical analysis.

Keywords: waterlogged archaeological leather, state of preservation, amino acids analysis, shrinkage temperature, acidity
measurement, scanning electron microscopy, statistical analysis.

Introduction

The term waterlogged archaeological leather normally defines leather that has lain in an anoxic wet environment during burial, resulting in water occupying its void space. It relates to material from both freshwater and marine sites. The degree of leather preservation at the point of excavation can vary from flexible, with a strong physical structure, to a non-cohesive fibrous mass, which lacks physical integrity. Factors such as type of burial environment and the original nature of the leather will strongly influence its condition, with biodeterioration and chemical hydrolysis influencing its decay. Material from burial contexts, such as soil particles and precipitated salts are normally included in the open network of the leather, making sampling for analysis a problematic exercise.

This contrasts with historical leather. Although it is often degraded, historical leather is normally much less physically altered in comparison to archaeological leather. Unlike archaeological leather, historical leather rarely contains either a wide range or a large amount of intrusive material. In part this explains why historical leather has been subject to extensive analysis, whereas archaeological leather has little recorded scientific analysis. Conservation methods used for waterlogged leather have also influenced analytical approaches. Treatment of waterlogged archaeological leather must be intrusive in order to provide an easy-to-handle and visually acceptable object. In the past, empirical analysis of leather condition has often produced successful treatment results (Ganiaris et al. 1982). This success may have disguised the need for an ordered scientific approach to assessing the condition of waterlogged archaeological leather. Indeed, it may be argued that there is limited value in determining accurate condition ranking for a group of archaeological leathers, if it is a costly and time consuming exercise that ultimately has minimal influence on either the treatment regime or its outcome.

Conservators will always support cheap, reliable and easy-to-use simple tests that help to determine the finer points of a treatment. The condition of leather reflects the state of its structural protein (collagen) and it is important to correlate this with both its physical properties and its appearance. The condition of the collagen can be determined by complex analysis, but it would be interesting to determine if the results of such analyses supported the outcomes of simple analytical techniques, as this may help to facilitate recommendations for a simple analysis regime to assess leather condition. Any such guidelines for simple assessment should require a small sample, be quick to institute, inexpensive and capable of use by the layman, rather than the specialist scientist.

Statistics have been proved a useful tool for answering questions in many disciplines. In practice through an interactive process one studies the data in hand, examines it using some statistical method, decides to look at it another way by either transforming them, taking only a part of them or by even applying a different analysis method. Different methods are being used to bring out different aspects of the data, to ask and answer different questions about the "population" they came from and predict accurately future observations (make inference) by minimizing the time and effort needed. By using statistics the researcher has sound methodological tools that enable him to make accurate conclusions on the underlying process that generates the data itself (Berthold and Hand 1998).

Conservation science studies the nature of the object materials and the chemical and physical processes leading to their breakdown (Larsen 1998). Assessment of the condition of the objects before and/or after conservation is of great importance (Nikitina 1981, English Heritage 1995, Suenson-Taylor et al. 1999, AIC 1999), as any treatment should be based on this assessment. The criteria chosen for the estimation of the objects' condition must therefore be basic to the material and symptomatic of its condition or factors of deterioration (Suenson-Taylor et al. 1999). In other words, the scientific investigation should be based on representative analysis that provides reliable and verifiable results.

Many techniques have been used to determine the condition of historical leather. These are: the determination of the pH, the sulfate content, the free fat content, the total moisture content (Van Soest et al. 1984, Florian 1987), the shrinkage temperature measurement (Borasky and Nutting 1949, Reed 1972, Nayudamma 1978, Haines 1987, Young 1990, Larsen et al. 1993, Larsen et al. 1994b, Larsen 1995, Malea et al. 1997), the denaturation temperature measurement (Chahine and Rottier 1995), the amino acids analysis (Larsen et al. 1989, 1995), the examination of cross sections under the optical microscope and examination of fibers under the scanning electron microscope (BLMRA 1957, Dempsey 1968, Reed 1972, Haines 1981, Cot et al. 1989, Alexander et al. 1993), the loss of infrared linear dichroism (Young 1992), the study of the chemical breakdown of collagen by using the Raman spectroscopy (Boghosian et al. 1999) and the Solid State Nuclear Magnetic Resonance Spectroscopy (Odlyha 1999).

The aim of the experimental work described in this paper is to test the correlation of the condition of waterlogged archaeological leather as pre-determined by a series of simple visual/physical tests as well as assessment by SEM photos with its condition as determined by various chemical and physical analyses. Statistical analysis of the results is carried out. The objective was to establish a set of minimal assessments, which could be easily used by conservators, in order to provide a clear guide to the degree of deterioration of waterlogged archaeological leather, without recourse to expensive or elaborate equipment. High Performance Liquid Chromatography (HPLC) amino acids analysis is carried out on waterlogged archaeological leather for the first time here and is supported by reference to comparative work, on historical and bookbinding leathers, carried out in the STEP and ENVIRONMENT programs (Larsen et al. 1992, 1993, 1995).

Materials and Methods

Fifteen samples of waterlogged archaeological leather were collected from two different sites in Great Britain (York) and Greece (Heraklion).

Identification of Animal Species

The animal type of the archaeological leather samples was determined – where this was possible – by examining the hair follicle pattern (BLMRA 1957, Haines 1981, Thomson 1995, Larsen 1996) and the SEM photomicrographs (Haines 1998). The majority of these were bovine and only one was thought to be sheep or goat (see Table 1). This data was not used in the Statistical Analysis due to ambiguous results in some instances.

Classification by Visual and Physical Methods

The samples were classified into three categories of preservation (C1-good condition, C2-intermediate state of preservation and C3-poor condition) (see Table 2), using simple subjective physical tests (Larsen and Vest 1995) although it has been reported by other scientists (Young 1990) that sometimes neither the physical appearance nor the feel give any indication of the extent of deterioration. The final ranking was based on a common assessment of three leather experts (Larsen 1996, Vest 1996, Vestergaard-Poulsen 1996). Terminology and methodology used here, was based on scientific research

reports of ENVIRONMENT Leather Project (Larsen and Vest 1995).

Simple physical tests were performed to test flexibility, strength and coherence of the fibers (Larsen and Vest 1995) in order to classify the samples:

- Flexibility of the samples was tested empirically by trying to bend/fold the leather.
- Tear strength was empirically tested by holding the leather, tearing it by hand then subjectively assessing the ease of doing this according to the following categories: easy, difficult, extremely difficult.
- Coherency was tested by scraping the grain with a fingernail and its removal was classified according to the following categories: easy, difficult, and extremely difficult.
- Coherency of the fibers was determined by cutting a fragment of the leather into small pieces with a scalpel, and then classifying it into one of the following categories: poor coherence, intermediate coherence, good coherence.

Classification Using the Scanning Electron Microscope

Scanning electron microscopy provides information on the surface microtopography of the specimen (Tite 1972, Cot et al. 1989, Cormia 1992). It allows the visual exploration of individual fibers within the bundle (Calnan 1991, Haines 1991) and has been used for degradation studies (Alexander et al. 1993). The preparation before examination with SEM requires dehydration of the sample (by successive baths of alcohol) and coating with gold or carbon to make the surface of the sample conductive. Samples were examined at x50, x250 and x600 magnifications using Philips 515 SEM coupled with an X-ray dispersive energy analyzer EDAX 9900

.

Table 1. List of the samples used in the present study, with leather type, origin and date where known. 1. R. Larsen et al., 1994a; 2. B. Haines, 1998; 3. R. Thomson, 1995; 4. R. Larsen, 1996

Sample number	Label recordings	Origin	Date	Leather type
Ref. Sample	Ref. "old new"	Denmark	1992	calf[1]
Ref. Sample	Ref. new	Denmark	1992	calf[1]
K1	La Thérèse	French shipwreck in Greece (Lianos, 1991)	1669	cattle[2]
K2	WH 91 20 764	Woodhall, U.K.	Medieval	cattle[2]
K3	WH 91 20 812	Woodhall, U.K.	Medieval	cattle[2]
K4	WH 94 20 1073 bag 4	Woodhall, U.K.	Medieval	cattle[2,3]
K5	WH 94 20 1640 box 1, bag 5	Woodhall, U.K.	Medieval	cattle[3]?
K6	WH 94 20 1640 box 1, bag 1	Woodhall, U.K.	Medieval	cattle[2,3]
K7	WH 94 20 1670	Woodhall, U.K.	Medieval	sheep/goat[2]
K8	WH 92 20 box 2, bag 2 511/590	Woodhall, U.K.	Medieval	cattle[2,3]
K9	WH 92 20 box 3, bag 6, 790	Woodhall, U.K.	Medieval	cattle[2,3]
K10	WH 91 20 box 8, bag 810 120	Woodhall, U.K.	Medieval	cattle[2,3]
K11	WH 91 20 bag 794	Woodhall, U.K.	Medieval	cattle[2,3]
K12	1d	Woodhall, U.K.	Medieval	cattle[2]
K13	3a	Woodhall, U.K.	Medieval	sheep[4]
K14	2	Woodhall, U.K.	Medieval	cattle[2]
K15	6a	Woodhall, U.K.	Medieval	cattle[2]

Estimation of leather condition is subjective (Vingelsgaard and Schmidt 1986) although it is believed that changes in appearance indicate a good or poor state of preservation (Bowes and Raistrick 1963). For this reason, in addition to the classification of the samples into three categories of preservation after simple physical and visual tests, a 'Blind Method' (Suenson-Taylor et al. 1999) was also used as a method for comparison. Three leather experts were asked to classify the same leather samples into C1, C2 and C3 classification using SEM photographs (Thomson 1998, Bugby 1998, Haines 1998). Classification was based on the degree and the type of splitting up of the fibers (Calnan 1991) (see Table 3)

574

Chemical and Physical Analysis

Apart from the macroscopic features of the samples it was useful to obtain information about their chemical and physical composition and relate it to changes caused by deterioration. The various chemical and physical analyses would then be compared with the visual/ physical and SEM classifications as an effort to correlate these assessments with the condition of leather. For this purpose, pH and the Shrinkage Temperature (Ts) were determined since both have been correlated with leather decay and can indicate its state of preservation (O'Flaerty et al. 1956, Bowes and Raistrick 1961a, Haines 1985, Sanders 1986, Florian 1987, Haines 1987, Raeder-Knudsen 1990, Young 1992, Stroz et al. 1993, Larsen 1993, Young 1998). Since collagen is the major component of skin and leather it should be expected that amino acid analysis would provide a useful tool in the study of its deterioration. Deteriorated leather may be characterized by containing large amounts of ammonia and by an altered amino acids distribution compared to that of new leather.

Determination of acidity (pH)

Leather pH was determined by a method partly derived from standard international test methods used for newly made leather. This test has been used on archaeological leathers to decide the conservation treatment (Van Soest et al. 1984, Van Dienst 1985). The pH measurement was carried out by means of a pH-mV-C meter, type ELE International Model 3070 with automatic temperature correction. The amount of leather needed is fixed at 1/20 of the total solution (Hallebeek 1992). The material was mechanically removed as loose fibers from a vertical cross-section of the complete sample, after removal of any burial material, if present. The pH measurement was taken twice for each leather sample.

Determination of the Hydrothermal Stability (Shrinkage Temperature: Ts)

The hydrothermal stability of collagen in skin or leather can be defined by the shrinkage temperature (Ts), since Ts is a measure of the stability of the bonds maintaining the structure of the collagen chains (Larsen et al. 1992, 1993). Deformation of the collagen is apparent as shrinkage of the fibers when they are heated (Sanders 1986, Florian 1987, Raeder-Knudsen 1990, Sykes 1991).

Table 2. Classification of the fifteen leather samples into three preservation groups after the performance of physical tests. Group C1 corresponds to the best-preserved samples, group C2 to the samples with intermediate deterioration and group C3 to the most heavily deteriorated samples.

Sample s	Preservation state	Physical condition after simple tests
K1	C3	Coherent fibers but present little strength
K2	C1	Good resistance to the physical tests
K3	C2	Enough strength but not too coherent fibers at the grain side
K4	C2	Grain side in good condition, reasonable good/coherent fibers
K5	C2	Coherent fibers
K6	C3	Poor condition
K7	C2	Coherent fibers
K8	C1	Flexible, nice long coherent fiber
K9	C2	Loose fibers but they do not fall apart
K10	C2	Although the sample can be torn, some fibers remain still together
K11	C1	Flexible, presents strength, coherent fibers
K12	C3	Poor condition
K13	C2	Reasonably good
K14	C2	Inner part coherent, the rest easily can be torn
K15	C2	Although the fibers can easily be split, they are hardly fall apart

Table 3. Classification of the leather samples after examination of the SEM photomicrographs. Preservation state C1 determines samples well preserved with coherent structure and fibers packed into bundles. Group C2 determines samples in a moderate state of preservation with structure that presents some sticking of the fibers and clumping of the bundles. Group C3 determines the most deteriorated samples that present severe sticking of the fibers and clumping of the bundles and /or fragmentation of the fibers.

Sample	Preservation state	Microscopic examination (SEM)
K1	C3	Fibers deteriorated and loose
K2	C2	Marked sticking of the fibers within the bundle and clumping of the bundles
K3	C2	Marked sticking of the fibers and clumping of the bundles
K4	C1	Dense but open up fiber structure
K5	C3	Fibers and fibril bundles visible but fractured
K6	C3	Compact, stuck bundles with fractured areas
K7	C2	Coherent structure, some sticking of the fibers
K8	C1	Dense but open up fiber structure
K9	C1	Dense fiber structure with some sticking and clumping of the fiber bundles
K10	C2	Sticking and clumping of the fiber bundles which are coated with debris
K11	C1	Dense but open up fiber structure
K12	C3	Bundles showing sticking and coated with debris
K13	C3	Fine fibers deteriorated and loose
K14	C1	Dense, coherent but open up fiber structure
K15	C3	Fragment, decayed fibers coated with debris

In the present study, the determination of the Ts by the micro-hot table technique (MHT) was carried out by means of a Zetopan research M/S microscope with a Linkam TMS 90/TH 600 heating stage connected to a precision temperature control system. A heating rate of 2°C per minute was set. Three temperatures transitions were recorded for each sample: when single fibers started to move; when fiber groups increased their mobility; and cessation of activity within the system. Measurements were taken twice for each sample and Ts was defined as the start temperature of the main interval (Borasky and Nutting, 1949; Chahine and Rottier, 1992; Larsen et al., 1993).

Amino acids analysis

All samples were analyzed by High Performance Liquid Chromatography (HPLC). Larsen and his collaborators (Larsen et al. 1989, 1992, Larsen 1993) proved that it is possible to analyze corium collagen. The method involves a routine method of hydrolysis to produce amino acids which can be separated and analyzed by means of High Performance Liquid Chromatography (HPLC).

Approximately 0.2 mg of each sample was analyzed. To avoid interference with other proteins (i.e. keratin and elastin) which may be present in the grain layer, all the samples were taken from the corium. These were hydrolyzed for 24 hours in sealed, evacuated ampoules at 110°C in 300 µl 6M redistilled HCl containing 0.05% phenol, as described in detail by Larsen et al. (1989). The analyses were performed on Waters HPLC equipment by ion exchange chromatography and amino acids were detected by fluorescence following post-column derivatization with ortho-phthaldialdehyde (OPA). The elution profile of the amino acids is reported in percent mole (see Table 4).

Statistical analysis

In an attempt to quantify the condition of the leather samples and to correlate it with their physical features statistical analysis was used. The aim was to identify either an analytical method or a portion of the data that could be used as an index of deterioration.

The small number of samples tested, in relation to the large number of variables (data), presented significant problems for statistical analysis. Exploratory data analysis took place first. This graphically (Box-Plots) examined the relationship between variables without modeling and contributed to the identification of any data abnormalities that would make it difficult or impossible to carry out further data analysis.

The statistical methods used are:

- Logistic Regression, to investigate whether the probability of classifying leather in one of the three categories of preservation is dependent on some of the variables. It is a method widely used for analyzing multivariate data when the response is measured in the binary scale (only two possible values – to belong at a preservation category C1 instead of C2 or to C2 instead of C3). McCullagh and Nelder (1989), Hosmer and Lemeshow (1965) and Draper and Smith (1967) present theory supporting this method in some detail. Logistic Regression was performed separately for each of the two types of classification (visual/physical and SEM classification).

- Principal Components Analysis was used in order to reduce the number of the variables for the prediction of the state of preservation given the small number of leather samples under study. The focus of this method is to find a set of standardized linear combinations of the original variables, called Principal Components, which explain a large amount of the variance of the data (Mardia et al. 1979).

- Discriminant Analysis was used in order to develop a model that would help predict the preservation state of leather. Such a model uses as input the Principal Components resulting from the previous statistical method (Linear combinations of - Discriminant Functions F1 and F2) as variables to identify the differences between the three states of preservation. The existence of differences between the preservation groups was tested via the Wilk's lambda. In addition the F statistic was used to test the equality of centroids for each pair of groups. The success of the classification was evaluated using a) the percentage of leathers classified in the correct preservation group and b) the cross-validation where a leather sample is classified into a preservation group according to the discrimination functions computed from all the leathers except this one. The percentage of the correctly classified and misclassified leathers was examined.

The S-plus and the Spss software were used for the statistical analysis.

Results and Discussion
Visual examination and physical tests:
The results from visual examination and simple physical tests were used to classify the leather samples into three groups of differing preservation state (C1-good condition, C2-intermediate state of preservation and C3-poor condition) (see Table 4). Although some authors (Sully and Suenson-Taylor 1998) suggest an increase in the number of preservation states, only three different states of preservation were set here due to limited number of samples.

Scanning electron microscopy (S.E.M.)
Considerable effort was made to define the state of preservation of each leather sample, and to classify them into three categories using only their SEM photomicrographs (see Table 3). The classification for each sample differed considerably when fiber pictures were taken into account. This lack of agreement with the estimated condition of the leather samples based on visual examination could probably be explained by the fact that minute samples are not always representative of the total condition of the sample (Hodges 1968, Baer and Low 1982). This explanation is in agreement with the opinion of some leather experts who advocate that it is not possible to identify specific deterioration of the leather from changes in the microscopic appearance (Haines 1998).

Table 4 (rotated landscape table). Classification and experimental data for the fifteen archaeological leather samples. The data are presented in two panels that together form one table sharing the same row labels.

Panel A — classification, pH, T_s and amino acid content (Hyp … Phe)

	State vls/phys.	State SEM	pH	Ts	Hyp	Asp	Thr	Ser	Glu	Pro	Gly	Ala	Val	Met	Ile	Leu	Tyr	Phe
Ref. "old new"					9,42	4,61	1,69	3,20	7,49	12,34	33,28	10,89	2,13	0,61	1,21	2,50	0,41	1,31
(SD)					(0,15)	(0,05)	(0,03)	(0,05)	(0,06)	(0,09)	(0,61)	(0,12)	(0,04)	(0,04)	(0,03)	(0,05)	(0,03)	(0,03)
Ref. new					9,54	4,5	1,66	3,45	7,5	12,55	32,96	11,16	2	0,6	1,15	2,4	0,4	1,26
K1	3		5,4	63	9,23	4,94	1,97	3,61	7,71	12,55	33,19	10,62	2,19	0,64	1,27	2,61	0,25	1,3
K2	1		6,45	72	9,83	5,37	2,21	3,51	8,4	11,76	31,61	10,68	2,24	0,66	1,35	2,93	0,32	1,33
K3	2		7,5	85	8,96	5,14	1,93	3,59	7,87	12,12	33,01	10,79	2,27	0,65	1,39	2,79	0,35	1,4
K4	2		5,73	78	9,42	4,83	1,74	3,54	7,61	12,63	33,49	10,92	2,04	0,65	1,22	2,53	0,31	1,28
K5	2		6,26	85	9,14	5,08	1,93	3,73	7,72	12,03	32,7	10,79	2,24	0,7	1,38	2,8	0,34	1,38
K6	3		5,29	60	8,53	5,94	2,26	3,86	8,13	11,58	31,1	10,39	2,39	0,8	1,61	3	0,66	1,56
K7	2		4,6	80	9,8	5,01	2,13	3,46	7,85	11,91	32,82	10,93	2,17	0,63	1,24	2,67	0,25	1,28
K8	1		6,77	68	9,73	5,15	1,83	3,54	7,85	11,91	33,51	11,07	2,09	0,61	1,23	2,5	0,26	1,22
K9	2		4,7	83	9,34	4,98	1,77	3,55	7,73	12,25	33,59	10,87	2,1	0,64	1,31	2,53	0,26	1,3
K10	2		6,1	84	8,64	5,72	2,4	3,9	7,85	11,4	31	10,72	2,56	0,75	1,62	3,04	0,5	1,55
K11	1		5,2	81	9,59	4,97	1,84	3,54	7,8	12,28	32,98	10,92	2,26	0,65	1,25	2,6	0,26	1,32
K12	3		6,75	62	9,4	5,32	1,83	3,54	8,05	11,98	33,58	11,08	2,15	0,62	1,21	2,49	0,29	1,22
K13	3		6,6	74	9,47	5,09	1,81	3,55	7,95	12,19	33,28	10,96	2,13	0,62	1,29	2,58	0,28	1,32
K14	2		5,2	77	7,82	6,52	2,42	3,79	8,47	10,72	30,08	10,69	2,79	0,76	1,88	3,48	0,56	1,75
K15	2		6,7	85	9,08	5,19	2,04	3,73	8,14	12,62	31,27	10,44	2,43	0,7	1,43	2,95	0,35	1,39

Panel B — His … Orn, B/A, Coll.cont, TPC and ratios

	His	Hyl	Lys	Arg	Ada	Abu	bAla	4Abu	6Aha	Orn	B/A	Coll.cont	TPC	Arg/Orn	Lys/Ada	Pro/bAla	Hyp/bAla	(Pro+Hyp)/bAla
ref. "old new"	0,54	0,72	2,62	5,04							0,69(0,004)	.						
(SD)	(0,02)	(0,05)	(0,05)	(0,06)														
Ref. new	0,55	0,67	2,63	4,94	0	0	0,01	<0,01	0	0,06	0,69	0,5	%	82,33		1255	954	2209
K1	0,44	0,45	2,23	4,5	0,07	0	0,02	0	0	0,21	0,57	0,47	0,05	21,43	31,86	627,5	461,5	1089
K2	0,5	0,41	1,86	4,6	0,18	0	0,05	0,01	0	0,21	0,5	0,44	0,05	21,90	10,33	235,2	196,6	431,8
K3	0,51	0,44	1,96	4,46	0,11	0	0,02	0,05	0	0,17	0,53	0,57	%	26,23	17,81	606	448	1054
K4	0,47	0,51	1,95	4,64	0,08	0	0,02	0	0	0,11	0,57	0,42	%	42,18	24,37	631,5	471	1102,5
K5	0,53	0,42	2,02	4,66	0,11	0	0,02	0,01	0	0,27	0,55	0,27	%	17,26	18,36	601,5	457	1058,5
K6	0,72	0,5	2,16	4,38	0,14	0	0,05	0,02	0	0,23	0,5	0,43	%	19,04	15,43	231,6	170,6	402,2
K7	0,51	0,43	2,02	4,52	0,13	0	0,03	0,02	0	0,18	0,54	0,45	%	25,11	15,54	397	326,66	723,66
K8	0,39	0,47	1,75	4,6	0,11	0	0,04	0,02	0	0,13	0,52	0,42	%	35,38	15,90	297,75	243,25	541
K9	0,51	0,46	1,82	4,6	0,11	0	0,03	0,03	0	0,21	0,54	0,39	0,11	21,90	16,54	408,33	311,33	719,66
K10	0,66	0,52	2,22	4,48	0,09	0	0,15	0,01	0	0,22	0,53	0,52	%	20,36	24,66	76	57,6	133,6
K11	0,42	0,49	1,76	4,7	0,11	0	0,1	0,01	0	0,14	0,54	0,52	%	33,57	16	122,8	95,9	218,7
K12	0,36	0,42	1,68	4,43	0,13	0	0,05	0,02	0,01	0,14	0,49	0,55	%	31,64	12,92	239,6	188	427,6
K13	0,45	0,45	1,75	4,52	0,14	0	0,02	0,01	0	0,14	0,52	0,27	0,07	32,28	12,50	609,5	473,5	1083
K14	0,75	0,41	2,12	4,22	0,22	0	0,09	0,07	0,02	0,36	0,45	0,5	0,08	11,72	9,63	119,11	86,88	206
K15	0,57	0,5	2,05	4,79	0,12	0	0,03	0,01	0	0,19	0,55	0,5		25,21	17,08	420,66	302,66	723,33

Table 4. Experimental data for the fifteen archaeological leathe samples. Classification of the samples into three groups of preservation after visual physical examination and after the SEM microphotographs. Group 1 corresponds to the best-preserved samples, group 2 to the samples with intermediate deterioration and group 3 to the most heavily deteriorated samples. "Ref. new" corresponds to new leather sample and "Ref. old new" to artifically aged leather (Chahine and Rottier 1996).

Degree of acidity:

To a certain extent, pH reflects the degree of hydrolytic breakdown in the leather (Larsen 1993, 1995). Singley (1988) states that a safe pH range for archaeological waterlogged leather from freshwater environment is between pH 3 and 6, while later studies on historical leathers (Hallebeek 1992) showed that a safe pH range lies between pH 4 and 8. For historical leather it is reported that when pH values are above 8 then the leather becomes darker in color, tends to be stiff and cracks (Bowes and Raistrick 1961b). When pH decreases there is a loss of strength in leather. This is supported by the fact that low-pH leathers had greatly reduced shrinkage temperature (Ts) (Bowes and Raistrick 1961b).

The pH values of the leather samples in this study lie between 4.6 and 7.5 with the majority of them concentrated between 5.0 and 7.0. None of the recorded values provides an indication of the degree of acidic deterioration of the leather. However, if archaeological leather is waterlogged, hydrolysis may be assumed to take place to some degree without the catalytic effect from acids. Since amino acid analysis revealed that all the samples showed signs of oxidative breakdown, then it may be that the release of ammonia has masked the acidity of the leather (Larsen 1999) or that the aqueous burial environment has influenced the retention (lack of retention) of acidic products in the leather. No correlation was found between pH values and shrinkage temperatures (Ts) and/or classification into the three different state of preservation: C1, C2 and C3.

Shrinkage temperature (Ts):

Shrinkage temperature was recorded for all the leather samples (see Table 5). The values for the samples in this study ranged between the 60°C and 85°C. No one correlation was evident between the different states of preservation (C1, C2 and C3) and the shrinkage temperatures, although it is known that the shrinkage temperature is a valuable indicator of the extent of deterioration (Larsen et al. 1993).

It was not possible to deduce any conclusions about possible acidic deterioration of the leather samples.

Previous studies of leather structure and deterioration have shown that a correlation exists between the chemical composition of leather and the shrinkage temperature (Harrington and Von Hippel 1961, Bowes and Raistrick 1961a, Nayudamma 1978, Larsen 1995). They have also shown an interdependence between the shrinkage temperature and the iminoacids hydroxyproline (Hyp) and proline (Pro), (Positive correlation- decrease of the iminoacids values is followed by a decrease in the shrinkage temperature and vice-versa). In the present study, only two samples (K6 and K14) showed low shrinkage temperatures and a decrease in iminoacids Hyp and Pro.

Another element that was examined in the shrinkage temperature measurements was the total shrinkage interval ΔTt, i.e. the interval between the very first and the very last sign of shrinkage activity, which corresponds to the difference Te-Ts (Te stands for the temperature where the shrinkage activity of the whole system stops and Ts for the initial temperature where fibers show shrinkage activity) (see Table 5).

The total shrinkage interval varies considerably and for one sample (K14) is as large as 35°C. These differences in stability may, apart from experimental errors, be due to:
- The initial treatment of the skin.
- Non-uniformity in tannage.
- A non-uniform degree of deterioration (Larsen et al. 1993, Vest 1999) which usually describes samples with a low degree of deterioration.

Only three of the samples (K2, K3 and K12) present a narrow shrinkage range (of 5° to 10°C) indicating a more uniform deterioration (Young 1990).

Table 5. *Shrinkage Temperature Measurements for the fifteen leather samples. The first column represents the initial shrinkage activity of the fibers, the second one the shrinkage temperature, and the third one the final shrinkage activity of the whole system.*

Sample	Initial Shrinkage Activity	Ts	Final Shrinkage Activity
K1	46	63	67
K2	71	72	82
K3	80	85	90
K4	65	78	89
K5	70	85	90
K6	60	60	85
K7	60	80	92
K8	60	68	86
K9	72	83	90
K10	60	84	92
K11	72	81	89
K12	60	62	70
K13	63	74	85
K14	60	77	95
K15	65	85	92

Amino acids analysis:

Previous work has shown that the amino acid distribution for archaeological leather is similar to that expected for new leathers (Larsen et al. 1989). Table 4 presents the amino acid distribution for all the samples as well as these of the two reference samples, one new calf vegetable tanned skin and one artificially aged leather for comparison (Larsen et al. 1994c). The amino acid analysis by HPLC in this study (see Table 4) can be summarized as follows:

- The amino acids Asp, Glu, Thr and Ser present higher values than the new samples (reference samples).
- The B/A ratio (the ratio of the basic to the acidic amino acids: $\sum$Arg,Hyl,Lys/$\sum$Asp,Glu) is rather low. The normal range for B/A ratio for new leathers is 0.70 (Larsen 1995). It stands below 0.60 for the majority of the samples and is below 0.50 for two of them. This means that there is a decrease of the basic amino acids and an increase of the acidic ones. This altering in the amino acid distribution normally happens during oxidative breakdown. In the present study these values are not related to the visual/physical or SEM classification.

In general terms, amino acid analysis confirmed the results of other workers. In part, the results recorded could be explained by the resistance of the collagen molecule to thermal and chemical denaturation and the interdependence of the iminoacids Hyp and Pro (Harrington and Von Hippel 1961, Nayudamma 1978, Pearson 1987). Additionally, the increased values of Asp and Glu in relation to the low B/A ratio suggest that the leather has undergone oxidative deterioration (Larsen et al. 1989, 1992, Larsen 1993). Interpreting the results of the amino acid analysis is complicated by the fact that deterioration can follow several reaction routes (Larsen 1999) and because animal fibers may vary in composition as a result of genetic, nutritional and environmental differences (Crewther et al. 1965). On the other hand, more recent work on another collageneous material (historical parchment) reported that samples exhibiting small chemical modifications may have undergone extensive physical damage (Boghosian 2007).

Statistical analysis:

To make sense of the large amount of collected data (pH measurement, Ts measurement, HPLC analysis) in relation to the number of samples statistical analyses were performed. Minimizing the data by selecting certain amino and imino acids or by eliminating their breakdown products was not an easy task, as all the data were equally important given that this was the first time this kind of analysis had been performed on waterlogged archaeological leathers.

Box Plots

The study of the Box-plots revealed the following: In the case of the Shrinkage Temperature (Ts), there is a discrimination of the third group of classification C3 (poor preservation state) from the two other groups of preservation C1 and C2. The C3 group has considerable lower Ts values. This observation is clear only in the case of the samples classified by visual/physical examination (see Figure 1). The analysis of variance proved that the values of the shrinkage temperature (Ts) differ significantly between the three condition categories using visual/physical examination F(2,12) = 23.003, p < .05. In contrast, there is no statistical difference in the Ts values between the three condition categories using SEM examination, F (2, 10.078) = 1.1.590, p > .05 (The assumption of the homogeneity of variance is violated; therefore, the Brown-Forsythe F-ratio is reported).

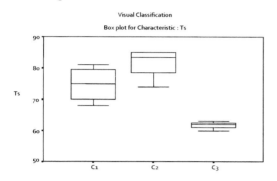
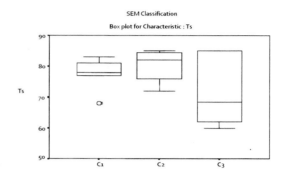

Figure 1. *Box-Plots of shrinkage temperature (Ts) after classification into three condition categories using visual/physical (left graph) and SEM examination (right graph). Discrimination is clear between C1 and C3 after visual/physical classification of the samples. Analysis of variance verified this result.*

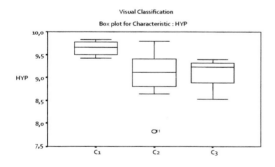
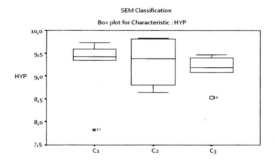

Figure 2. *Box-Plots of aminoacid Hydroxyproline (Hyp) after classification into three condition categories using visual/physical (left graph) and SEM examination (right graph). Although the graphic display shows discrimination between C1 and C3 after visual/physical and SEM classification of the samples, this was not verified by the analysis of variance.*

In the case of the iminoacid Hydroxyproline (Hyp), discrimination can be observed in the graphic display between the preservation groups C1 and C3 (between the well and the poorly preserved samples), after both visual/physical and SEM examination (see Figure 2). The analysis of variance showed that the values of the iminoacid Hydroxyproline (Hyp) do no differ significantly between the three condition categories using visual/physical examination F(2,12) = 1.945, p > .05.

Similarly, there is no statistical difference between the three condition categories using SEM examination $F(2,12) = 0.102$, p > .05.

The values of the amino acid Serine (Ser) are, in both types of assessment, very concentrated in the C1 group. Discrimination between the preservation groups C1 and C3 can be observed in the graphic display (see Figure 3). The analysis of variance showed that the values of the aminoacid Serine (Ser) do no differ significantly between the three condition categories using visual/physical examination, F (2,3.677) = 1.218, p > .05 (The assumption of the homogeneity of variance is violated; therefore, the Brown-Forsythe F-ratio is reported). Similarly, there is no statistical difference between the three condition categories using SEM examination F (2,12) = 0.435, p > .05.

Discrimination in the graphic display can be observed between the values of the amino acid Arginine (Arg) of the preservation groups C1 and C3 for the visually/physically assessed samples (see Figure 4). The analysis of variance showed that the values of the aminoacid Arginine (Arg) do no differ significantly between the

three condition categories using visual/physical examination F(2,12) = 1.607, p > .05. Similarly, there is no statistical difference between the three condition categories using SEM examination $F(2,12) = 0.077$, p > .05.

From the above results it can be seen that discrimination is usually apparent between the two extremes groups of preservation C1 and C3 (good and poor state of preservation respectively). Samples from the intermediate state of preservation (C2) can be difficult to classify as they combine qualities of both groups and consequently they could be classified either in group C1 or C3.

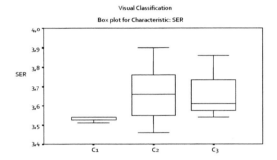
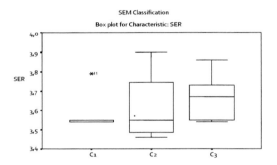

Figure 3. *Box-Plots of amino acid Serine (Ser) after classification into three condition categories using visual/physical (left graph) and SEM examination (right graph). Analysis of variance could not verify the discrimination appeared in the graphic display between C1 and C3 after visual/physical classification of the samples.*

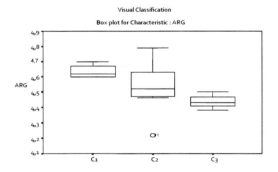
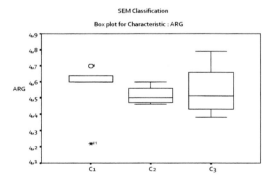

Figure 4: Box-Plots of amino acid Arginine (Arg) after classification into three condition categories using visual/physical (left graph) and SEM examination (right graph). Analysis of variance did not verify the discrimination appeared in graphic display between C1 and C3 after visual/physical classification of the samples.

The discrimination due to Hydroxyproline probably verified its stabilizing role in the collagen molecule. Arginine on the other hand is known to be affected by oxidation while Serine is usually related to the animal species and the presence of keratin. It would be worthwhile to further investigate

if these amino acids could be used to discriminate between the various states of preservation.

Logistic Regression
The Logistic Regression results did not provide a clear discrimination among the

582

various states of preservation. Furthermore, the aim here was the discrimination among the three states of preservation and not a discrimination based on a binary scale (only two possible values – to belong at a preservation group C1 instead of C2 or C2 instead to C3).

Principal Components

The principal components analysis considers a smaller number of linear combinations of the original variables which when taken together, explain a large amount of the variance of the original data. In our analysis, the first six linear combinations (Principal Components) explain the 93.30% percent of the observed variance whereas the first five explain the 89.24 % of the observed variance (see Table 6). It was decided to explore the effect of the first six components instead of the first five ones in the discriminant analysis and to investigate which of them could be used in predicting the preservation state of the leather samples (see Figure 5). Table 7 (see Table 7) presents the weight-significance of each variable into each Principal Component.

Discriminant Analysis

In order to find the differences between the three categories, Discriminant Analysis was applied to the six Principal Components from the previous step as its original variables (see Table 8 and Table 9). This analysis develops a discriminant model (Functions F1 and F2) that is then used to

classify leather samples into one of the preservation categories (C1, C2 and C3) previously identified in this study.

Discriminant Analysis showed a highly significant difference between the three group centroids for both types of assessment (see Figure 6 and Figure 7). By the classification results it can be seen that although the 93.3% of the samples are correctly classified, only the 46.7% are cross-validated (see Table 10), when applied to visually classified samples. This means that the discriminant functions are not reliable and cannot be used to predict the preservation group membership of other deteriorated leathers.

Similarly, when the method is applied to leathers classified by SEM photographs, although 60.0% of the samples are correctly classified, only 20.0% are cross-validated (see Table 11). So these functions cannot be used to classify other deteriorated leathers. The analysis of a larger number of leathers could either validate the conclusions or bring out new elements on the importance of the measurements for the prediction of the preservation state. However it should be noted that the three preservation groups (C1, C2 and C3) seem to be better discriminated when using the visual/physical assessment as a classification method than the SEM assessment (see Figure 6 and Figure 7).

Table 6. *The left column presents the Principal Components (PC). The right column depicts the Cumulative Proportion which is the percentage explained by the Components.*

Importance of Components			
	Standard Deviation	Proportion of Variance	Cumulative Proportion
PC. 1	3.9114	0.5884	0.5884
PC. 2	1.9234	0.1423	0.7307
PC. 3	1.1996	0.0553	0.7860
PC. 4	1.1856	0.0541	0.8401
PC. 5	1.1663	0.0523	0.8924
PC. 6	1.0271	0.0406	0.9330
PC. 7	0.8008	0.0247	0.9577
PC. 8	0.6195	0.0148	0.9725

Table 7. Loadings of the variables for the first 6 Principal Components. The statistical software (S-plus) used for the analysis doesn't report loadings/weights less than 0.1.

	Loadings of the variables for the first 6 Principal Components					
Variables	**PC.1**	**PC.2**	**PC. 3**	**PC.4**	**PC.5**	**PC.6**
pH	-	-	-0.187	-0.512	0.172	-0.609
Ts	-	0.160	-0.699	-	-0.346	-
Hyp	0.225	-	-	-	-	0.339
Asp	-0.243	-0.125	0.126	-	-	-
Thr	-0.227	-	-	-	-	0.269
Ser	-0.204	0.244	-	-0.113	-	-0.201
Glu	-0.170	-0.259	-0.106	-0.280	0.304	0.167
Pro	0.212	0.206	-	-	0.220	-
Gly	0.237	-	0.128	0.174	-0.120	-0.178
Ala	0.156	-0.258	-	-	-0.481	-
Val	-0.238	-	-0.154	-0.102	-	-
Met	-0.228	0.188	-	-	-	-
Ile	-0.251	-	-	-	-	-
Leu	-0.244	-	-0.203	-	-	-
Tyr	-0.230	-	0.207	-	-	-0.141
Phe	-0.247	-	-	-	-	-
His	-0.238	0.131	-	-	-	-
Hyl	-	0.401	0.198	-0.300	-0.230	-
Lys	-0.157	0.309	-	0.254	0.169	-
Arg	0.164	0.224	-0.362	-0.205	0.101	0.207
Ada	-0.157	-0.349	-0.164	-	0.143	0.198
BAla	-0.137	-	-	-0.335	-0.506	0.316
4/Abu	-0.148	-0.268	-0.177	0.230	-0.209	-0.326
Orn	-0.213	-	-0.170	0.318	-	-
A/B	0.167	0.367	-0.109	0.175	-	-
Coll.Con	0.220	-	-0.118	-0.242	-	-

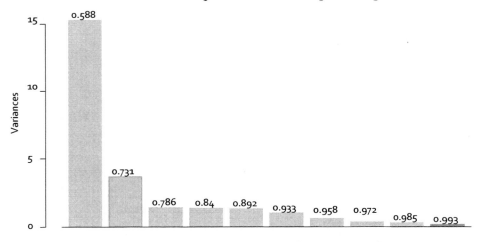

Relative Importance of Principal Components

Figure 5. Plot of the first Principal Components.

Table 8. *Coefficients of the first six Principal Components for the two Discriminant Functions (PC. refers to the Principal Components) after visual/physical classification.*

	Standardized Canonical Discriminant Function Coefficients	
	Function 1	Function 2
PC.1	0.188	0.696
PC.2	-0.089	-0.176
PC.3	1.205	-0.017
PC.4	-0.131	-0.713
PC.5	0.877	-0.215
PC.6	0.003	0.644

Table 9. *Coefficients of the first six Principal Components for the two Discriminant Functions (PC. refers to the Principal Components) after SEM classification*

	Standardized Canonical Discriminant Function Coefficients	
	Function 1	Function 2
PC.1	0.030	0.424
PC.2	0.310	-0.011
PC.3	0.385	0.705
PC.4	-0.168	0.341
PC.5	0.968	-0.266
PC.6	-0.466	-0.360

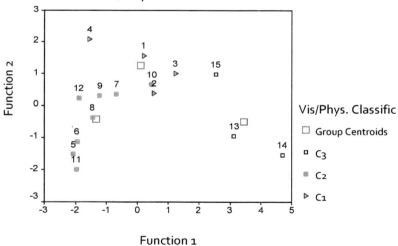

Canonical Discriminant Functions

Visual/Physical Classification

Figure 6. *Group centroids and classification in Preservation Groups C1, C2 and C3 using two Discriminant Functions.*

585

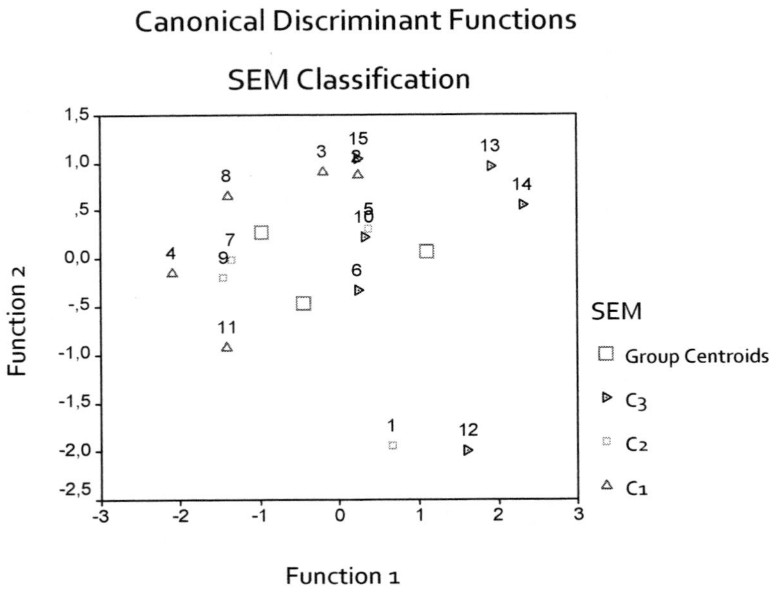

Canonical Discriminant Functions

SEM Classification

Figure 7. Group centroids and classification in Preservation Groups C1, C2 and C3 using the two Discriminant Functions.

Table 10. Percentage of the correctly classified leathers and percentage after the cross-validation. Statevis refers to the classification type (visual/physical examination), while 1, 2 and 3 refer to the three preservation groups C1, C2 and C3.

Classification Results [b,c]

				Predicted Group Membership			Total
				1	2	3	
Original	Count	STATEVIS	1	4	0	0	4
			2	1	7	0	8
			3	0	0	3	3
	%	STATEVIS	1	100.0	0	0	100.0
			2	12.5	87.5	0	100.0
			3	0	.0	100.0	100.0
Cross-validated[a]	Count	STATEVIS	1	1	3	0	4
			2	4	4	0	8
			3	1	0	2	3
	%	STATEVIS	1	25.0	75.0	0	100.0
			2	50.0	50.0	0	100.0
			3	33.3	0	66.7	100.0

a. Cross validation is done only for those cases in the analysis. In cross validation, each case is classified by the functions derived from all cases other than that case.

b. 93.3% of original grouped cases correctly classified.

c. 46.7% of cross-validated grouped cases correctly classified.

586

Table 11. *Percentage of the correctly classified leathers and percentage after the cross-validation. StateSEM refers to the classification type, while 1, 2 and 3 refer to the three preservation groups C1, C2 and C3.*

Classification Results[b,c]

				Predicted Group Membership			Total
				1	2	3	
Original	Count	STATESEM	1	3	1	1	5
			2	2	1	1	4
			3	0	1	5	6
	%	STATESEM	1	60.0	20.0	20.0	100.0
			2	50.0	25.0	25.0	100.0
			3	0	16.7	83.3	100.0
Cross-validated[a]	Count	STATESEM	1	1	2	2	5
			2	2	0	2	4
			3	1	3	2	6
	%	STATESEM	1	20.0	40.0	40.0	100.0
			2	50.0	0	50.0	100.0
			3	16.7	50.0	33.3	100.0

a. Cross validation is done only for those cases in the analysis. In cross validation, each case is classified by the functions derived from all cases other than that case.

b. 60.0% of original grouped cases correctly classified.

c. 20.0% of cross-validated grouped cases correctly classified.

Conclusions

In conclusion:

- Visual/physical examination of leather condition remains a subjective assessment.

- Examination of the fibers under the scanning electron microscope is a useful tool for observing the internal structure of the leather, but because it is based on minute samples, it is not always representative of their total condition.

- Degree of acidity lay within the safe range and did not predict deterioration as defined by the classification method.

- The samples tended to produce large shrinkage intervals (ΔT), which may be explained by a lack of uniformity in deterioration or in tannage, or in differences in stability as result of the initial treatment of the skin.

- Box-plots revealed that for the Shrinkage Temperature there is a clear discrimination between the preservation group C3 and groups C1 and C2, for the visually/physically classified leather samples, indicating a correlation between the visual/physical assessment of condition and the shrinkage temperature.

- The Logistic Regression analysis didn't provide discrimination among the various states of preservation.

- Discriminant analysis showed a highly significant difference between the groups C1, C2 and C3 for both type of assessment. The results of the cross-validation techniques applied are not considered sufficient and hence do not allow to use the discriminant functions for predicting the preservation group membership of other deteriorated leathers.

- Statistical analysis needs to increase its sample data for both quantity and representativeness of the samples.

In general, this study has revealed the problems associated with the analysis of waterlogged archaeological leather and has shown that empirically categorizing leather condition is unpredictable and highly subjective. It has also shown that the use of more complex analytical procedures can reveal more information about the condition of waterlogged archaeological leather but they do not provide a clear ranking of its degree of deterioration and its overall condition. To do this the analytical approach needs to be considerably more refined. Many more samples should be examined in order to produce results that can be statistically assessed. As stated by Larsen et al. (2002) a successful outcome will very much depend on the amount of data available for model building and the subsequent correlation analysis. It is important that many different techniques – advanced as well as simple- are applied to a large number of samples in different states of preservation. This will require extensive cooperation between both conservators/restorers and scientists, and an efficient flow of data and software between the different research groups. One way of achieving this may be, as in the case of IDAP (Bechmann and Larsen 2007), to establish a network of interested conservators/restorers and scientists and to build a central database containing all experimental data and software for all members of the network.

Until this time, simple physical tests will continue to aid conservators in their selection of conservation procedures, even though they are not reproducible.

Acknowledgments

The authors would like to thank Mr. P. Fisher, University of Cardiff, Dr. V. Kilikoglou, NSCR Democritos, Dr. R. Larsen and Mrs. D. Poulsen, Konservatorskolen Denmark, for their support and contribution in Shrinkage Temperature measurement, Scanning Electron Microscopy and High Performance Liquid Chromatography respectively. Thanks are also due to Mr. R. Thomson, L.C.C., Ms. A. Bugby and Ms. B. Haines[†] for their contribution to the classification of the samples and to Ms. A. Wallace for her advice on scanning electron microscopy.

References

AIC, (1999), American Institute for Conservation- code of ethics and guidelines for practice. Available: http://palimpsest.stanford.edu/aic/pubs/ethics.html

Alexander K.T.W., Covington A.D., Garwood R.J. and Stanley A.M., (1993), The Examination of Collagen ultrastructure by Cryo-Scanning Electron Microscopy in: XXII IULTCS Congress Proceedings, Porto Alegre Brazil 16-20 November 1993, pp 1-16.

Baer N. S. and Low M.J. D., (1982) Advances in scientific instrumentation for conservation: an overview, in: N. S. Brommelle and G. Thomson (eds.) Preprints of IIC Congress on Science and Technology in the service of conservation. Washington 3-9 September 1982, London: IIC, pp 1-5.

Bechmann D. J. and Larsen R., (2007), The IDAP website – Data collection and sharing of knowledge, in R. Larsen (ed.), School of Conservation, The Royal Academy of Fine Arts, Improved damage assessment of parchment IDAP, Assessment, data collection and sharing of knowledge, Research Report no18, Copenhagen, European Commission-Directorate General for Research I-Environment, 2007, pp 13-16.

Berthold M. and Hand D., (1998), Intelligent Data Analysis, Berthold, M. and Hand, D (eds.), Springer-Verlag publications, Heidelberg.

BLMRA, (1957), Hides, Skins and Leather under the Microscope, Milton Park, Egham, Surrey.

Boghosian S., Garp T. and Nielsen K., (1999), Study of the chemical breakdown of collagen and parchment by Raman Spectroscopy, in: Preprints for the Advanced Study Course. School of Conservation Royal Academy of Fine Arts – European Commission-Directorate General XII-Environment and Climate Program 'Methods in the Analysis of the Deterioration of Collagen based Historical Materials in relation to Conservation and Storage' 6-10 July 1999, Copenhagen, pp 73-89.

Boghosian S., (2007), Structural damage of parchment at the molecular level assessed by Raman Spectroscopy, in Rene Larsen (ed.), School of Conservation, The Royal

Academy of Fine Arts, Improved damage assessment of parchment IDAP, Assessment, data collection and sharing of knowledge, Research Report no18, Copenhagen, European Commission-Directorate General for Research I-Environment, 2007, pp 105-109.

Borasky R. and Nutting G.C., (1949), Microscopic Method for Determining Shrinkage Temperatures of Collagen and Leather, in Journal of American Leather Chemists Association, Vol. 44, pp 830-841.

Bowes J. H. and Raistrick A.S., (1961a), The action of heat and moisture on leather. Part I. The storage of a variety of commercial leathers at 40^0C and 100% R.H., in Journal of American Leather Chemists Association, Vol. 56, pp 32-44.

Bowes J. H. and Raistrick A.S., (1961b), The action of heat and moisture on leather. Part III. The effect of pH on the deterioration of vegetable, chrome, semichrome, and chrome retan leathers, in Journal of American Leather Chemists Association, Vol. 56, pp 632-644.

Bowes J. H. and Raistrick A. S., (1963), The action of heat and moisture on leather. Part IV. The effect of chrome content and detannage by sodium lactate on the resistance of chrome leather to moist heat, in Journal of American Leather Chemists Association, Vol. 58, pp 190-201.

Bugby A., (1998), Personal Communication.

Calnan C. N., (1991), Ageing of vegetable tanned leather in response to variations in climatic conditions, in C. Calnan and B. Haines (eds.) Leather: Its composition and changes with time, Northampton, The Leather Conservation Centre, pp 41-50.

Chahine, C. and Rottier C., (1992), Changes in thermal stability during artificial ageing with pollutants: a DSC study, in P. Hallebeek et al. (eds.) Preprints of the ICOM Interim Symposium on Leathercraft and Related objects, V&A

Museum London 24-25 June 1992, London: ICOM., pp.6-10.

Chahine C. and Rottier C., (1995), DSC Measurements, in ENVIRONMENT-Leather Project EV5V-CT94-0514, Progress Report, pp145-159.

Chahine C. and Rottier C., (1996), Artificial Ageing, in ENVIRONMENT-Leather Project EV5V-CT94-0514, Research Report No 6, pp33-38.

Cormia R.D., (1992), Problem-Solving Surface Analysis Techniques, in Advanced Materials & Processes 12/92, pp16-23.

Cot J., Marsal M. and Aramon C., (1989), A Study of the Grain Layer using a Scanning Electron Microscope (SEM) fitted with an Energy-Dispersive X-Ray Analyser: Part I. The Contribution to Quality Improvement in Defective Chrome Tanned Leathers, in Journal of the Society of Leather Technologists and Chemists, Vol.73, pp 42-46.

Crewther W. G., Fraser R. D. B., Lennox F. G. and Lindley H., (1965), Amino acid composition. The chemistry of keratins, in Advances in Protein Chemistry, Vol. 20, pp 191-346.

Dempsey M., (1968), Leather and Light Microscopy, in Journal of American Leather Chemists Association, Vol. 63, No 12, 1968, pp 667-692.

Draper N. R. and Smith H., (1967), Applied Linear Regression, Willey Publications.

English Heritage, (1995), Guidelines for the care of waterlogged archaeological leather, in English Heritage-Archaeological Leather Group Scientific and Technical Publications Guideline No.4.

Florian M-L. E., (1987), Deterioration of organic materials other than wood, in C. Pearson (ed.), Conservation of Marine Archaeological Objects, London, Butterworths, pp 39-46.

Ganiaris H., Keene S. and Starling K., (1982), A Comparison of some Treatments for Excavated Leather, in The Conservator, 6, pp12-23.

Haines B. M., (1981), The Fibre Structure of Leather, Northampton, The Leather Conservation Centre.

Haines B. M., (1985), The structure of leather and its deteriorations, in Hackens et al. (eds.), The Conservation of Library and Archive Property, European Intensive Course, Rome 3-12 April 1980, PACT 12, pp163-184.

Haines B., (1987), Shrinkage Temperature in Collagen Fibers, in Leather Conservation News, Vol.3, No 2, pp1-5.

Haines B. M., (1991), The structure of collagen, in C. Calnan and B. Haines (eds.), Leather: Its composition and changes with time, Northampton, The Leather Conservation Center, pp 5-10.

Haines B. M., (1998), Personal Communication.

Hallebeek P., (1992), Moisture uptake/release and chemical analysis, in STEP Leather Project First Progress Report, pp 99-127.

Harrington W. F. and Von Hippel P. H., (1961), Structure of collagen and gelatine, in Advances in Protein Chemistry, 16, pp 30-94.

Hodges H., (1968), Artifacts- An introduction to early materials and technology, 3rd Edition, London, J. Baker.

Hosmer D. W. and Lemeshow S., (1965), Applied Logistic Regression, Willey Publications.

Larsen R., Barkholt V. and Nielsen K., (1989), Amino Acids Analysis of Leather. Preliminary Studies in Deterioration, Accelerated Ageing and Conservation of Vegetable Tanned Leather, in Das Leder, pp 153-158.

Larsen R., Vest M., Jensen A.L. and Nielsen K., (1992), Amino Acids Analysis, in First Progress Report. STEP Leather Project, March 1992, pp 19-48.

Larsen R., (1993), Evaluation of the correlation between natural and artificial ageing of vegetable tanned leather and determination of parameters for standardization of an artificial ageing method: STEP Leather Project, in European Cultural Heritage Newsletter on Research, Vol. 7, No 1-4, pp 19-26.

Larsen R., Vest M. and Nielsen K., (1993), Determination of Hydrothermal Stability (Shrinkage temperature) of Historical Leather by the Micro Hot Table Technique, in Journal of the Society of Leather Technologists and Chemists. Vol.77, No 5, pp 151-156.

Larsen, R., Vest, M. and Calnan, C., (1994a), Materials. In: STEP Leather Project. Protection and Conservation of European Cultural Heritage. Research Report No1. European Commission Directorate-General for Science, Research and Development, pp. 11-30.

Larsen R., Vest M. and Nielsen K., (1994b), Determination of Hydrothermal Stability (Shrinkage temperature), in STEP Leather Project. Protection and Conservation of European Cultural Heritage. Research Report No1, European Commission Directorate-General for Science, Research and Development, pp 151-164.

Larsen R., Vest M., Nielsen K. and Jensen A. L., (1994c), Amino Acid Analysis, in STEP Leather Project. Protection and Conservation of European Cultural Heritage. Research Report No1, European Commission Directorate-General for Science, Research and Development, pp 39-57.

Larsen R., (1995), Fundamental Aspects of the Deterioration of Vegetable Tanned Leather, PhD Thesis, The Royal Danish

Academy of Fine Arts School of Conservation.

Larsen R. and Vest M., (1995), Historical Materials and Visual Assessment, in ENVIRONMENT- Leather Project EV5V-CT94-0514, Progress Report, pp 7-11.

Larsen R., (1996), Personal Communication.

Larsen R., (1998), The science of Conservation-Restoration, in K. Borchersen (ed.), Preprints of the Jubilee Symposium 18-20 May 1998, Copenhagen, Konservatorskolen Det Kongelige Danske Kunstakademi. Konservatorskolen Det Kongelige Danske Kunstakademi, pp 77-85.

Larsen R., (1999), Personal Communication.

Larsen R., Poulsen D. V., Odlyha M., Kurt N., Wouters J., Puchinger L., Brimblecombe P. and Bowden D., (2002), The Use of Complementary and Comparative Analysis in Damage Assessment of Parchments, in R. Larsen (ed.), Microanalysis of Parchment, London, Archetype, 2002, pp 165-179.

Malea E., Stassinou A., Kilikoglou V., Ioannidis I.A. and Watkinson D., (1997), Preliminary Report on the Examination of Leather Bookbindings belonging to the National Library of Athens, in Postprints of the 4th Interim Meeting of the ICOM Committee for Conservation Group 10, Conservation of Leathercraft and Related Objects, Amsterdam 5-8 April 1995, pp 50-56.

Mardia K. V. Kent J. T. and Bibby J. M., (1979), Multivariate Analysis, London, Academic Press.

McCullagh P. and Nedler J. A., (1989), Generalised Linear Models, 2nd Edition. London, Chapman and Hall.

Nayudamma Y., (1978), Shrinkage Phenomena. The Chemistry and Technology of Leather, Vol. II- Types of Tannages, New York, R.E. Krieger Publishing Company, pp 28-65.

Nikitina K. F., (1981), Conservation of Archaeological Leather in the State Hermitage Museum, in ICOM 6th Triennial Meeting Preprints, 81/19/2, Ottawa, pp 1-10.

Odlyha M., (1999), Study of chemical changes in leather and parchment by Solid Phase Nuclear Magnetic Reasonance Spectroscopy (NMR), in Preprints for the Advanced Study Course, School of Conservation Royal Academy of Fine Arts – European Commission-Directorate General XII-Environment and Climate Program 'Methods in the Analysis of the Deterioration of Collagen based Historical Materials in relation to Conservation and Storage' 6-10 July 1999, Copenhagen, pp 103-117.

O'Flaerty F., Troddy W. and Collar R. M., (1956), Deterioration, in Reinohold (ed.), Chemistry and Technology of Leather, Vol. IV, New York, Reinohold.

Pearson C., (1987), Conservation of Marine Archaeological Objects, IIC (ed.), London, Butterworths.

Raeder-Knudsen L., (1990), Conservation of the Tollund-Man, in Leather Conservation News, Vol. 6, No 2, pp 1-7.

Reed R., (1972), The Physical Examination of Parchment and Leather. In Reed R. (ed.), Ancient Skins, Parchments and Leathers, London, Seminar Press, pp 283-323.

Sanders S., (1986), Preventing metal ion catalysed degradation of leather, in P. Hallebeek (ed.), Symposium on Ethnographic and Waterlogged Leather. Amsterdam 9-11 June 1986, Amsterdam, CL-ICOM, pp 79-86.

Singley K., (1988), Leather, in The Conservation of Archaeological Artifacts from Freshwater Environments, Michigan,

Lake Michigan Maritime Museum, pp 79-84.

Stroz M. D., Glew R. H., Williams S. L. and Saha A. K., (1993), Comparisons of preservation treatment of collagen using the Collagenase-SDS-Page technique, in Studies in Conservation, 38, pp 45-54.

Suenson-Taylor K., Sully D. and Orton C., (1999), Data in Conservation: the missing link in the process, in Studies in Conservation, 44, No 3, pp 184-195.

Sully D. and Suenson-Taylor K., (1998), An Interventive Study of Glycerol Treated Freeze-Dried Leather, in C. Bonnot-Diconne, X. Hiron, Q. K. Tran and P. Hoffmann (eds.), Proceedings of the 7th ICOM-CC Working Group on Wet Archaeological Materials Conference, Grenoble, 1998, pp 224-231.

Sykes R. L., (1991), The Principles of Tanning, in C. Calnan and B. Haines (eds.), Leather: Its composition and changes with time, Northampton, The Leather Conservation Center, pp 10-12.

Thomson R., (1995), Personal communication.

Thomson R., (1998), Personal Communication.

Tite M.S., (1972), Methods of Physical Examination in Archaeology, London, Seminar Press.

Van Dienst E., (1985), Some remarks on the conservation of wet archaeological leather, in Studies in Conservation, 30, pp 86-92.

Van Soest H. A. B., Stambolov T. and Hallebeek P. B., (1984), Conservation of Leather, in Studies in Conservation, Vol. 29, No 1, pp 21-32.

Vest M., (1996), Personal Communication.

Vest M., (1999), Personal Communication.

Vestergaard-Poulsen D., (1996), Personal Communication.

Vingelsgaard V. and Schmidt A.-L., (1986), Removal of Insecticides from furs and skins. Registration of Conservation condition, in P. Hallebeek (ed.), Symposium on Ethnographic and Waterlogged Leather, Amsterdam 9-11 June 1986, Amsterdam, ICOM, pp 51-61.

Young G.S., (1990), Microscopical Hydrothermal Stability Measurements of Skins and Semi-Tanned Leather, in Postprints of ICOM Committee for Conservation Group 18, Vol. II, pp 626-631.

Young G. S., (1992), Loss of Infrared Linear Dichroism in Collagen Fibres as a Measure of Deterioration in Skin and Semi-Tanned Leather Artifacts, in Materials Research Society Symposium Proceedings, Vol. 267, pp 859-867.

Young G. S., (1998), Thermodynamic characterization of skin, hide and similar materials composed of fibrous collagen, in Studies in Conservation, 43, pp 65-79.

Questions and answers

Lars Andersen: I had a comment on the shrinkage temperature. This method was made for recent leather and it gives very good results on recent leather for evaluating the degradation rate but I have a problem with using it on archaeological leather because of mineral deposits in the leather fibers and things like that. They react in a completely unpredictable way and I would like to ask if anyone else has had this problem of using this method with archaeological leather? It's always a problem when you take a very nice method that has been used in one field and then apply it to another field.

Ingrid Wiesner: Lars, I think in the 1997 WOAM Wethers made an analysis about the mineral content and the shrinkage temperature and she found some sort of correlation on this.

A Comparative Study of Various Impregnation and Drying Methods for Waterlogged Archaeological Leather

Angela Karsten* and Karla Graham
English Heritage, Fort Cumberland, Fort Cumberland Road, Portsmouth, PO4 9LD, UK
*E-mail: angela.karsten@english-heritage.org.uk

Liz Goodman and Helen Ganiaris, Museum of London Archaeology,

Kelly Domoney, former University College London/Museum of London intern

Abstract

The aim of this study was to compare different treatment and drying methods using parameters such as shrinkage, flexibility, appearance, time, effort and equipment. It also seemed an opportune time to consider the environmental impact of current leather treatments.

The first part of this study was carried out by English Heritage. Treatments included 20% glycerol, 20% PEG and no impregnation. Half the samples in each treatment category were pre-treated using 5% Na_2EDTA. The leather was dried using vacuum freeze drying, non-vacuum freeze drying, air drying and controlled air drying.

The second part of this study was carried out by the Museum of London. The leather was treated using 20% glycerol followed by vacuum freeze drying, non-vacuum freeze drying or air drying. The drying methods were separated into best practice and real life scenarios typical for bulk treatment.

The results of both studies are intended to contribute to informed decision making on treatment regimes and drying methods, providing choices and alternatives appropriate to the type and quantity of leather.

Keywords: Leather, Conservation, Air drying, Vacuum freeze drying, Non-vacuum freeze drying

1. Introduction

This project examined the effects of different treatment and drying techniques on waterlogged archaeological leather. It aimed to provide comparative data on the efficacy of the most commonly used remedial conservation methods for waterlogged archaeological leather using parameters such as shrinkage, flexibility, appearance, time, effort and equipment.

2. Background

Leather from archaeological sites in the UK is most likely to come from anaerobic waterlogged deposits where little or no oxygen is present. The aim of remedial conservation is to remove all the water so that the leather is stable in ambient environmental conditions to facilitate further study and to enable deposition at an appropriate repository. Over the years many different methods have been used to conserve archaeological waterlogged leather. Currently, the most common technique used in the UK and northern Europe is a pre-treatment of either glycerol or polyethylene glycol (PEG) in water followed by vacuum freeze drying.

The initial costs of purchasing a freeze dryer and high running costs means that only a limited number of institutions in the UK have freeze dryers or can offer vacuum freeze drying as a service. The vacuum freeze drying of waterlogged leather is perceived by archaeological contractors as expensive and cited as the reason for not conserving leather. While other drying methods exist, the lack of comparative data has resulted in reluctance by both conservators and archaeological contractors to use alternative methods. Backlogs of un-conserved leather are being created and these present a number of problems:

- Waterlogged leather is prone to mould and bacteria growth that can damage the leather and poses a health hazard.
- It may not be possible to carry out assessment by a researcher as some details may not become visible until the leather is dry.
- As the leather cannot be deposited at the appropriate repository (museum), the archaeological unit must take on the resources required for storage and curation.

English Heritage (as the UK Government's advisor on the historic environment) and the Museum of London are working together on a project to address this issue and provide informed advice to archaeologists, curators and conservators. Experimental work to support this project was divided into two parts: the first part, carried out by English Heritage, addressed a number of commonly used pre-treatments and four different drying methods. The second part of this study, carried out by the Museum of London, following on from the results of the English Heritage work, focused on one pre-treatment and separated the drying methods into best practice and real life scenarios, typical for bulk treatment.

3. The English Heritage Trial
3.1 Sample material and condition
The leather used for the English Heritage trial was donated by Dean Sully, lecturer in conservation at University College London (UCL). It was collected by UCL in 2003 from discarded material on the spoil heap of an excavation in Novgorod, an urban site in North West Russia.

All 89 bags of leather comprised of off cuts and fragments coming from three different locations on the excavation, which is

indicated by the codes NE, NF and T. During visual examination it became evident, that all the leather from area T was much more friable and fragmented than the leather from the other two areas. The leather was cleaned using running water and brushes and did not require any further washing.

3.2 Recording
The following parameters were chosen to compare the various treatments: shrinkage, flexibility, appearance, time and effort. Furthermore a condition score, CARS (criterion anchored rating scale) originally adapted by Suenson-Taylor and Sully (1996) was used to record the condition of each piece before and after treatment.

All pieces were photographed and drawn before conservation. In order to establish the flexibility before and after treatment, a flexibility test was devised [1]. For this study flexibility is defined as the degree in change of movement when leather is suspended over an edge.

3.3 The trial
PEG and glycerol were chosen as the impregnation medium at a concentration of 20% for three days. Some samples did not receive any pre-treatment and were dried from the wet state (see Table 1). To evaluate the effect with regards to shrinkage of the complexing agent disodium ethylene diamine tetra acetic acid (Na_2EDTA) on leather, half the samples were pre-treated with Na_2EDTA. Four drying methods were chosen for this study: air drying, controlled airdrying using saturated salt solutions, vacuum freeze drying and non-vacuum freeze drying. Sample selection was random, with the exception for the vacuum freeze drying method for the leather labeled T.

3.3.1 Pre-treatment

The mineral content of wet archaeological leather is sometimes considered to be a problem, which can result in iron staining and brittleness. Complexing agents are used to reduce the mineral content, which is also thought to prevent future problems of the oxidation of iron compounds especially during storage. This study focused on the use of EDTA only, as it seems to be the material most widely used and works in a pH range of 3-6 which is considered safe for leather.

Table 1: Overview of treatment and drying methods (English Heritage)

Pre-treatment method	Number of samples in each category	Drying method	Number of samples in each category
No impregnation	14	Air drying	23
5% Na$_2$EDTA	15	Controlled air drying	15
20% glycerol	15	Vacuum freeze drying	26
20% PEG400	15	Non-vacuum freeze drying	23
5% Na$_2$EDTA 20% glycerol	15		
5% Na$_2$EDTA 20% PEG400	15		

A literature review confirmed that EDTA was commonly used in the past (Elmer 1980, Ganiaris et al 1982, v. Dienst 1985, Wouters 1986, Jenssen 1987, Singley 1988, Hamilton 2000, Godfrey 2002, Hovmand & Jones 2001, Peacock 2001, Rodgers 2004). Often the reason for an EDTA treatment is not given. Informal discussions with several conservators did however reveal that it is used for one or more of these reasons:

- To lighten the color of the leather.
- To produce a more natural looking artifact.
- On stiff leather, to produce a more flexible artifact.
- When contamination with metal corrosion products has taken place from nearby objects or metal fittings of the same object.

Half the samples were pre-treated with a 5% solution of Na$_2$EDTA for 2hours, followed by 48h rinse in running tap water.

3.3.2 Impregnation

A vast variety of bulking and dressing agents have been used on waterlogged leather in the past. A 20% solution of PEG400 (w/v) or 20% glycerol (v/v) was chosen as the bulking agent for this study for three days at room temperature.

3.3.3 Drying

Past drying methods are as varied as past impregnation methods and include among others drying from solvents. Freeze drying of leather is widely used and considered to be a cost effective way of drying large quantities of leather while at the same time producing satisfactory results in terms of appearance.

All leather was dried as found, for example folded pieces were not laid out flat nor weighted down. The weight of each piece was recorded every day throughout the trial. The end point was established when one or more of the following parameters were noted:

- The leather felt and looked dry.

- Two constant weights were measured.
- All ice crystals had disappeared.

Vacuum freeze drying: The leather was frozen in a domestic chest freezer for two days and then placed on acid free tissue lined trays inside the otherwise empty freeze drying chamber. As all the leather from region T was found to be more friable than the leather from the other two regions NE and NF it was decided to deviate from the random sample selection in this case and vacuum freeze dry all the leather from region T.

Non-vacuum freeze drying: This was undertaken in a domestic chest freezer with the addition of silica gel and a fan (see Figure 1). The average temperature inside the chest freezer was -25°C. The leather was placed on thin polyethylene foam (Plastazote®) inside open mesh baskets, which were stacked on top of each other. The baskets were put between the fan and the desiccated silica gel (4.2kg split between the baskets), to allow cold air to be gently blown over the leather towards the silica gel, in order to absorb moisture and lower vapor pressure in order for sublimation of the ice to occur (Diesen and Storch 1997).

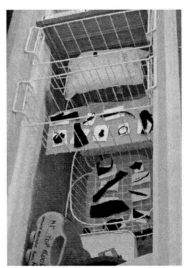
Figure 1. Chest freezer arrangement

Slow air drying: At ambient conditions this was carried out on polyethylene foam (Jiffy Foam®) lined tray with a polythene cover loosely draped on top (see Figure 2). The tray was placed away from direct sunlight.

Figure 2. Slow air drying

Controlled air drying: This was carried out inside a humidity chamber with the saturated salt solution placed at the bottom of the chamber and the leather above it on a grid (see Figure 3). The solutions were changed after two days to slowly lower the humidity in increments [2].

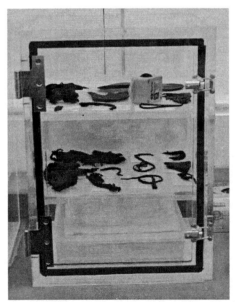
Figure 3. Controlled air drying, humidity chamber

3.4 Results
3.4.1 Condition score
Of the 89 items, 38 condition scores increased following treatment (43%), 22 condition scores decreased (25%) and 29 condition scores remained unchanged

(32%). The changes in condition score occurred in the following areas:

- Increases in value occurred mainly from improvements in the cohesivity and friability values.
- Decreases in value occurred mainly in the flexibility value.
- Items from area T decreased in condition score across all three categories.

The best performing pre-treatment for improved condition was 5% Na₂EDTA 20% glycerol where 64% of the condition scores increased. The highest percentage of items decreasing in condition score occurred with no impregnation. The controlled air drying and non-vacuum freeze drying methods both performed well with approximately half of the items increasing in condition score. A third of the items dried by air drying and vacuum freeze drying also increased in condition score. Vacuum freeze drying resulted in the highest percentage of items decreasing in condition score although, the selection of all the poor condition T area items for freeze drying may account for the low score. Controlled air drying resulted in the

lowest percentage of items decreasing in condition score.

3.4.2 Shrinkage
When looking at the shrinkage values per pre-treatment (see Table 2) it can be concluded that the smallest shrinkage was achieved by 20% glycerol impregnation and the largest shrinkage by 5% Na₂EDTA. Evaluating the drying methods the smallest shrinkage values were achieved following air drying and the largest by controlled air drying (see Table 3).

It is widely accepted that leather will experience some shrinkage during treatment. The mean shrinkage value of 7.37% is acceptable. Individual shrinkage values are in some cases too high, but a more defined treatment, which is designed for the individual condition of each object, can overcome this problem. This was however not the purpose of this study and the difference in shrinkage values from one piece to another is a well known fact when carrying out batch treatment of leather.

Table 2. Mean shrinkage values (%) by pre-treatment

Pre-treatment method	Mean shrinkage values (%)
20% glycerol	5.26
5% Na₂EDTA 20%glycerol	6.93
20% PEG400	6.94
5% Na₂EDTA 20% PEG400	7.47
No impregnation	8.43
5% Na₂EDTA	9.2

Table 3: Mean shrinkage values (%) by drying method

Drying method	Mean shrinkage values (%)
Air drying	6.17
Non-vacuum freeze drying	7.52
Vacuum freeze drying	7.66
Controlled air drying	8.43

3.4.3 Flexibility
Overall, 38% of the samples changed in flexibility, all of which were decreases in flexibility. The smallest decrease of flexibility occurred with the 5% Na₂EDTA

alone and the highest decrease in flexibility occurred with 20% PEG (53% of samples). By drying method, a loss in flexibility resulted from all drying methods and the difference between them was not significant.

3.4.4 Appearance

All leather looked acceptable after treatment and was of a natural brown color. Some items seem to have a slight red-brown tinge; these had mainly undergone Na_2EDTA pre-treatment. As color was not recorded in a standard way before treatment, it is not clear to what extent this color was already present in the wet, untreated leather.

3.4.5 Evaluation of treatment time

Since the pre-treatment and impregnation time was the same for all sample batches, only the drying time differed. Vacuum freeze drying was the fastest method, closely followed by air drying. Non-vacuum freeze drying took the longest, whilst controlled air drying was only a day shorter (see Table 4). For the purposes of the trial, the leather was weighed every 24 hours. However, in reality the leather would be weighed every other day or at least twice a week. The amount of monitoring would depend upon staff expertise, type of equipment and volume of material being dried.

Table 4: Mean treatment time (days) by drying method

Drying method	Mean drying time (days)
Vacuum freeze drying	4.4
Air drying	5.6
Controlled air drying	8.2
Non-vacuum freeze drying	9.1

3.5 Observations for English Heritage trial

All the impregnation methods worked well. Preparation time was minimal and all methods are equally suitable for batch or individual treatment. A point to consider is the use of Na_2EDTA as a standard treatment: this trial showed increased shrinkage and flexibility values. This is not surprising as it was already reported in 2001 (Hovmand and Jones 2001) that Na_2EDTA removes some minerals which leads to a loosening up of the fiber network and leather that can contract more. Furthermore, it does not only prolong the overall treatment time, but the required wash afterwards uses quite a lot of water and thereby adds to the overall treatment time and costs having environmental and sustainability considerations. The use of a complexing agent (such as Na_2EDTA) should therefore be limited to exceptional cases and not used as a standard treatment.

As can be expected, the non- impregnated batch resulted in rather high shrinkage values and for that reason, an impregnation should always be carried out. For the relatively small fragments in this trial it was evident that all drying techniques are suitable for large scale treatment, with the exception of controlled air drying. This drying technique was the most labor intensive method and needs improvement. Non-vacuum freeze drying worked well and this process could be sped up by gently manipulating the shape of the leather. Freeze drying was a very rapid method of drying; the leather felt rather dry and brittle when it first came out of the freeze dryer but improved after a few days. Air drying worked well when carried out with care and attention.

4. The Museum of London Trial

For the Museum of London case study, the aim was to repeat the work carried out at English Heritage focusing on drying methods and using material from excavations that was more likely to resemble leather found on UK sites (e.g. larger fragments and whole soles, uppers etc). The main body of work compared drying methods for leather that had been pre-treated with glycerol. A second smaller set from a different excavation was carried out to make some observations on air drying without glycerol.

4.1 Sample material, condition and recording

Sixty leather samples from the site of the former City of London Boys' School (BOY86) were chosen for the research. The leather had been stored wet with adhered burial dirt for over 20 years since excavation. Five contexts are represented within the sample groups, with the majority of the samples (40) representing a single context. Samples were assigned a number from 1 – 60 and randomly distributed across the six experiments in order to minimize bias in assessing condition. Samples consisted of shoes (uppers and soles) and leather working waste.

Samples were covered in large amounts of burial dirt as they had not undergone initial washing by finds processors in the 1980s. Much of the leather had mould growth on top of the burial deposit (see Figure 4). All samples underwent cleaning with soft brushes in running water. Due to health and safety concerns over the effects of mould, a risk assessment was completed and appropriate personal protection equipment and procedures were followed.

All recording was carried out in a similar way to the English Heritage trial (see 3.2). The end point of the experiments was determined once two constant weights (or slight gain in weight) were measured, all ice crystals had disappeared and the leather felt dry to touch. Samples were documented and assessed after 24 hours in order to allow the leather to acclimatize to atmospheric conditions.

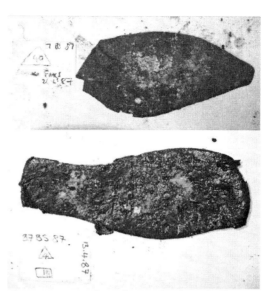

Figure 4. Examples of typical white fluffy mould growth covering leather samples

4.2 The trial

4.2.1 Pre-treatment and impregnation

All samples underwent impregnation with 20% glycerol in tap water for 48 hours, as per standard Museum of London treatment. After 48 hours all samples, except those selected for air drying, were placed in a conventional chest freezer at -25°C in preparation for freeze drying. Air drying scenarios were conducted immediately after impregnation.

Figure 5. Terram® bags and impregnation in Stewart® boxes

The following six experiments were conducted, each representing a best case or real life scenario to bulk dry waterlogged leather (see Table 5). Following the English Heritage method, the leather was laid out on surfaces but not flattened or compressed.

Table 5. *Overview of treatment and drying methods (Museum of London)*

Drying technique	Scenario	No. of samples
Vacuum freeze drying	***Best case*** Empty freeze dryer	10
	Real life Full freeze dryer with standardized drying time	10
Non-vacuum freeze drying in conventional chest freezer	***Best case*** Empty chest freezer with silica gel and fan	10
	Real life Full chest freezer without silica gel or a fan	10
Air drying	***Best case*** Semi-controlled air drying from wet state	10
	Real life Uncontrolled air drying from wet state	10

Vacuum freeze drying, best case scenario: Samples were placed in isolation in the centre of the freeze drying chamber.

Vacuum freeze drying, real life scenario: Samples were dried in accordance with the Museum's standardized procedure for bulk processing. Sample bags were placed on one of three shelves and dried in a packed freeze dryer amongst 50 bags of leather and/or wood (see Figure 6).

Figure 6: *Vacuum freeze drying experiment, real life scenario*

Non-vacuum freeze drying, best case scenario: Samples were placed on trays in the centre of an empty low-temperature chest freezer normally used for pest eradication (see Figure 7). The freezer had a fixed thermostat which maintained the temperature of the freezer to -40°C. 20kg of silica gel was placed at the bottom of the chamber.

After 15 days a portable fan was inserted in the chamber to act as an additional energy source to investigate if this would further lower the vapor pressure and increase the rate of sublimation; when this did not appear to work the leather was transferred to English Heritage.

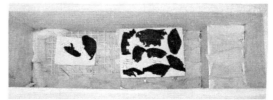

Figure 7. *Non-vacuum freeze drying experiment, best case scenario*

Non-vacuum freeze drying, real life scenario: Samples were placed on a plastic tray without a cover and stacked amongst boxes and bags of other archaeological material within a conventional chest

602

freezer at -25°C (see Figure 8). The freezer lid was opened frequently during the experiment as the freezer was in normal operation.

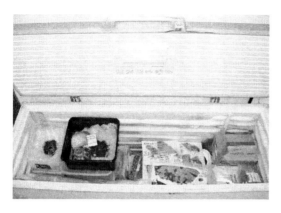

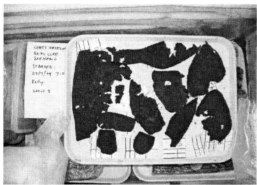

Figure 8:.*Non-vacuum freeze drying chamber: packed chamber with tray of samples placed on top*

Air drying, best case scenario: Samples were spaced out on nylon-net trays within an open Plastazote® (polyethylene foam) shelf structure (see Figure 9). The structure was covered with low density perforated polypropylene flow wrap sheeting in order to reduce the drying rate and help prevent shrinkage. Perforations in the sheeting allowed for air circulation. The structure was placed in a dark, well-ventilated storage facility without environmental controls (akin to a garage) in order to reduce mould growth. The store was chosen as it was likely to replicate best case facilities within an archaeological contract firm. Weight and shrinkage were measured again after 20 days because the samples had been relocated to the conservation laboratory immediately after

the experiment (the location for real life air dried leather).

Air drying, real life scenario: Samples were dried out on newspaper among a bulk load of leather in ten stacked plastic seed trays (see Figure 10). Each tray was full with some samples overlapping. The stack was placed in the corner of the archaeological conservation laboratory at the Museum of London and subject to warmer indoor conditions. The indoor environment was selected as it was likely to represent a real life scenario within a busy contract firm whereby space and supplies are limited. Weight and shrinkage were measured again after 20 days and compared to the results for best case air-dried leather.

Figure 9. *Air drying real life scenario: Plastazote® structure and holding store at the Museum of London*

4.3 Results
4.3.1 Condition assessment
Vacuum freeze-dried leather: There were no major differences in condition between real life and best case scenarios using CARS. In general all samples retained the

603

same physical integrity before and after drying. Flexibility was the main difference between the two groups with 30% of best case samples seeing a decrease in flexibility compared to 100% of real life samples retaining the same acceptable level. Based on visual assessment there was no obvious difference in condition between the two groups. After drying, both groups resulted in light-colored, flexible leather with minimal shrinkage and curling.

Figure 10: Air drying real life scenario: stack of trays and location in the corner of archaeological conservation laboratory, Museum of London

Air-dried leather: There were two main differences between the air-dried groups in terms of CARS rating. The physical integrity decreased for 30% of real life dried samples whilst 100% of best case remained the same. The decrease in score was apparent as cracks on the surface and around edges. Real life samples suffered a decrease in flexibility for 30% of samples whilst 100% of best case samples retained acceptable flexibility. There was a general improvement in cohesivity and friability for both groups.

After drying both groups were very dark in color compared to the freeze-dried samples (see Figure 11). Real life samples were visibly more curled and distorted than the best case samples. Ten days after the condition score was taken, both groups saw a dramatic change in flexibility with the majority of samples becoming brittle as they acclimatized to the warmer laboratory conditions. Both groups suffered from mould growth with half of best case samples having 75–100% surface coverage compared to 20% of real life samples (see Figure 12).

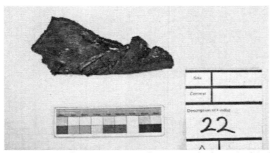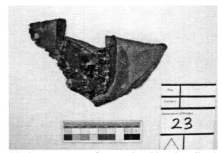

Figure 11. Color comparison between darker air-dried and lighter vacuum freeze-dried leather (both real life drying scenarios)

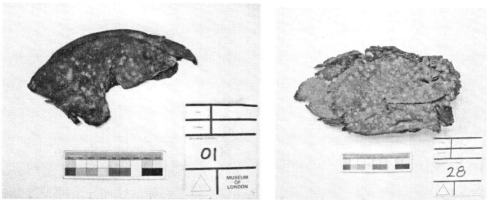

Figure 12. Examples of mould growth on air-dried best case and real life scenarios

Non-vacuum freeze-dried leather: There were no major differences in the CARS results between the best case and real life samples. The real life group showed no difference in the pre and post treatment scores whilst the best case group improved slightly on both cohesivity and friability. Visually the results were similar to the vacuum freeze-dried samples.

4.3.2 Shrinkage
Shrinkage was assessed on a visual rather than quantitative basis due to the variety of factors influencing behavior of leather such as cut of skin, original use, burial environment and tanning procedure. In general samples air dried in uncontrolled conditions suffered greater shrinkage than samples air dried in semi-controlled conditions; however after ten days of acclimatizing to warmer laboratory conditions best case air-dried samples underwent similar shrinkage values to real life air-dried samples.

Both vacuum and non-vacuum freeze-dried groups had limited shrinkage compared to air-dried groups. Real life freeze-dried samples had slightly less shrinkage than best case samples. For all samples, shoe soles underwent less shrinkage compared to shoe uppers and leather working waste.

4.3.3 Evaluation of treatment time
Freeze-dried groups: The time taken relates to how full the freeze dryer is,

therefore the best case was complete within 48 hours compared to the standard two week procedure for real life vacuum-dried leather.

Air-dried groups: The results of both the best case and real life indicate that most of the water is lost within the first few days. It was realized that although it was thought that the best case samples had reached equilibrium and were fully dry, when the samples were transferred to the warmer, drier laboratory conditions, further water was lost.

Non-vacuum freeze drying groups: A number of problems were encountered with this drying method, all of which increased the drying time. The best case non-vacuum freeze-dried group was initially done in a chest freezer that was set at -40°C, but the rate of loss was so small that it would have taken more than six months to dry. These samples were transferred to a different freezer to continue the experiment. It was also noted in the real life experiment that the drying rate also depended on whether the samples were covered or not.

4.4 Supplement to Museum of London trial: effect of no pre-treatment with glycerol
4.4.1 Samples and air drying method
To further consider the effect of pre-treatments, a trial was carried out to air

605

dry leather without pre-treating with glycerol. The English Heritage trial showed that a pre-treatment with either PEG or glycerol produced better results. This was repeated to confirm this observation and to determine whether mould growth is more likely to occur when air drying material treated with glycerol or whether it occurred (as happened with the BOY86 leather) because it had been present as a result of long term wet storage.

Twenty-five leather samples from a London site (SWI97), identified as shoe fragments and leather working scraps, were selected. The samples were cleaned, recorded and assessed as described above. The air drying methods from the previous scenarios were followed. Because the leather was from another site, it was acknowledged that this may not be a fair comparison. Therefore, five samples were pre-treated with glycerol and air dried as per the real life scenario to allow some comparisons to be made to the previous experiments.

4.4.2 Results
Both non-impregnated groups suffered from a severe reduction of flexibility (100% of the samples) and increased brittleness. In both groups the leather samples most affected were those with a thickness of less than 2mm. Curling was not a factor in the previous air drying scenarios. 100% of the leather samples treated with glycerol retained acceptable flexibility.

All the samples from all three scenarios experienced considerable shrinkage. However, the glycerol treated samples appear to have suffered from less shrinkage than those from the untreated groups. There was no mould growth on any of the samples.

The untreated real life samples took between 1 and 3 days to dry, while the untreated best case sample took between 2 and 7 days. The pre-treated real life samples also took only 2–3 days to dry.

4.5 Observations for Museum of London trial
All air-dried and freeze-dried groups resulted in stable objects with intact fibers. Air-dried leather groups however, were not as aesthetically pleasing compared to freeze-dried groups in terms of color and shape retention. On the whole all features of the air-dried leather could be identified by the researcher except for folded sections of more complete objects. As air-dried leather was more brittle, folded sections could not be manipulated without physically damaging the leather. In contrast freeze-dried leather was suppler and could be examined by hand without damage.

The greatest shrinkage was from the air-dried leather in both the real life and best case. It is possible that the shrinkage from the best case air-dried leather would have been less, if the leather had not continued to dry in an uncontrolled manner. All the freeze dried groups had some shrinkage but this will be influenced by a number a different factors such as burial environment or where the leather came from on the skin.

Non-vacuum freeze drying can be time-inefficient and would not be useful to process bulk loads, particularly as sublimation occurs at a faster rate when leather is exposed by being placed on top of other items in the freezer compartment. For smaller groups of leather this method may be useful and will likely result in leather with a more aesthetically pleasing appearance than air-dried items.

5. Conclusion
This study was instigated by a general concern that wet archaeological leather was not receiving treatment because of the perception that treatment is expensive. The results from both trials have had slightly varying results which is largely due to the inherent variability of the material

we are dealing with. However the general assessment by the working party is that there are options for treating wet leather that can be presented to the archaeological community.

There are some general conclusions that can be drawn:

- Pre-treatment with Na$_2$EDTA is not required routinely.
- A pre-treatment (glycerol or PEG400) is required.
- Leather that has been stored for a long period may have mould; mitigation measures will be required to deal with this.
- In appearance and flexibility, the best results were generally with freeze-dried leather but air-dried leather, done with care, can have good results.
- Shrinkage may be a less useful diagnostic tool for judging results because it is dependent on many inherent factors.
- Vacuum freeze drying is less labor intensive than air drying; air drying requires less equipment (no freezer or freeze dryer) but requires ventilated laying out space and daily attention.
- Non-vacuum freeze drying can produce good results but can also take a long time. It is best suited to small quantities of material.
- Some categories of leather (e.g. waste fragments, soles, simple shapes) can be expected to have good results with air drying, done with care; more complex shapes and thinner, delicate leather and objects made of composite materials will generally have better results with vacuum freeze drying.
- Standard treatment methods for leather and wood composite objects should be used. These objects are not suitable for pre-treatment with a low

concentration of bulking agents and air drying.

Results suggest that with careful assessment and guidelines for registering finds, leather could be divided into groups that could be air dried, and individual finds that would have better results with freeze drying. It must be stressed however that air drying requires time, laying out space, a well-ventilated area and vigilance to watch for mould growth. Although a freeze dryer requires a large initial outlay, in person time freeze drying is much more cost effective than the other methods discussed here.

A number of European institutions routinely use air drying and have devised methods to ensure a good result (Goubitz 1997, Domoney 2009). In the UK, Dana Goodburn Brown has devised a method of air drying that produced good results for some categories of material. This method prevented the curling sometimes observed on air-dried material particularly those made of thinner leather (Goodburn Brown, pers. comm).

The environmental impact of conservation standards and treatments is now under scrutiny. More work is needed in this area but the reduction of water usage by eliminating the routine use of a complexing agent is a positive step. Freezers and freeze dryers require higher energy consumption but the cost/benefit over air drying (which requires heated and/or ventilated spaces) has not been calculated.

It is planned that the revision of the English Heritage guidelines on treatment of waterlogged organic materials will present all options for treatment of leather based on this work, with a flow chart that will help archaeological units, particularly those faced with large quantities of leather. The method of treatment depends on a variety of parameters such as type, quantity and condition of the leather, time, budget, available equipment and staffing. With limited budgets and financial pressures, it is essential that the right decisions are made for conservation of excavated materials so that all material that requires treatment is treated in good time. Leather is a relatively small part of most excavation archives and initiatives that ensure that all leather is retained for future research should be encouraged.

Notes

[1]   Initially it was planned to carry out a tear test. Given the limited number of sample leather and the irregular size of each sample, this method was disregarded and a flexibility test devised: Each piece of leather was secured to a metallic cabinet with a magnet and then suspended over the edge of the cabinet. The degree it bent down was read on a protractor that was placed behind the cabinet. If the leather did not move at all or pointed upwards, the value 0 was assigned, as no change in movement took place. If the leather had some creases or cracks, that predetermined its flexibility or folding ability, Not Applicable (NA) was assigned. For all other pieces a value of 1°–90° was recorded.

[2]   The use of saturated salt solutions for the conditioning of showcases is widely reported (Aastrup 1987; Aastrup and Hovin Stub 1990; Crehan 1991 a; Crehan 1991 b; Piechota 1992). Their use enables the accurate conditioning of environments which can be used for the slow drying of sensitive materials. Three different solutions were used, each creating a specific relative humidity (RH) inside the chamber: barium chloride – 90%RH, potassium iodide – 70%RH and magnesium nitrate – 55%RH. The solutions were changed after two days to slowly lower the humidity in increments. The leather was to be left in the humidity chamber for one week after the solution had been changed to magnesium nitrate.

Acknowledgements

The authors would like to thank the following people Luisa Duarte (UCL), Dana Goodburn Brown (AMTEC), Maarit Hirvilammi (Turun Museokeskus, Finland), Jackie Keily (Museum of London), Quita Mould (Barbican Research Associates), Jane Sidell (English Heritage), Paul Simpson (Isle of Wight Council Museum Service), Dean Sully (UCL), Jacqui Watson (formerly English Heritage).

References

Aastrup E.E., (1987), Is it worth-while re-looking at salt solutions as buffers for humidity control of showcases?, in Preprints 8th Triennial Meeting International Council of Museums, pp 853-858

Aastrup E.E. and Hovin Stub K.E., (1990), Saturated salt solution for humidity control of showcases: conditions for a successful system, in Preprints 9th Triennial Meeting International Council of Museums, pp 577-582

Crehan J., (1991 a), Controlling relative humidity with saturated calcium nitrate solutions, WAAC Newsletter 13, Number 1, pp 17-18

Crehan J., (1991 b), Update and feedback: controlling humidity with saturated calcium nitrate solutions, WAAC Newsletter 13, Number 2, pp 11-12

Dienst van E., (1985), Some remarks on the conservation of wet archaeological leather, Studies in Conservation Volume 30, 1985, pp 86-92

Diesen C. and Storch P., (1997), A simple method for the freeze drying of archaeological leather: experiments and suggestions for further research, Leather Conservation News, No 2, pp 5-7.

Domoney D, (2009), Waterlogged archaeological leather: a comparative study of drying treatments and methodologies, unpubl MSc dissertation, University College London

Elmer J.Th., (1980), Die Gefriertrocknung von Nassleder-Bodenfunden aus dem Bereich der Archaeologie, in Konservering og restaurering af laeder, skind og pergament. Konservatorenskolen det Kongelige Danske Kunstakademi, Kopenhagen, pp 212-225

Ganiaris H., Keene S. and Starling K., (1982), A comparison of some treatments for excavated leather, The Conservator 16, pp 12-23

Godfrey I., Kasi K., Richards V., (2002), Iron removal from waterlogged leather and rope recovered from shipwreck sites in Hoffmann P., Spriggs J.A., Grant T., Cook C., Recht A. (editors), Proceedings of the 8th ICOM Group on Wet Organic Archaeological Materials Conference, Stockholm 2001, Bremerhaven, pp 439–470

Goubitz O., (1997), What is wrong with freeze-drying? in Hallebeek P. (editor), ICOM Working Group on the Conservation of Leather and Related Materials, Interim Conference, Amsterdam, Paris, pp 36-37

Hamilton D., (2000), Conservation of cultural materials from underwater sites: science and technology in historic preservation, in Williamson R.A and Nickens P.R. (editors), Advances in Archaeological and Museum Science Volume 4, New York, Kluwer Academic/ Plenum Publishers, pp 216-217

Hovmand I. and Jones J., (2001), Experimental work on the mineral content of archaeological leather, in Wills B. (editor), Leather Wet and Dry: Current treatments in the Conservation of Waterlogged and Desiccated Archaeological Leather, London, Archetype Publications Ltd., pp 27-36

Jenssen V., (1987), Conservation of wet organic artefacts excluding wood, in Pearson C. (editor), Conservation of Marine Archaeological Objects, London, Butterworth & Co Ltd., pp 122-163

Karsten A. and Graham K., (2010) (forthcoming), The leather drying trial: a comparative study of various impregnation and drying methods for waterlogged archaeological leather. English Heritage Research Department Report Series, Portsmouth: English Heritage

Peacock E., (2001), Water-degraded archaeological leather: an overview of treatments used at Vitenskapsmuseum (Trondheim). in Wills B. (editor), Leather Wet and Dry: Current Treatments in the Conservation of Waterlogged and Desiccated Archaeological Leather, London, Archetype Publications Ltd., pp 11-26

Piechota D., (1992), Humidity control in cases: buffered silica gel versus saturated salt solutions, WAAC Newsletter 15, Number I, pp 19-21

Rodgers B.A., (2004), The Archaeologist's Manual for Conservation: a Guide to Non-toxic Minimal Intervention Artefact Stabilization, New York, Kluwer Academic

Singley K., (1988), The Conservation of Archaeological Artefacts from Freshwater Environments, Michigan, Lake Michigan Maritime Museum

Suenson-Taylor K. and Sully D., (1997), The use of condition score to determine glycerol concentration in the treatment of waterlogged archaeological leather: an experimental solution, in Hoffmann P., Grant T., Spriggs J.A., Daley T. (editors), Proceedings of the 6th ICOM Group on Wet Organic Archaeological Materials Conference, York 1996, Bremerhaven, pp 157-172

Wouters J., (1986), A comparative investigation of methods for consolidation of wet archaeological leather: Application of freeze-drying to PEG impregnated leather, in Hallebeek P.B. (editor) Symposium on Ethnographic and Waterlogged Leather, 9, 10, 11 June 1986, Amsterdam, Netherlands, Amsterdam, ICOM, pp 61-69

Questions and answers

Ian Godfrey: A question for Liz about objects that have been treated with glycerol in the past. We've had problems at the museum years down the track because of glycerol leading to desiccation and brittleness. I was just wondering what your experience was at the Museum of London?

Liz Goodman: At the Museum of London we've been using glycerol since the eighties and looking at the long-term so far it seems to be okay. It's one of those things where we keep thinking it would be really nice to go back and have a look and really do a proper assessment but just looking at the anecdotal evidence, things seem to be okay. It was chosen because of the better shrinkage value.

Ian Godfrey: This is just really to let anyone know if they've got a lot of leather that they want analyzed in some way we'd certainly be happy to participate in a study that might use FTIR and artificial neural networks to assess leather. Anyone who wants to supply some samples, we'd be very happy to run the spectra, feed them through the program and then distribute the results. So please feel free to contact us.

Liz Goodman: Just to say that, as was demonstrated by my talk, we have some leather that's been sitting around for over a decade that we'd volunteer for any experiments you'd like to do.

5.8

Efficiency and Quality in a Batch Treatment: The Conservation of Over A Hundred Leather Shoes and Fragments

Jessica Lafrance
Canadian Conservation Institute, 1030 Innes Road, Ottawa, Ontario, K1A 0M5, Canada
Email: jessica.lafrance@live.ca

Abstract
In late 2008 nearly 400 organic objects from the Old Songhees Reserve site in Victoria, British Columbia, arrived at the Canadian Conservation Institute for treatment. Over half of these objects were leather shoes and fragments covered with corrosion and heavily iron stained. The treatment of 112 of these objects is the topic of this paper. Treatment included individual mechanical cleaning of each shoe, followed by mass chloride removal, iron corrosion stain removal, impregnation with polyethylene glycol, reshaping, freeze drying, and final consolidation and repair. Employing batch treatment methods for many of the conservation steps reduced time and material costs while careful planning, balanced decision making and monitoring ensured that the quality of the treatment was not reduced.

Keywords: leather, iron staining, iron corrosion, batch treatment, chlorides, efficiency, ammonium citrate

1. The Old Songhees Reserve & Objects
1.1 Old Songhees Reserve
Located in the Inner Harbor of Victoria, British Columbia, the Old Songhees reserve was a prominent and important part of the city from 1843 to 1911. Historically much of the city of Victoria was Songhees territory. When Fort Victoria was built in the 1840s the Songhees families created one village in the Inner Harbour. This village was sometimes referred to by Europeans as Lekwungen, or Stamish Village. In late 1844, the village moved to the other side of the harbor and became a reserve (Keddie 2003). The reserve, home of the Songhees people, grew over time to become a center for other visiting native peoples from the coastal and northern areas of British Columbia. Until the reserve was relocated in 1911, the Old Songhees Reserve was a meeting place, a location for celebrations and a center for trade in Victoria.

1.2 The Objects
The objects from the Old Songhees Reserve site (Borden Number DcRu-25) were recovered during archaeological investigations preceding the construction of a spa and residences. The leather objects were found in a metal cistern located in a small ravine on the site. It was suggested by the archaeologists that the items in the cistern may have been *"dumped shortly after the smallpox epidemic of 1862 in an effort to sanitize the site"* (I.R Wilson Consultants Ltd. 2006). An assessment of the possible personal hazards associated with treating objects connected to an infectious disease was carried out and it was determined that the probability of viable smallpox bacteria was very low.

The cistern itself had disintegrated onto the objects resulting in iron corrosion products and staining on the leather surface and interiors. Some pieces of leather were embedded in remaining fragments of the cistern. Apart from the damage due to the presence of corrosion products, other physical and chemical deterioration was apparent;
- visible and heavy chloride contamination
- waterlogged condition
- exposure of the leather grain
- splitting and cracking

611

- crumbling and fragmentation of exposed edges
- severe warping and folding
- areas of loss

Figure 1. *Visible chlorides on the surface of a sole.*

Figure 2. *Section of a shoe showing many signs of severe deterioration.*

2. Creating a Batch Treatment

The objects arrived at the laboratory in late 2008. The leather objects numbered over 200 and the first treatment was carried out on 112 of the shoes and larger shoe fragments. To develop and implement an efficient batch treatment, the steps, methods, and materials needed to be well planned and researched prior to beginning the work to ensure that all possibilities were anticipated and the project flowed at a good pace. This batch treatment plan needed to address the needs of all objects and ensure the use of reliable and compatible materials. The final plan included mechanical cleaning of the solid corrosion, iron corrosion stain removal, chloride removal, impregnation, reshaping, drying, consolidation and minor repairs. After searching the literature and consulting with other staff, the following treatment steps and materials were chosen based on positive recommendations, previous success rates and ease of use.

1. Sorting of objects into two groups to allow for the continuous treatment of objects.
2. Full immersion of the objects in water to begin the process of chloride removal, and to ensure the objects were completely waterlogged.
3. Removal of corrosion products and other debris from the surface and interior of objects using a Cavitron ultrasonic dental scaler, dental tools and brushes in running water.
4. Immersion of cleaned objects in monitored chloride removal baths.
5. Soaking cleaned objects in a 2% w/v solution of dibasic ammonium citrate (diammonium citrate or citric acid diammonium salt) in water to remove iron corrosion stains.
6. Impregnation of de-chlorinated objects with a 20% v/v solution of polyethylene glycol (PEG) 400 plus 1% v/v of Hostacor IT to inhibit the corrosion of iron nails and other iron fasteners.
7. Reshaping of objects using Ethafoam inserts and stretchy medical gauze.
8. Drying of objects using a vacuum freeze dryer.
9. Further reshaping following drying using a Preservation Pen and Bionaire ultrasonic humidifier.
10. Consolidation of friable areas using a 2% w/v solution of Klucel G in ethanol applied by brush or syringe.
11. Repairs and reinforcements using reactivated strips of Reemay coated with a 50:50 w/w mixture of Lascaux 498 HV and 360 HV.

The properties of some of the materials and why they were chosen will be discussed in greater detail in the remainder of this paper.

3. Treatment
3.1 Mechanical Cleaning

The corrosion products on the surface of these objects were well bonded to the leather. This prevented the safe mechanical removal of this material using small hand tools. The Cavitron ultrasonic dental scaler, which is regularly used when cleaning waterlogged organics, was employed with varying tips and power settings to efficiently remove corrosion products. As is visible in Figure 3, this tool was very effective in liberating the shoes from the heavy iron corrosion. While time consuming, Mardikian et al (2004) pointed out that leather with corrosion products on the surface must be thoroughly, mechanically cleaned in order to achieve good results from chemical removal of iron corrosion stains.

3.2 Removal of Chlorides

The objects from this site were heavily impregnated with chlorides, some of which had precipitated on the surface prior to arrival at CCI. Based on the visible level of contamination it was necessary to create a treatment step dedicated to monitored chloride removal. Chlorides can act as a catalyst for the production of sulfuric acid

causing solubilization of collagen (M-L.E Florian 1987). It can also cause physical damage to the structure as it precipitates on the surface.

Figure 3. *Child's shoe before and after mechanical cleaning.*

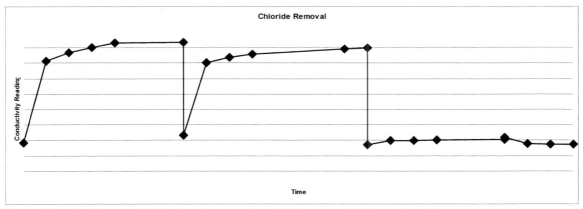

Figure 4. *Conductivity graph indicating changes in the chloride content of the leather objects.*

The removal of chlorides was carried out through the immersion of the artifacts in successive 75 L tap water baths. A submersible pump was placed in the bath and a timer was used to agitate the water for one hour, four times a day. This agitation reduced the concentration of

chlorides in the water surrounding each object and increased the rate of desalination while the intermittent running of the pump avoided heating the water and subjecting the leather to higher temperatures which might cause shrinkage or grow mould. The conductivity of the bath was monitored regularly using a Hanna Dist WP Conductivity/TDS instant read meter. Once equilibrium was reached the water was changed. This was carried out until there was no increase in conductivity after a bath change - a total of 3 months for Group 1, and 2 months for Group 2. While Group 1 was being de-chlorinated Group 2 was cleaned. The bulk of the chlorides were removed from the objects at this point and any it is likely any remaining chlorides would be removed during chemical corrosion stain removal and impregnation with PEG (McLeod et al, 1987).

3.3 Removal of Iron Corrosion Stains

When considering the removal of iron corrosion stains from these shoes several options presented themselves.

1. Do nothing. Leave the stains in place as they may be beneficial to the leather (Bardet et al 2009) and the need for removal is mainly aesthetic.
2. Remove the stains as, it was best stated by Wight (1978), iron stains may often become centers for accelerated chemical and physical decay of the substrate.
    a. Remove the stains using a 2% w/v solution of dibasic ammonium citrate (Newton 1987, MacLeod et al 1993, Godfrey 2001, Mardikian et al 2004) followed by thorough rinsing.
    b. Remove the stains using a 5% w/v sodium dithionite solution (SDT) (sodium hydrosulphite or sodium sulfoxykate) combined with a 2% w/v ethylenediaminetetraacetic acid solution (EDTA) (Selwyn & Tse 2008) followed by thorough rinsing.

Option 1, to leave the stains in place, was not chosen. It was decided that the stains should be removed to prevent any future problems.

Sodium dithionite removes iron corrosion stains very effectively but decomposes very quickly as the acidity of the solution increases due to reaction with water and oxygen (Selwyn, Tse 2008). Based of the high level of corrosion staining on the leather and the limited working time of the solution each shoe would have to be individually immersed in a sodium dithionite/EDTA solution several times to achieve the desired results. To carry out this process several times for 112 objects would require an immense amount of materials, resources, and time.

Ammonium citrate, though not as strong a sequestering agent, is an effective chelate. Both dibasic (pH 4.5 -5.5) and tribasic (pH 7.0) ammonium citrate solutions were tested for effectiveness and the dibasic was found to remove more iron stains from these particular objects. It is known that the higher the pH the stronger the chelate but pre treatment testing seemed to show otherwise with these objects. When discussing the use of low pH ammonium citrate solutions on leather Rabin (1983) states that *"the increased potential of the solution may be due more to the acidity than the material's ability as a chelate"*. A pH of 3-6 is considered safe when working with leather (Ganaris, H., 1982) so it was decided to use the more effective dibasic ammonium citrate. The objects would be monitored for signs of deterioration.

A 2% w/v solution of dibasic ammonium citrate was prepared in a large polyethylene tub. As in the case of the chloride removal, a submersible pump was inserted with the objects to circulate the solutions at timed intervals. One stained and heavily degraded shoe was chosen for monitoring from each group. Over-softening and crumbling of the leather

614

would indicate deterioration was occurring in the solution

Figure 5. Shoe before and after mechanical cleaning and iron stain removal.

The reduction in staining of the object and color of the solution were monitored daily for change. Once the changes had ceased, the objects were thoroughly rinsed in water for several days. The rinse water was also monitored for color change and the rinsing was complete when the water was clear. A new solution of ammonium citrate was prepared and the objects were re-immersed. After two immersions in ammonium citrate the stains were significantly reduced and no further stain removal was required. Following further rinsing, it was assumed that any chelate remaining in the leather would be removed during immersion in the polyethylene glycol solution.

This method was very effective in removing iron corrosion staining from the leather objects with no detrimental effects.

Table 1. Length of immersion and rinsing cycles during iron corrosion stain removal.

| Group | Time Displayed in Days | | | |
	Immersion 1	Rinsing	Immersion 2	Rinsing
1	5	9	4	10
2	5	5	4	10

3.4 Polyethylene Glycol Impregnation and Vacuum Freeze-drying

3.4.1 Polyethylene glycol

A 75L 20% v/v solution of PEG 400 was prepared and Hostacor IT (1% v/v) was added to prevent the PEG-induced corrosion of any ferrous attachments. The solution was monitored for darkening and biological activity. Two of the largest objects from each group were chosen for weight monitoring to determine when PEG uptake was complete. For both groups this step took a little over two and half weeks.

The solution did darken significantly which may have been caused by the leaching of tannins by residual ammonium citrate or the acidic PEG solution (Mardikian 2004). Consultation with colleagues however suggested that the solution was only slightly darker than normal when treating large amounts of leather (Personal communication). When removed from the bath the objects were briefly rinsed to remove excess PEG from the surface.

3.4.2 Reshaping

Before freeze-drying, all the shoes and soles were reshaped and supported while still wet using stretchy medical bandages (Supercrinx), various thicknesses of Ethafoam and cotton twill tape. The shoes were then frozen.

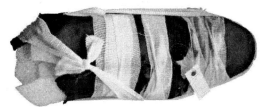

Figure 6. Shoe displayed in Figure 5 after having been reshaped using Supercrinx and foam.

3.4.3 Freeze Drying

The capacity of the freeze drier at the Canadian Conservation Institute allowed all of the objects in each group to be dried together. The specimen chamber was -25 °C, the condenser was -73 °C and the pressure was 1.5 Pa. The leather objects required from 3 days to 2 weeks to freeze-dry. During this time the objects were monitored and as the weights stabilized objects were removed.

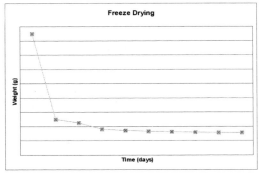

Figure 7. *Graph displaying moisture loss from leather during freeze drying.*

The slight moisture gain after removal from the freeze dryer was also monitored and objects were left in the lab environment untouched until the weight stabilized. The shrinkage of flat objects such as soles and other small fragments were assessed through the measurement of the surface area before and after freeze-drying, expressed as a percentage. The measurements were calculated based on tracings made of the objects before and after treatment. For example, the sole to the right shrank 7.7% based on the change in surface area. Calculations showed the average shrinkage of these objects to be between 7 and 10%.

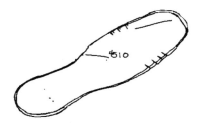

Figure 8. *Tracing of a sole before and after treatment to record shrinkage.*

3.5 Further Stabilization

Following freeze drying many of the shoes required further reshaping, consolidation, adhesion, and support.

3.5.1 Reshaping

Using a Preservation Pen humidifier, light humidity was applied to misshapen areas of the objects to adjust the shape. Foam and weights were used to hold the objects in their new form until the leather had dried.

3.5.2 Consolidation

On the dry and friable leather grain and areas where delamination or loss of the original surface had occurred a 2% w/v solution of Klucel G in ethanol was applied as a consolidant. Based on the frequency of its use in leather conservation, the viscosity of the solution, the extent of penetration and the ease of preparation and application, Klucel G was the best material for the task. The fluid solution was applied by either brush or syringe .

Figure 9. *Heel area of a boot upper after consolidation.*

3.5.3 Adhesion and Support

Tears, joins, and weak areas requiring support were reinforced using Lascaux 360HV and 498HV on Reemay paper. A 50:50 w/w mixture of the two Lascaux products was applied by brush to the Reemay on a sheet of Mylar. This was then set aside to dry. When needed, strips of any size were cut from the sheet and reactivated using acetone. Once reactivated, small strips were put in place using tweezers and dental tools while large strips or "patches" were applied by hand using a silicone release paper backing. Release paper was set on top of the strip or patch and weights were placed to ensure good contact between the adhesive and the leather. When partially dry the weights and release paper were removed.

Once completely dry, these repairs were colored using the same 50:50 mixture of Lascaux products tinted with acrylic paints. The repairs were tinted a compatible color so they would not catch the eye but would remain easily distinguishable.

Figure 10. Shoe displayed in Figures 5 & 6 after treatment.

4. Efficiency and Quality of the Treatment
By employing well planned treatment steps and thoroughly researched materials the batch treatment of these objects required far less time than initially estimated. Using the official estimate for this project nearly ten weeks was saved. Reducing the time for treatment did not reduce the overall quality of the work. This was determined using a numerical evaluation of the objects by the author and peers.

Traditionally the amount of shrinkage is one factor used to determine the success of a leather treatment along with an assessment of the color, surface texture and flexibility. This assessment visually evaluated other parameters such as a change in shape, friability, delamination, staining and corrosion products present. A system employing values between 6 and 1 was chosen, and the following defined the worth of each number.

6. Excellent condition: no negative shape change, surface not friable, no delamination, no staining, no corrosion products.
5. Good condition: minimal or no negative shape change, surface not friable, no delamination, no or very minimal staining, no corrosion products.
4. Standard: some negative shape change, minimal areas of friable surface, little or no delamination, minimal staining, no corrosion products.
3. Tolerable: some negative shape change, minimal to moderate areas of friable surface, little to moderate delamination, minimal to moderate staining, some corrosion products may be present.
2. Deteriorated: moderate negative shape change, moderate areas of friability surface, moderate delamination, moderate staining, corrosion products may be present.
1. Severely deteriorated: severe negative shape change, moderate to severe areas of friable, moderate to severe delamination, moderate to severe staining, corrosion products may be present.

Each object was evaluated and assigned a *before treatment* and *after treatment* value and these values were then compared individually and overall. Colleagues were asked to evaluate a selection of 10 shoes. Qualitatively this assessment proved that the batch treatment was successful with 95% of the objects moving from the lower to the higher half of the value scale by at least two value markers. In all cases the condition of each object was significantly improved.

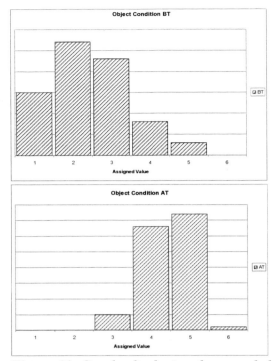

Figure 11. *Graphs displaying the recorded shift in the condition of these objects.*

5. Conclusion

The balance that was found between object needs and batch steps led to the success of this treatment. The methods and materials employed effectively allowed for the desalination, cleaning, stain removal, impregnation and stabilization of over one hundred leather objects and created a well developed treatment for leather objects from this site. Batch treatments are not new but achieving good results with reduced resources (supplies, space and staff) is becoming increasingly necessary in today's work environment.

Employing batch treatments allows for greater output while not comprising the quality of the work. With proper planning, batch treatments can be used to address the treatment of a range of objects of the same material type but varying in condition.

References
Bardet, M. et al, (2009), Nuclear Magnetic Resonance and Electron Paramagnetic Resonance as Analytical Tools to Investigate Structural Features of Archaeological Leathers, Analytical Chemistry, Volume 81, No. 4, 2009, pp 1505-1511.

Fawcett, E., (1912), Some reminiscences of old Victoria (1912), Toronto, W. Briggs.

Florian, M-L.E., (1987), The underwater environment; Deterioration of organic materials other than wood, in Pearson, C. (editor), Conservation of Marine Archaeological Objects, London, Butterworths, 1987, pp 44-46.

Ganaris, H., S. Keene and K. Starling, A comparison of some Treatments for Excavated Leather, The Conservator, No 6, 1982, pp 12-23

Godfrey, I. et al, (2002), Iron Removal from Waterlogged Leather and Rope Recovered from Shipwreck Sites, in Hoffman, P. et al (editors), Proceedings of the 8th ICOM Group on Wet Organic Archaeological Materials Conference, Bremerhaven, International Council of Museums, Committee for Conservation Working Group on Wet Organic Archaeological Materials, 2002, pp. 439-470.

Keddie, G., (2003), Songhees Pictorial: A History of the Songhees People as Seen by Outsiders, 1790-1912, Victoria, Royal British Columbia Museum.

MacLeod, I. D., Fraser, F.M., and V.L. Richards, (1989), The PEG-water solvent system: effects of composition on extraction of chloride and iron from wood and concretion, in MacLeod, I.D. (editor), *Conservation of Wet Wood and Metal, Freemantle, Western Australian Museum, 1989, pp 245-263.*

MacLeod, I. et al, (1994), Observations on the extraction of iron and chloride from composite materials, in Hoffman, P. et al (editors), Proceedings of the 5th ICOM

Group on Wet Organic Archaeological Materials Conference, Bremerhaven, International Council of Museums, Committee for Conservation Working Group on Wet Organic Archaeological Materials, 1994, pp. 199-211,

Mardikian, P., et al, (2005), A Preliminary Investigation into the Effects of Diammonium Citrate on Waterlogged Leather from the H.L Hunley Submarine (1864), in Hoffman, P. et al (editors), Proceedings of the 9th ICOM Group on Wet Organic Archaeological Materials Conference, Bremerhaven, International Council of Museums, Committee for Conservation Working Group on Wet Organic Archaeological Materials, 2005, pp 513-531.

Newton, C.L., (1987), Chemical Cleaning of Wet Leather, Journal of the International Institute for Conservation – Canadian Group, Ottawa, Vol 12, 1987, pp 3-8.

Rabin, P.M., (1983), A Study of Iron Stain Removal from Marble Using Various Chelating Agents, Kingston, Queen's University.

Selwyn, L. and S. Tse, (2009), The chemistry of sodium dithionite and its use in conservation, Reviews in Conservation, No. 9, 2009, pp 61-74.

Wright, J.A. and J.F. Hanlan, (1978), Poly (vinyl pyrrolidone) as an aid in Removal of Stains from Textile and Ceramic Materials, Journal of the International Institute for Conservation – Canadian Group, Ottawa, Vol 4, No 1, 1978, pp 32-36.

Questions and answers

Suzanne Grieve: Just have a practical comment for Jessica. The technique that I learned and used at the Hunley and that I published on for the last WOAM for freeze-drying leather shoes in particular was to insert shoe forms that you can get at department stores and such and also I used a type of plastic called Bivac and you can use a hairdryer on it to melt it and shape it and I found that that worked better than the foam because you have less surface area and it dries faster and more efficiently. And then also the bandages, I found also that using any type of organic material on cloth or tape like that especially during PEG impregnation, when you were shaping it, caused either mold or uneven areas of pooling on the shoe, especially during freeze-drying so I used Teflon tape, or plumbers tape, around the shoes.

Jessica LaFrance: I did think about using the shoe inserts but the shoes – the full shoes, especially the heels because they were so worn – were too deteriorated to put in and remove a full insert so that's why I chose the foam because I could actually cut it into pieces and insert one piece at a time for easy removal. We didn't have any problems with the Supercrinx. It was only applied after the object had been immersed in PEG and rinsed so I didn't have any problems with any sort of mold growth because the Supercrinx was put on right before the object went into the freezer. I didn't have any problems with marking but I definitely will try the Teflon tape because that sounds quite interesting. The nice thing about the Supercrinx is that it's actually self adhesive. You don't need to tie anything you just wrap it and it adheres to itself.

Shanna Daniel: A practical question for Jessica. How low did you get your solution level before you took out the leather? I'm speaking about desalination.

Jessica LaFrance: With the leather I managed to get it down to the level of the regular tap water.

Emily Williams: I have a question for both Liz and Jessica and that is that while I think all of us in this room understand that batch treatments are a part of life and a necessity, one of the things that I often find with collections managers and archaeologists is that the term "batch treatments" often affects their concept of the value of the pieces. A piece that has to have its own approach and is a one off is cared for differently. The batch treated materials often get the least care, get shunted to the side and I wondered if other people or if the two of you had noticed this or if you had ideas about combating that kind of perception?

Liz Goodman: Unfortunately, in the UK we've gone down the route of commercial archaeology. It started in the nineties and we are now stuck with a very, very commercial system which, to be honest, is done by price. Therefore we have no choice and, let's be honest, if they find organics most of the project managers cringe. They deeply hate it because they can't just dry and pack and leave it for maybe assessment/conservation at a later date so we have to go down the batch treatment approach. I would like to be able to persuade them that actually these are just as important and actually some of them are very good about it but unfortunately commercial processes just cover up any other type of processes we have going on.

Jessica LaFrance: I think the problem also starts with the archaeologists or curators who send you these objects. Often you can tell by just their assessments of the objects that they don't deem them very worthy. They basically throw them in a box all together. There is less care for these objects that they send to you in a batch than there is for the one object they send to you ahead of time. There was also the problem with this lot that when they applied they said there would be 200 objects, when they arrived there were actually 400 objects, so the time that we allotted for 200 is now actually diluted for

a lot more. So I think that even though it does seem that they are less important, that's something we should try to change. Just because you do it in a batch doesn't mean that the quality is any less than what you do individually.

Jim Spriggs: I just wanted to make a comment about batch treatment as well. I don't have a problem with batch treatment. It's a convenient and successful action to treat leather from one site to another providing they are the same dates, same sort of condition and come from the same sort of environment. You can obviously divide the leather out with the thicker sole parts divided from the thinner upper parts and so on and so forth. But beyond that you conduct an assessment and then you batch treat so it is a conservation choice not just a matter of convenience necessarily. But what I do have a slight problem with, and I hope that the English Heritage publication doesn't go down this line, is actually suggesting that archaeologists do their own treatments. I'm not sure, Liz, whether that's what you were going to suggest. I think in certain cases that may become necessary but only as long as there are other resources there to oversee it and see that it goes smoothly. Just one other point, can I say that we ran a survey some years ago of all the treated leather that we'd done in York since the early seventies using a whole range of techniques but ending up principally with glycerol and freeze-drying and we found that over time the glycerol treated dried leather doesn't stand up terribly well. There are changes. From the point of view of pure longevity, one of the earlier treatments we used, which was solvent dehydration followed by impregnation with a solvent soluble oil called Bavon, created by the leather industry, came out far and away the best in terms of color of the leather, its survival, its flexibility and its lack of fragmentation. I wouldn't recommend this treatment to anybody for a moment because of the expense, the hazard and so on but in terms of the long-term survival of the leather, it came out tops.

Liz Goodman: Just in response to Jim's comment. Creating this flow diagram (for English Heritage), strangely enough, we often seemed to come to "Consult a conservator" and there was only one instance that it suggested that you could air-dry but it mostly ended with them having to consult a conservator. If I had my way, we would have to treat it all but I know that there are some units which have such major problems. And the thought of the working group was "at the moment we don't know if it's even being kept after a quick assessment and if it means that the unit dries it and keeps it so that it's there for the future that is better than disposal."

Jim Spriggs: Just a quick response...a one word response. You don't just find leather in waterlogged deposits and if units are digging up waterlogged deposits with tons of leather in it what about all the wood and other organics which possibly need the same kind of treatments but not by the archaeological units.

Elizabeth Peacock: Just a comment about batch treatments of waterlogged leather. In Trondheim, we've been batch treating waterlogged leather for 35 years—it is the rule as opposed to the exception but we don't advertise that. It is how we do it.

5.9

The Conservation of Thule Skin Clothing from the Sanirajak Site, Nunavut

Tara Grant
Canadian Conservation Institute, 1030 Innes Road, Ottawa, ON, Canada, K1A 0M5
e-mail: tara.grant@pch.gc.ca

Abstract

Excavations in the summer of 2007, at Sannirajaq (Hall Beach), Nunavut, uncovered a mother-lode of Thule artifacts frozen beneath a thick layer of ice. One important component of this site was the 49 well preserved skin artifacts. Many of the artifacts were largely intact clothing including fur parkas, bird skin inner parkas, gut skin anoraks, fur trousers, boots, mittens, belts and bags. The skin clothing presented the usual conservation problems which occur when treating wet, dirty, fragile, 3-dimensional artifacts. In addition, the skin artifacts presented special conservation problems due to their proximity to several well-preserved burials. The possibility of hazardous biological contamination combined with an extremely unpleasant odor necessitated special safety and cleaning processes. This paper will present the history, deterioration processes, analysis, safety concerns, conservation and restoration of these garments.

Key words

Thule, cleaning, skin, gut, feather, sodium bicarbonate, sodium dodecyl sulfate, polyethylene glycol 400, freeze-drying, anthrax, smallpox, cadeverine, putresine.

Introduction

Archaeological excavations of prehistoric Thule sites in the Canadian Arctic often produce skin artifacts that survive in good condition as a result of their burial in permafrost conditions. More unusual is the discovery of equally well-preserved bodies. Materials from these sites are usually heavily impregnated with fats and oils from sea mammals but artifacts from sites containing burials may also be contaminated with the degradative products from corpses. These products may not only present a biological hazard to the conservator but most definitely present an olfactory problem, a revolting smell, which makes handling or storing these artifacts without treatment impossible. This paper discusses the overall conservation treatment of the skins, a more detailed discussion of the gut artifact as well as the research and special precautions taken to deal with both the biological contamination from the burials and the resulting repugnant smell.

Description of the artifacts

In 2007 the Canadian Conservation Institute received a collection of forty-nine well –preserved skin, feather and gut artifacts excavated from Hall Beach, Nunavut. The Inuktitut name is Sanirajak which means the shoreline. The hamlet is located on the coast of Melville Peninsula, a north-eastern projection of mainland Canada. The artifacts included clothing fragments, boots, boot liners, mittens, belts, satchels, pants, parkas and anoraks.

Description of the site

The site is large. It is comprised of approximately 12 Thule semi-subterranean winter houses aligned in a row with associated middens and other features. There are a few earlier Dorset houses behind the Thule houses. The Thule people were the ancestors of the modern Inuit. Migrating from Alaska around 1000-1200 years ago, they had distinct tools and houses which allowed them to successfully adapt to the harsh climate and sparse resources. The house that was excavated in 2006 and 2007 was Feature 15 located at the end of the row and partially covered by a later, larger house. Based on the style of the architecture and artifacts, Feature 15 dates from between 1000 and 1400 AD. Radio-carbon dates for the house still remain to be done.

During excavation it was discovered that Feature 15 had been perfectly preserved by a 1 to 2-foot thick layer of ice which had covered the contents of the house prior to the roof collapsing. The contents included baleen baskets, soapstone lamps, ulus, pendants, harpoon heads, gaming pieces, bladder floats, snow goggles, muskox horn wick trimmers, inscribed ivory, bone and wood tools as well as the skin and gut clothing. In addition the house contained the remains of eight individuals in one corner of the structure, probably representing an extended family. While the cause of death is unknown starvation, drowning, disease or food poisoning from an Inuit delicacy, igunaq, a fermented walrus meat, have been suggested.

Nunavut archaeological permits require that as soon as human remains are found all excavation must cease and the archaeologist must ask for permission from the nearest community, the Inuit Heritage Trust as well as the Government of Nunavut in order to proceed. All three parties agreed to allow the excavation to continue with the proviso that the remains were to be reburied in the site at the end of the excavation. Fortunately the excavation site was located on one of the three manned DEW line military stations now called the North Warning System. The base contains extensive offices, living quarters and the large radar system which tracks all airborne objects entering Canadian airspace as well as monitoring

the other 27 unmanned stations. The base was able to provide the archaeologist with specialized equipment necessary to deal with the unexpected finds such as large storage containers, chest freezers and a HEPA suit and mask.

Two major problems arose due to the close proximity of burials, one being the potential health problems of material contaminated by well-preserved human remains and the second being the revolting smell.

Health concerns
A literature search yielded a sparse amount of information and dealt, mainly, with excavation of European burials. According to the literature, burials without coffins generally contain no viable infectious agents (Healing 1995). Only burials in sealed coffins where soft tissues or liquids remained were of concern. In the European context archaeologists were concerned with plague, cholera, typhoid, tuberculosis, anthrax and smallpox. The first four diseases do not survive long in burials and do not generally present a hazard to the archaeologist (Healing 1995).

Of the remaining two, anthrax is a bacillus associated with soil and herbivores. It can be passed to humans and carnivores through the consumption of contaminated animals or by contact with anthrax spores. While the bacillus only survives for a few minutes to an hour inside a dead body, escaping blood can form highly resistant spores. The spores can survive in dry conditions for up to 110 years and up to 50 years in the soil (Kneller 1998). They are more commonly found in funerary objects made from animals such as woolen garments and horsehair-stuffed pillows.

Smallpox is a virus which can be caught by inhaling the virus usually from an infectious person. A viable smallpox virus can survive for up to 13 year in skin lesions (Kneller 1998). A 400 year-old intact smallpox virus was discovered in a skin lesion of an infant mummy found in Naples however the virus was no longer able to reproduce or cause disease (Arriaza 2007). An intact virus was found in a 100 year-old Spitalfields excavation but it was also considered not viable as it could not be cultured in the lab (Reeve 1993). The World Health Organization (WHO) believes that the survival time for an infectious smallpox virus at temperate ambient temperatures is less than 2 years and that survival of the virus in humid or wet conditions is likely shorter (Young 1998). While burial in permafrost will likely allow a virus to survive for longer periods even this period may be significantly less than 100 years. Recent searches for both a viable smallpox virus and the 1918 pandemic influenza virus in victims buried in permafrost resulted only in severely damaged segments of the virus being recovered. The nucleic acids (DNA and RNA) of a virus are damaged and fragmented even when frozen for long periods of time (Arriaza 2007).

It was noted that there were more health risks associated with lead dust and coffin wood containing mould and parasite eggs than from infectious diseases. Archaeologists excavating the Christchurch crypts were found to have elevated levels of lead in their blood streams (Reeve 1993). It was recommended that archaeologists wear personal protective equipment consisting of disposable overalls, safety helmets, gloves, goggles and a high quality mask.

This dealt with the health risks associated with non-frozen European burials but not with the possible risks of long-term preservation in permafrost. One of the problems with conservation is that we often deal with unusual materials and situations which are not common, so finding a person with the specific expertise to give advice for this particular situation was difficult. There is information on dealing with modern remains, there is information on dealing with remains which are not well-preserved and there is information on partially preserved but not frozen remains but the potential health risks of a frozen, well-preserved individual was not really covered. A search for information started with the CCI Health and Safety officer and swiftly passed through five people ending up at the Canadian Science Centre for Human and Animal Health, a department in the Canadian version of the U.S. Centre for Disease Control, located in Winnipeg. Their conclusion was that there was almost no health risk in dealing with this material provided that general clean hygiene practices were followed and basic personal protective equipment was worn. This was based on the excavation being a Classic Thule site at least 500 years old. The early date of the site, the isolated northern location, and the lack of European artifacts or material in the collection indicate that there was no European contact. This eliminated the modern European diseases such as plague, cholera, typhoid, tuberculosis, and smallpox. The lack of domesticated animals eliminated the possibility of anthrax.

The Canadian Science Centre for Human and Animal Health stated that:
> ....there would be minimal risk of acquiring a harmful pathogen from this type of excavation. As long as proper personal protective equipment (PPE) is used there is no risk, generally ice crystals will destroy the integrity of the bacterial and/or viral cell wall leaving inactive organisms. Any RNA/DNA which would be left from any organism would be very fragmented and unable to replicate. The only micro-organism which could survive this type of harsh treatment would be bacterial spores, Nunavut not being a normal place where

spores would be found it would be extremely unlikely that there would be any spores in a high enough concentration to cause infection. Proper PPE and working under a Biosafety cabinet or fumehood would be the best type of protection to ensure no cross contamination. …. (Theriault 2007)

All cleaning was conducted in a Class 1 HEPA (High Efficiency Particulate Air) biochamber or a reverse flow HEPA unit. These units are suitable for low and moderate risk biological agents. Air is drawn into the chamber and expelled through three filter-fan units on the top of the chamber. The filters are composed of a foam pre-filter to capture larger particles, a 8 cm thick HEPA filter rated to 99.99% efficient at capturing airborne particles 0.3 microns or larger and a 5 cm charcoal filter to absorb odors. A gauge on the front of each filter unit measures the flow of air and indicates when the filters need to be changed. Units are required to be professionally certified for a velocity of 50 cms/sec ± 5 (100 feet/minute ±10) across the working face of the unit. Units are certified in a specific location in the laboratory and cannot be moved without recertification.

Smell
The second problem was the unpleasant smell. There are two degradative amine compounds responsible for the foul odor: putrescine (1, 4-butanediamine, $NH_2(CH_2)_4NH_2$) and cadaverine (1, 5-pentanediamine, $NH_2(CH_2)_5NH_2$) (Ballard 1996). Both are produced by the breakdown of amino acids in living and dead organisms. The compounds are not particularly toxic but the smell is revolting even in small quantities. The chemicals are soluble in water and would presumably be removed by cleaning with the standard detergent process used for fatty skins. However, even small residues can contribute to persistent odors which become noticeable in high RH conditions so an alternative process to deal with the smell was researched.

Mary Ballard, a textile conservator at the Smithsonian Institute in Washington, D.C., developed a deodorizing process for both proteinic and cellulosic materials (Ballard 1996). Protein-based material can be deodorized in a bath of sodium bicarbonate while cellulosic materials are rinsed in sodium carbonate. According to Mary Ballard the mild alkali likely causes breakdown and volatilization of the amine short chain hydrocarbons responsible for the smell (Ballard 1992). The baths are dilute solutions of 20 g/L in water. The reduction in the smell is supposed to be almost instantaneous.

Conservation treatment
This article describes three artifacts treated from this collection: a child's fur and bird skin parka, a fur boot and an adult gut anorak.

Description of Artifacts
The child's parka is actually two hooded jackets layered on top of each other. The outer parka is composed of multiple diagonal panes of seal fur with a few sections of caribou fur. The broad panes are combined with narrower stripes of darker fur to form a decorative pattern. The inner parka is composed of untanned caribou skin in the torso and whole bird skins with the feathers still attached in the sleeves and hood. There is more than one type of bird skin present although they have not been identified yet. A similar garment from Greenland was identified as containing 5 different bird skins including arctic loon, snow goose, cormorant, mallard, and the king eider (Ammitzboll 1991). Any bird skin could be used however the diving birds were preferred to land or non-diving birds due to their tougher skins. Bird skin parkas were reversible with the feathers worn out in warm (around or above freezing), wet weather and worn inward during

cold, dry weather. The feathers are turned inward in this parka indicating that the deaths likely occurred during cold weather.

Figure 1. Child's Parka before treatment

The child's parka is in good condition but the smell was extremely bad. It was wet, dirty and had some fatty deposits on the surface. There is significant hair loss, exposing the epidermis, probably from abrasion during burial. The back of the parka and the bottom hem of the jacket front had most of the fur remaining. The hem of the parka had been folded under the jacket during burial and the fur had survived. There are several rips and holes in the skins and along the seams. Many of the seams are loose and opening.

Figure 2. Boot before treatment

The boot is composed of two distinct layers; a furless sole stitched to a vamp both made of de-furred seal skin while the upper cuff of the boot is made of caribou fur. It has two patches – one on the heel and one on the toe. The boot is more degraded with massive hair slippage and loss. It was chosen for treatment as it

was the smelliest of the 49 artifacts. The artifact was wet, dirty and fatty.

Figure 3. Boot before treatment

Figure 4. Gut anorak before treatment

The third artifact is an adult anorak made of gut. It is sewn of vertical strips of gut. The shoulder strips run continuously from the front to back hem. The garment has drawstrings at the hood face and waist to make it waterproof. Gussets were inserted in the neck to improve mobility. There are large areas missing including the sleeves, part of the hood and a large section from the waist. The hole at the waist occurred before burial as the hem is knotted to keep the sections together. There are several stitched repairs. The garment was wet, dirty, coated in fat, crumpled, torn and smelled badly.

Gut

As gut is less well known in the conservation literature the material will be described in more detail. Gut parkas are made from the intestines of various sea mammals, most commonly seals, sea lions and walrus. As Sanirajaq is a well-known walrus hunting site the parka is most likely made from walrus intestines. Gut parkas were water-proof garments worn over fur parkas to protect the wearer against the rain and from sea-spray while paddling a kayak.

The intestines of sea mammals are composed of three layers; the inner soft muscosa, the sub mucosa and the external muscularis externa. The soft muscosa contains the glands and absorb nutrients. The two outer layers have different orientations of their collagen structure which contributes to the strength and elasticity of the gut. The sub mucosa contains large collagen fiber bundles arranged in a double helix at 45 degrees to each other giving extreme elasticity and allowing the gut to withstand great strain while the muscularis externa is a specialized muscle tissue containing collagen fiber bundles arranged in a circular pattern on the interior and longitudinal fiber bundles running parallel to the gut on the exterior allowing contraction and relaxation to force food along (peristalsis) and giving the gut strength, toughness and the ability to withstand high pressures (Morrison 1986). When dry, gut is brittle and tears easily. In use it was worn in damp or humid conditions which allowed the material to maintain some flexibility and strength however it was not uncommon for a person to need 2 or 3 anoraks a year.

The gut is prepared for use by washing and then by scraping to remove the inner soft mucosa. The intestines are then knotted, inflated and allowed to dry. Drying at warm temperatures will cause the material to turn a translucent amber color and is referred to as "summer" gut. "Winter" gut, dried below freezing, is opaque and white. Summer gut is less flexible than winter gut. After drying the gut was slit to provide a long, narrow band of material which could be sewn vertically or in a continuous horizontal spiral. The garments were sewn with sinew which swells when wet providing a tight, waterproof seam

Although the structure of gut differs from skin, the material is predominantly collagen and can be treated with the same cleaning and bulking treatment as the skin garments.

Fiber Shrinkage Temperature

The fiber shrinkage temperatures (T_s) of the three artifacts were measured on the new Thermal Microscopy/Image Analyzer at CCI. Each dot on the graph represents an image of the fiber taken every 30 seconds with a temperature increase of 2 C°/minute (so each dot represents a 1° C increase). A small sample of a single fiber is placed in the analyzer. On the computer image the fiber image is selected, outlined and the outline is filled to determine the area of measurement. The computer calculates the total number of pixels visible within the fiber outline every 30 seconds. As the fiber shrinks the pixel number decreases. This method is much more sensitive than the old method of visually determining onset temperature. With the old visual method normal undegraded seal shrank around 60° C. With the new more sensitive method the T_s of undegraded seal skin is around 55°C. The onset fiber shrinkage temperature of the child's parka was 50°C while the T_s of the boot was around 45°C. No undegraded T_s standards are known for walrus gut. The T_s of the walrus gut anorak was 63.4°C. No modern walrus was available for comparison although a sample of modern cow gut gave a T_s of 59.9° C. All artifacts showed a fairly narrow range of shrinkage temperature indicating uniform deterioration. The fiber shrinkage temperatures of all artifacts indicate that the artifacts are hydrothermally stable with T_s close to that of undegraded skin and well above room temperature. High fiber shrinkage temperatures are a good indication of the ability of the skins to handle chemical and detergent treatments without shrinking.

Sample 1356

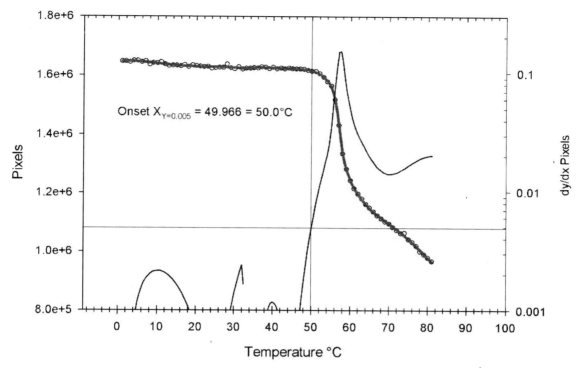

Figure 5. *Fiber Shrinkage Temperature graph for Child's Parka*

Deodorizing

Initially, the artifacts were put in a water bath for an hour to relax the folds and to remove loose dirt. The next step was to deodorize the artifacts by immersing them in a sodium bicarbonate bath of 20 g/L for approximately 30 minutes. The liquid was agitated around the artifact with a brush. The pH of the solution was around 8.0 (Orion EA 940). The pH was monitored at 15 minute intervals while the artifact was immersed to ensure that the solution did not become more alkaline. According to Mary Ballard the sodium bicarbonate preferentially reacts with the amine degradation products before reacting with the protein substrate. At the end of the bath there was a significant reduction in the smell of the two skin artifacts although they still smelled slightly. The gut anorak no longer smelled. All wash waters were disposed of down the drain while wearing a HEPA mask followed by running water and finished with a cup of bleach (hypochlorite) and more flushing.

Cleaning

The second step was washing the artifacts in a detergent. A 0.5% w/v sodium dodecyl sulfate detergent (SDS) was chosen. SDS is an anionic detergent. It removes dirt and fats from skin quickly and efficiently and the residues of the detergent are easier to remove from the skins during rinsing. SDS can only be used on artifacts with a high T_s as the detergent can cause temporary lowering of the shrinkage temperatures of the skins of up to 10°C, with the result that very degraded skins can shrink at room temperature in an SDS solution. The surface was cleaned with a brush or cavitron while in the detergent solution. The bath lasted for an hour for each of the artifacts.

Rinsing

Extensive rinsing is needed to remove the detergent residues, even for SDS. The artifacts were placed in a running water bath overnight (approximately 17 hours). It was not possible to rinse the artifacts in the HEPA unit due to the volume of water needed. Although after cleaning any potential health risks should have been eliminated, the artifacts were removed from the HEPA unit and placed in the water bath while wearing a HEPA mask. The treatment was conducted in a lab where exposure to other people was minimal. Once immersed in water there would be minimal exposure. The next day both the deodorizing bath and the detergent were repeated for both artifacts. This was followed by more extensive rinsing of four days to ensure the removal of all residues.

Bulking
The artifacts were then placed in 20% v/v polyethylene glycol 400 for 24 hours to replace the water and bulk out the cell wall to minimize shrinkage. On removal, the artifacts were rinsed briefly to remove excess PEG from the surface, tamped dry to remove excess water and reshaped. The artifacts were returned to a three dimensional shape by stuffing with plastic wrap and plastic bags and tying the artifact with stretchy medical bandages. Bubble pack should not be used for reshaping as it expands under vacuum. The gut anorak was thinner and when wet tended to cling to itself. The anorak was reshaped while floating in the PEG bath. Two sealed polyethylene tubes, slightly stuffed with plastic bags, were carefully inserted inside the anorak. The artifact was then removed and briefly rinsed. All the artifacts were then wrapped in polyethylene and frozen at -22°C.

Freeze-Drying
The skin artifacts were vacuum freeze-dried (Virtis General Purpose Freeze-dryer) at -25°C for the specimen chamber, -74°C for the condenser and 1.5 Pa. Simply air-drying wet artifacts causes compression and shrinkage of the skin. Water has a high surface tension and prefers to stick to the collagen surface. In a weakened cell structure the water, as it evaporates pulls the collagen fibers closer together, compressing and shrinking the skin. In freeze-drying the water is in its frozen state - ice. Freeze-drying sublimates the ice directly to a gas without going through a liquid phase thereby avoiding any surface tension problems. The child's parka took 15 days, the boot 8 days while the gut anorak took 7 days to freeze-dry. Progress was monitored by weighing every day until the weight stabilized.

Conclusions and After Treatment
The treatment of these artifacts was only partially successful. The obnoxious smell has been significantly reduced in the skin artifacts although there is still a faint odor from the boot and a stronger odor from the child's parka. The thick patch on the toe of the boot is the most aromatic and this is probably due to insufficient cleaning on the inside of the toe and the sewn edges of the patch. The feathers on the interior of the sleeves of the child's parka could also not be cleaned sufficiently to remove all of the decomposition products due to the awkward location. Wet cleaning of the parka could not continue indefinitely as the seams were beginning to loosen and individual feathers were detaching. Cleaning of the feathers will continue using a small suction disc to remove moisture. The gut anorak did not smell at all after drying.

Final cleaning, restoration and structural analysis still remains to be done for all the artifacts. X-radiographs were done of the child's parka to try to distinguish the seams of the inner garment. Unfortunately, there are so many folds and seams that it is not possible to accurately distinguish the inner seams. Reshaping of the anorak has begun using a cold mister (Bionaire Preservation

Pencil). The gut is humidified, finger pressed flat and clamped or weighted until dry. It is slightly stiff but has some flexibility.

Figure 6 Child's Parka after treatment

Figure 7. Boot bottom after treatment

Figure 8. Gut anorak after treatment

Acknowledgements
Karen Wittke (archaeologist), Julie Ross(Chief Archaeologist, Department of Culture, language, Elders and Youth CLEY, Nunavut), Dr. Douglas Stenton (Director of Heritage CLEY, Nunavut), The Hamlet of Hall Beach, The Inuit Heritage Trust, Mary Ballard (Senior Textile Conservator, CAL, Smithsonian Institute), and staff at CCI; Greg Young, Maureen MacDonald, Season Tse, Carl Bigras, Mylene Choquette and Carmen Li

References
Ammitzboll, T. et al., (1991) Clothing in Peder et al (editors), The Greenland Mummies, Montreal, McGill-Queens University Press, pp 127-131.

Arriaza, B. and Pfister, L-A., (2007) Working with the Dead: Health Concerns in Cassman V., N. Odegaard and J. Powell (editors), Human Remains: Guide for Museums and Academic Institutions, Toronto, AltaMira Press-Rowman and Littlefield Publishers, Inc, pp 205-221.

Ballard, M., (1996) Dead Walter's Clothes, in IIC Archaeological Conservation and Its' Consequences: Summaries of the Posters at the Copenhagen Congress, 26-30 August pp 1.

Ballard, M., (1992) unpublished Treatment Proposal for Walter Weir's Burial Clothes.

Healing, T. D., Hoffmand., P and Young, S., (1995) The Infection Hazards of Human Cadavers in Communicable Disease Report Review, Vol 5, RN 5, London, pp 61-68.

Kneller, P, (1998) Health and safety in church and funerary archaeology in Cox (editor), Grave Concerns: death and burial in England 1700 to 1850, London, Council for British Archaeology Research Report 113, pp 181-189.

Morrison, L., (1986) The Conservation of Seal Gut Parkas, The Conservator, Vol 10, No. 10, pp 17-24.

Reeve, J. and Adams, M., (1993) The Spitalfields Project, Vol 1, London, Council for British Archaeology Research Report 85, Council for British Archaology, pp 17-21

Theriault, S., (2007) personal correspondence via e-mail, Nov 12, 2007.

Young, S.E.J., (1998) Archaeology and Smallpox in Cox (editor), Grave Concerns: death and burial in England 1700 to 1850, London, Council for British Archaeology Research Report 113, pp 190-196.

Questions and answers

Suzanne Grieve: Tara, could you just comment on how you transported the skins from the excavation site to the laboratory?

Tara Grant: Unfortunately, I wasn't actually on the site the year she found everything. I was there the year before when we found almost nothing. So that was one of the other benefits of being so close to Hall Beach when she kept calling me and saying "What so I do now? I've found a polar bear rug and can I fold it over or roll it?" So I was advising her over the phone. Basically everything was on coroplast supports, packed with moss and then covered in plastic and then foil and then it was shipped in a cooler on an airplane. So that kept it frozen until we got it.

5.10
Conservation of Waterlogged Elephant Tusks

Ian Godfrey[*], **Kalle Kasi and Sophie Lussier**
(dec.)
Western Australian Museum, Shipwreck Galleries, 45-47 Cliff St FREMANTLE, WESTERN AUSTRALIA 6160
E-mail:* ian.godfrey@museum.wa.gov.au

C. Wayne Smith
Texas A & M University, Archaeological Preservation Research Laboratory, Center for Maritime Archaeology and Conservation, College Station, TX 77843-4352, USA

Abstract
Over the period 1996 - 1999 an assortment of waterlogged elephant tusk fragments, ranging in condition from slightly to highly degraded, were treated with traditional conservation consolidants and in-situ polymerization techniques involving the use of siloxanes/silicone oils. The treated tusks were stored for 11 years before being subjected to an assessment of their condition and the effects of the conservation treatments. Scanning electron microscopy, x-ray fluorescence spectroscopy and Fourier transform infrared spectroscopy were used to determine the extent of penetration of consolidants and to relate the extent of penetration to the effectiveness of the conservation treatments. This paper reports the findings of this long-term study and makes recommendations concerning the treatment of waterlogged elephant tusks.

Keywords: waterlogged ivory, plastination, silicone oils, scanning electron microscopy, Fourier transform infrared spectroscopy, penetration of consolidants

Dedication
This paper is dedicated to the memory of Sophie Lussier, a very talented conservator, colleague and friend who completed most of the traditional conservation treatments applied to experimental tusk fragments described in this paper. Sophie came to the Western Australian Museum in 1995 as an intern in order to complete the requirements for her Master of Art Conservation from Queen's University in Canada. Following an impressive internship, Sophie was employed in the WA Museum as an objects conservator before moving to the Art Gallery of Western Australia. Her death at the young age of 35 robbed all those who knew Sophie of the pleasure and fun of her company for the many more years that we all not only expected, but also wanted greatly. Sophie's sense of humor, practical jokes and lively personality brightened so many lives. Her friendship, warmth, compassion, willingness to always help others and of course her contagious laugh are over-riding memories that are treasured by all of those people who were fortunate enough to have known and loved Sophie. While her life was far too brief, the wonderful memories of shared good times have helped to ease some of the pain and sense of loss at her untimely passing.

1. Introduction
While archaeological bone and ivory have been studied extensively, most studies have been directed towards determining the suitability of these materials for use in dating, genetic, dietary and habitat studies (Röttlander 1976, Schoeninger et al. 1989, Bartsiokas and Middleton 1992, Pate and Schoeninger 1993, Lebon et al. 2010).

Early chemical studies of archaeological ivory attempted to link analytical data to provenance determination (Baer and Indictor 1974, Baer et al. 1978) while infrared and electron spin resonance spectroscopic techniques have been used to gain information regarding the thermal and environmental deterioration of archaeological ivory (Baer et al. 1971, Robins et al. 1983).

Further studies have characterised the nature of deterioration of bone and ivory, linked to the burial environment (Weiner and Goldberg 1990, Turner-Walker 1998a, 1998b) but very few however, have been directed towards relating the nature and extent of deterioration to an appropriate conservation treatment (Turner-Walker 2009).

Waterlogged elephant tusks are notoriously difficult to conserve. Collagen loss, breakdown of the inorganic matrix, mineral exchange, the cone-in cone structure and the presence of degraded layers of differing compositions and densities all have an impact on the effectiveness of conservation treatments. Drying stresses often lead to delamination and sometimes catastrophic disintegration of the tusks.

A recent study assessed a range of conservation treatments applied to small fragments of waterlogged mammoth mandibles, femur, radius and tooth (Daniel 2007). While details of the analytical procedures and precise outcomes of these analyses were not described, the mammoth remains were described as being sub-fossilised, retaining only "… a minute amount of organic material (collagen) and hydroxyapatite, but not enough to retain any structural support". A range of potential consolidants were tested on small mammoth fragments. Consolidants used included polyvinyl acetate (PVA), Acryloid B-72 (ethyl methacrylate methyl acrylate copolymer), Starbond EM-02 (a cyanoacrylate, type of superglue), Paleo-bond (a cyanoacrylate), polyvinyl butyral (PVB), Rhoplex WS-24 (acrylic emulsion), silicone oil, methyltrimethoxysilane (MTMS) and

MTMS with dibutyltin diacetate (DBTDA). MTMS was recommended as the preferred consolidant.

The study reported in this paper commenced in 1996, with the conservation treatments completed in 1999. A suite of waterlogged ivory pieces, recovered from the wreck site of the Dutch East Indiaman *Vergulde Draeck* (1656) in 1972, was chosen for this study (Table 1). Excavation of the *Vergulde Draeck* wreck site revealed a total of 119 tusks and tusk fragments, part of the general cargo carried by this vessel. Following excavation, all tusks and tusk fragments were stored in freshwater containing a fungicide (Panacide) while awaiting treatment. Since 1992 untreated tusks have been stored in fresh water with no added fungicide.

Large tusk fragments were sectioned to provide samples for analysis, parallel treatments and as controls. A subsequent study described the range of chemical and structural changes that occurred in one highly degraded tusk fragment from this shipwreck (Godfrey et al. 2002). In the tusk fragment examined in the 2002 study, small amounts of collagen were retained in the outer, iron-impregnated layers with none in the core of the fragment, iron corrosion products permeated the outer layers of the tusk, iron ions replaced calcium in the inorganic matrix producing vivianite, increases in crystallinity were observed and isolated pockets of pyrite were detected.

Prior to the application of a range of conservation treatments, representative samples of the tusk fragments were dried and powdered so that the chemical composition and the extent of degradation of the tusks could be determined. Analytical techniques applied to the powdered samples included Fourier transform infra-red (FTIR) spectroscopy, solid state nuclear magnetic resonance (NMR) spectroscopy, automated powder X-ray diffraction (APD), scanning electron microscopy (SEM) and elemental analyses. Apart from powdering, no additional sample preparation was required for any of the above analytical procedures. This meant that all components in the samples were analysed with no discrimination on the basis of solubility or preferential extraction. Results of these analyses will be reported in a future publication.

Based on these analyses and subsequent observations of the cross-sectional surfaces of the tusk fragments when they were sectioned for conservation treatment, the degree of degradation of the respective tusk fragments were broadly classified as either slight, slight-moderate, moderate or high. Images below indicate the differences in appearance of tusk fragments given these classifications (Figure 1).

Figure 1. Pre-treatment classification of wet ivory samples (a) GT 4161 A2 = 'slightly degraded'; (b) GT 1379-2 ='moderately degraded'; (c) GT 4161 B1 = 'highly degraded'

Tusk fragments were soaked in solutions of gelatin, Rhoplex AC-235 (acrylic emulsion) and Primal MV-23-LO (acrylic emulsion), plastinated following the procedures pioneered by Gunter von Hagens (Von Hagens et al. 1987) and treated with silicone oils according to the procedures developed at Texas A & M University (Smith 2003). The respective fragments were impregnated initially in 5% solutions of gelatin, AC-235 and MV-23, with progressive increases in solution concentrations to 30% over 3 months, with total impregnation times of 4 months. In order to keep the gelatin in solution the temperature of the impregnation bath was elevated (30-45°C) as the concentration was increased.

Further samples were dehydrated in alcohol before being plastinated at room temperature from a solution of methylene chloride using Biodur S10 silicone polymer, S3 hardener and S6 fast gas cure. Following dehydration with acetone, silicone oils were also applied to four tusk fragments. Two fragments were treated in the Texas A&M laboratories using SFD-1 silicone oil containing MTMS (5%) with duplicates treated in the Western Australian Museum laboratories using siloxane Q1-3563 containing MTMS (9%). Control samples were stored in water for the duration of the impregnation regimes. Following impregnation with gelatin, AC-235 and MV-23 the samples, including the controls, were wrapped tightly with elasticized bandages and sealed in plastic bags. The samples were bandaged to provide physical support to the consolidating medium during drying. The bags were changed at three monthly intervals and then resealed to allow very slow drying to continue. After one year a pinhole was placed in each replacement bag to accelerate the drying process. The plastinated samples were placed in a desiccator containing self-indicating silica gel while curing took place. A summary of the samples, their treatment and changes in mass during treatment and drying is provided below (Table 1).

Table 1. *Samples and treatments*

Sample	Extent of degradation*	Applied treatment	Pre-treatment wet mass (g)	Post-treatment mass (g)	Mass loss (%)
GT 1380 B1	slight	gelatin	338	267	21.0
GT 1380 B2	slight	control	554	432	22.0
GT 1380 B3	slight	MV-23-LO	606	454	25.1
GT 4161 A1	slight	AC-235	2792	2347	15.9
GT 4161 A2	slight	plastination	3002	2692	10.3
GD1132/137 3A	slight	Silicone oil SFD-1	568	N/A	N/A
GD1132/137 3B	slight	Siloxane Q1-3563	951	N/A	N/A
GT 1380 A1	slight-moderate	gelatin	505	440	12.9
GT 1380 A2	slight-moderate	MV-23-LO	943	827	12.3
GT 1379-1	moderate	plastination	896	833	7.0
GT 1379-2	moderate	AC-235	976	844	13.5
GT 1379-3	moderate	control	1057	912	13.7
GT 4161 B1	high	plastination	804	756	6.0
GT 4161 B2	high	AC-235	1431	1200	16.1
GT 1373A	high	Silicone oil SFD-1	611	N/A	N/A
GT 1373B	high	Siloxane Q1-3563	838	N/A	N/A

* As indicated by the appearance of the transverse surfaces

Only the plastination and silicone oil/siloxane treatments were successful. For all other treatments, the tusk fragments were characterized by delamination, exfoliation of the outer layers, splitting and cracking (Figure 2). While there was some internal splitting in two of the plastinated samples this was attributed to problems with the impregnation medium, which became very viscous during the treatment. Despite this there was no delamination or surface loss from the outer layers of the plastinated specimens.

All fragments were stored in the air-conditioned laboratories of the Department of Materials Conservation, Western Australian Museum until further analyses were conducted in 2009/2010, 10-13 years after the fragments were initially treated. There had been no visible change in the condition of the fragments that had been treated with silicone-based polymers over that period.

In order to determine the effectiveness and penetration of the treatments, tusk fragments treated via plastination, silicone oils/siloxanes and with Rhoplex AC-235 were sectioned and analysed via SEM, FTIR and x-ray fluorescence (XRF) spectroscopy. This paper reports the results of these analyses.

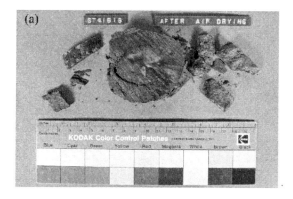

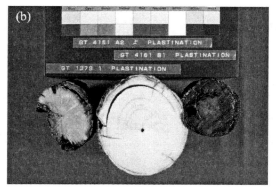

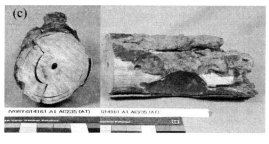

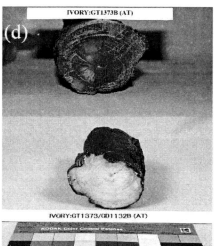

Figure 2. Post-treatment images: (a) Air-dried control GT 4161 B; (b) Plastinated samples, from left to right, GT 1379-1, GT 4161 A2 and GT 4161 B1; (c) Rhoplex AC-235 treated sample GT 4161 A1; and (d) Siloxane-treated samples GT1373B and GD1132/GT1373B.

2. Experimental

Middle cross-sections (x2) of treated samples GT1379-1, GT 4161 B1, GT 4161 B2, GT 1373 A and GT 1373 B were cut by careful hand sawing (Figure 3), embedded in epoxy resin and dry polished to a 1200 grit finish using silicone carbide papers and a rotary grinder. The embedded sections were then carefully vacuumed to remove all loose powder and any residues from the polishing paper. Middle sections were used for the analyses in order to gain an indication of the extent of consolidant penetration into the center of the fragments.

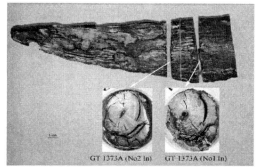

Figure 3. Sectioning of GT 1373A prior to analysis

In addition to polishing treated tusk cross-sections, control samples were also prepared. A sample of modern, untreated ivory was polished as a primary control to determine baseline levels of chemical components. A second control was prepared by embedding together and polishing tusk sections taken from an untreated tusk and from fragments that had been treated with silicones (Figure 4). This second control was used to determine if any polishing residues remained on the untreated fragment or if silicon and/or other elements had smeared or had been otherwise transferred from one piece to another during the polishing process. This test was necessary to ensure that the presence of any silicon in the inner regions of the treated tusk fragments was due solely to migration of the impregnants during treatment and not due to transfer during the polishing process.

637

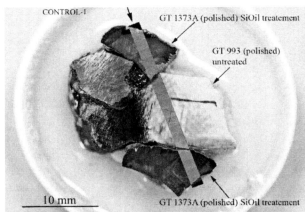

Figure 4. *Embedded control samples to check on smearing of silicones and/or retention of silicon polishing residues. The SEM analytical paths are indicated by lines and arrows.*

The polished silicone oil/siloxane/plastinated samples were analyzed by environmental SEM/EDAX and FTIR to determine the extent of penetration of the respective consolidants. As SEM was not appropriate to determine the penetration of the organic polymer Rhoplex AC-235, samples were taken at regular intervals across the section and examined by FTIR spectroscopy.

2.1. Scanning Electron Microscopy/Electron Dispersive X-ray Analysis (SEM/EDAX)

Each mounted and dry-polished ivory cross section was examined using a Philips XL40 CP variable pressure scanning electron microscope equipped with a Robinson scintillator back-scatter electron detector and an EDAX energy dispersive (EDS) system. The microscope was operated at 0.5mbar and 30kV at a working distance of approximately 10 mm. One digital electron micrograph (SEM) and four energy dispersive x-ray analyses (EDAX) were collected as the primary data for every mapping frame (approximately 1.5 mm) at a magnification of 150 as the environmental SEM scanned a straight path across each cross-section. Mounted specimens, with the scanning paths highlighted and associated data are shown in the results section below (Figures 6, 7, 9).

2.2. FTIR Analysis

Pin-head size samples were taken at regular intervals across representative pieces and examined using a Perkin Elmer Spectrum 100s FTIR spectrometer. The sample spectra were collected using a UATR accessory with 1 bounce Diamond/KRS-5 crystal combination, accumulated over 4 scans. The spectral range was 4000-400 cm^{-1} with a resolution of 4 cm^{-1}. Small ivory samples (~1mm^2) were taken for FTIR analysis with a 2 mm wide steel chisel. No other sample preparation was necessary except for the application of good contact between the sample and the ATR crystal under the ATR pressure arm. The Spectrum v6.3.5 software package from Perkin Elmer Inc was used to collect the spectra with the ATR correction applied and conversion from transmittance (%T) as its ordinate to absorbance units (A). The OPUS v6.5 IR package from Bruker Optik GmbH was used to calculate peak intensities by setting up the integration method 'L' with the baseline from 1215 to 480 cm^{-1} for silicone oil/siloxane/plastination treatments and from 1800 to 480 cm^{-1} for the Rhoplex AC-235 treatment. A FTIR spectrum of modern, undegraded ivory is shown below (Figure 5).

In order to obtain information about the relative degree of consolidant incorporation, it was necessary to compare the intensities of signals corresponding to the incorporated materials (silicones and acrylics) with those of the ivory substrate. As the SEM data indicated that the phosphorous content was uniform across each of the cross-sections, FTIR signals for the various phosphate absorptions were examined to determine which of these signals was least affected by the incorporated chemicals. The phosphate splitting peaks at approximately 600 cm^{-1} and 560 cm^{-1} were chosen. In order to minimize any impacts associated with changes in crystallinity, which would be reflected in changing intensities of the respective phosphate splitting peaks, the sum of the intensities of the phosphate peaks were compared with the signal intensities of incorporated materials. For plastinated and silicone oil/siloxane treated samples, the intensity of the signal at approximately 800 cm^{-1} was used to determine the relative silicon content while the ester signal at approximately 1730 cm^{-1} was used to estimate the extent of acrylic (Rhoplex) incorporation.

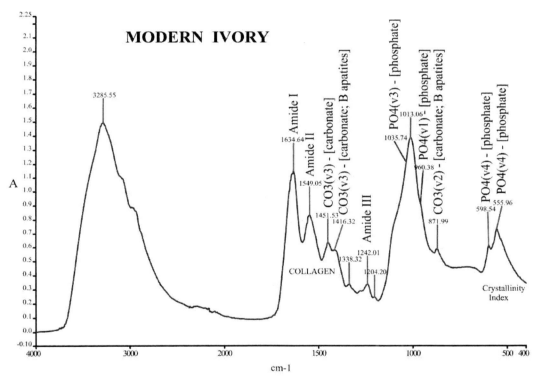

Figure 5. FTIR spectrum of modern, undegraded ivory with characteristic peaks highlighted

2.3. XRF Analysis

A Bruker TRACeR® III-V energy dispersive X-ray fluorescence (XRF) analyzer was used, prior to sampling the ivory for FTIR analyses, to detect the presence of phosphorous, sulfur, calcium and iron (Figure 10). The operating parameters are as follows: Rhodium tube and Silicon PIN diode detector with a resolution of ~180 eV FHWM for 5.9 keV X-rays (@ 1000 counts per second) over an area of ~6 mm^2 with all analyses conducted at 15 keV, 15 μA, using a 0.025 mm titanium filter in the X-ray path and a 180 second live-time count. The collected data was graphed using Bruker ASX Artax software.

3. Results and Discussion

Although final weights were not measured for the silicone oil/siloxane treated samples, the post-treatment mass loss for other similarly degraded samples gave an indication of the incorporation of the treatment chemicals (Table 1). In comparing the slightly degraded samples, the control lost 22% of its mass on drying, with similar mass losses recorded by the samples treated with gelatin and MV-23, an indication that very little additional material had been incorporated into these samples. The plastinated sample only lost about 10% of its wet mass, a little under half that of the control, while the sample treated with Rhoplex AC-235 lost nearly 16% of its mass on drying. For the slight/moderate and moderately degraded fragments, all samples, with the exception of the plastinated sample, lost 12-13% of their mass after drying. As for the slightly degraded sample, the more degraded plastinated samples, moderately and highly degraded, lost approximately half the mass of the control (7% and 6% respectively) after drying, again indicating that there had been significant incorporation/retention of silicones in the tusk fragment.

As none of the conventional treatments were successful and the mass loss on drying for most samples indicated that very little of the treatment chemicals had been incorporated into the ivory matrix, only the sample treated with Rhoplex AC-235 was analyzed further for comparison with the silicone-treated samples.

3.1. Analyses of Silicone-treated Samples

SEM/EDAX and FTIR analyses gave useful and complementary information about the extent of consolidant incorporation in the treated samples. Use of the SEM/EDAX gave a complete picture of the elemental distribution across a sample, allowing conclusions to be drawn about the extent and distribution of silicon incorporation in the matrix, the loss of calcium, the phosphorous presence and the incorporation of iron. For example, the data obtained from analysis of the highly degraded siloxane-treated sample GT 1373 B demonstrated a very good correlation between the loss of calcium, the increase in iron and the retention of phosphorous, particularly in the outer areas of the tusk fragments, indicating that iron had replaced calcium in the inorganic matrix (Figure 6). Interestingly, and not surprisingly in these areas of mineralogical change, more silicon was also present after treatment. It is likely that the higher degree of degradation and therefore the greater porosity in these outermost areas is the major factor contributing to increased silicon incorporation. However, whereas the iron concentration is highest in the outermost areas, tapering off in the core of the samples, the silicon concentration is remarkably consistent throughout the core, indicating that stabilization of the tusk fragments is not confined to the outer skin. SEM/EDAX analysis of plastinated samples GT 4161 B1 and GT 1379-1 (Figure 7) also demonstrated the relatively uniform distribution of silicon throughout the samples.

In addition to demonstrating the extent of silicon incorporation, SEM/EDAX also confirmed the presence of vivianite and pyrite in some of the more degraded tusk fragments.

While the SEM could be programmed to progressively scan across a surface, taking 4 readings in every 1.5 mm section, much more effort and individual work was required to accumulate the corresponding FTIR data. Although less data points were taken, the FTIR analyses (Figure 8) conclusively supported the SEM findings (Figure 6), showing the presence of large amounts of silicon in the outer regions of sample GT 1373 B2 and uniform incorporation of silicon through the ivory core.

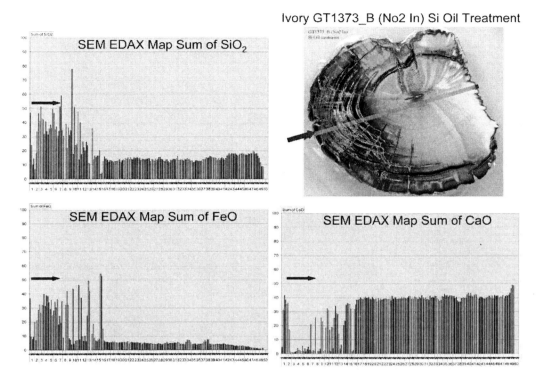

Figure 6. *SEM/EDAX analysis of siloxane-treated ivory GT 1373 B (subsample 2) showing the relative amounts of silicon, iron and calcium. The sampling path is indicated by the arrow and shading across the ivory surface*

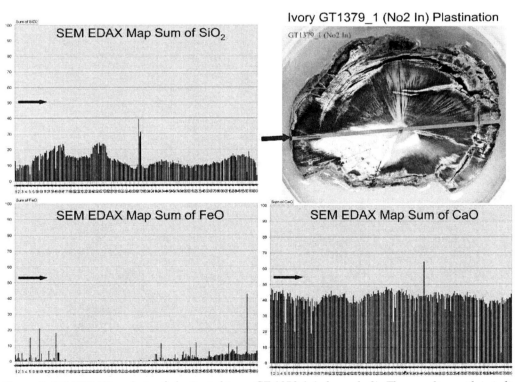

Figure 7. *SEM/EDAX analysis of plastinated ivory GT 1379-1 (subsample 2). The sampling path is indicated by the arrow and shading across the ivory surface.*

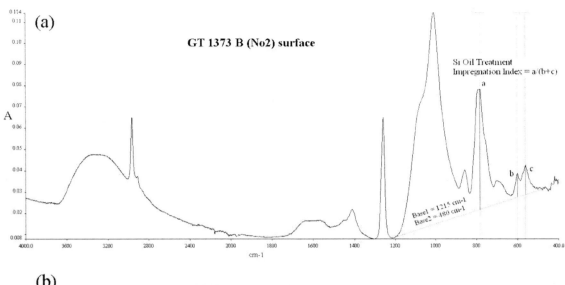

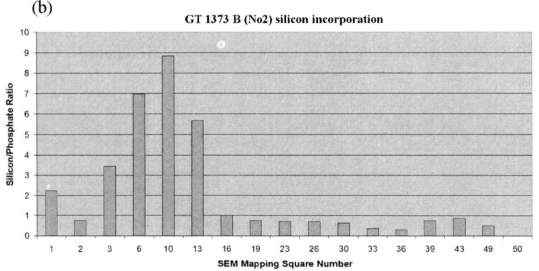

Figure 8. (a) FTIR spectrum of GT 1373 B2; (b) Graph showing the amount of silicon present relative to retained phosphate. The sampling path is shown in Figure 6 above.

Additional information regarding the extent of deterioration of the ivory, particularly changes in the collagen content, alterations in crystallinity and carbonate concentrations could also be determined by examination of the FTIR spectra. The results of these analyses will be reported in a subsequent publication.

The SEM/EDAX and FTIR data were consistent for all plastinated and silicone oil/siloxane treated fragments examined as part of this study. The data provide strong evidence for the effective consolidation and support given by these cross-linked polymers to the complex mix of components and structures present in degraded ivory.

3.2. Analyses of Rhoplex-treated Ivory

Cutting and embedding of the Rhoplex-treated ivory was complicated by the fragility of the sample. Because the Rhoplex had not effectively stabilized the ivory it was difficult to retain the section as a whole, with the ivory tending to fall apart when cut into sections. The extent of the deterioration and separation of the internal layers is clearly evident in the embedded cross-section of sample GT

4161 B2 (Figure 9). Although SEM/EDAX analysis could not reveal the extent of Rhoplex impregnation, it was undertaken to determine the relative amounts of iron incorporation and calcium loss.

FTIR analysis of samples taken at regular intervals across the surface of the cross-section revealed that the Rhoplex only penetrated 1 mm into the ivory matrix and in a small number of internal areas where pre-existing cracks had provided an easy pathway for migration of the consolidant (Figure 9). Although these cracks provided a pathway for the Rhoplex to penetrate into the inner parts of the ivory sample, no effective consolidation occurred in those regions. Thus despite the presence of degraded outer layers Rhoplex was unable to penetrate the ivory matrix. Extensive surface delamination and large internal cracks occurred despite carefully controlled, slow air-drying.

Combined XRF and FTIR analyses confirmed earlier findings that collagen degradation appears to be related to the presence or absence of iron (Godfrey et al. 2002). In ivory samples used in this study in which only small amounts of iron corrosion products were present, collagen degradation followed the expected pattern, with greater collagen loss in the outer, more exposed layers and more collagen retention in the inner core. The opposite occurred in more degraded, iron-rich ivory however, where strong collagen signals (at approximately 1650 and 1540 cm^{-1}) are present in the FTIR spectrum in the outer, iron-rich areas (Figure 10, A) while significant collagen degradation has occurred deeper in the ivory in areas containing no iron (Figure 10, B).

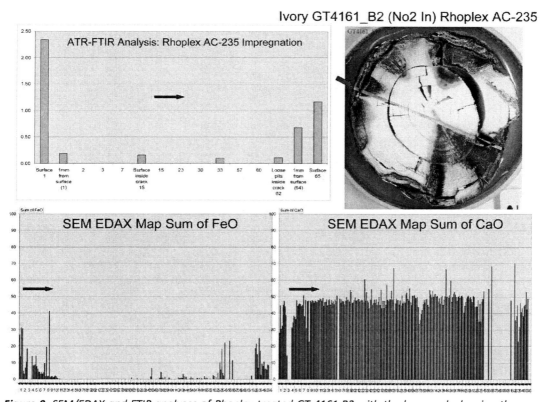

Figure 9. SEM/EDAX and FTIR analyses of Rhoplex-treated GT 4161 B2 with the bar graph showing the amount of Rhoplex present relative to retained phosphate. The sampling path is indicated by the arrow and shading across the ivory surface.

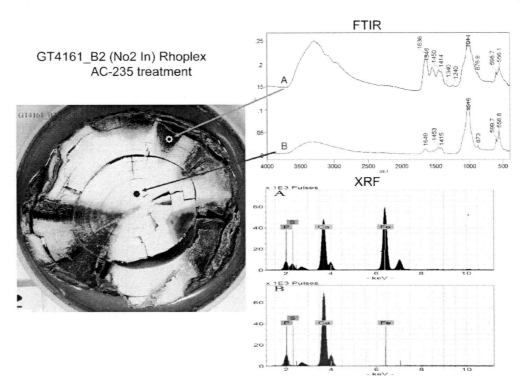

GT4161_B2 (No2 In) Rhoplex
AC-235 treatment

FTIR

XRF

Figure 10. XRF and FTIR analyses of Rhoplex-treated GT 4161 B2 showing the relationship between collagen retention and iron incorporation.

4. Conclusions

The complex ivory structure, combined with non-uniform degradation and the associated markedly different physical and chemical properties throughout the waterlogged ivory tusks, have made it very difficult to develop appropriate conservation treatments for these problematic materials. Whereas different treatments have been developed for waterlogged wood, depending on the extent of degradation of the wood, no such option appears likely for waterlogged tusks. The very dense structure of slightly degraded ivory inhibits penetration by consolidants and the immensely different properties and non-uniformity/complexity of waterlogged ivory tusks makes it almost impossible to tailor specific treatments for particular ivory artifacts.

The ability of the silicones to penetrate the often very dense areas of the ivory and when cross-linked, to effectively bind together layers of very different compositions and consistencies has resulted in an effective treatment for ivory tusks regardless of the extent of deterioration. There were no visible signs of deterioration or change in condition of the plastinated/silicone oil treated tusk fragments more than 10 years after their conservation. They have remained in good condition.

Of the two silicon-based treatments, the silicone oils method has a number of advantages. It is generally safer and more 'user friendly' than plastination as it does not require high vacuums and very low temperatures during the impregnation stage. Even though only water-pump vacuum pressure was used in our laboratories during the siloxane impregnations, care must still be taken to ensure that the MTMS cross-linker is not lost during this stage of the process. Indeed, MTMS was added on a number of occasions during the vacuum impregnation

644

stage in order to ensure that subsequent cross-linking would be effective.

It would be worthwhile to investigate the use of other monomer/polymer impregnations, followed by *in-situ* polymerization/crosslinking as possible alternatives to the use of silicones and also to determine the effectiveness of humectants in minimizing drying stresses and delamination (Turner Walker 2010).

References

Baer N.S. and Indictor N., (1974), Chemical Investigations of Ancient Near Eastern Archaeological Ivory Artifacts, in C.W. Beck (editor), Archaeological Chemistry, Advances in Chemistry Series, no. 138, Washington DC, American Chemical Society, 1974, pp 246-245.

Baer N.S., Indicator T., Franz J.H. and Appelbaum B., (1971), The Effects of High Temperature on Ivory, Studies in Conservation, Vol. 16, 1971, pp 1-8.

Baer N.S., Jochsberger, T. and Indictor N., (1978), Chemical Investigations on Near Eastern Archaeological Ivory Artifacts. Fluorine and Nitrogen Composition, in G.F. Carter (editor), Archaeological Chemistry 11, Advances in Chemistry Series, no. 171, New York, American Chemistry Society, 1978, pp 139-149.

Bartsiokas A. and Middleton A.P., (1992), Characterisation and Dating of Recent and Fossil Bone by X-ray Diffraction, Journal of Archaeological Science, Vol. 9, 1992, pp 63-72.

Daniel S.L., (2007), A Mammoth of a Project: The Conservation of a Columbian Mammoth, Master of Arts thesis, Texas A & M University, College Station, Texas, 2007, pp 1-88.

Godfrey I.M., Ghisalberti E.L., Beng E.W., Byrne L.T. and Richardson G.W., (2002), The Analysis of Ivory from a Marine Environment, Studies in Conservation, Vol. 47, 2002, pp 29-45.

Lebon M., Reiche I., Bahain J.-J., Chadefaux C., Moigne A.-M., Fröhlich F., Sémah F., Schwarcz H.P. and Falguères C., (2010), New Parameters for the Characterisation of Diagenetic Alterations and Heat-induced Changes of Fossil Bone Mineral Using Fourier Transform Infrared Spectrometry, Journal of Archaeological Science, Vol. 37, 2010, pp 2265-2276.

Pate R.D. and Schoeninger M.J., (1993), Stable Carbon Isotope Ratios in Bone Collagen as Indicators of Marine and Terrestrial Dietary Composition in South-Eastern South Australia: A Preliminary Report, in B.L. Fankhauser and J.R. Bird (editors), Archaeometry: Current Australasian Research, Occasional Papers in Prehistory No 22, Canberra, Australian National University, 1993, pp 38-44.

Robins G.V., Del Re C., Seeley N.L, Davis A.G. and Hawari J.A.-A, (1983), A Spectroscopic Study of the Nimrud Ivories, Journal of Archaeological Science, Vol. 10, 1983, pp 385-395.

Röttlander R.C.A., (1976), Variation in the Chemical Composition of Bones as an Indicator of Climatic Change, Journal of Archaeological Science, Vol. 3, 1976, pp 83-88.

Schoeninger M.J, Moore K.M., Murray M.L. and Kingston J.D., (1989), Detection of Bone Preservation in Archaeological and Fossil Samples, Applied Geochemistry, Vol. 4, 1989, pp 281-292.

Smith C.W., (2003), Archaeological Conservation Using Polymers: Practical Applications for Organic Artifact Stabilization, Texas A & M University, College Station, Texas, 2003, pp 1-144.

Turner-Walker G., (1998a), The West Runton Fossil Elephant: A Pre-Conservation

Evaluation of its Condition, Chemistry and Burial Environment, The Conservator, Vol. 22, 1998, pp 26-35.

Turner-Walker G., (1998b), Pyrite and Bone Diagenesis in Terrestrial Sediments: Evidence from the West Runton Freshwater Bed, Bulletin of the Geological Society of Norfolk, Vol. 48, 1999, pp 3-26.

Turner-Walker G., (2009), Degradation Pathways and Conservation Strategies for Ancient Bone from Wet Anoxic Sites, in K. Straetkvern and D.J. Huisman (editors), Proceedings of the 10th ICOM Group on Wet Organic Archaeological Materials Conference, Amsterdam, 2007, Amersfoort, Rijksdienst voor Archeologie, Cultuurlandschap en Monumenten (RACM), 2009, pp 659-676.

Turner-Walker G., (2010), personal communication.

Von Hagens G., Tiedemann K. and Kriz W., (1987), The Current Potential of Plastination, Anatomy and Embyrology, Vol. 175, 1987, pp 411-421.

Weiner S. and Goldberg P., (1990), On-site Fourier Transform-Infrared Spectrometry at an Archaeological Excavation, Spectroscopy, Vol. 5, 1990, pp 46-50.

Questions and answers

Carlos Cabrera Tejedor: A question for Ian. First of all, thank you very much for your presentation and for your analysis. I am very grateful for your analysis and I am eager to have your paper. Regarding the plastination, if I understand the technique properly, I believe that the poor result that you obtained is because the polymer was mixed with the catalyst first and that's why he had to maintain the -40°C because if you don't maintain -40°C then it reacts and polymerizes. So he maintains the -40°C temperature for two reasons: to keep the mixture from reacting and because he's dealing with corpses. And I believe that that is the reason why if you try to perform plastination at room temperature you get bad results.

Ian Godfrey: That's not actually correct. The catalysis is done later. It is purely a cross-linker that is put in with it and the plastination brew, or soup, if you like, you can use it for years if you maintain it below -30°C. I spoke with the chap from Murdock University to say "why did you do it at room temperature?" And he said "I just thought because it's a dense material if we do it at room temperature, it will be more fluid. The material won't be as viscous and so you'd get better penetration." So he did it with the best of intentions but we had done a plastination before at -30°C and it worked beautifully. But the catalysis it definitely after and it's done very, very slowly. They normally use a gas cure so that it will penetrate through. There is no catalysis in that initial bath because they can use that bath over and over again for a couple of years with just the monomer.

Carlos Cabrera Tejedor: Thank you, Ian. I never did it, I just read the papers and was referring to those.

Khoi Tran: Ian, you showed us pyrite in the ivory and you don't have any efflorescence as we do. So I wondered does the plastination create a sort of barrier against the oxidation of the pyrite?

Ian Godfrey: It may do, I'm not sure.

Anthony Crawshaw: If anyone else has any suggestions about how we deal with that mammoth tusk we showed you in our presentation, we'd be very grateful.

5A

Excavation and Stabilization of a 17th Century Wicker Basket: New Application of a Known Method.

Jill Barnard (Museum of London), Liz Goodman (Museum of London Archaeology) and Nancy Shippen (formerly a Museum of London Intern)
Email:
lgoodman@museumoflondon.org.uk

In 2006 a rare surviving 17th century willow basket was discovered during part of a controlled archaeological excavation. The basket was positioned at the bottom of a brick lined sump and filled with concretions of soil and glass debris and had to be block lifted (see figure 1).

Figure 1. Excavation of basket

The basketry was too fragile in its waterlogged state to be self-supporting, therefore a 2.5cm layer of concretion was left on the inside to prevent collapse during treatment (see figure 2). Immersion was inappropriate so the basket was sprayed with 20% PEG 200 and 20% PEG 4000 for a total of 2 months and vacuum freeze dried.

Figure 2: Initial clean before stabilization

Treatment meant that the basket was now stable but fragile. In addition the remaining/supporting soil matrix obscured any details (see figure 3), and so a method to remove it had to be devised.

Figure 3. Post freeze drying

Due to the method of PEG application and the nature of the material it was unclear as to how much the PEG had impregnated the structure. Further cleaning and the need to consolidate the basket were investigated. Initially hand tools were used to thin the soil block; however, there were concerns that the pressure applied to the structure was too great and risked damaging the willow.

Figure 4. Micro sandblaster (air abrasive)

Figure 5. Exterior during final cleaning

Aluminium oxide powders are commonly used to cut through corrosion products on archaeological objects. Discussions with visiting representatives from PESL and Crystal Mark Inc suggested an approach using softer abrasive powders in a micro sandblaster to clean the concretion away from the willow. Glass beads have been used to remove soil matrix from palaeontology and ethnographic specimens. Using spherical glass beads (44 microns) is less harsh on the surface of the willow less likely to become embedded.

Some areas of the basket could be cleaned just using compressed air without glass beads and this worked rapidly and gently, removing the soil without harming the basket material (see figure 5). However, air abrasion proved difficult on the delicate outer surface, as the basket needed consolidation with Butvar B98 (polyvinyl butyral) 5% in IMS throughout the process and the control of the air-abrasive was not fine enough. Mechanical cleaning using a bamboo skewer or scalpel allowed for more control, easily consolidating areas that appeared fragile.

While the delicate exterior required gentle mechanical cleaning and consolidation, encrustation on the interior necessitated harsher cleaning with the micro sandblaster. The delicate exterior was wrapped to protect the surface during the process (see figure 6). The interior of the basket was air abraded using minimum flow of glass beads at a low setting of pressure (see figure 7). Some encrustations were left where the basket was determined to be too fragile. The interior and exterior was again consolidated with Butvar B98 5% in IMS, and the interior base was further consolidated with Butvar B98 10% in IMS to stabilize it. The completed object was then supported on a conservation mount (see figure 8) made from Epopast 400 (epoxy resin putty pre-mixed with glass fibres) and pigmented to match the willow.

Figure 6. Protecting the cleaned exterior during treatment

648

Figure 7. Detail of cleaning the interior

Figure 8. Completed object

Questions and answers

Chris Wilkins: My question is: what was the pressure that you were using with the glass powder and did you find that the use of the glass powder tended to polish the surface of the basket?

Nancy Shippen: With the pressure, it was the lowest setting on the airbrasive machine so it was just 0, 1, 2. I mean it was very low pressure. The glass beads didn't really polish the surface. They really worked well at removing the encrustation. I was very careful not to go too far. I was very careful of that and afterwards as I say came back with a scalpel and bamboo skewers and things like that to really get the rest of it. There was a little bit of the outer bark of the willow occasionally when it was just kind of a loose structure anyway would tend to come off a little bit in the process but for the most part, it was really effective.

Cliff Cook: How did you get the bead out of the basket?

Nancy Shippen: It was the compressed air.

Cliff Cook: No, how did you clean it out of the basket afterward. It must have collected in the bottom of the basket when you were doing the interior.

Nancy Shippen: I covered the interior –the base on the inside with layers of plastazoate and other things--to protect it and so it wouldn't get residual air and beads hitting it but also that made it very simple to clean out as well. Occasionally I needed to blow it out with the compressed air but in general there wasn't that much accumulation because of the protective layers.

Jim Spriggs: A comment and a question. I found that rather than using an abrasive for this sort of process using vacuum tweezers but just putting the tube on the outlet rather than the inlet gives you a nice steady stream of air which you can control quite finely. But my question is, you say that the concretion on the inside of the basket was harder than that on the outside and I'm just wondering whether there's a chance that the concretion could have been related to some final use of the basket? Sometimes basketry was deliberately lined with clay to contain liquids or pastes.

Nancy Shippen: Yes, it could be a possibility. It was found at a glass factory so there were lots of pieces of glass, remnants and things like that. So I don't know how that would have come in to play with what you are saying.

Jim Spriggs: It could be used to hold silica or something like that.

Liz Goodman: The whole matrix was that material so it's unlikely. I actually did the basket lift on site. The soil was actually

649

completely filled with that matrix that was on the interior. We had to clear it all away so it's unlikely that the interior is anything special because it was completely surrounding the basket.

Elizabeth Peacock: I just wondered how you applied the final consolidant?

Nancy Shippen: Mostly just with using a brush.

Ship Caulking: A Project Focusing on the "Leftovers" from Ship Conservation Projects.

Anette Hjelm Petersen
The Conservation Department, The National Museum of Denmark
E-mail: anette.hjelm.petersen@natmus.dk

Introduction:

Nine ships from the late Viking Age to the early Middle Ages were excavated in Roskilde harbour during 1996-97 (Bill *et al* 1998). Among the ships in the find (Roskilde 1-9), is the largest Viking warship ever found, Roskilde 6 (dated by dendro chronology to AD1015-1025), and a large merchant ship, Roskilde 4 (dated by dendro chronology to AD 1108-1113; figure1). All of the ships still had intact caulking material, preserved *in situ*. The aim of the project [1] is to focus on this traditionally "leftover" material from Danish ship finds, to investigate if any information is hidden in these wooly strings covered in tar. At first glance it is wool spun in more or less the same way. Some seem to be made of unspun yarn, some are two or more threads twisted together, others are woven textile. When is textile and when is unspun yarn used as caulking material? Is the difference to be found in whether it was used in a warship or a merchant ship? Lots of questions are waiting for an answer connected to this material.

Caulking material is placed between the planks to keep the ship watertight. Caulking laid into the seams of a clinker-built ship during assembly of the planks is <u>inlaid caulking</u>, if placed after building of the ship it is <u>driven caulking</u> [2].Caulking is most often made of wool soaked in tar, but moss is also known to have been used.

Figure 1. *Roskilde 4 during excavation. Roskilde 4 is a large merchant ship from beginning of the 12th century (Photo Credit: Viking Ships Museum, Roskilde).*

In Denmark, clinker-built ships have been conserved for ages. The excavation and documentation procedure has traditionally involved dismantling of the ships followed by conservation of the individual timbers before reassembling for exhibition. Traditionally, the caulking material has been removed before documentation of the planks in order to look for tool marks on the wood under the wool (Petersen and Straetkvern, 1998). The conservation of caulking material is generally only done when the piece is a woven textile. The conservation treatment consists of removing the tar, impregnation with 4% PEG 400 followed by freeze-drying. Other caulking material is packed from the wet state, with the ID-number from the plank where it was located, in Cryovac, a polyolefin formulation perforated shrink film, in which it remains for later storage, and either air-dried or freeze-dried. The tar remains on the untreated caulking.

Observations from the Roskilde Ships

The caulking material from the Roskilde Ships is very varied; sometimes it is found as woven textile sometimes as loosely spun wool. The caulking in figure 2, from the Roskilde Ship 4 has not yet been dried, but is in the wet state as it was when removed from the plank. The figures 3, 4, 5, show wool fibres, from the Roskilde Ship 4. They clearly show that the material is in fact wool. The tar has not been removed from the fibres prior to examination with a microscope. The caulking in figure 6 is air-dried. It resembles the caulking from Roskilde 4 in being a non-woven caulking, but is made from six thin spun yarns instead of the four fuller more loosely spun yarns in the Roskilde 4 caulking.

Figure 2. Caulking from the Roskilde Ship 4, 1480x362

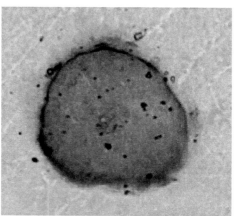

Figure 3. Cross section (40X)

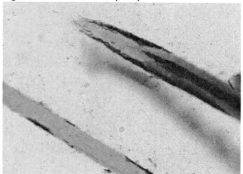

Figure 4. Longitudinal section (20X)

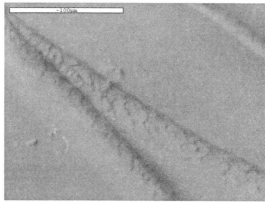

Figure 5. SEM recording (750X)

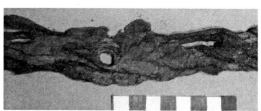

Figure 6. The caulking from the Roskilde Ship 6, 1480X362.

In a sample from the Roskilde ship 7 (dated by dendro chronology to 1270), both textile and unspun yarn are used in a connected caulking. This caulking has been conserved (figure 7).

Figure 7. Caulking from the Roskilde Ship 7, 1483X37.

In another sample from Roskilde Ship 5 (figure 8), the conserved, inlaid caulking material is woven textile. The caulking consists of two layers of textile. The top caulking (as seen on the photo) is woven in 2/2 twill. The bottom caulking is in 1/2 twill, with many weaving errors. The warp is Z-spun, the weft is S-spun. The edges of the caulking are very clearly defined and therefore the material appears to be cut for the purpose. Several S-spun, 2-ply sewing threads, fig. 9, were found in the material from the Roskilde ship 5 (dated to AD1131-1136).

Figure 8. *Caulking from the Roskilde Ship 5, 1481X179. The holes are from the iron nails holding the planks together. This indicates that it is an inlaid caulking,*

Figure 9. *Sewing thread from the Roskilde Ship 5 1481X179*

The figures 10-12 show the various designs of caulking material. Investigations will perhaps show if it is the time or place of the building of the ship that decides the shape of the caulking. The caulking from Roskilde 5, figure 10 consists of many tightly and a few loosely spun yarns, in a way that is rarely seen in the Roskilde Ships material. A much coarser yarn is used for this woven caulking figure 11, than what is normally seen in caulking material from the Roskilde ships. In the caulking from the Roskilde Ship 5, presumed to be a driven caulking shown in figure 12, the textile was folded and driven in between the planks. It was not unfolded before conservation but preserved in the shape in which it was found. It has been examined and there are no seams to indicate what the original purpose of this textile was. The weaving can still be determined as a 2-2 twill. The caulking

was cleaned in water using an ultrasound cleaner.

Figure 10. *Caulking from the Roskilde Ship 5*

Figure 91. *A conserved woven caulking from a scarf (the joint between two planks, lengthwise) from the Roskilde Ship 1 (dated to AD 1450).*

Conclusions

Textiles from this time period, AD 1015-1450, are very rarely found in Denmark. The caulking material made from textile is always examined, in the hope of finding the origin of sails. The rest of the material is often described as being wool from sheep or other domestic animals. More information could be added. It would be interesting to know if the amount of wool and the technique used to produce a caulking change from the lower to the upper planks of the hull. Also it would be interesting to know whether the wool was selected for this use, or if any old scrap of wool would do as caulking material. After all, the tarred wool is what keeps the water out of the ship. Today the builders of clinker-built Viking ships do not use as much wool in the caulking, as is seen in archaeological finds [3]. They copy everything else on the ship, but claim that it would be impossible to fit as much wool in the caulking groves of the planks as the Vikings did! The examination of the caulking material from the Roskilde ships will hopefully show that caulking material, in any shape, is well worth preserving. Just like other part of the ship the caulking has an important story to tell, it is just waiting to be told.

Figure 12. *Presumed driven caulking from Roskilde 5, 1481X46.*

Notes:
1) The project is part of a master's degree at the School of Conservation in Denmark and will be finished in 2011-2012.
2) This term is used by the "Viking Ships Museum" in Roskilde.
3) This is according to the boat builders working in the "Vikings Ships Museum in Roskilde"

References

Bill J., Gøthche M., Myrhøj H.M. (1998) *The largest ship find in Northern Europe,* "Nationalmuseets arbejdsmark 1998", p.136

Bojesen-Koefoed I., Petersen A.H. (2002) *Caulking,* "Maritime Archaeological newsletter from Roskilde", 18, 2002 p.46-47

Petersen A.H., Strætkvern K. (1998) *Archaeological workshop on the museum Island, Roskilde,*"Nationalmuseets arbejdsmark 1998", p.159

Questions and answers

Ian Godfrey: I was wondering if you have any plans to extract the wool or the caulking and just see the nature of the tars, or if there are any tars used as well?

Anette Peterson: I will, and there is tar. I would like to find out what kind of tar. I have also preserved some of the tar that was still on the planks and I would like to know if it was the same that they used to soak the wool. You never know because it can be different